ENCYCLOPEDIA OF
BIRDS

ENCYCLOPEDIA OF
BIRDS

400 SPECIES FROM AROUND THE WORLD

Consultant editor: Per Christiansen

amber
BOOKS

This edition first published in 2009

Published by
Amber Books Ltd
United House
London N7 9DP
United Kingdom
www.amberbooks.co.uk
Instagram: amberbooksltd
Facebook: www.facebook.com/amberbooks
Twitter: @amberbooks

ISBN: 978-1-78274-654-6

Project Editor: Sarah Uttridge
Editorial Assistant: Kieron Connolly
Picture Research: Terry Forshaw and Natascha Spargo
Designer: Anthony Cohen

Printed in China

6 8 10 9 7 5

Cover Picture Credits:
Front cover: Bald Eagle (Johnny Johnson/Getty Images)
Back cover: Close-up of a bird's wing (Mycteria/Shutterstock)

CONTENTS

SPLENDID FAIRY WREN

GOLDEN PHEASANT

Introduction

Birds, or class Aves, make up a very large group of vertebrate animals, and today around 10,000 species are known. Birds vary enormously in size and appearance, from the tiny Bee Hummingbird to the Ostrich, and from Birds of Paradise to Penguins. Yet, a bird is instantly recognizable to everyone. A bird is a vertebrate animal, in which only the hind-limbs are used for locomotion, either on the ground or in water, whereas the forelimbs have become modified into wings. Birds lay hard-shelled eggs, as opposed to reptile eggs, which have softer shells. Birds are warm-blooded and actively regulate their body temperature, and usually maintain a much higher body temperature than mammals, typically around 41°C. They have four-chambered hearts, and a highly advanced lung system, where the lungs themselves are relative small and inflexible, but have large distensions, known as airsacs, which lie in the body cavity and also penetrate into many of the bones in the skeleton and in special hollows around the brain. Inhalation of air takes place into the posterior airsacs, from where the air is directed to the lungs, then to other airsacs, and finally out through the windpipe again. The bird lung-system is more efficient than that of mammals. In most species, the skeleton is lightweight and hollow because of the airsacs, which is a great adaptation for flying, but Penguins have more solid bones, like mammals. Birds are also characteristic in having a beak, and in a number of unusual skeletal structures – in the structure of the shoulder girdle and pelvis, for example, and in having a wishbone, which is actually fused collarbones. The nervous system is well developed and the brain is quite large in many species. Some birds are quite intelligent, such as many Crows and Parrots, which can even use tools for a variety of purposes.

The Bee Hummingbird is barely larger than many pollinating insects. Yet it has all the anatomical characteristics of other birds.

The Ostrich is the world's largest bird. A member of the more primitive palaeognathe birds, it is descended from flying ancestors, which lived in Europe and Asia.

The scales along the feet of the Rock Ptarmigan have been transformed into feathers. This is true of many birds, including some breeds of domestic chickens.

The defining hallmark of birds is the feather. Feathers grow from papillae in the skin, and are found only in certain areas, called feather beds or pterylae, whereas other areas are naked, and are covered by feathers growing from the pterylae. Feathers are moulted at regular intervals, most often once a year, and males of many birds switch from a rather drab plumage outside the breeding season to more colourful plumage during the breeding season. Like hair, feathers are made from a horny material called keratin, but feathers are made from a different kind of keratin from hair and reptile scales. New research has shown that birds have two kinds of scales along their legs. The large scales on top of the foot are biochemically similar to feathers, and may be modified into feathers, as in the Rock Ptarmigan, whereas the small scales under the feet are more similar to reptile scales. The feathers serve many purposes. Along the wings, they become very large and strong, and their individual barbs are held together with small hooklets, forming a smooth surface. The vanes are strongly asymmetrical, and the anterior vane is much narrower than the posterior one, so the feather can be used in gliding and flying. This is a flight feather. In flightless birds, these feathers are usually more simple and open, and cannot be used for flying. Other feathers covering the wings and body also have vanes held together with hooklets, but have symmetrical vanes, and are called coverts. They protect the bird from wind and water, like an overcoat. Underneath are softer, fluffier feathers without hooklets, called down. They insulate the bird, so it can maintain a stable body temperature, even under extremely cold conditions. There are many other kinds of specialized feathers, serving a multitude of different purposes.

The rise and evolution of birds

The origin of birds has been a subject of intense debate and controversy among scientists, but today, there is overwhelming evidence to support the theory that birds originated from small theropod or predatory dinosaurs. The most primitive bird known to science is the world famous *Archaeopteryx* from the Late Jurassic Period (155–150 million years ago). *Archaeopteryx* had long feathers along its arms, which were very similar to flight feathers in birds today. It also had long feathers in its tail, and its body was covered in fluffy feathers. But it also had jaws lined with small teeth; a long, bony tail instead of a pygostyle or parson's nose; and long fingers with claws, like a reptile. *Archaeopteryx* showed a wonderful mix of characters and although universally regarded as the most primitive bird, it must have been distinctly un-birdlike in many respects.

Archaeopteryx is known from eight skeletal specimens, all from the Late Jurassic Period of Bavaria in southern Germany. This is the Berlin specimen, discovered in 1877.

When birds evolve to become flightless, like Australia's Emu, their plumage reverts to a more primitive stage with open, fluffy feathers, similar to those of their theropod dinosaur ancestors.

At 18kg (40lb), the Mute Swan is one of the largest flying birds. Yet it is dwarfed by *Argentavis,* from 8–10 million years ago, which may have weighed as much as an adult human.

Since the late 1960s, an abundance of small theropod dinosaurs have been found, many of which look very similar to *Archaeopteryx* and other primitive birds from the Jurassic period (208–145 million years ago) and Cretaceous period (145-65 million years ago). Scientists have identified almost 200 characters in the skeleton shared by primitive birds and birdlike theropod dinosaurs. Significantly, many characters previously believed to be strictly avian – for instance the pygostyle, the wishbone, or special bones in the wrist –≠have been found in a variety of small theropods.

In China, the Liaoning beds from the early Cretaceous period (around 120–130 million years ago) have yielded many small theropods, and they have shown scientists for the first time what these creatures really looked like. They looked nothing like the popular images in countless books and films, but were covered in fluffy feathers, more primitive than those of any bird today. Some theropods also had 'real' feathers along their arms and tails, which looked quite similar to those of modern flightless birds, such as emus. But some appear to have had true flight feathers along their arms – could they fly? This is a question still hotly debated among scientists.

Since the 1980s, many small, primitive birds have been found, and scientists can now reconstruct the early history of birds in much greater detail than previously. Some time in the Late Jurassic period, at least 160 million years ago, small feathered theropods began evolving large feathers on their arms, probably for gliding between branches in the treetops. These animals were almost certainly warm-blooded, and had wishbones and lungs with airsacs, almost like birds today.

Gradually, they began to fly, and such a stage is represented by *Archaeopteryx.* Like

A bird's plumage provides warmth but also camouflage. This Snowy Owl is conspicuous on a dark background, but would be hidden on the open, ice-filled tundra where it lives.

its theropod ancestors, *Archaeopteryx* probably fed on insects and small creatures, but soon birds began to diversity ecologically. *Jeholornis* from the Early Cretaceous of China looked similar to *Archaeopteryx* but ate seeds. These primitive birds still had long bony tails and arms with clawed fingers, and were probably very clumsy fliers.

Flying

Flight became the most important driving force in early avian evolution. Birds soon evolved true wings with fused fingers, the tail became short and stumpy, forming the pygostyle, because such a tail is much more efficient for manoeuvring in the air. The body became more compact; the centre of gravity moved forwards from the hips to the chest, so the bird became better balanced in the air; and the shoulder girdle and wishbone became adapted for flying. Finally, the birds rapidly became smaller. *Archaeopteryx* and *Jeholornis* had been crow-sized, but most later birds in the Early Cretaceous were the size of sparrows.

In the Cretaceous period, the Enaniornithes were the most common birds. This group included some primitive forms with toothed jaws, but most were almost modern in appearance. Ecologically, they were very diverse, and some ate seeds or plants, some ate insects, and others probably lived on fish. In the Late Cretaceous period, birds were probably common throughout much of the world, sharing the skies with the pterosaurs. In the Late Cretaceous of Europe and North America lived also the Hesperornithiformes. They were large birds, which had become highly adapted for life in water. They had very small, stumpy wings and could not fly, but had large, wide feet for swimming. They looked very similar to modern Loons, but still had small teeth in the beak. Towards the end of the Cretaceous, the enaniornithines and other early bird groups went extinct. By this time, the modern birds, the Neornithes, had already evolved. This was the only group to survive the great extinction that also killed off the dinosaurs and pterosaurs, along with many other life forms. The Neornithes is the group to which all extant birds belong, and this group evolved in the Cretaceous period but became diverse only after the extinction of the dinosaurs and other bird groups. It is divided into two large groups, the Palaeognathae, containing the large flightless ratites, such as the Ostrich and Emu, the Kiwis, and

Most birds build a nest from twigs or leaves, but some roost under ground. The Sand Martin is capable of tunnelling far into sandy banks along rivers, lakes or coasts.

the tinamous, which can fly. The other group is the Neognathae, to which most birds belong. The systematics of the Neognathae is still a hotly debated subject among scientists, but normally, the group is divided into 26 major groups called orders – for example, the Gaviiformes (loons) or the Strigiformes (owls). Of those, 23 are represented in this book, along with the palaeognathine order Struthioniformes. Despite the enormous amount of research being done on birds, scientists still disagree on how those 26 orders are related to each other. It would appear, however, that the Galliformes (fowl) and Anseriformes (waterfowl) are more primitive than the other neognathe bird orders.

Distribution and ecology

Birds are found virtually all over the globe and in every conceivable type of environment, from scorching deserts to the freezing cold of the poles, from high in the mountains to the open oceans. However, unlike many mammals, no bird is adapted for a life underground, although several roost in burrows, often made by mammals, but some dig their own tunnels, such as the Sand Martin. Although some birds are active at night – for instance, Owls and Nightjars – most birds are active only during the day, and rest during the night. Unlike mammals, birds usually do not fall into a deep sleep, but sleep for brief periods at a time, interrupted by sudden wakening. This so-called vigilant sleep allows birds to be alert to approaching dangers. Most birds migrate seasonally, to escape unfavourable conditions such as drought or winter, and some migrate many thousands of miles.

Like other palaeognaths, the Brown Kiwi has a primitive skull. It also has a primitive, furlike plumage and a highly developed sense of smell, which is unusual among birds.

Unlike most mammals, birds cannot move their eyes. Birds have full-colour vision, and the cone cells in their eyes can detect green, red and blue. The often very colourful plumage of many species, and male in particular, is used as communication signals to other birds, mainly within the same species, but also to other species. However, unlike mammals, birds also have special cone cells that can detect ultraviolet light, and many birds have plumage patterns that are visible only in ultraviolet light. Thus, many birds actually look different to the birds themselves than they do to us.

Many birds are territorial, and males actively defend a territory against intruders, usually males of the same species, but occasionally also other birds as well. Males typically announce their right to a territory by singing, which is attracts females. Singing takes place in a muscular chamber in the throat known as the syrinx. Singing loudly is extremely laborious, and the pulse of a singing Robin or Sparrow soars to hundreds of heartbeats a minute. Sound and visual communication are much more important in birds than in most mammals, which often communicate by smell. In contrast, most birds have a rather poorly developed sense of smell. Some birds, such as the Kiwi, have an excellent sense of small and use it when foraging for prey in the ground.

Feeding ecology is enormously varied among birds, and has been an important factor in their evolution. Many small passerines hunt insects and other creepy crawlies, and typically have slender, pointed bills. Others birds eat seeds, and often have strong, heavy bills, whereas species feeding on plants, such as Ducks and Geese, have wide, flat bills. Owls and raptors prey on large, vertebrate prey, and have strong, hooked bills for tearing flesh. Some birds, such as Sun Birds and Hummingbirds, rely on nectar and pollen, and often have very long, thin and curved bills for probing deeply into flowers, and long, brushy tongues for collecting nectar. They are mainly tropical species, and several are important pollinators.

All birds breed on land, and even the ocean-going albatrosses and terns have to come ashore to roost. The vast majority of birds are monogamous, forming pairs that typically last for one breeding season. Some birds will mate for life – the Wandering Albatross, for instance. However, males of monogamous species often cheat on their partner, and thus father more offspring. Some species may be polygamous, typically species in which the female is not dependent on the male for rearing the chicks. Unlike mammals, male parental care is common in birds, and both parents often take turns incubating the eggs and feeding the chicks. Most birds build a nest from twigs, straw, leaves or earth, but some lay their eggs on bare ground or rock, and the male Emperor Penguin uses its feet to incubate their single egg. Chicks are often born almost naked and helpless, known as altricial, and are totally dependent on their parents for food, warmth and protection for several weeks after hatching. In other birds, such as Kiwis and Ostriches, the chicks are precocial and the chicks are able to move around and feed soon after hatching. In megapodes, the chicks leave the egg flying, looking like a miniature adult.

Some birds, like the Sooty Tern, spend large parts of their lives on the open ocean, travelling thousands of miles. Yet all must come ashore to lay and roost. No bird can bear live young.

How this book works

The format for all the entries that follow is similar, enabling comparisons to be made easily. The birds are not grouped on the basis of their common names, however, because this is unreliable; in many cases, a species may be known under a variety of different common names. Furthermore, different subspecies may also be accorded separate common names, adding to the confusion. This approach also avoids the inevitable linguistic problems in cases where the same species is known under different common names in neighbouring countries. The entries here are actually grouped by order, on an A-Z basis, which has the advantage of ensuring that closely related species, linked as members of the same order, can be found together.

Penguins have small, stiff, arrow-shaped feathers, which repel water and protect against the cold. This male Emperor Penguin is keeping his chick warm with his bellyfold.

Steppe Eagle

• ORDER • Accipitriformes • FAMILY • Accipitridae • SPECIES • *Aquila nipalensis*

Steppe Eagles are an adaptable and successful species – equally at home in grasslands or cities, and happy to make a meal of any available food.

VITAL STATISTICS

LENGTH	62–74cm (24.4–29.1in)
WINGSPAN	1.6–1.9 m (5.2–6.2ft)
SEXUAL MATURITY	At least 1 year
NUMBER OF EGGS	1–3 eggs
INCUBATION PERIOD	45 days
FLEDGLING PERIOD	55–56 days
NUMBER OF BROODS	1 a year
TYPICAL DIET	Birds, mammals, insects and carrion
LIFE SPAN	Up to 41 years in captivity

WHERE IN THE WORLD?

Steppe Eagles get their name from their preference for such dry open habitats as those found on the Russian steppes. They breed mainly in Central Asia, from eastern Europe through to Kazakhstan.

CREATURE COMPARISONS

It is while they are in flight that you are most likely to be able to tell a juvenile Steppe Eagle from an adult. The underside of an adult's wing is dark, tipped with grey-black 'primary feathers'. A juvenile's wing is paler brown with a broad, white band.

Juvenile Steppe Eagle

WINGS
The eagles' wings are tipped with finger-like primary feathers. These are splayed to reduce friction and give more control in the air.

EYES
Steppe Eagles have remarkable eyesight. It is believed that they can spot a grasshopper, from the air, 100m (328ft) away.

LEGS
Unusually for birds of prey, Steppe Eagles have legs adapted for hunting on the ground as well as for catching prey in mid-air.

HOW BIG IS IT?

SPECIAL ADAPTATION

These magnificent birds are one of the few species of eagle to nest on the ground. This might sound dangerous, but adaptability is an important survival tactic. Steppe Eagles can – and do – take advantage of a wide range of environments, even nesting in cities.

Martial Eagle

• **ORDER** • Accipitriformes • **FAMILY** • Accipitridae • **SPECIES** • *Polemaetus bellicosus*

These magnificent birds of prey are Africa's largest known species of Eagle – easily powerful enough to kill and carry away a small antelope.

VITAL STATISTICS

WEIGHT	6.5kg (14.3lb)
LENGTH	78–86cm (30.7–33.8in)
WINGSPAN	2.5m (8.2ft)
SEXUAL MATURITY	5–6 years
INCUBATION PERIOD	47–53 days
FLEDGLING PERIOD	59–99 days
NUMBER OF EGGS	1 egg every 2 years
HABITS	Diurnal, non-migratory
TYPICAL DIET	Small mammals, birds and reptiles
LIFE SPAN	Typically 16 years

WHERE IN THE WORLD?

Limited numbers are found throughout sub-Saharan Africa, especially Zimbabwe and South Africa. They can adapt to life in parched, savannah grasslands as well as mountains.

CREATURE COMPARISONS

Ornithologists can guess how old Martial Eagles are by the colour of their plumage and the number of speckles on their breast. As a general rule, older birds have more speckles and darker plumage. Juveniles (shown) are grey above, with more white below.

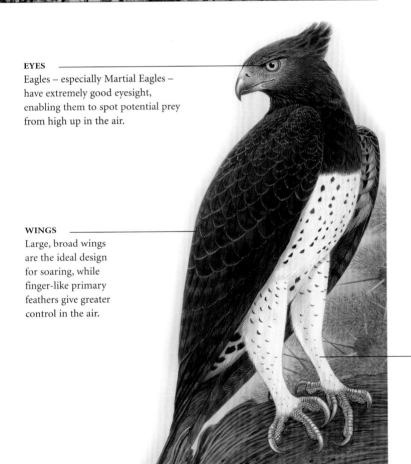

EYES
Eagles – especially Martial Eagles – have extremely good eyesight, enabling them to spot potential prey from high up in the air.

WINGS
Large, broad wings are the ideal design for soaring, while finger-like primary feathers give greater control in the air.

LEGS
Many birds of prey have completely bare or partially bare legs so their feathers do not get matted with blood.

Juvenile Martial Eagle

HOW BIG IS IT?

SPECIAL ADAPTATION
Martial Eagles, in common with many birds of prey, use their sharp talons to hold down and kill their prey. Holding their claws outstretched while in flight, they can grab even quickly moving prey with relative ease.

Mandarin Duck

• **ORDER** • Anseriformes • **FAMILY** • Anatidae • **SPECIES** • *Aix galericulata*

VITAL STATISTICS

WEIGHT	
MALES	630g (22.2oz)
FEMALES	520g (18.3oz)
LENGTH	41–49cm (16.1–19.3in)
WINGSPAN	65–75cm (25.6–29.5in)
SEXUAL MATURITY	1 year
INCUBATION PERIOD	28–30 days
FLEDGLING PERIOD	40–45 days
NUMBER OF EGGS	9–12 eggs
NUMBER OF BROODS	1 a year
TYPICAL DIET	Plants, insects and small invertebrates
HABITS	Diurnal/ crepuscular, migratory

These exotic and handsome birds take their name from the males' colourful plumage, which resembles the traditional costume of a Chinese civil servant.

WHERE IN THE WORLD?

Mandarins belong to a group of perching ducks, which nest in tree cavities close to water. They were originally found in China, Japan and Siberia, but populations of zoo escapees are now found in Europe.

CREATURE COMPARISONS

It is hard to believe that this dowdy, unassuming duck is a Mandarin. While male birds are resplendent in 'costumes' of orange, purple, blue and green, females of the species must make do with plainer attire. However, their olive-grey plumage provides ideal camouflage when they are nesting.

Female

HEAD
During courtship, males raise their brilliantly coloured head crests. In flight, these are safely tucked away, giving a more streamlined shape.

BILL
Male Mandarins have a bold, orange bill, tipped with white. The bill of the female is lighter, with a less obvious pale tip.

ORANGE 'SAILS'
This pair of spectacular, orange 'sails' are really enlarged wing feathers. They are folded down when the Mandarin is in flight.

HOW BIG IS IT?

SPECIAL ADAPTATION
Mandarins are related to Wood Ducks, and, like them, they prefer forest or woodland habitats. Because of this, they have rather unusual feet. Like most water fowl, they still have webbed toes, but these are particularly long and tipped with sharp claws, for grasping branches.

Wood Duck

VITAL STATISTICS

WEIGHT	635–681g (22.3–24oz)
LENGTH	47–54cm (18.5–21.3in)
WINGSPAN	70–73cm (27.6–28.7in)
LAYS EGGS	February–March in the South and March–April in the North
SEXUAL MATURITY	1 year
INCUBATION PERIOD	30 days
NUMBER OF EGGS	6–15 eggs
NUMBER OF BROODS	2 a year are possible in the southern part of the range
TYPICAL DIET	Nuts, fruit, aquatic plants and aquatic insects
LIFE SPAN	Typically 4 years

CREATURE COMPARISONS

In their breeding plumage, male Wood Ducks look like some exotic Eastern species. In fact, they have often been compared to the Mandarin Duck. Females (shown below, right) are duller, but just as appealing, with a bushy head crest and shiny, olive-grey upper parts.

Male (left) and female (right)

There are many people who consider these colourful American swamp ducks to be one of the most beautiful of all species of waterfowl.

WHERE IN THE WORLD?

Wood Ducks are found throughout North America from Nova Scotia to the Gulf of Mexico. Birds nest in trees in flooded swamps, marshes and ponds.

BODY
Male Wood Ducks (shown here) can be easily be differentiated from females as they have bolder plumage and red eyes.

HEAD
Both male and female adult birds have a crest on their head. However, the males' are iridescent green, blue and purple.

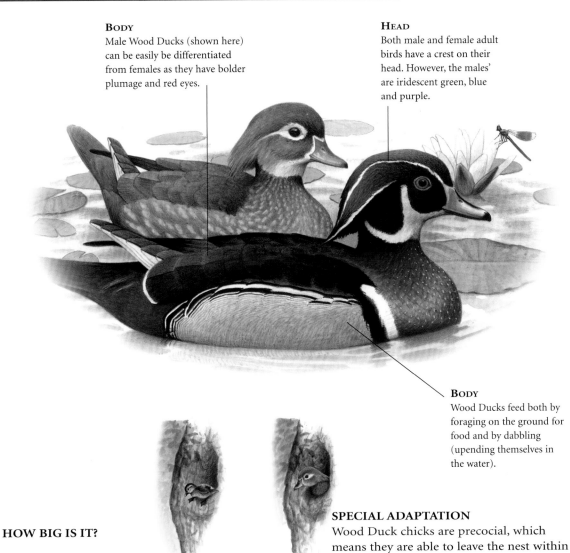

BODY
Wood Ducks feed both by foraging on the ground for food and by dabbling (upending themselves in the water).

HOW BIG IS IT?

SPECIAL ADAPTATION

Wood Duck chicks are precocial, which means they are able to leave the nest within 24 hours of hatching. Because they nest in tree cavities, the ducklings must jump down and make their way to water. However, because they are so light, they are normally able to do this without injury.

Pintail (Northern)

• ORDER • Anseriformes **• FAMILY •** Anatidae **• SPECIES •** *Anas acuta*

VITAL STATISTICS

WEIGHT	
MALES	900g (31.7oz)
FEMALES	700g (24.7oz)
LENGTH	51–62cm (20.1–24.4in)
WINGSPAN	79–87cm (31.1–34.2in)
SEXUAL MATURITY	1 year
LAYS EGGS	April–June
INCUBATION PERIOD	22–24 days
FLEDGLING PERIOD	40–45 days
NUMBER OF EGGS	7–9 eggs
NUMBER OF BROODS	1 a year, but a second clutch is possible if the first fails
TYPICAL DIET	Insects and invertebrates in summer, aquatic plants and seeds in winter

With their slimline bodies, elongated tails and skilful aerial acrobatics, the elegant Pintail Duck is often referred to as 'the greyhound of the air'.

WHERE IN THE WORLD?

Lakes, rivers and wetlands are perfect habitats for Pintail Ducks. Found across Europe, Asia and North America, some birds are residents, but many migrate to North Africa, Asia and Latin America.

CREATURE COMPARISONS

Pintail chicks (shown) are precocial, which means that they are able to swim and feed from the time they hatch. Despite this, they offer easy pickings for predators, such as foxes and crows, and it is estimated that only half of all chicks survive long enough to breed.

Pintail chicks

WINGS
Pintails are very fast fliers, holding their wings at a swept-back angle in the air, rather than straight out.

TAIL
The Pintails' scientific name, *Anas acuta* means duck sharpen in Latin, in reference to the males' distinctive, pointed tail.

LEGS
Dabbling ducks, like Pintails, upend themselves in water to feed. To help, their feet are set well back on the body.

HOW BIG IS IT?

SPECIAL ADAPTATION

With their shorter tails and mottled, light brown plumage, female Pintails look very similar to many other species of female waterfowl. The reason for such drab coloration is safety. It is the females' job to incubate the eggs, so it is important that they are well camouflaged.

Shoveler (Northern)

• ORDER • Anseriformes **• FAMILY •** Anatidae **• SPECIES •** *Anas clypeata*

VITAL STATISTICS

WEIGHT	
MALES	470g–1kg (16.6oz–2.2lb)
FEMALES	470–800 g (16.6–28.2oz)
LENGTH	44–52cm (17.3–20.5in)
WINGSPAN	73–82cm (28.7–32.3in)
SEXUAL MATURITY	1 year
LAYS EGGS	April–June, depending on location
INCUBATION PERIOD	22–23 days
NUMBER OF EGGS	9–11 eggs
NUMBER OF BROODS	1 a year
TYPICAL DIET	Aquatic vegetation, insects, crustaceans and molluscs
LIFE SPAN	Up to 13 years

Shovelers are also known as spoonbill ducks because of their unique bills, which are large and shaped like a spatula.

WHERE IN THE WORLD?

Northern Shovelers breed on wetlands in Europe, northern and central Asia and North America. Some birds are resident while others winter in northeastern and south Africa, southern Asia and the Americas.

CREATURE COMPARISONS

Apart from their spatula-shaped bills, male Shovelers look remarkably similar to male Mallards, with their arresting green and chestnut plumage. In fact, in the USA, some hunters call them 'neighbour's Mallards' because they give the Shovelers to their neighbours and keep the tastier Mallards for themselves.

Male Mallard

BODY
In appearance, male Northern Shovelers (shown here) are dramatically different to the female birds, which have mainly brown mottled plumage.

HEAD
The striking, iridescent green head of the male Northern Shoveler makes these birds one of the more recognizable species of Duck.

BILL
Shovelers' bills are lined with comb-like lamellae, which filter food from the water as they sweep their bills from side to side.

HOW BIG IS IT?

SPECIAL ADAPTATION
Dabbling ducks, like Shovelers, have their legs set far back on their bodies so that they can upend themselves to feed, with ease. This makes them quite bottom heavy so, while they are strong fliers, getting airborne needs an energetic run-up, often across water.

Common Teal

• **ORDER** • Anseriformes • **FAMILY** • Anatidae • **SPECIES** • *Anas crecca*

VITAL STATISTICS

WEIGHT	300–400g (10.6–14.1oz)
LENGTH	34–38cm (13.4–15.0in)
WINGSPAN	55–60cm (21.7–23.6in)
NUMBER OF EGGS	8–10 eggs
INCUBATION PERIOD	21–23 days
NUMBER OF BROODS	1 a year
TYPICAL DIET	Small aquatic animals, aquatic plants
LIFE SPAN	Up to 16 years

The Common Teal is the smallest of the dabbling ducks, and a familiar sight across much of Europe.

WHERE IN THE WORLD?

The Common Teal breeds across much of northern Europe and Asia. Birds from northern and eastern areas usually migrate to southwestern Europe for the winter.

CREATURE COMPARISONS

During the breeding season, the male has grey flanks and back, and a lighter grey underside with darker spots along the breast. The wings are also greyish with white and green stripes along the upper side. The head is handsomely chestnut with a green cheek. The underside of the tail is yellow. Females are much drabber and are mottled brown and grey.

Wings

WINGS
The adult male can be recognized even at a distance by his small size and white stripe across the shoulder.

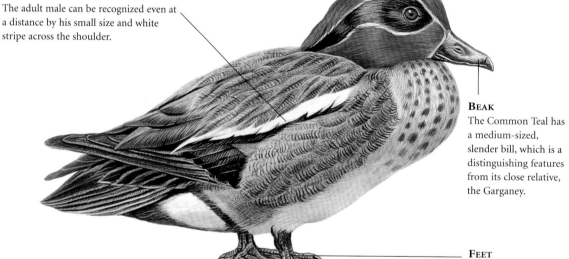

BEAK
The Common Teal has a medium-sized, slender bill, which is a distinguishing features from its close relative, the Garganey.

FEET
The short legs are set far back on the body, and its large feet are webbed for efficient swimming.

SPECIAL ADAPTATION

The male performs a courtship dance on the water to attract a female. He shakes his head and utters a high-pitched call, raises his tail and finally raises his head.

HOW BIG IS IT?

Baikal Teal

• ORDER • Anseriformes **• FAMILY •** Anatidae **• SPECIES •** *Anas formosa*

VITAL STATISTICS

WEIGHT	360–520g (12.6–18.2 oz)
LENGTH	39–43cm (15.4–16.9in)
WINGSPAN	57–70cm (22.4–27.6in)
NUMBER OF EGGS	6–9 eggs
INCUBATION PERIOD	23–25 days
NUMBER OF BROODS	1 a year
TYPICAL DIET	Aquatic plants, grasses, seeds, water insects and worms
LIFE SPAN	Unknown

It is not surprising that scientists named the Baikal teal *formosa,* because this is the Latin word for beautiful.

WHERE IN THE WORLD?

The Baikal Teal breeds in eastern Siberia from the Yenisey Basin and eastwards to the Kamchatka Peninsula, but migrates south for the winter to Japan, the Koreas and northeastern China.

CREATURE COMPARISONS

The male is strikingly beautiful, and has bright yellow and green markings on the face, while the top of the head is mottled dark green and black. The throat is chestnut with dark spots, the flanks and breast are greyish-blue, the wings are slate-grey or bluish, and there are long red, brown and creamy feathers on the shoulders. Females are much drabber, and have a brownish, speckled plumage.

Female

WINGS
Males have a bright green band on the wing, which can be seen only during flight.

BEAK
The bill is large and flat, and has serrated edges for biting off aquatic plants and capturing small creatures.

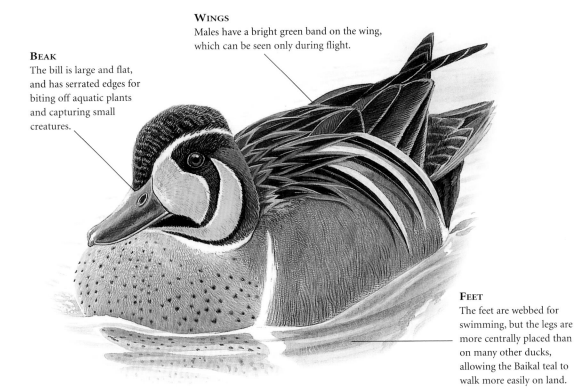

FEET
The feet are webbed for swimming, but the legs are more centrally placed than on many other ducks, allowing the Baikal teal to walk more easily on land.

HOW BIG IS IT?

SPECIAL ADAPTATION

The male uses his stunning colour to attract females during the breeding season. During courtship displays, he dances and struts before the female, throwing his head backwards.

Eurasian Wigeon

• ORDER • Anseriformes **• FAMILY •** Anatidae **• SPECIES •** *Anas penelope*

VITAL STATISTICS

WEIGHT	700–1000g (26.5–35.3oz)
LENGTH	42–50cm (16.5–19.7in)
WINGSPAN	70–80cm (27.6–31.5in)
NUMBER OF EGGS	6–12 eggs (usually 8–9)
INCUBATION PERIOD	22–25 days
NUMBER OF BROODS	1 a year
TYPICAL DIET	Mainly different grasses, but also leaves, roots and seeds
LIFE SPAN	Up to 10 years

This Eurasian Wigeon is often seen along coasts in northern Europe during the winter season, sometimes in huge flocks of thousands of birds.

WHERE IN THE WORLD?

The Wigeon breeds in the northern part of Europe and Asia, even well within the Polar Circle. As winter approaches, they migrate south to mid- or southern Europe, North Africa and even to Southeast Asia.

CREATURE COMPARISONS

This species of dabbling duck is vividly coloured, and in the breeding season, the male has a chestnut or reddish head and neck, with a yellow stripe across the top of the head. The upper side and flanks are greyish, and the wings have a bright white patch and are black towards the rear. The underside is pinkish and the belly is white. The plumage of females is light brown and much drabber.

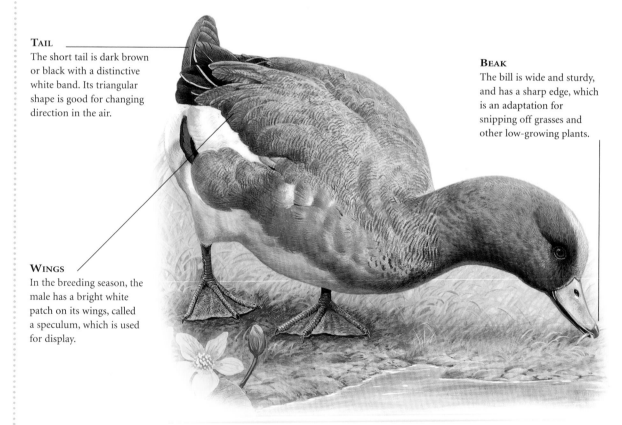

TAIL
The short tail is dark brown or black with a distinctive white band. Its triangular shape is good for changing direction in the air.

WINGS
In the breeding season, the male has a bright white patch on its wings, called a speculum, which is used for display.

BEAK
The bill is wide and sturdy, and has a sharp edge, which is an adaptation for snipping off grasses and other low-growing plants.

Female

HOW BIG IS IT?

SPECIAL ADAPTATION

The male is very colourful during the breeding season. His bright colours attract females, but also make him more visible to predators. Outside the breeding season the males become much drabber, and tend to resemble females.

Mallard

With their waddling walk and their renowned quacking call, Mallards are probably the most famous and distinctively duck-like of all duck species.

VITAL STATISTICS

WEIGHT	
MALES	1.2kg (2.6lb)
FEMALES	975 g (34.4oz)
LENGTH	50–60cm (19.7–23.6in)
WINGSPAN	81–95cm (31.9–37.4in)
SEXUAL MATURITY	1 year
LAYS EGGS	February–May, depending on location
INCUBATION PERIOD	27–28 days
NUMBER OF EGGS	4–18 eggs
NUMBER OF BROODS	1 a year
TYPICAL DIET	Plants and insects
LIFE SPAN	Typically 3 years but up to 20

WHERE IN THE WORLD?

Found throughout North America, Europe and Asia, Mallards have also been introduced – with great success – to Australasia. Northern birds usually migrate south in winter.

CREATURE COMPARISONS

The plumage of the male Mallard is so different to the females' that it used to be believed that the two birds belonged to different species. However both have a patch of purple on the speculum (part of the flight feathers), which is visible at rest.

Female with her young

BODY
With their unremarkable, mottled brown plumage, it can be hard to distinguish one species of female duck from another. Males like this one are more colourful though.

LEGS
Like most species of water fowl, Mallards have short legs and webbed feet, which are set well back on the body.

FEET
Mallards splay out their feet when they land, using them like water skis to slow themselves down as they hit the surface of the water.

HOW BIG IS IT?

SPECIAL ADAPTATION
Mallards are dabbling ducks, which means they feed by upending themselves in water and grazing on the food below. Their broad bills are lined with keratinous plates, called lamellae, and as their tongues pump water through the bill, tiny invertebrates and seeds are trapped inside.

Garganey

• **ORDER** • Anseriformes • **FAMILY** • Anatidae • **SPECIES** • *Anas querquedula*

VITAL STATISTICS

WEIGHT	350–500g (12.3–17.6oz)
LENGTH	37–41cm (14.6–16.1in)
WINGSPAN	58–70cm (22.8–27.6in)
NUMBER OF EGGS	7–11 eggs (usually 8–9)
INCUBATION PERIOD	21–23 days
NUMBER OF BROODS	1 a year
TYPICAL DIET	Mainly aquatic plants, grasses, and small aquatic invertebrates
LIFE SPAN	Up to 10 years

The Garganey, a small dabbling duck, is strongly migratory, and abandons its breeding grounds in Europe when winter approaches.

WHERE IN THE WORLD?

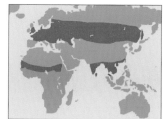

The Garganey is common in Europe (except northern Scandinavia, the Iberian Peninsula and the coast of the Mediterranean), and extends across central Asia. It winters in central Africa and Southeast Asia.

CREATURE COMPARISONS

The adult male is very beautiful. The top of the head is brown, and a broad, white stripe extends across the eye and down the neck. The throat is mottled with white and light brown, and the chest is also light brown. The flanks are grey, and there are long, loose feathers near the shoulders with a greyish-blue tint and a white stripe. Females are much drabber and are mottled brown with a grey neck.

BEAK
The wide bill is grey, and the upper bill has slightly serrated edges, helping the duck bite off plants.

WING
The wing has a pale bluish patch, called a speculum, which is edged in white. It is used for display during the breeding season.

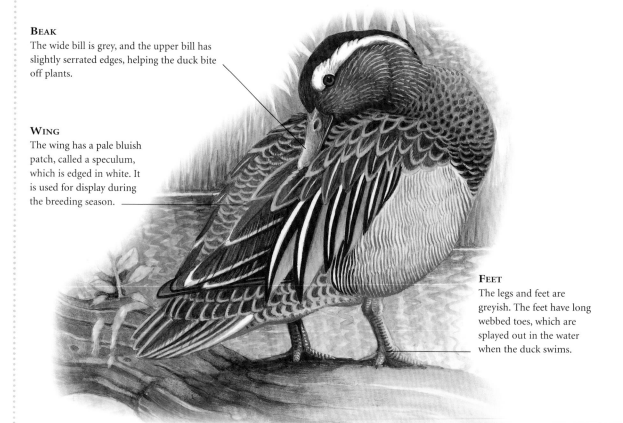

FEET
The legs and feet are greyish. The feet have long webbed toes, which are splayed out in the water when the duck swims.

Female Garganey

HOW BIG IS IT?

SPECIAL ADAPTATION

A bright patch of feathers on each of the males' wings is used as display to females in the breeding season, but it is also highly visible in flight. This helps the birds in a flock to stay in contact with each other.

Greylag Goose

VITAL STATISTICS

WEIGHT	2.3–5.5kg (5.1–12.1lb)
LENGTH	74–87cm (29.1–34.3in)
WINGSPAN	147–175cm (57.9–68.9in)
NUMBER OF EGGS	4–8 eggs (usually 4–6)
INCUBATION PERIOD	27–29 days
NUMBER OF BROODS	1 a year
TYPICAL DIET	Strictly herbivores, feeding on grasses, leaves, roots, seeds and fruit
LIFE SPAN	Up to 20 years

This goose is known for being the bird that was used by the world-renowned scientist, Konrad Lorenz, for his ground-breaking studies of animal behaviour in the 1930s.

WHERE IN THE WORLD?

The Greylag Goose is found in central and eastern Europe, and it is also widely distributed across much of Asia, except the northern parts. It no longer seems to breed in southwestern Europe.

CREATURE COMPARISONS

The Greylag Goose is a large bird, with a greyish head, neck, breast and upper and underside. However, the underside of the tail is white. The wings are darker grey with a silvery-grey leading edge on the large wing feathers. The male and female are similar, but males are often distinctly larger.

Adult Greylag

BEAK
The long bill is orange-pink or yellow in geese from Europe, while it is decidedly pink in geese from Asia.

WINGS
The wings are large and wide, giving the goose a fast, powerful flight, and enabling it to undertake long migrations.

BODY
The Greylag Goose has a large, stocky body, and stores fat under the skin before migrating south.

HOW BIG IS IT?

SPECIAL ADAPTATION

The Greylag Goose is one of the last waterfowl to migrate south in autumn in large 'v'-shaped formations. This delay is probably the origin of its popular name, from the English word laggard, which means loiterer.

Snow Goose

• **ORDER** • Anseriformes • **FAMILY** • Anatidae • **SPECIES** • *Anser caerulescens*

VITAL STATISTICS

WEIGHT	1.9–5.2kg (4.2–11.5lb)
LENGTH	66–85cm (26.0–33.5in)
WINGSPAN	135–165cm (53.1–65.0in)
NUMBER OF EGGS	3–10 eggs (usually 4–6)
INCUBATION PERIOD	23–26 days
NUMBER OF BROODS	1 a year
TYPICAL DIET	Grasses, leaves, seeds, aquatic plants, insects
LIFE SPAN	Up to 10 years

The large, white Snow Goose has two subspecies, which differ from each other in size, and breeds in the high Arctic.

WHERE IN THE WORLD?

The Lesser Snow Goose breeds in the high Arctic, on the northeastern coast of Siberia and in western and northern Canada. The Greater Snow Goose breeds in eastern Canada and on the west coast of Greenland.

CREATURE COMPARISONS

The Snow Goose has a uniformly white plumage, with distinctive black wing tips. The legs and beak are yellow or yellowish pink. Males are similar to females. Curiously, there appear to be two colour types. Most Lesser Snow Geese are white, but a pale blue-grey form is also common. They appear not to interbreed. The blue-grey form is very rare in the Greater Snow Goose.

Blue-grey Lesser Snow Goose

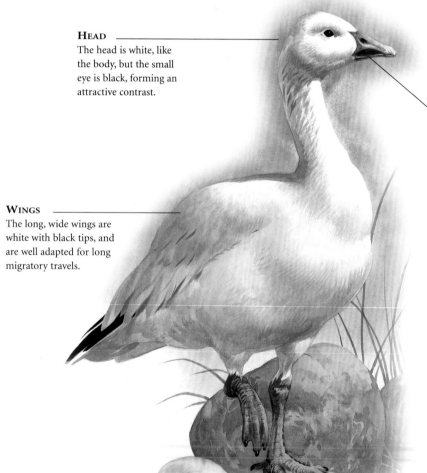

HEAD
The head is white, like the body, but the small eye is black, forming an attractive contrast.

BEAK
The short bill is stout and strong, and has a cutting edge along the upper bill for shearing off grasses and other plants.

WINGS
The long, wide wings are white with black tips, and are well adapted for long migratory travels.

HOW BIG IS IT?

SPECIAL ADAPTATION

Snow Geese pair for life, and build a large, round nest on a high spot, enabling them to look out for predators such as the Arctic fox. The birds have to feed intensively so that they can raise their goslings in the short Arctic summer.

Tufted Duck

• ORDER • Anseriformes • FAMILY • Anatidae • SPECIES • *Aythya fuligula*

VITAL STATISTICS

WEIGHT	760g (26oz)
LENGTH	40–47cm (15.7–18.5in)
WINGSPAN	70–80cm (27.6–31.5in)
NUMBER OF EGGS	8–12 eggs
INCUBATION PERIOD	24–27 days
NUMBER OF BROODS	1 a year
TYPICAL DIET	Snails and other molluscs, aquatic insects, some plant matter and seeds
LIFE SPAN	Up to 15 years

The Tufted Duck, a type of diving duck, is often seen in large flocks on lakes and ponds or near coastal areas.

WHERE IN THE WORLD?

The Tufted Duck is common throughout northern Europe and Asia, extending eastwards to the Sea of Okhotsk. It is sometimes found along the coasts of Canada and the USA in winter.

CREATURE COMPARISONS

During the breeding season, the adult male's head and neck, back, upper side of the wings and tail are jet black, while the lower side of the wings, belly and breast are strikingly white. Females are dark brown with pale flanks and a white belly. Outside the breeding season, the males become drabber, and resemble females to a greater extent.

Female (top), male (bottom)

HEAD
The male Tufted Duck has a tuft of long feathers along the back of the head, which has given this species of bird its popular name.

WINGS
A wide, white band along the entire back edge of the male's black wings is visible only during flight.

FEET
The feet are large and webbed for swimming, and are set far back on the body, giving the duck an awkward waddle on land.

HOW BIG IS IT?

SPECIAL ADAPTATION
The males' conspicuous head-crest of long feathers is used in display to females during the breeding season. He will raise and lower the crest, while bobbing his head.

27

Scaup (Greater)

• **ORDER** • Anseriformes • **FAMILY** • Anatidae • **SPECIES** • *Aythya marila*

VITAL STATISTICS

WEIGHT	1kg (2.2lb)
LENGTH	42–51cm (16.5–20in)
WINGSPAN	71–80cm (27.5–31.5in)
SEXUAL MATURITY	2 years
INCUBATION PERIOD	26–28 days
FLEDGLING PERIOD	40–45 days
NUMBER OF EGGS	8–10 eggs
NUMBER OF BROODS	1 a year
TYPICAL DIET	Aquatic plants; occasionally molluscs, especially in winter
LIFE SPAN	Up to 8 years

Greater Scaups are a gregarious species. They are most often seen across northern sea coasts where they breed, gathering in marshes and brackish, saltwater bogs.

WHERE IN THE WORLD?

These ducks breed in northern Europe, Asia and sub-Arctic areas of North America, preferring saltwater to freshwater. Populations overwinter in southern Europe, eastern China and southern USA.

CREATURE COMPARISONS

Female Scaups differ from males by their brown breasts and the patch of white around their bill. However, when Scaups and Tufted Ducks are side by side, identifying species is more difficult because males and females have similar plumage.

Female Scaups (top), Tufted Ducks (bottom)

BILL
Greater Scaups are also sometimes known, colloquially, as Blue Bills due to the pale blue tint on their bills.

HEAD
During the breeding season, the plumage on the head of the male Scaup is almost black, with an iridescent green sheen.

BODY
From a distance, male breeding plumage appears black and white. Up close, grey vermiculation (worm-like patterns) are visible on the back.

HOW BIG IS IT?

SPECIAL ADAPTATION

Scaups feed by diving for food underwater. Their bodies are therefore much more streamlined than those of other ducks. Even their wings are shorter than those of dabbling ducks, to prevent them from getting in the way when the birds plunge into the depths.

Brent Goose

VITAL STATISTICS

WEIGHT	1.3–1.7kg (2.9–3.7lb)
LENGTH	56–61cm (21.7–24.0in)
WINGSPAN	110–120cm (43.3–47.2in)
NUMBER OF EGGS	3–5 eggs
INCUBATION PERIOD	24–26 days
NUMBER OF BROODS	1 a year
TYPICAL DIET	Seaweeds, eel-grass, grasses, moss, lichen
LIFE SPAN	Up to 13 years

The Brent Goose breeds in the high Arctic, and there are two distinct species. These can be distinguished by the colour of the breast.

WHERE IN THE WORLD?

It breeds across the Arctic, from Siberia, Scandinavia, the east and west of Greenland, Alaska and northern Canada. It winters in northwest Europe, North America and eastern Asia.

CREATURE COMPARISONS

The Brent Goose is a small, dark species with a black head and neck, and a white collar around the throat. The lower part of the tail is white, and the back and upper side of the wings are brown. Some have a white breast, but the most common species, which breeds in northern Siberia, has a pale brown or greyish-brown breast.

Pale grey-brown belly

WINGS
The wings are large and elongate, and are well adapted for undertaking long migrations of thousands of kilometres.

FEET
The large grey feet have long webbed toes, which are excellent for fast efficient swimming and paddling.

BEAK
The Brent Goose has a short, delicate touch-sensitive bill, which it uses to pluck seaweeds and grasses.

HOW BIG IS IT?

SPECIAL ADAPTATION

Brent Geese feed extensively on eel-grasses, and can often be seen swimming about in shallow coastal waters while continuously upending. In this position, they stretch their long neck to reach down to feed off the eel-grasses.

Canada Goose

• ORDER • Anseriformes **• FAMILY •** Anatidae **• SPECIES •** *Branta canadensis*

VITAL STATISTICS

WEIGHT	
MALES	3.2–6.5kg (7–14.3lb)
FEMALES	2.5–5.5kg (5.5–12.1lb)
LENGTH	90cm–1m (35.4 in–3.3ft)
WINGSPAN	1.6–1.7 m (5.2–5.6ft)
SEXUAL MATURITY	3 years
INCUBATION PERIOD	28–30 days
FLEDGLING PERIOD	40–48 days
NUMBER OF EGGS	4–7 eggs
NUMBER OF BROODS	1 a year
TYPICAL DIET	Grass, leaves and seeds
LIFE SPAN	Typically 6 years

The widespread Canada Goose is just as famous for its evocative honk and yodelling calls as it is for its distinctive black and white plumage.

WHERE IN THE WORLD?

Although Canada Geese are natives of North America, populations have settled in northern Europe, eastern Siberia, eastern China and Japan. They enjoy a wide range of habitats, but usually nest beside water.

CREATURE COMPARISONS

Although there has been much debate on the subject, it is now accepted that there are seven sub-species of Canada Goose. The Aleutian Cackling Goose (shown) was originally considered a sub-species of the Canada Goose but, in July 2004, it was reclassified as a separate species, *Branta hutchinsii.*

WINGS
Canada Geese are most often seen at dusk, flying with long, slow wing beats, back home to their nests to roost.

NECK
A long neck enables this adaptable bird to take advantage of a wide range of food, from underwater vegetation to overhanging leaves.

FEET
Large, webbed feet are designed both to spread the birds' weight on muddy ground and propel them through water.

Aleutian Cackling Goose

HOW BIG IS IT?

SPECIAL ADAPTATION

Generally, birds of the same species are larger the further north they are found. This natural adaptation helps to keep the birds warm. The Canada Goose is the exception to the rule, as southern races tend to be larger, such as this Giant Canada Goose (shown).

Hawaiian Goose

• ORDER • Anseriformes • FAMILY • Anatidae • SPECIES • *Branta sandvicensis*

VITAL STATISTICS

WEIGHT	1.4–2.5kg (3.1–5.5lb)
LENGTH	56–70cm (22.0–27.6in)
WINGSPAN	105–135cm (41.3–53.1in)
NUMBER OF EGGS	3–5 eggs
INCUBATION PERIOD	27–29 days
NUMBER OF BROODS	1 a year
TYPICAL DIET	Grasses, leaves, fruit, berries, sometimes insects and spiders
LIFE SPAN	Up to 30 years

This goose is the official bird of the US state of Hawaii, and is known locally as the Nene.

WHERE IN THE WORLD?

The Hawaiian Goose is found only on the islands of Hawaii and Maui in the Pacific Ocean. Geese were once also present on the Hawaiian islands of Kaua'i and O'ahu, but they have since disappeared.

CREATURE COMPARISONS

The adult male has a black head and a pale orange cheek. The throat is handsomely adorned with white and black stripes, while the breast is pale buff with large, greyish-brown patches along the flanks. The wings are dark brown to black. Females are similar to males, but usually slightly drabber, and are distinctly smaller in size.

Male Hawaiian Goose

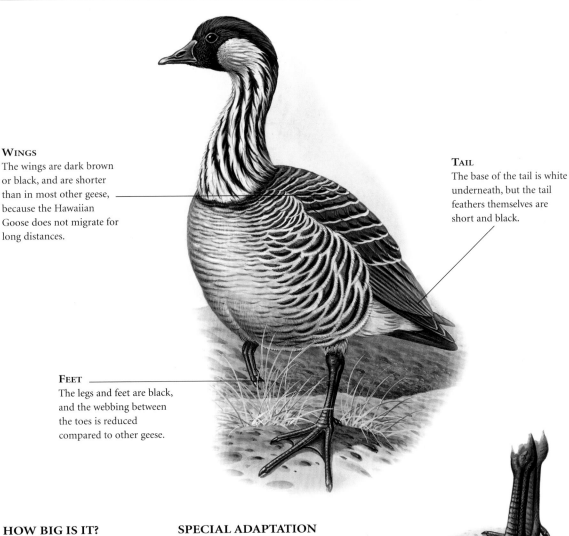

WINGS
The wings are dark brown or black, and are shorter than in most other geese, because the Hawaiian Goose does not migrate for long distances.

TAIL
The base of the tail is white underneath, but the tail feathers themselves are short and black.

FEET
The legs and feet are black, and the webbing between the toes is reduced compared to other geese.

HOW BIG IS IT?

SPECIAL ADAPTATION

Geese usually have fully webbed toes, but the Hawaiian Goose has much reduced webbing. This is an adaptation for living on land and walking on old volcano lava-plains, instead of paddling around in shallow water.

Mute Swan

• **ORDER** • Anseriformes • **FAMILY** • Anatidae • **SPECIES** • *Cygnus olor*

VITAL STATISTICS

WEIGHT	
MALES	11.5kg (25.3lb)
FEMALES	9kg (19.8lb)
LENGTH	1.4–1.6m (4.6–5.2ft)
WINGSPAN	2–2.4m (6.6–7.9ft)
SEXUAL MATURITY	
MALES	3 years
FEMALES	4 years
LAYS EGGS	March–May
INCUBATION PERIOD	34–38 days
NUMBER OF EGGS	5–7 eggs
NUMBER OF BROODS	1 a year
TYPICAL DIET	Aquatic plants, grass, insects; occasionally amphibians and small fish
LIFE SPAN	Typically 10 years

With its exquisite beauty and form, it is easy to see why Ancient Britons regarded Mute Swans as sacred. Even today, these graceful birds are one of Britain's most popular residents.

WHERE IN THE WORLD?

Mute Swans are common in temperate regions of western Europe, but less prevalent in eastern Europe and Asia. They have also been introduced into North America, South Africa and Australasia.

CREATURE COMPARISONS

The bulbous, black knob at the base of the Mute Swans' bill helps ornithologists to identify males and females. Females have a larger knob than the males. Juveniles of either sex don't develop this feature until they reach sexual maturity.

BILL
The Mute Swans' orange bill helps differentiate them from Whooper Swans and Bewick's Swans, which have yellow bills.

NECK
The elegant, long neck is held straight while in flight, but usually in an 's' shape on the ground.

BODY
Male Mute Swans, known as cobs, are one of the heaviest flying birds. Females, called pens, are much lighter.

Female (top), juvenile (bottom)

HOW BIG IS IT?

SPECIAL ADAPTATION
Mute Swans bodies are bottom heavy. This lets them feed by upending themselves in water (a technique called dabbling) and grazing on the aquatic vegetation, below. Their long necks give them access to food sources that other dabbling birds, such as Mallards, cannot reach.

Harlequin Duck

• ORDER • Anseriformes • FAMILY • Anatidae • SPECIES • *Histrionicus histrionicus*

VITAL STATISTICS

WEIGHT	500–800g (17.6–28.2oz)
LENGTH	38–50cm (15.0–19.7in)
WINGSPAN	57–75cm (22.4–29.5in)
NUMBER OF EGGS	4–10 eggs (usually 5–7)
INCUBATION PERIOD	26–29 days
NUMBER OF BROODS	1 a year
TYPICAL DIET	Snails, aquatic insect larvae, crayfish
LIFE SPAN	Unknown

This duck is known by almost a dozen different names, but is most often called Harlequin Duck in Europe and Lords and Ladies in North America.

WHERE IN THE WORLD?

The Harlequin Duck is found in coastal areas of eastern Russia, along the southern coasts of Greenland, on Iceland, and on both the northeastern and northwestern coasts of North America.

CREATURE COMPARISONS

The male is most colourful. The side of his face and neck and along his upper back are slate-blue, the flanks are chestnut, and his tail and wings are dark slate-grey. There are numerous bright white markings along his face and throat, and at the base of his wings. Females are much drabber and have a brownish-grey plumage with a white patch on her cheek.

Juvenile Harlequin Duck

BEAK
The bill is short and stout, and is well adapted for searching for small creatures among the rocks in fast-moving water.

BODY
The Harlequin Duck has a compact, heavy-set body, which provides good insulation in the cold rivers.

FEET
The feet are large and webbed, and are used for paddling and diving under the surface in pursuit of prey.

HOW BIG IS IT?

SPECIAL ADAPTATION

This colourful duck appears very conspicuous, but bobbing around on the surface of the fast-moving streams where it lives, the many colours and patterns make it blend into the constantly changing backdrop of blue-grey water.

Smew

• ORDER • Anseriformes • FAMILY • Anatidae • SPECIES • *Mergellus albellus*

VITAL STATISTICS

WEIGHT		
MALES	700g (24.7oz)	
FEMALES	580g (20.4oz)	
LENGTH	38–44cm (15–17.3in)	
WINGSPAN	56–59cm (22–23.2in)	
SEXUAL MATURITY	2 years	
LAYS EGGS	From May	
INCUBATION PERIOD	26–28 days	
NUMBER OF EGGS	5–11 eggs	
NUMBER OF BROODS	1 a year	
TYPICAL DIET	Fish and insects in the winter	
HABITS	Diurnal, migratory	

The stylish, cracked-ice breeding plumage of the male Smew makes these little ducks one of Britain's most eagerly anticipated – but rare – winter visitors.

WHERE IN THE WORLD?

These attractive little ducks breed in trees, close to the fish-rich rivers of northern Europe and Asia. In September, populations fly south for the winter, finding shelter in inland lakes and seas.

WINGS
The Smew's agility in the air enables it to nest beside tree-shrouded lakes that would be inaccessible to larger birds.

CREATURE COMPARISONS

Male Smews, in their black and white breeding finery, are unmistakable. Females (shown) with their brown-grey bodies, white cheeks and chestnut head are easy to confuse with other water fowl, especially Ruddy Ducks. Males in their eclipse plumage, which occurs after breeding, look similar to females.

BILL
Smews' bills are shorter than those of other sawbills like the Red-Breasted Merganser. This is because they eat smaller prey.

BODY
The word smew is believed to be a corruption of the word small, referring to the bird's compact size.

Female Smew

HOW BIG IS IT?

SPECIAL ADAPTATION

Smews belong to a group of ducks known as sawbills. The name comes from the serrated edges that run along the length of their bills. Typically, there is also a small hook at the tip of the bill. These adaptations enable sawbills to grip prey more easily.

Goosander

VITAL STATISTICS

WEIGHT	
MALES	1.7kg (3.7lb)
FEMALES	1.3kg (2.9lb)
LENGTH	58–68cm (22.8–26.8in)
WINGSPAN	78–94cm (30.7–37in)
SEXUAL MATURITY	2 years
INCUBATION PERIOD	30–32 days
FLEDGLING PERIOD	60–70 days
NUMBER OF EGGS	8–11 eggs
NUMBER OF BROODS	1 a year
TYPICAL DIET	Fish
LIFE SPAN	Up to 9 years

Goosanders are expert hunters – and they need to be. Goosander chicks require around 33kg (72lb) of fish to fuel their change into adults.

WHERE IN THE WORLD?

These ducks are found in northern and central Europe, northern Asia and western North America. Preferred habitats are lakes, rivers and estuaries, with mature trees for nesting in.

CREATURE COMPARISONS

Goosanders are also called Common Mergansers and the resemblance to their Red-Breasted cousins is clear. These handsome birds are also related to the Smew which, at first glance, could not look more different. However, all three species are sawbills, and are expert divers that sport a handsome crest.

Smew

HEAD
It is easy to distinguish male Goosanders from females. Males have a dark green head, and females have a brown head.

CREST
The birds' bulky crest, which stretches from the crown to the nape of the neck, makes the Goosanders' head appear wedge shaped.

NECK
The Goosander's long neck is obvious when the bird is in flight. When it is swimming, the neck is often folded down.

HOW BIG IS IT?

SPECIAL ADAPTATION
Along with other species of Merganser, Goosanders are known as sawbills. This is a reference to the tooth-like lamellae along the cutting edges of their bills, which help them grip prey. A hook on the end of the bill works just like a fishing hook.

Red-crested Pochard

• **ORDER** • Anseriformes • **FAMILY** • Anatidae • **SPECIES** • *Netta rufina*

VITAL STATISTICS

WEIGHT	750–1200g (26.5–42.3oz)
LENGTH	53–57cm (20.9–22.4in)
WINGSPAN	90–105cm (35.4–41.3in)
NUMBER OF EGGS	6–12 eggs
INCUBATION PERIOD	25–26 days
NUMBER OF BROODS	1 a year
TYPICAL DIET	Mainly aquatic plants, seeds, also small creatures
LIFE SPAN	Up to 10 years

Adult male Pochards are among the most beautiful of all ducks, but the females of the species are drab.

WHERE IN THE WORLD?

Isolated populations are found in parts of central and northern Europe, but the duck is more common in Spain. It is also found in parts of the Middle East, but the largest populations are found in Southeast Asia.

CREATURE COMPARISONS

The adult male is most handsome, and has a golden-red head, black neck and breast, and a bright red bill. The flanks are white, and the back and wings are brownish. The tail is black. Females look entirely different, and are uniformly pale brown with a white cheek and throat. The top of the head is darker brown.

Female

WING
The male has a wide, bright white band along the back edge of the wing, which is visible only during flight.

HEAD
The male has a beautiful red head, and the feathers on top of the head can be raised to form a crest.

LEGS
The legs are bright orange-red and the feet are wide and webbed as an adaptation for swimming.

HOW BIG IS IT?

SPECIAL ADAPTATION
Unlike most other pochards, the Red-crested Pochard has a rather narrow, elongated bill. This is probably because they feed mainly on water plants instead of small creatures.

Comb Duck

• ORDER • Anseriformes **• FAMILY •** Anatidae **• SPECIES •** *Sarkidiornis melanotos*

This unusual looking duck is formally known as the Knob-billed Duck and is widespread in the tropics. It is the only known species of the genus *Sarkidiornis*.

VITAL STATISTICS

LENGTH	56–76cm (22.0–29.9in)
WINGSPAN	95–120cm (37.4–47.2in)
NUMBER OF EGGS	6–20 eggs (usually 10–15)
INCUBATION PERIOD	26–29 days
NUMBER OF BROODS	1 a year
TYPICAL DIET	Aquatic plants, grasses, also insects, worms, crayfish and even small fish
LIFE SPAN	unknown

WHERE IN THE WORLD?

The Comb Duck is found in wetlands across tropical South America; Africa south of the Sahara desert; Madagascar; and southern Asia from Pakistan to Laos and the southernmost regions of China.

CREATURE COMPARISONS

This unusual-looking duck has a white neck with lots of small, dark brown spots and a shiny white breast. The upper part of the body and wings are glossy bluish-black. There is a rusty brown or reddish band on the hind part of the wing. Birds from South America have dark brown or black flanks, and birds from Africa and Asia have greyish-blue flanks. Males are similar to females, but have stronger colours and are larger.

Female Comb Duck

HEAD
The white head is freckled with dark spots, and the eyes are handsomely dark.

BEAK
The most conspicuous feature of the Comb Duck is the huge knob on top of the bill. This is present only in the male of the species.

FEET
The feet are large and webbed for swimming, but the legs are set wide apart and the toes are strong, allowing the bird to perch on branches.

HOW BIG IS IT?

SPECIAL ADAPTATION

The huge, strange-looking fleshy comb on the males' bill is used to attract females during the breeding season. This would appear to be its only function, because it is not used in feeding.

Eider (Common)

• ORDER • Anseriformes • FAMILY • Anatidae • SPECIES • *Somateria mollissima*

VITAL STATISTICS

WEIGHT	2.2kg (4.8lb)
LENGTH	60–70cm (23.6–27.5in)
WINGSPAN	95cm–1 m (37.4 in–3.3ft)
SEXUAL MATURITY	2–3 years
LAYS EGGS	May–June
INCUBATION PERIOD	25–28 days
NUMBER OF EGGS	4–6 eggs
NUMBER OF BROODS	1 a year
TYPICAL DIET	Mussels, clams and other aquatic invertebrates
LIFE SPAN	Typically 18 years

The soft, warm breast feathers of the female Eider have long been used to fill quilts. They are also useful for keeping the Eider warm in its harsh living environment.

WHERE IN THE WORLD?

Eiders breed and nest close to the sea, thriving in the cold, inhospitable waters of northern Europe, Asia and North America. Large flocks may move south in the winter to avoid pack ice.

CREATURE COMPARISONS

Female Eiders are predominantly brown with barred backs. Outside the breeding season, from July to November, males take on a duller, blackish-brown coloration. Both sexes can still be readily distinguished from other ducks by their body size and wedged head shape.

Female (above), male (below)

BODY
Breeding Eider males are unmistakable with their dramatic black-and-white plumage and green patches on the nape of the neck.

BILL
Eiders are one of the more bulky ducks, with large, rounded bodies, a short neck, big head and a powerful bill.

FEET
Like most water fowl, Eiders have legs set well back on their bodies. This makes them efficient swimmers.

HOW BIG IS IT?

SPECIAL ADAPTATION

Eiders use their webbed feet to help them dive deep in search of mussels and clams. Thanks to their design, Eider bills are powerful enough to make short work of the toughest shell, which the Eiders shatter to get at the soft flesh inside.

Shelduck (Common)

• **ORDER** • Anseriformes • **FAMILY** • Anatidae • **SPECIES** • *Tadorna tadorna*

VITAL STATISTICS

WEIGHT	1–1.5kg (2.2–3.3lb)
LENGTH	58–67cm (22.8–26.4in)
WINGSPAN	100–115cm (39.4–45.3in)
NUMBER OF EGGS	8–12 eggs (usually 8–10)
INCUBATION PERIOD	28–30 days
NUMBER OF BROODS	1 a year
TYPICAL DIET	Mainly marine snails, worms and crayfish
LIFE SPAN	Up to 15 years

The vividly coloured Shelduck is found in coastal areas, and easily draws attention because of its size and beautiful plumage.

WHERE IN THE WORLD?

The Shelduck is widespread and quite common in coastal areas in temperate Europe, and across much of temperate Asia. In winter, many populations migrate south to subtropical regions.

CREATURE COMPARISONS

This large duck is very beautiful and, in adult males, the lower part of the neck and the flanks and tail are bright white. There is a striking chestnut band around the breast and upper back, and the wing tips are black. The head and upper neck and two large areas on the upper back are dark green. The bill is strikingly red. Females are similar, but smaller and drabber.

Adult (top), juvenile (bottom)

BEAK
Both sexes have a large red bill, but the males have a large knob at the base of their bill.

HEAD
The head is dark green in colour, starkly contrasting with the very abrupt transition to the white lower neck.

FEET
The orange or pinkish legs are short and sturdy and the feet are large and webbed, so are well adapted for swimming.

HOW BIG IS IT?

SPECIAL ADAPTATION

This large, colourful duck often builds its nest underground, for example in such places as abandoned rabbit burrows. Sometimes it will even nest in a fox burrow, but the fox leaves the ducks alone as a neighbourly gesture!

White-faced Whistling Duck

• **ORDER** • Anseriformes • **FAMILY** • Dendrocygnidae • **SPECIES** • *Dendrocygna viduata*

VITAL STATISTICS

WEIGHT	450–800g (15.9–28.2oz)
LENGTH	38–48cm (15.0–18.9in)
WINGSPAN	58–78cm (22.8–30.7in)
NUMBER OF EGGS	4–13 eggs (usually 8–10)
INCUBATION PERIOD	25–28 days
NUMBER OF BROODS	1 a year
TYPICAL DIET	Aquatic plants, grasses, insects, snails, crayfish
LIFE SPAN	Up to 20 years

The colourful White-faced Whistling Duck can often be seen in huge flocks, numbering thousands of birds, on their way to good feeding grounds.

WHERE IN THE WORLD?

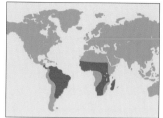

This duck is common in much of Africa south of the Sahara desert, but is not found in the rainforest-belt of central Africa. It is also widespread in South America, apart from the Andes Mountains.

CREATURE COMPARISONS

This duck has a white face and upper part of the neck, while the back of the head is dark brown or black. The anterior part of the breast and back are brown with dark markings, and the belly, most of the wings and the tail are dark brown to black. The legs and beak are grey. Females and males are similar, but the males tend to be smaller.

Juvenile

BEAK
The bill is long and sturdy, and is black at the base but becomes grey towards the tip.

WINGS
Unlike most ducks, the White-faced Whistling Duck has broad wings along their entire length, giving the bird a rather slow flight.

HEAD
The head has a characteristically white face, and the neck is long, enabling the bird to reach plants under the water's surface.

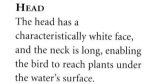

HOW BIG IS IT?

SPECIAL ADAPTATION
The White-faced Whistling Duck is highly gregarious, and flocks of thousands of birds arrive each morning to their favourite food sites. Living in flocks also gives good protection against predators.

Swift

VITAL STATISTICS

WEIGHT	35–50g (1.2–1.8oz)
LENGTH	16–17cm (6.3–6.7in)
WINGSPAN	32–40cm (12.6–15.7in)
NUMBER OF EGGS	1–4 eggs (usually 2–3)
INCUBATION PERIOD	18–23 days
NUMBER OF BROODS	1 a year
TYPICAL DIET	All kinds of flying insects
LIFE SPAN	Up to 17 years

CREATURE COMPARISONS

The Swift has a uniformly dark brown to almost blackish upper and underside of the body. The underside of the wings is dark and often has a greyish hue, with paler edges on the large wing feathers. The throat is pale whitish. The legs are very short and the wings are extremely long and narrow. Males and females look almost identical.

Juvenile

The Swift is a true high-flyer, and spends most of its time in the air. In fact, it is even able to sleep on the wing.

WHERE IN THE WORLD?

The Swift is found throughout most of Europe, except the high north, across central Asia, the Middle East, northern Africa, and northwestern China. It spends the winter in southern Africa.

WINGS
Very long narrow wings give the Swift a very fast and manoeuvrable flight, perfect for chasing flying insects in the air.

LEGS
The very short legs are adapted for clinging to vertical surfaces, but they make it difficult for the Swift to take off from the ground.

BEAK
The bill is very short and pointed, but the mouth is wide, and can be expanded even further when the bird is hunting insects in the air.

HOW BIG IS IT?

SPECIAL ADAPTATION

The Swift hunts insects in the air at high speeds. It can store insects in a pouch under its chin, and so can continue to catch many insects at a time before flying back to the nest to feeds its chicks.

Ruby-throated Hummingbird

• **ORDER** • Apodiformes • **FAMILY** • Trochilidae • **SPECIES** • *Archilochus colubris*

VITAL STATISTICS

WEIGHT	2–6g (0.1–0.2oz)
LENGTH	7–9cm (2.8–3.5in)
WINGSPAN	8–12cm (3.1–4.7in)
NUMBER OF EGGS	2 eggs
INCUBATION PERIOD	16–19 days
NUMBER OF BROODS	2–3 a year
TYPICAL DIET	Mainly nectar but also small insects and spiders
LIFE SPAN	Up to 5 years

The tiny Ruby-throated Hummingbird is no larger than a ping pong ball, but beats its wings 80 times a second when flying.

WHERE IN THE WORLD?

The Ruby-throated Hummingbird is found in the eastern part of the USA, extending into southern Canada. It winters in southern Mexico, Central America and northern South America.

CREATURE COMPARISONS

This beautiful little bird has a bright, metallic green upper side and wings, while the underside is whitish, often with a green hue along the sides and towards the tail. Males are easily distinguished from females by having a bright red throat (females have a uniformly white throat). Juvenile males resemble females.

Female (right), juvenile male (left)

TAIL
The short, wide, fan-shaped tail enables the bird to perform fast manoeuvres in the air.

WINGS
Short, narrow wings give this bird an extremely fast, elegant flight, and it can even fly backwards.

BEAK
The very long, straight bill is well adapted for poking deep into flowers in search of nectar.

HOW BIG IS IT?

SPECIAL ADAPTATION

A swivelling shoulder joint allows the Ruby-throated Hummingbird to tilt its wings. When the bird hovers, its wing-tips describe a figure-of-eight'. With its wings tilted forwards and downwards, the bird moves ahead.

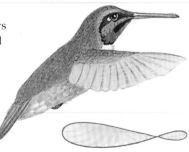

Bee Hummingbird

• **ORDER** • Apodiformes • **FAMILY** • Trochilidae • **SPECIES** • *Mellisuga helenae*

VITAL STATISTICS

WEIGHT	1.9–2.8g (0.07–0.1oz)
LENGTH	5.2–6.6cm (2.0–2.6in)
WINGSPAN	3.2–3.8cm (1.3–1.5in)
NUMBER OF EGGS	2 eggs
INCUBATION PERIOD	14–23 days
NUMBER OF BROODS	1 a year
TYPICAL DIET	Nectar, tiny insects and spiders
LIFE SPAN	Up to 7 years

Hummingbirds are famous for their tiny stature, and the Bee Hummingbird is often regarded as the smallest bird in the world.

WHERE IN THE WORLD?

This tiny hummingbird is found on only two West Indian islands, the large island of Cuba, and the smaller Isla de la Juventud, often called the Island of Youth in English.

CREATURE COMPARISONS

This Bee Hummingbird has a compact body. Males have a bright red band around the back of the neck and along the throat, and a black collar around the throat. The upper side is brilliantly bluish green. The breast and belly are white. Females are larger and drabber than males, and have a green upper side and a white underside. The legs are short and the feet are small and weak.

Female Bee Hummingbird

WINGS
The wings are short and narrow, and are powered by huge muscles. They can be rotated 180° for incredibly agile flight.

BEAK
The bill is long and slender, and is used to probe deep into flowers for nectar, which it collects with its long tongue.

TAIL
The tail is short and forked at the tip, and is usually cocked while hovering.

HOW BIG IS IT?

SPECIAL ADAPTATION

The Bee Hummingbird is positively tiny. Males weigh only 1.95g (0.07oz) on average, while females weigh an average of 2.65g (0.093oz). For their size, they have huge flight muscles, which allow them to hover.

Sword-billed Hummingbird

• **ORDER** • Apodiformes • **FAMILY** • Trochilidae • **SPECIES** • *Ensifera ensifera*

VITAL STATISTICS

WEIGHT	12g (0.4oz)
LENGTH	15cm (6in)
LAYS EGGS	Coincides with months when flowers bloom
INCUBATION PERIOD	Around 14–19 days
FLEDGLING PERIOD	Around 17–19 days
NUMBER OF EGGS	2 eggs
NUMBER OF BROODS	2 a year, but males may mate with several females each year
TYPICAL DIET	Nectar
HABITS	Diurnal/ crepuscular; non-migratory but move locally to find food
LIFE SPAN	Unknown

The colourful Sword-billed Hummingbird from the Andes has one remarkable claim to fame: it is the only species of bird to have a bill longer than its body.

WHERE IN THE WORLD?

This bird lives on páramo shrubland and in humid, Andean Mountain forests, some 2500–3000m (8200–9840ft) above sea level. Populations range from Venezuela to Bolivia.

CREATURE COMPARISONS

In common with other species of Hummingbird, Sword-Bill Hummingbirds make nests of foliage and moss, bound together with cobwebs. These are moulded into tiny cup shapes, which are built in trees or shrubs. The cup shape prevents both eggs and chicks from falling out of the nest.

Sword-Billed Hummingbird nest

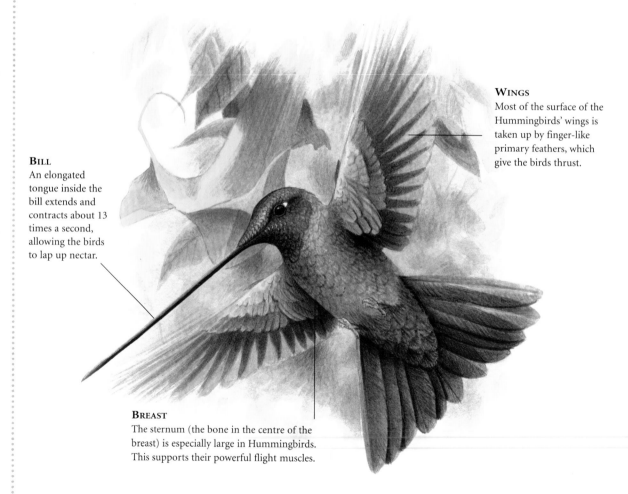

BILL
An elongated tongue inside the bill extends and contracts about 13 times a second, allowing the birds to lap up nectar.

WINGS
Most of the surface of the Hummingbirds' wings is taken up by finger-like primary feathers, which give the birds thrust.

BREAST
The sternum (the bone in the centre of the breast) is especially large in Hummingbirds. This supports their powerful flight muscles.

HOW BIG IS IT?

SPECIAL ADAPTATION

The bill of the Sword-billed Hummingbird is adapted to feed on flowers with particularly long petals, like fuchsias. Although this allows Hummingbirds to feed on plants that other birds cannot reach, such an extreme adaptation does create problems. At rest, for example, birds must hold their bills downwards, to prevent neck strain.

Giant Hummingbird

• ORDER • Apodiformes • FAMILY • Trochilidae • SPECIES • *Patagona gigas*

As the name suggests, this is the largest of all hummingbirds, but the Giant Hummingbird is still small compared to many other birds.

VITAL STATISTICS

WEIGHT	18–20g (0.6–0.7oz)
LENGTH	21–24cm (8.3–9.4in)
WINGSPAN	27–33cm (10.6–13.0in)
NUMBER OF EGGS	1–2 eggs
INCUBATION PERIOD	20–25 days
NUMBER OF BROODS	1 a year
TYPICAL DIET	Nectar, small insects, caterpillars and spiders
LIFE SPAN	Up to 10 years

WHERE IN THE WORLD?

A mountain-dwelling species, the Giant Hummingbird lives along western South America in the Andes Mountains at elevations of 2000–3800m (6500–12,500ft).

CREATURE COMPARISONS

The Giant Hummingbird is drabber than most other species of hummingbird. The upper side of the wings is dark and the body and head are golden orange or yellowish-brown, with a pattern of smaller darker spots and stripes. The lower part of the tail is pale cream, but the upper part is brown. Females are similar to males, but have more spots on the underside.

Drab colours

TAIL
The tail is very large and wide for a hummingbird, and plays an important part in manoeuvring during flight.

BEAK
The bill is very long and straight, and is used to probe deep into flowers for nectar. Giant Hummingbirds mainly gather nectar from bromeliad flowers.

FEET
Like most hummingbirds, the Giant Hummingbird has very short legs and small feet adapted for perching.

HOW BIG IS IT?

SPECIAL ADAPTATION

In order to conserve energy to survive cold nights in the mountains the Giant Hummingbird's body temperature drops. In the morning, it must be warmed by the Sun before it is able take flight.

Red-billed Streamertail

• ORDER • Apodiformes • FAMILY • Trochilidae • SPECIES • *Trochilus polytmus*

VITAL STATISTICS

WEIGHT	5.2g (0.2oz)
LENGTH	22–30cm, including tail (8.7–11.8in)
LAYS EGGS	October–March
INCUBATION PERIOD	14–21 days
FLEDGLING PERIOD	Around 21 days
NUMBER OF EGGS	2 eggs
NUMBER OF BROODS	Up to 3 a year are possible
CALL	Loud, metallic-sounding 'ting, ting, ting'
TYPICAL DIET	Nectar
HABITS	Diurnal, non-migratory

Streamertails are the national bird of Jamaica, where they are known locally as 'Doctor birds', after their long tail feathers, which resemble the coats of old-style medics.

WHERE IN THE WORLD?

Found from western to central Jamaica, the Red-billed Streamertail is a common sight. Birds tolerate a wide range of habitats wherever there are flowering plants, from mountains to plains.

CREATURE COMPARISONS

Apart from insects, hummingbirds, like the Red-billed Streamertail, have the highest metabolism of any animal while they are airborne. This means they need to consume vast amounts of nectar to fuel their rapidly beating wings. In fact, Hummingbirds spend much of their lives close to starvation.

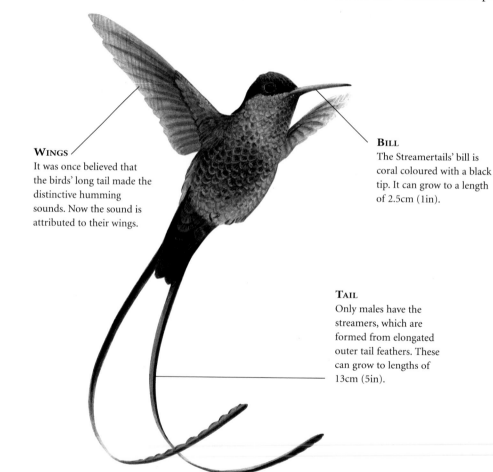

WINGS
It was once believed that the birds' long tail made the distinctive humming sounds. Now the sound is attributed to their wings.

BILL
The Streamertails' bill is coral coloured with a black tip. It can grow to a length of 2.5cm (1in).

TAIL
Only males have the streamers, which are formed from elongated outer tail feathers. These can grow to lengths of 13cm (5in).

A hovering Red-billed Streamertail

HOW BIG IS IT?

SPECIAL ADAPTATION

In common with all hummingbirds, the Red-billed Streamertail needs a calorie-rich diet and nectar, which is high in sugar, provides this. To reach the nectar, birds have an elongated bill and a specially adapted, extendable tongue, allowing them to access nectar deep within the flowers.

Brown Kiwi

• ORDER • Apterygiformes **• FAMILY •** Apterygidae **• SPECIES •** *Apteryx australis*

VITAL STATISTICS

WEIGHT	1.5–4kg (3.3–8.8lb)
LENGTH	50–65cm (19.7–25.6in)
HEIGHT	36–41cm (14.2–16.1in)
NUMBER OF EGGS	1–2 eggs (usually just 1)
INCUBATION PERIOD	70–85 days
NUMBER OF BROODS	1 a year
TYPICAL DIET	Worms, insect, spiders, fallen fruit, seeds, even crayfish, small amphibians and fish
LIFE SPAN	Up to 30 years

CREATURE COMPARISONS

Kiwis are unusual-looking birds. They are related to ostriches and emus, and, like them, are unable to fly. Being strictly nocturnal, all kiwis lack strong colours. The Brown Kiwi has a uniformly brown plumage, with few darker markings. The plumage looks strange for a bird because the small feathers are elongate and triangular, with an open structure, and at a distance they appear almost hair-like.

Male

In several respects, the peculiar, ground-dwelling Brown Kiwi resembles a mammal more than it resembles a bird.

WHERE IN THE WORLD?

The Brown Kiwi is one of five species of Kiwi. All are found only in New Zealand. There are three sub-species of Brown Kiwi living on the South Island and on the nearby Stewart Island.

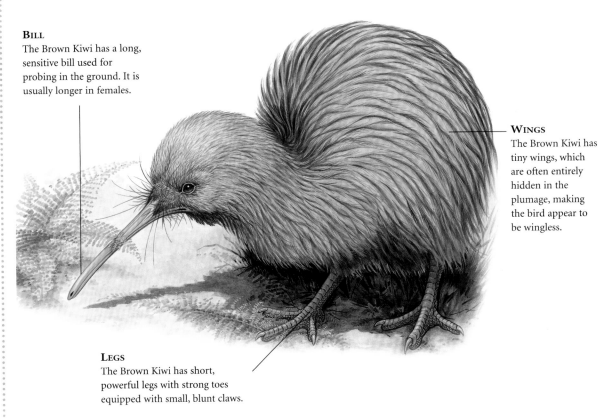

BILL
The Brown Kiwi has a long, sensitive bill used for probing in the ground. It is usually longer in females.

WINGS
The Brown Kiwi has tiny wings, which are often entirely hidden in the plumage, making the bird appear to be wingless.

LEGS
The Brown Kiwi has short, powerful legs with strong toes equipped with small, blunt claws.

HOW BIG IS IT?

SPECIAL ADAPTATION
Unlike most birds, the kiwi has a keen sense of smell. The nostrils are found at the tip of the long bill, with which the bird probes for worms and insects in the ground, detecting them by smell and touch.

European Nightjar

• **ORDER** • Caprimulgiformes • **FAMILY** • Caprimulgidae • **SPECIES** • *Caprimulgus europaeus*

The European Nightjar is the only member of its family across much of northern Europe and southern Asia.

VITAL STATISTICS

WEIGHT	50–100g (1.8–3.5oz)
LENGTH	26–28cm (10.2–11.0in)
WINGSPAN	50–55cm (19.7–21.7in)
NUMBER OF EGGS	2 eggs
INCUBATION PERIOD	17–20 days
NUMBER OF BROODS	2 a year
TYPICAL DIET	It feeds on a variety of flying insects at night, primarily moths
LIFE SPAN:	Up to 8 years

WHERE IN THE WORLD?

The European Nightjar is found across much of Europe and central Asia. A migratory bird, it usually arrives in northern Europe in April. It winters in southeastern Africa, as far south as the Cape Province.

CREATURE COMPARISONS

The plumage on the body is mottled grey with stripes of buff and brown. The wings are brownish with long dark stripes. Adult males have distinctive white spots on the wing tips and along the edge of the tail feathers. These are absent in females, and in young males, these areas are buff. The variable, mottled plumage provides excellent camouflage on the ground.

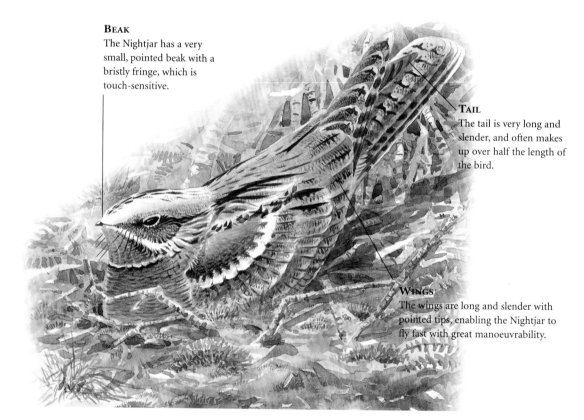

BEAK
The Nightjar has a very small, pointed beak with a bristly fringe, which is touch-sensitive.

TAIL
The tail is very long and slender, and often makes up over half the length of the bird.

WINGS
The wings are long and slender with pointed tips, enabling the Nightjar to fly fast with great manoeuvrability.

Adult male

HOW BIG IS IT?

SPECIAL ADAPTATION

The Nightjar is active at night, but during the day it rests motionless on the ground, blending in almost perfectly with the vegetation and dead leaves. If disturbed, it may open its huge mouth and emit a loud, snake-like hissing sound.

Tawny Frogmouth

• **ORDER** • Caprimulgiformes • **FAMILY** • Podargidae • **SPECIES** • *Podargus strigiodes*

The Tawny Frogmoth, a relative of the Nightjar, is a large, scary-looking bird that hunts by night by swooping down on its prey like an owl.

VITAL STATISTICS

WEIGHT	175–675g (6.2–23.8oz)
LENGTH	35–53cm (13.8–20.9in)
WINGSPAN	55–75cm (21.7–29.5in)
NUMBER OF EGGS	1–3 (usually 2)
INCUBATION PERIOD	27–33 days
NUMBER OF BROODS	1 a year
TYPICAL DIET	Large insects, spiders, centipedes, amphibians, lizards, small snakes, rodents
LIFE SPAN	Up to 20 years

WHERE IN THE WORLD?

The Tawny Frogmouth is found in the southern part of New Guinea and across large parts of Australia and Tasmania.

CREATURE COMPARISONS

The most conspicuous features of this strange bird are its huge head and its enormous mouth, which is bright yellow inside. The plumage is mottled greyish-brown with lighter and darker stripes and patterns. It has large, conspicuous stiff bristles above the beak. Males and females are similar, but the females are smaller and drabber.

Juvenile

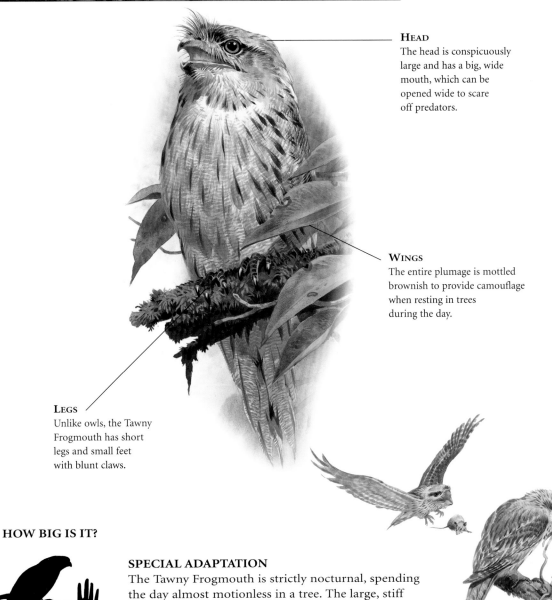

HEAD
The head is conspicuously large and has a big, wide mouth, which can be opened wide to scare off predators.

WINGS
The entire plumage is mottled brownish to provide camouflage when resting in trees during the day.

LEGS
Unlike owls, the Tawny Frogmouth has short legs and small feet with blunt claws.

HOW BIG IS IT?

SPECIAL ADAPTATION
The Tawny Frogmouth is strictly nocturnal, spending the day almost motionless in a tree. The large, stiff bristles above the beak are touch-sensitive, and help the birds catch prey in the dark.

Oilbird

• **ORDER** • Caprimulgiformes • **FAMILY** • Steatornithidae • **GENUS AND SPECIES** • *Steatornis caripensis*

VITAL STATISTICS

LENGTH	35–45cm (13.8–17.7in)
WINGSPAN	1–1.15m (3.3–3.8ft)
SEXUAL MATURITY	1 year
INCUBATION PERIOD	30–33 days
FLEDGLING PERIOD	90–125 days
NUMBER OF EGGS	2–4 eggs
NUMBER OF BROODS	1 a year
TYPICAL DIET	Mainly fruit from oil palm and laurel trees
HABITS	Nocturnal, non-migratory
LIFE SPAN	Typically 12–15 years

In Trinidad, this curious bird is known as 'diablotin' or 'little devil', in reference to its eerie, nocturnal cries, which sound like howls of pain.

These gregarious birds live in remote, mountain areas of Guyana, Venezuela, Colombia, Ecuador and Peru. They are also found in the Caribbean (in northwestern Trinidad) roosting in coastal caves.

CREATURE COMPARISONS

Young Oilbirds are fed on such a rich diet that they become extremely plump. Typically a squab will weigh in at half as much again as a fully grown adult bird. In fact, its taxonomic name, *Steatornis*, means fat bird.

Juvenile

TAIL
Extra long wings help carry Oilbirds over long distances as they embark on regular, nocturnal expeditions, foraging for food.

EYES
The bodies of young Oilbirds used to be farmed for lamp oil, which is how the species got its unusual name.

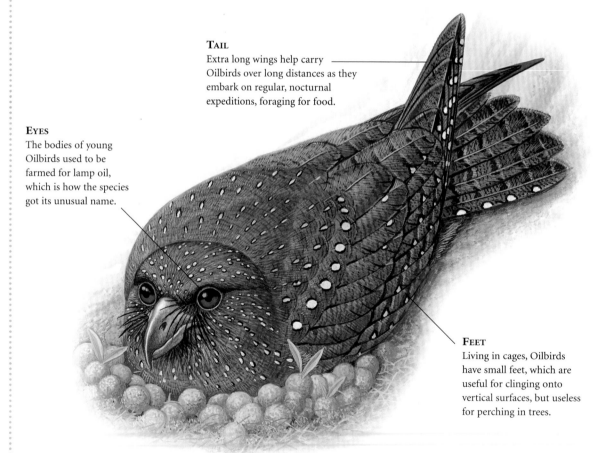

FEET
Living in cages, Oilbirds have small feet, which are useful for clinging onto vertical surfaces, but useless for perching in trees.

HOW BIG IS IT?

SPECIAL ADAPTATION
Although they hunt by sight, Oilbirds also use echo-location to find their way around the gloomy caves in which they roost. An Oilbird's echo-location works on a much lower frequency than that used by bats and is audible to humans as a series of loud clicks.

Little Auk

• **ORDER** • Charadriiformes • **FAMILY** • Alcidae • **GENUS AND SPECIES** • *Alle alle*

VITAL STATISTICS

WEIGHT	170g (6oz)
LENGTH	19–21cm (7.5–8.3in)
WINGSPAN	34–38cm (13.4–15in)
INCUBATION PERIOD	28–31 days
FLEDGLING PERIOD	23–30 days
NUMBER OF EGGS	1 egg
NUMBER OF BROODS	1 a year
TYPICAL DIET	Planktonic crustaceans and some fish
HABITS	Diurnal, migratory
LIFE SPAN	Unknown

They may be no bigger than Starlings, but Little Auks are a hardy breed, making their homes in the ice-laden seas of the North Atlantic.

WHERE IN THE WORLD?

Little Auks spend their winters in the cold, open seas of the North Atlantic Ocean. They breed on rock cliffs or sometimes in crevices under scree, and congregate in large, over-crowded colonies.

CREATURE COMPARISONS

To help keep them warm in the chilly Atlantic waters, Auk chicks have a covering of thick down, a fine, thermal layer that lies beneath the tougher, outer feathers of adult birds. Together, these layers creates a dense, insulating plumage.

Auk chicks

HEAD
With their round, almost neckless heads and throat sacs bulging with stored food, little Auks can look oddly frog-like.

BELLY
White underparts help protect the bird from predators, and make it harder for prey to spot them from the water.

LEGS
When they come in to land, LIttle Auks stand upright, with a similar stance to their Southern Hemisphere cousins, the Penguins.

HOW BIG IS IT?

SPECIAL ADAPTATION
Adult Little Auks sometimes travel great distances to feed their chicks, so it makes sense to be able to carry as much as possible once they have found a rich source of food. A specially adapted throat sac enables them to carry and store supplies.

Puffin (Atlantic)

• **ORDER** • Charadriiformes • **FAMILY** • Alcidae • **SPECIES** • *Fratercula arctica*

VITAL STATISTICS

WEIGHT	400g (14oz)
LENGTH	28–34cm (11–13.4in)
WINGSPAN	55cm (21.6in)
SEXUAL MATURITY	4–5 years
LAYS EGGS	April–May
INCUBATION PERIOD	39–45 days
NUMBER OF EGGS	1 egg
NUMBER OF BROODS	1 a year, as long as there is enough food
TYPICAL DIET	Small fish, especially sand eels
LIFE SPAN	Typically 20 years

Don't be fooled by these brightly coloured clowns of the sea. Despite their comical appearance, these extraordinary seabirds are agile, skilled hunters.

WHERE IN THE WORLD?

Puffins are pelagic, which means they spend most of their lives in the open sea. During the breeding season, they head for the coastlines of Europe, northern Russia and the northeastern USA.

CREATURE COMPARISONS

During the breeding season, adult male birds use their colourful bills to attract a mate. This is not a necessity for juvenile Puffins, so in their first year, they look very similar to adults in winter plumage, with smaller, darker bills and grey cheeks.

Adult in winter (top), juvenile (right)

BILL
The Puffin's multi-coloured bill is much larger and brighter during the breeding season. In the winter, it is smaller and yellowish.

WINGS
Small, broad-tipped wings are a typical seabird adaptation. This makes Atlantic Puffins both strong fliers and skilled swimmers.

FEET
Puffins use their strong, clawed feet to dig themselves a burrow in which to nest and lay their eggs.

HOW BIG IS IT?

SPECIAL ADAPTATION
The upper part of a Puffin's bill has a serrated edge. By holding the fish in place between its tongue and the upper bill, the Puffin can continue fishing until its mouth is full of wriggling fish without losing any of its catch.

Guillemot (Common)

• ORDER • Charadriiformes • FAMILY • Alcidae • SPECIES • *Uria aalge*

Guillemots are so numerous that, in their breeding colonies (loomeries), as many as 20 birds may occupy just 1 sq m (10.75 sq ft).

VITAL STATISTICS

WEIGHT	690g (23.3oz)
LENGTH	38–46cm (15–18.1in)
WINGSPAN	61–73cm (24–28.7in)
SEXUAL MATURITY	5 years
LAYS EGGS	March–July, depending on location
INCUBATION PERIOD	28–37 days
NUMBER OF EGGS	1 egg
NUMBER OF BROODS	1 a year
TYPICAL DIET	Fish, crabs and squid
LIFE SPAN	Typically 24 years

WHERE IN THE WORLD?

Ornithologists disagree on how many sub-species of Common Guillemot there are, but most populations live around the Atlantic, with fewer on the Pacific coastline. Preferred habitats are rocky shores and cliffs.

CREATURE COMPARISONS

Some Common Guillemots sport a pair of what look like bold, white spectacles around their eyes during the breeding season. However, these Bridled Guillemots are not a separate sub-species, but a different morph, or form. This variation in plumage becomes more common the further north that the birds breed.

Bridled Guillemot

BILL
Guillemots carry one fish at time, lengthways in the bill, with the tail hanging out over the tip of the bill.

WINGS
Guillemot chicks leave the nest in a dramatic style by plunging from the cliff, with only downy wings to slow their fall.

FEET
To land on narrow cliff faces, Common Guillemots approach with bodies erect, paddling the air with their feet, to slow their descent.

HOW BIG IS IT?

SPECIAL ADAPTATION

Common Guillemots do not build traditional nests – their colonies are so crowded that there is simply not the space. Instead they lay their eggs on rock ledges. These eggs come in a variety of colours but are all pear-shaped, so they roll in circles, rather than off the ledge.

Blotches **Spots** **Scribbles** **Mixed marks**

Stone–Curlew

• ORDER • Charadriiformes **• FAMILY •** Burhinidae **• SPECIES •** *Burhinus oedicnemus*

VITAL STATISTICS

WEIGHT	470g (16.6oz)
LENGTH	40–44cm (15.7–17.3in)
WINGSPAN	81cm (31.9in)
SEXUAL MATURITY	1–3 years
INCUBATION PERIOD	24–26 days
NUMBER OF EGGS	1–3 eggs
NUMBER OF BROODS	1–2 a year
TYPICAL DIET	Worms, insects, small reptiles, mammals and bird's eggs
HABITS	Nocturnal/ crepuscular, migratory
LIFE SPAN	Typically 6 years

Birdwatchers should not be fooled by the familiar sounding, shrill 'kur-lee' call of the Stone-Curlew. These big pretenders are not really Curlews at all.

WHERE IN THE WORLD?

Patchy populations of this crow-sized birds are found in lowland regions across Europe, from southern Britain to Russia and into Asia. Most northern populations migrate to North Africa for the winter.

CREATURE COMPARISONS

With their large heads, long yellow legs, falcon-like eyes and long wings and tails, Stone-Curlews look unusual. Juveniles tend to be paler than their adult counterparts, with less black in their plumage. The black and white bars under the wings are also less prominent.

Juvenile

BODY
From above, Stone-Curlews look brown but, during the breeding season, they display their black and white underparts to attract a mate.

LEGS
Despite having long legs, usually associated with wading species, Stone-Curlews are equally at home on dry land.

KNEES
Curlews belong to the Family Burhinidae . The name means thick knees, in reference to the prominent knee joints in their elongated legs.

HOW BIG IS IT?

SPECIAL ADAPTATION

Stone-Curlews are crepuscular, meaning that they do most of their hunting at dawn or dusk. In order to take in as much of the available light as possible, their eyes are particularly large for a bird of their size. This enables them to hunt while other birds sleep.

Little Ringed Plover

• **ORDER** • Charadriiformes • **FAMILY** • Charadriidae • **SPECIES** • *Charadrius dubius*

VITAL STATISTICS

WEIGHT	30–50g (1.1–1.8oz)
LENGTH	14–16cm (5.5–6.3in)
WINGSPAN	42–48cm (16.5–19in)
NUMBER OF EGGS	4 eggs
INCUBATION PERIOD	22–26 days
NUMBER OF BROODS	2 a year
TYPICAL DIET	Insects, worms, spiders, small crayfish
LIFE SPAN	Up to 10 years

The tiny and speedy Little Ringed Plover breeds near lakes, streams and also in man-made structures such as gravel pits.

WHERE IN THE WORLD?

The Little Ringed Plover is widespread throughout Europe, except northern Scandinavia, and across large parts of Asia and the Middle East. It is absent from western Britain.

CREATURE COMPARISONS

The Little Ringed Plover has a light brown upper side of the wings, back and top of the head, while the breast and belly are white. The throat is white with a distinctive black collar. The face has handsome markings of black and white. Males and females are similar. This bird looks superficially very similar to the Ringed Plover, but it is distinctly smaller.

Little Ringed Plover

BEAK
The Little Ringed Plover has a short bill, the dark colour of which distinguishes it from the Ringed Plover.

LEGS
The Little Ringed Plover has long, light brown legs for running at speed over the sand in pursuit of small insects.

WINGS
The wings are long and narrow, and lack the white band found in the Ringed and Kentish Plover.

HOW BIG IS IT?

SPECIAL ADAPTATION

The Little Ringed Plover often breeds on open ground, where it can get very hot in summer. The adults soak their feathers in water, and cool off their chicks with their wet belly feathers.

55

Ringed Plover (Common)

• **ORDER** • Charadriiformes • **FAMILY** • Charadriidae • **SPECIES** • *Charadrius hiaticula*

VITAL STATISTICS

WEIGHT	64g (2.2oz)
LENGTH	18–20cm (7.1–8in)
WINGSPAN	35–41cm (13.8–16in)
SEXUAL MATURITY	1 year
LAYS EGGS	May–July
INCUBATION PERIOD	23–25 days
NUMBER OF EGGS	3–4 eggs
NUMBER OF BROODS	2–3 a year
TYPICAL DIET	Aquatic invertebrates, insects and spiders
LIFE SPAN	Typically 5 years

With their striking plumage, Ringed Plovers are one of the easiest waders to identify, although spotting them in their natural habitat is a challenge.

WHERE IN THE WORLD?

Like many waders, Plovers make their homes on sandy estuaries and coastlines. They breed throughout northern Europe and on the Arctic cost of Canada, but overwinter in southern Africa.

CREATURE COMPARISONS

The bold, black bands visible around the head and neck of the adult Ringed Plovers do not develop until the birds' first winter. The rings of young, juvenile Plovers' are generally dark brown, rather than black, and do not go all the way around the head.

Juvenile

WINGS
The dramatic, white wing bars make it possible to distinguish Common Ringed Plovers from Little Ringed Plovers in flight.

BILL
Plovers have short bills that they use to pluck their food from the surface.

FEET
Surprisingly, for species that breed primarily in marshes and on river estuaries, the feet of the Ringed Plover are not webbed.

HOW BIG IS IT?

SPECIAL ADAPTATION

Plover eggs are heavily camouflaged and, from a distance, resemble stones. However, if this fails to deter predators, adult birds have a clever trick. They pretend to have a broken wing so that they look like easy pickings and lead predators away from the nest.

Semipalmated Plover

• **ORDER** • Charadriiformes • **FAMILY** • Charadriidae • **SPECIES** • *Charadrius semipalmatus*

VITAL STATISTICS

WEIGHT	47g (1.7oz)
LENGTH	17–19cm (6.7–7.5in)
SEXUAL MATURITY	Probably 1 year
LAYS EGGS	May–June
INCUBATION PERIOD	Around 28 days
NUMBER OF EGGS	4 eggs for first clutch, fewer if a second are laid
NUMBER OF BROODS	1 a year, but a second clutch is possible if the first fails
CALL	Two-toned 'chu-wee' whistle
TYPICAL DIET	Worms, insects and crustaceans
HABITS	Diurnal, migratory

CREATURE COMPARISONS

It is a sad fact that many bird species are either now critically endangered or their numbers are falling, due to polluted waterways or the loss of traditional habitats. However, Semipalmated Plovers are not under threat, thanks to their opportunist eating habits and their widespread distribution.

Successful plovers

The plump-breasted Semipalmated Plover, a shore bird, can be found along coasts and river estuaries.

WHERE IN THE WORLD?

Semipalmated Plovers make their nests on open ground, beaches or mudflats across Arctic and sub-Arctic Canada and North America. They migrate south, as far as Patagonia, for the winter.

NECK
Semipalmated Plovers are also known, colloquially, as ring-necks because of the single black band that runs around their neck.

WINGS
Although they nest on the ground, Plovers will regularly fly over their territory to warn rival males to stay away.

FEET
The Semipalmated part of the Plovers' name refers to the fact that the birds' feet are only partly webbed.

HOW BIG IS IT?

SPECIAL ADAPTATION

Semipalmated Plovers have an unusual hunting technique. They hold one foot off the ground and use the other to vibrate the surface. This may look odd, but it is a very effective method of flushing any insects in the area out of cover, making them easier to catch.

Eurasian Dotterel

• **ORDER** • Charadriiformes • **FAMILY** • Charadriidae • **SPECIES** • *Charadrius morinellus*

The Eurasian Dotterel is an unusual bird because the females are larger and have more attractive plumage than males and play no part in rearing the chicks.

VITAL STATISTICS

WEIGHT	55–80g (1.9–2.8oz)
LENGTH	20–22cm (8–8.7in)
WINGSPAN	45–50cm (17.7–19.7in)
NUMBER OF EGGS	2–4 eggs (usually 2–3)
INCUBATION PERIOD	**24–28** days
NUMBER OF BROODS	2–3 a year
TYPICAL DIET	Insects, snails, worms, spiders, some fruit and seeds
LIFE SPAN	Up to 7 years

WHERE IN THE WORLD?

The Eurasian Dotterel breeds in open areas such as tundra in the high north, from Norway in the west to eastern Siberia in the east, and on suitable mountain plateaus. It winters in North Africa and the Middle East.

CREATURE COMPARISONS

The head and neck are brownish with a pale stripe across the chest and a chestnut-coloured breast. There is a conspicuous white stripe across the eye. The belly is dark brown or black, and the back and wings are brown. The legs are long and yellowish, and the feet are small. Unusually, females are larger than males, and have brighter plumage.

Male

WINGS
The wings are elongate and slender, enabling the Eurasian Dotterel to fly fast and migrate long distances.

BODY
The body is plump, and can easily be recognized by the chestnut colour of its breast.

TAIL
The tail is broad and the tail feathers have white edges. The tail is used for steering during flight.

HOW BIG IS IT?

SPECIAL ADAPTATION

Unlike most birds, the female Eurasian Dotterel courts the male, and lays eggs in a nest. She then leaves the brooding and raising of young to the male, and goes in search of another male to mate again.

Curlew (Eurasian)

• ORDER • Charadriiformes • FAMILY • Charadriidae • SPECIES • *Numenius arquata*

VITAL STATISTICS

WEIGHT MALES	770g (27.2oz)
FEMALES	1 kg (2.2lb)
LENGTH	48–57cm (19–22.4in)
WINGSPAN	89cm –1.1m (35 in–3.6ft)
SEXUAL MATURITY	2 years
LAYS EGGS	April–May
INCUBATION PERIOD	27–29 days
NUMBER OF EGGS	4 eggs
NUMBER OF BROODS	1 a year
TYPICAL DIET	Worms, molluscs, crabs; some fruit and seeds
LIFE SPAN	Typically 5 years

The elegant Curlew is a long-legged wader perfectly adapted for life on the seashore, where its plaintive cry is often heard, drifting along the coast.

CREATURE COMPARISONS

Eurasian Curlews are the largest species of European wader within their range. Although males and females of the species look similar, females are the larger, thanks to an extra long bill, which can be up to 5cm (2in) bigger than the bill of the male.

Male (left) and female (right)

WHERE IN THE WORLD?

Marshes, mudflats and meadows are the preferred habitat of the Curlew. Populations are resident in temperate regions in Britain, Ireland and coastal Europe, but others migrate south for the winter.

EYES
Eyes on the side of the head give a wide field of vision, which helps the Curlew spot danger more easily.

BODY
It may look dramatic, but the barred, grey-brown plumage provides the Curlew with perfect camouflage in both muddy and sandy environments.

FEET
Three, long, forwards-facing toes and one balancing backwards-facing toe help the Curlew to walk on uneven, muddy surfaces.

HOW BIG IS IT?

SPECIAL ADAPTATION

Special cells, called Herbst's Corpuscles, make the tip of the Curlew's bill sensitive enough to find food deep in the mud. The size and shape of the bill is adapted for a specific diet, so it is not competing with other sandpipers for the same food.

Golden Plover (European)

• ORDER • Charadriiformes • FAMILY • Charadriidae • SPECIES • *Pluvialis apricaria*

VITAL STATISTICS

WEIGHT	220g (7.8oz)
LENGTH	26–28cm (10.2–11in)
WINGSPAN	72cm (28.3in)
SEXUAL MATURITY	1 year
LAYS EGGS	April–June
INCUBATION PERIOD	28–31 days
NUMBER OF EGGS	3–4 eggs
NUMBER OF BROODS	1 a year
TYPICAL DIET	Invertebrates, especially worms and beetles; occasionally seeds and berries
LIFE SPAN	Typically 4 years

During the breeding season these elegant waders show their true colours, replacing their drab winter plumage with a handsome coat of gold.

WHERE IN THE WORLD?

Golden Plovers are a common sight on Europe's moorlands, wet pastures and river estuaries. Breeding as far north as Siberia, populations tend to move south into warmer regions, for the winter.

CREATURE COMPARISONS

In summer, Plovers may look resplendent in their shimmering, golden plumage, but in winter they favour a more sober look. In their winter plumage, adults and juveniles look similar, although the belly and flanks of young birds are often finely barred.

Adult in winter plumage

WINGS
An argument over which bird is faster, the Grouse or the Golden Plover, inspired *The Guiness Book of Records*. (The Grouse is faster.)

FEET
Golden Plovers have been compared to clockwork toys because of their habit of running, then stopping abruptly to search for food.

BILL
A short bill is better adapted for pecking at insects or seeds than for probing deep into the ground for worms.

HOW BIG IS IT?

SPECIAL ADAPTATION

Without a long, probing bill, Plovers have developed another way to catch worms. They make rapid patting motions on the earth with their feet. Worms associate the vibrations with rain, and come to the surface to avoid drowning only to be pounced on by a Plover.

Grey Plover

• ORDER • Charadriiformes • FAMILY • Charadriidae • SPECIES • *Pluvialis squatarola*

VITAL STATISTICS

WEIGHT	150–250g (5.3–8.8oz)
LENGTH	27–31cm (10.6–12.2in)
WINGSPAN	60–70cm (23.6–27.6in)
NUMBER OF EGGS	4 eggs
INCUBATION PERIOD	24–26 days
NUMBER OF BROODS	1 a year
TYPICAL DIET	Crayfish, snails, worms, insects and insect larvae
LIFE SPAN	Up to 20 years

The Grey Plover is a strongly migratory bird, and can be found in coastal areas almost all over the world.

WHERE IN THE WORLD?

The Grey Plover breeds in the high north, and is found all over the Arctic. It flies south for the winter, and may then be found in almost any region of the world, even Australia and New Zealand.

CREATURE COMPARISONS

During the breeding season, the male has a jet-black underside, while the flanks and side of the neck are strikingly white. The upper side of the body and wings are mottled black and white. The female is similar, but is dark brown instead of black. Outside the breeding season, both sexes become much drabber, and have a paler greyish plumage with darker spots.

Juvenile

BILL
The Grey Plover has a short, stout bill for probing after prey in the sand and crushing small prey.

TAIL
The tail is long and tapering and is white underneath but has a black and white pattern above.

BODY
The underside of the body is dark in both sexes during the breeding season, but becomes pale outside the breeding season.

HOW BIG IS IT?

SPECIAL ADAPTATION
The Grey Plover has a remarkable defence. It nests on the ground, and if a predator comes close to the nest, the adults will pretend to limp away with a broken wing, thus luring the predator away from the chicks.

Blacksmith Lapwing

• **ORDER** • Charadriiformes • **FAMILY** • Charadriidae • **SPECIES** • *Vanellus armatus*

VITAL STATISTICS

WEIGHT	125–225g (4.4–8oz)
LENGTH	28–31cm (11.0–12.2in)
WINGSPAN	60–70cm (23.6–27.6in)
NUMBER OF EGGS	2–4 eggs
INCUBATION PERIOD	24–26 days
NUMBER OF BROODS	1 a year
TYPICAL DIET	Snails, water insects, crayfish, small mussels, worms, small frogs and fish
LIFE SPAN	Up to 20 years

The Blacksmith Lapwing is unusually long-legged, and it is one of the few plovers to live as a wading bird.

WHERE IN THE WORLD?

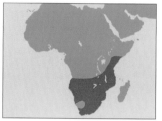

The Blacksmith Lapwing is widespread in southern Africa, from Kenya through Tanzania and Zambia to Angola in the west, extending all the way south to the Cape of Good Hope in South Africa.

CREATURE COMPARISONS

The Blacksmith Lapwing has a striking pattern of black and white. The head, throat and breast, and most of the wings are black, while the forehead, back of the neck and belly are white. The inner part of the wings is greyish. The legs are black and stilt-like. Unusually, the females are larger than males, but otherwise the sexes look similar.

Juvenile

TAIL
The short, narrow tail is white with a black tip, and is held high when the bird is wading in shallow water.

LEGS
The Blacksmith Lapwing has much longer legs than most plovers, an adaptation for wading in shallow water.

BILL
The bill is short and stout, and is often used to crack the shells of snails and small shellfish.

HOW BIG IS IT?

SPECIAL ADAPTATION

The Blacksmith Lapwing reacts to the presence of other lapwings within its territory with aggression. It swoops down, uttering its characteristic alarm call, which sounds like a hammer hitting an anvil, hence the bird's name.

Lapwing

• ORDER • Charadriiformes **• FAMILY •** Charadriidae **• SPECIES •** *Vanellus vanellus*

The Lapwing is easily recognized by its shiny feathers and long head crest, and is a common sight in many European countries.

VITAL STATISTICS

LENGTH	28–31cm (11.0–12.2in)
WINGSPAN	45–58cm (17.7–22.8in)
NUMBER OF EGGS	4 eggs
INCUBATION PERIOD	23–27 days
NUMBER OF BROODS	1 a year
TYPICAL DIET	Insects, spiders, earthworms, snails, grubs
LIFE SPAN	Up to 17 years

WHERE IN THE WORLD?

The Lapwing is a resident of Western Europe, but extends its breeding range across central Russia to the Sea of Okhotsk, and into Japan and southeastern China, and also into northern Africa.

CREATURE COMPARISONS

This Lapwing is a familiar sight in many European countries, and is easily recognized by the shiny, blackish-green plumage on the back and wings, and the tall, black feather-crest on the head. The underside is white, except for the throat, which has a similar colour to the back. The cheeks are white but the anterior face is black. Males are similar to females, but have a larger head crest.

Female

WINGS
The wings are long and greenish-black above, but white and black below, making the bird harder to see from the ground.

HEAD
The head is small and round, and has a very distinctive backwards-pointing crest of feathers.

LEGS
The orange-red legs are long for wading in grass and shallow water, and the feet are rather small.

HOW BIG IS IT?

SPECIAL ADAPTATION
The tall, narrow head crest could be a defence against predators. When the bird walks around picking at food items on the ground, the crest makes it appear as if the beak is pointing upwards, as if the bird was on the alert and looking around.

Snowy Sheathbill

• **ORDER** • Charadriiformes • **FAMILY** • Chionidae • **SPECIES** • *Chionis alba*

VITAL STATISTICS

WEIGHT	450–775g (16–27.3oz)
LENGTH	34–41cm (13.4–16in)
WINGSPAN	75–80cm (29.5–31.5in)
NUMBER OF EGGS	1–4 eggs (usually 2–3)
INCUBATION PERIOD	28–32 days
NUMBER OF BROODS	1 a year
TYPICAL DIET	Carrion, fish, birds' eggs and chicks, seal afterbirths, droppings, feathers
LIFE SPAN	Unknown

CREATURE COMPARISONS

The Snowy Sheathbill is perfectly adapted for life in regions permanently covered with ice and snow. The entire body, wings and tail are uniformly white, and the only other colour on the body is the bare skin wattles near the eye, which are pinkish. The legs are blue-grey or brownish, and the strong bill is yellow with a black tip. Males and females are similar, but males are larger.

Snowy Sheathbill in flight

This white Snowy Sheathbill may be beautiful to look at but it is a predator that eats other birds' eggs and chicks.

WHERE IN THE WORLD?

The Snowy Sheathbill is found on Elephant Island, the South Shetland Islands, South Orkney Islands and South Georgia, and it also lives along the Antarctic Peninsula.

BILL
The yellow bill is very large, heavy and powerful, and is used for scavenging and for breaking open eggs.

HEAD
There is a distinct area of bare, warty pinkish skin at the base of the bill.

BODY
The Snowy Sheathbill has a waterproof outer covering of feathers, and a thick undercoat of grey down to insulate it against the cold.

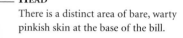

HOW BIG IS IT?

SPECIAL ADAPTATION

The Snowy Sheathbill is a fierce predator that attacks other birds using both its large strong bill and a sharp spur on each hand at the front of the wing.

Crab Plover

VITAL STATISTICS

WEIGHT	230–325g (6.5–11.5oz)
LENGTH	38–41cm (15–16in)
SEXUAL MATURITY	Unknown
LAYS EGGS	April–July
INCUBATION PERIOD	28–30 days
NUMBER OF EGGS	1–2 eggs
NUMBER OF BROODS	1 a year
TYPICAL DIET	Crabs; occasionally aquatic invertebrates
CALL	Far-travelling 'ha-how' and melodic 'prooit'
HABITS	Nocturnal/ crepuscular, some daytime feeding during breeding season. Migratory
LIFE SPAN	Unknown

These unique waders make their home in a few isolated regions of the world, where there are abundant supplies of crabs.

WHERE IN THE WORLD?

These distinctive birds breed on the coasts and islands of the Indian Ocean, Persian Gulf and Red Sea. Crab Plovers dig burrows in which to nest, so they prefer regions with sand dunes.

CREATURE COMPARISONS

With black and white plumage and long legs, Crab Plovers are elegant, if oddly proportioned, birds. Unusually for waders, chicks take a long time to fully fledge and juveniles (shown) depend on their parents for some time after leaving the nest.

Juvenile

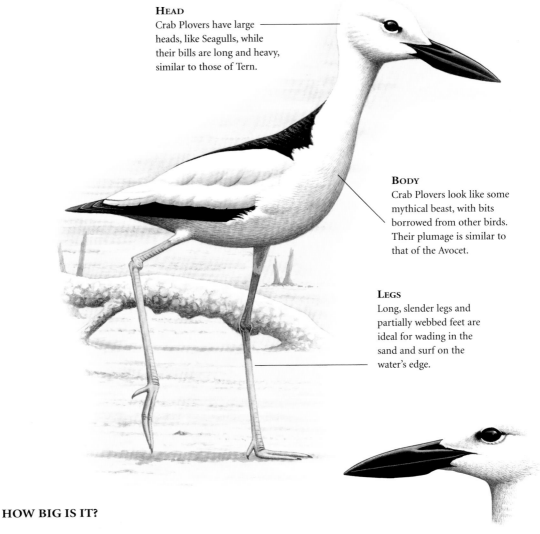

HEAD
Crab Plovers have large heads, like Seagulls, while their bills are long and heavy, similar to those of Tern.

BODY
Crab Plovers look like some mythical beast, with bits borrowed from other birds. Their plumage is similar to that of the Avocet.

LEGS
Long, slender legs and partially webbed feet are ideal for wading in the sand and surf on the water's edge.

HOW BIG IS IT?

SPECIAL ADAPTATION

Crab Plovers are true specialists that live almost entirely on a diet of crabs. Their chisel-like bill is perfectly adapted for the job of breaking open shells, their over-sized, muscular head acting like a hammer, powering each blow.

Oystercatcher (Eurasian)

• **ORDER** • Charadriiformes • **FAMILY** • Haematopodidae • **SPECIES** • *Haematopus ostralegus*

VITAL STATISTICS

WEIGHT	450g (16oz)
LENGTH	39–44cm (15.3–17.3in)
WINGSPAN	72–83cm (28.3–32.7in)
SEXUAL MATURITY	3–5 years
LAYS EGGS	April–May
INCUBATION PERIOD	24–35 days
NUMBER OF EGGS	2–5 eggs
NUMBER OF BROODS	1 a year
TYPICAL DIET	Mussels, cockles; occasionally crabs and worms
LIFE SPAN	Typically 12 years

Oystercatchers depend on coastal waters for their food. This means that a healthy population of Oystercatchers implies a healthy ecosystem.

WHERE IN THE WORLD?

These handsome birds breed on open, flat coastal estuaries in Europe and northern Asia. British populations tend to be resident, but others winter in Africa, the Middle East and southern Asia.

CREATURE COMPARISONS

With their black and white plumage, brilliant, orange bill, red eyes and pink legs, adult Oystercatchers are unmistakable. Juvenile birds are just as striking. However, their underparts are a muddy brown, with paler, almost yellow legs, and a paler bill with more black on the tip.

Adult (top), juvenile (bottom)

WINGS
In the air, Oystercatchers make a remarkable spectacle, as they fly in formation, with their white wing bars flashing.

BILL
These elongated bills vary in shape depending on what the bird eats. Parents pass these traits onto their young.

FEET
Oystercatchers have just three forwards-facing toes, which help to spread their weight and stop them sinking in the mud.

HOW BIG IS IT?

SPECIAL ADAPTATION

Despite their name, Oystercatchers do not eat oysters. They prefer mussels and cockles, and the shape of their bill varies depending on which they like to eat. Birds with long bills specialize in prising cockles apart while those with blunter bills hammer open the tougher mussel shells.

Ibisbill

• ORDER • Charadriiformes **• FAMILY •** Ibidorhynchidae **• GENUS AND SPECIES •** *Ibidorhyncha struthersii*

VITAL STATISTICS

WEIGHT	270–320g (9.5–11.3 oz)
LENGTH	39–41cm (15.3–16in)
SEXUAL MATURITY	Unknown
LAYS EGGS	Pairs start to nest in late March–early June
FLEDGLING PERIOD	45–50 days
NUMBER OF EGGS	2–4 eggs
NUMBER OF BROODS	1 a year
CALL	A loud, repetitive trilling is made during displays
TYPICAL DIET	Aquatic insects, crustaceans and small fish
HABITS	Diurnal, migratory
LIFE SPAN	Unknown

For many bird enthusiasts, just getting a peek at the elusive Ibisbill is the ornithological equivalent of reaching the summit of Mount Everest.

WHERE IN THE WORLD?

These unmistakable birds live on shingle banks in the river plateaux of Central Asia, from Kazakhstan to China. They typically nest at between 1700–4400m (5577–14435ft) above sea level.

CREATURE COMPARISONS

Although Ibisbills are not related to their famous namesakes, the Sacred Ibis (*Threskiornis aethiopicus*), it is easy to understand why early ornithologists compared the two. The species share a similar body shape and coloration, however, Sacred Ibis are found primarily in the Middle East.

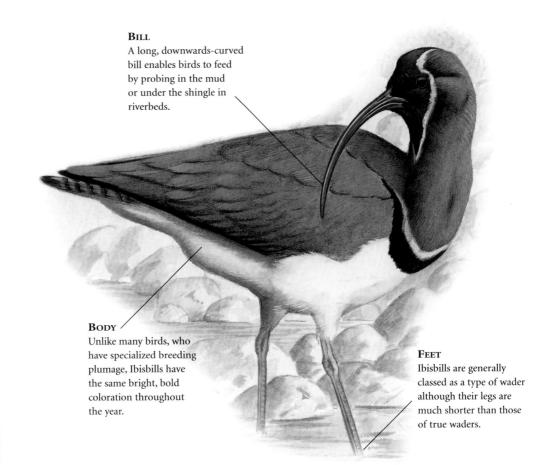

BILL
A long, downwards-curved bill enables birds to feed by probing in the mud or under the shingle in riverbeds.

BODY
Unlike many birds, who have specialized breeding plumage, Ibisbills have the same bright, bold coloration throughout the year.

FEET
Ibisbills are generally classed as a type of wader although their legs are much shorter than those of true waders.

Male Ibisbill

HOW BIG IS IT?

SPECIAL ADAPTATION
Despite their white bellies, red legs and black and white facial markings, Ibisbills can be surprisingly difficult to spot in their natural environment. This is because the bold patterns perfectly match the colours predominantly found in the birds' preferred habitat.

African Jacana

• ORDER • Charadriiformes • FAMILY • Jacanidae • GENUS AND SPECIES • *Actophilornis africana*

VITAL STATISTICS

WEIGHT	137–261g (4.8–9.2oz)
LENGTH	23–30cm (9–11.8in)
SEXUAL MATURITY	Probably 1 year
LAYS EGGS	December–April
INCUBATION PERIOD	20–26 days
FLEDGLING PERIOD	At least 30 days
NUMBER OF EGGS	3–5 eggs per clutch
NUMBER OF BROODS	Several clutches may be laid, with different male partners, until one is successful
CALL	A loud, mournful, whining sound on take off and landing
TYPICAL DIET	Worms, insects and spiders; occasionally seeds
HABITS	Diurnal, non-migratory
LIFE SPAN	Unknown

CREATURE COMPARISONS

Although their long legs and slender bodies look the same, juvenile African Jacanas lack the bright chestnut-brown plumage and blue bill of the adult birds. Their legs are also light grey rather than the blue-grey seen in Jacanas of breeding age.

Juvenile

The graceful African Jacana is also known as the Lily Walker because of its ability to walk on lily pads using its slender legs and long toes.

These sociable sub-Saharan birds gather in large groups in lagoons, stagnant pools and swamps, in fact, anywhere where floating vegetation can be found. Of the eight known species, only two live in Africa.

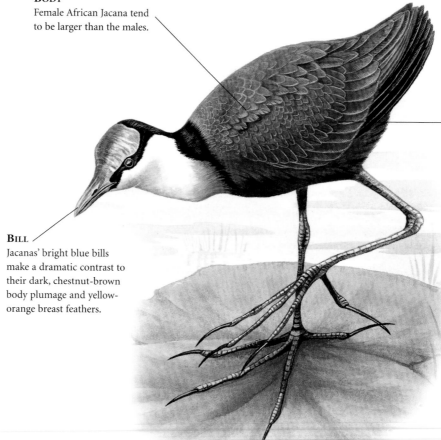

BODY
Female African Jacana tend to be larger than the males.

WINGS
Males have the job of caring for the young, incubating the eggs and carrying the chicks under their wings.

BILL
Jacanas' bright blue bills make a dramatic contrast to their dark, chestnut-brown body plumage and yellow-orange breast feathers.

HOW BIG IS IT?

SPECIAL ADAPTATION
Long legs and wide toes spread the birds' weight and enables African Jacanas to run across floating vegetation, such as lily pads. This gives Jacanas a great advantage over other species, as they can raise their young in regions where they are not directly competing for food.

Silver Gull

• ORDER • *Charadriiformes* • FAMILY • *Laridae* • SPECIES • *Chroicocephalus novaehollandiae*

VITAL STATISTICS

WEIGHT	375–550g (13.2–19.4oz)
LENGTH	40–45cm (15.7–17.7in)
WINGSPAN	91–97cm (35.8–38.2in)
NUMBER OF EGGS	1–5 (usually 3–4)
INCUBATION PERIOD	22–27 days
NUMBER OF BROODS	1–2 (usually 2)
TYPICAL DIET	Small fish, squid, insects, carrion, berries, garbage
LIFE SPAN	Up to 5 years

This is by far the most abundant gull in the waters off Australia, where it is known simply as Seagull.

WHERE IN THE WORLD?

The Silver Gull is found in all of Australia, New Zealand and parts of New Caledonia. It is mainly found near the coast, but is also frequently seen inland.

CREATURE COMPARISONS

The head, neck and underside of this gull are entirely white, whereas the wings are grey with dark wing tips. The tail is also white. The bill and legs are orange-red, and there is a handsome orange-red ring around each eye. The Silver Gull can be mistaken for a Pacific Gull or a Kelp Gull, but it is easily distinguished from them by its smaller size.

Juvenile Silver Gull

WINGS
The Silver Gull has large, narrow wings, giving it the fast, agile flight necessary for catching fish and insects.

BEAK
The bill is short and pointed with a slightly hooked tip for holding on to slippery fish and squid.

FEET
The large feet are webbed for efficient swimming, but are also used as air-brakes for slowing down.

HOW BIG IS IT?

SPECIAL ADAPTATION

Unlike large gulls, which live mainly on fish, the smaller Silver Gull often chases flying insects. Insects are packed with protein, and are a nutritious addition to its diet.

Black-headed Gull

• ORDER • Charadriiformes • FAMILY • Laridae • SPECIES • *Chroicocephalus ridibundus*

VITAL STATISTICS

WEIGHT	285–450g (10.1–16oz)
LENGTH	38–44cm (15.0–17.3in)
WINGSPAN	94–105cm (37–41.3in)
NUMBER OF EGGS	2–3 eggs
INCUBATION PERIOD	23–26 days
NUMBER OF BROODS	1 a year
TYPICAL DIET	Insects, worms, grubs, spiders, small fish, carrion, garbage
LIFE SPAN	Up to 32 years

Despite the name, this common, medium-sized gull does not have a black head but a brown one.

WHERE IN THE WORLD?

The Black-headed Gull is widespread across much of Europe, except northern Scandinavia and the Iberian Peninsula. It is also found along the coasts of eastern Canada.

CREATURE COMPARISONS

The Black-headed Gull has a dark brown face and upper part of the throat. The neck, breast and belly are white. The wings and back are light grey. Males are similar to females. It can be mistaken for the slightly larger Mediterranean Gull, which does have a jet-black head, but this species is found only in parts of southeastern Europe and in a few coastal areas.

Gulls fighting

BILL
The reddish bill is long and strong for feeding on a wide variety of animal and vegetable matter.

HEAD
The face and upper part of the throat are dark brown, not black, but young birds usually have only darker spots.

TAIL
The white tail is short and wide, and has a black tip while it is entirely white in the Mediterranean Gull, which looks otherwise similar.

HOW BIG IS IT?

SPECIAL ADAPTATION
The Black-headed Gull is an opportunist, and has adapted well to human settlements, where they feed on rubbish, scavenge fish or forage for earthworms when a farmer has ploughed a field.

Herring Gull

• ORDER • Charadriiformes **• FAMILY •** Laridae **• SPECIES •** *Larus argentatus*

VITAL STATISTICS

WEIGHT	Males: 1.2kg (2.6lb) Females: 948g (33.4oz)
LENGTH	54–60cm (21.2–23.6 in)
WINGSPAN	1.2–1.5 m (3.9–4.9 ft)
SEXUAL MATURITY	Usually 4 years
LAYS EGGS	April–June, but varies with location
INCUBATION PERIOD	28–30 days
NUMBER OF EGGS	1–5 eggs
NUMBER OF BROODS	1 a year
TYPICAL DIET	Fish, small mammals, eggs, insects, worms and scraps
LIFE SPAN	Typically 19 years

For many of us, the raucous cry of the Herring Gull will forever be associated with lazy summer days spent at the seaside.

WHERE IN THE WORLD?

These adaptable birds were once found only in coastal regions, but they are now increasingly seen in cities, feeding on garbage tips. Populations can be found across North America, Europe and parts of Asia.

CREATURE COMPARISONS

Big birds take a long time to mature. In the case of Herring Gulls, birdwatchers can observe the process as the seasons pass, and the juveniles' plumage gradually changes from speckled brown (shown) to white and grey, over a period of four years.

Juvenile

WINGS
There are 48 species of Gull. Herring Gulls have grey wings marked with white patches with black wing tips.

HEAD
Juvenile birds in their first winter have a dark bill and eyes. Adults have a pale yellow bill and eyes.

LEGS
Although it takes many winters for Herring Gulls to develop their adult breeding plumage, their legs and feet are always pink.

HOW BIG IS IT?

SPECIAL ADAPTATION
Adult Gulls store partly digested food in their crop (the extended, pouch-like part of the oesophagus). Chicks know, instinctively, that if they peck the red spot, near the tip of their parent's lower mandible, the adult will empty its crop into their open bill.

Audouin's Gull

• ORDER • Charadriiformes • FAMILY • Laridae • SPECIES • *Larus audouinii*

The large Andouin's Gull was once in serious danger of extinction, but in recent years it has become more numerous.

VITAL STATISTICS

WEIGHT	575–800g (20.3–28.2oz)
LENGTH	48–52cm (18.9–20.5in)
WINGSPAN	90–110cm (35.4–43.3in)
NUMBER OF EGGS	1–3 eggs (usually 2–3)
INCUBATION PERIOD	26–32 days
NUMBER OF BROODS	1 a year
TYPICAL DIET	Small fish and squid
LIFE SPAN	Unknown

WHERE IN THE WORLD?

Audouin's Gull is found on rocky islands and coasts along the Mediterranean. All young birds and many adults spend the winter along the Atlantic coast of northern Africa.

CREATURE COMPARISONS

The head, neck, breast and belly are white, while the wings are greyish. The legs and feet are dark grey-green. Males and females look similar, although the males are usually larger. It can be confused with the larger and much more common Herring Gull, but can be distinguished from this species by its stout red bill, dark legs and white patches along the dark wing feathers.

WINGS
The wings are large and narrow, giving this gull a fast and agile flight.

BEAK
Audouin's Gull has a short, stout, reddish bill it uses for snatching small fish from the surface of the sea.

FEET
The large feet are webbed and are used for swimming and for manoeuvring just above the waves during feeding.

Juvenile

HOW BIG IS IT?

SPECIAL ADAPTATION

Audouin's Gull feeds by flying close to the surface of the sea, and almost coming to a halt. It uses its large, webbed feet as air-brakes to slow down for feeding.

Common Gull

• **ORDER** • Charadriiformes • **FAMILY** • Laridae • **SPECIES** • *Larus canus*

VITAL STATISTICS

WEIGHT	290–580g (10.2–20.5oz)
LENGTH	40–46cm (15.7–18.1in)
WINGSPAN	96–120cm (37.8–47.2in)
NUMBER OF EGGS	2–3 eggs
INCUBATION PERIOD	22–26 days
NUMBER OF BROODS	1 a year
TYPICAL DIET	Small fish, crayfish, birds' eggs and chicks
LIFE SPAN	Up to 24 years

The Common Gull breeds along coastlines and large lakes, often in big noisy colonies.

WHERE IN THE WORLD?

The Common Gull breeds in northern Europe and across much of northern Asia. It is also found in the northwestern regions of the USA. It flies south for the winter.

CREATURE COMPARISONS

The Common Gull has an all-white breast and belly, while the back of the neck, the back and the upper side of the wings are grey. Adults have black wing tips. In winter, the adult birds are more greyish above, with faint dark stripes and spots. Males and females are similar. Juveniles are more mottled brownish and lack black wing tips.

Common Gull feeding young

BEAK
The bill is smaller than that of its close relative, the Herring Gull (seen on the left), and is not yellow but greenish-yellow.

WINGS
The Common Gull has large, narrow wings for efficient soaring and gliding above the waves

FEET
The legs and webbed feet of the Common Gull are greenish-yellow, not flesh-coloured as in the larger Herring Gull.

HOW BIG IS IT?

SPECIAL ADAPTATION

The Common Gull is an audacious thief, often stealing food from other, smaller seabirds, such as puffins. In this way, it avoids the effort of having to find the food itself.

Dolphin Gull

• **ORDER** • Charadriiformes • **FAMILY** • Laridae • **SPECIES** • *Leucophaeus scoresbii*

VITAL STATISTICS

WEIGHT	350–600g (12.3–21.2oz)
LENGTH	40–46cm (15.7–18.1in)
WINGSPAN	90–95cm (35.4–37.4in)
NUMBER OF EGGS	2–3 eggs
INCUBATION PERIOD	24–26 days
NUMBER OF BROODS	1 a year
TYPICAL DIET	Carrion, birds' eggs and chicks, fish, snails, mussels
LIFE SPAN	Up to 10 years

The Dolphin Gull is getting rarer in many places, and the entire world's population is now believed to be only around 40,000 birds.

WHERE IN THE WORLD?

The Dolphin Gull is found in southern South America, in south-central Chile, Tierra del Fuego, and the Falkland Islands. It is estimated that there are no more than 700 pairs left in Argentina.

CREATURE COMPARISONS

The Dolphin Gull is a somewhat small species of gull. It has a uniformly white head, neck and underside of the body. The wings are dark or slate-grey on the upper side, and are off-white on the under side, except for the dark wing tips. The bill and legs are yellow or yellowish-red. Males and females are similar, although the males may be slightly larger.

HEAD
The white head has an attractive red ring around the strikingly yellow eyes, which have a white iris.

BEAK
The bill is fairly stout, and has a distinct hook at the tip for tearing into food and cracking the shells of snails.

TAIL
The wide tail is white, and is important in manoeuvring, especially during slow flight and landing.

HOW BIG IS IT?

SPECIAL ADAPTATION
The Dolphin Gull nests on the ground in small colonies, making it vulnerable to predators. In many places, populations have declined rapidly because of introduced mink, rats or housecats.

Black-legged Kittiwake

• ORDER • Charadriiformes • FAMILY • Laridae • SPECIES • *Rissa tridacyla*

The Kittiwakes are the only type of gull that nest exclusively on cliffs and rocky ledges.

VITAL STATISTICS

WEIGHT	450–500g (15.9–17.6oz)
LENGTH	38–40cm (15.0–15.7in)
WINGSPAN	95–120cm (37.4–47.2in)
NUMBER OF EGGS	2 eggs
INCUBATION PERIOD	21–24 days
NUMBER OF BROODS	1 a year
TYPICAL DIET	Insects, worms, fish, squid, crayfish, carrion
LIFE SPAN	Up to 20 years

WHERE IN THE WORLD?

The Black-legged Kittiwake breeds in coastal areas in the North Pacific, North Atlantic and Arctic Oceans. In winter, many migrate south and may be seen along European shores.

CREATURE COMPARISONS

The Black-legged Kittiwake has dark brown to black legs, as the name implies, and a white head, neck, breast and belly. The back and upper side of the wings are grey, and the wing tips are black. Males are similar to females. This species, which may have reddish-grey legs, is often confused with the slightly smaller Red-legged Kittiwake, but it also has darker wings, a shorter bill and a larger head.

Black-legged Kittiwake feeding young

BEAK
The yellow bill is stout and powerful, with a slightly downwards-turned tip to grasp slippery fish and squid.

WINGS
The grey wings are long and narrow, giving the Black-legged Kittiwake a light, elegant flight.

FEET
The legs and feet are usually dark, but some specimens may have reddish-grey legs, and thus look similar to the Red-legged Kittiwake.

HOW BIG IS IT?

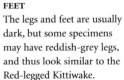

SPECIAL ADAPTATION

The Black-legged Kittiwake is a very common seabird in northern oceans. It breeds on hard-to-reach places, such as tall, steep cliffs, and is therefore safe from predators.

Avocet (Pied)

• **ORDER** • Charadriiformes • **FAMILY** • Recurvirostridae • **SPECIES** • *Recurvirostra avosetta*

VITAL STATISTICS

WEIGHT	280g (10oz)
LENGTH	44cm (17.3in)
WINGSPAN	67–77cm (26.4–30.3in)
NUMBER OF EGGS	3–4 eggs
INCUBATION PERIOD	35–42 days
NUMBER OF BROODS	1 a year
CALL	Loud 'klute-klute-klute'
TYPICAL DIET	Crustaceans, worms and insects
LIFE SPAN	Up to 16 years

These elegant waders get their curious common name from the black caps that were once worn by European lawyers, who were known as advocates.

WHERE IN THE WORLD?

The Avocet favours salty mudflats. It breeds throughout temperate Europe and Central Asia. Those in milder regions are residents, while others winter in southern Africa and Asia.

CREATURE COMPARISONS

Even experienced bird-watchers can have difficulty identifying bird species. For instance, in the air, it can be easy to mistake Avocets for Goosanders or Shellducks, which are also mainly black and white in colour. However, their long legs and extended bill differentiate them from other birds.

Avocet guarding eggs

BODY
Avocets are often referred to as Pied, because they have black-and-white plumage. This makes them easy to identify.

BILL
While other species of wading birds, such as Sandpipers, have straight or downwards-curving bills, the long black bill of the Avocet curves upwards.

LEGS
Many waders have red legs, but Avocets have grey-blue legs. These can be up to 10cm (4in) long.

HOW BIG IS IT?

SPECIAL ADAPTATION
The bill of the Avocet is packed with highly sensitive receptors so it can detect prey simply by sweeping its bill from side to side. It may also upend itself like a duck to reach food beneath the water.

Ruddy Turnstone

• ORDER • Charadriiformes **• FAMILY •** Scolopacidae **• SPECIES •** *Arenaria interpres*

VITAL STATISTICS

WEIGHT	85–150g (3.0–5.3oz)
LENGTH	22–25cm (8.7–9.8in)
WINGSPAN	50–57cm (19.7–22.4in)
NUMBER OF EGGS	3–4 eggs
INCUBATION PERIOD	23–27 days
NUMBER OF BROODS	1 a year
TYPICAL DIET	Small crayfish, insects, carrion
LIFE SPAN	19 years

The small, agile Ruddy Turnstone is a familiar wading bird seen along coastlines almost all over the world.

WHERE IN THE WORLD?

The Ruddy Turnstone breeds in Scandinavia, Estonia and the Arctic (in Alaska, Canada and Russia). It winters in western Europe, Africa, Australia, Asia and the Americas.

CREATURE COMPARISONS

The male Turnstone has a white head speckled with small black dots, black markings along the cheeks and a black throat. The upper side of the body is reddish-brown with black markings, and the underside is white. The legs are reddish. Females are similar to males, but drabber. The winter plumage is more drab and greyish.

The Ruddy Turnstone in flight

BEAK
The stout, flattened bill is used in searching for food on rocky shores.

WINGS
The Ruddy Turnstone has long, narrow wings, giving the bird a fast flight and enabling it to migrate long distances.

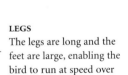

LEGS
The legs are long and the feet are large, enabling the bird to run at speed over sandy surfaces.

HOW BIG IS IT?

SPECIAL ADAPTATION

The Ruddy Turnstone has a flat, wide bill, perfectly suited to being used as a wedge to flip over small rocks and stones to reveal the small creatures that often hide underneath them.

Sanderling

• ORDER • Charadriiformes • FAMILY • Scolopacidae • SPECIES • *Calidris alba*

VITAL STATISTICS

WEIGHT	50–85g (1.8–3.0oz)
LENGTH	18–21cm (7.1–8.3in)
WINGSPAN	40–45cm (15.7–17.7in)
NUMBER OF EGGS	4
INCUBATION PERIOD	23–24 days
NUMBER OF BROODS	1 (sometimes 2)
TYPICAL DIET	Tidal zone invertebrates such as tiny insects, crayfish, plant matter
LIFE SPAN	Up to 12 years

The Sanderling, a type of Sandpiper, is a small wading bird that can be seen running endlessly back and forth across the sand to escape the waves.

WHERE IN THE WORLD?

The Sanderling breeds in the Arctic but migrates south for the winter, and can be seen along coastlines throughout much of the world. It is a common winter resident on many European coasts.

CREATURE COMPARISONS

The Sanderling is paler than all other Sandpipers. In summer, it has a pale reddish-brown head, back and throat, with lots of small black spots and stripes, while the wings are more greyish. The underside is white. Males and females are similar. In winter, the plumage is much paler and greyish-white. The sanderling can be confused with a Dunlin, but has a shorter bill.

Juvenile

BILL
The Sanderlings' bill is short and sturdy for a Sandpiper, and is used for probing after insects in sand and mud.

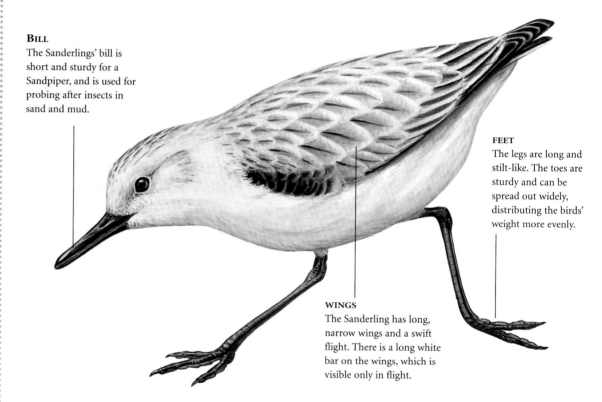

FEET
The legs are long and stilt-like. The toes are sturdy and can be spread out widely, distributing the birds' weight more evenly.

WINGS
The Sanderling has long, narrow wings and a swift flight. There is a long white bar on the wings, which is visible only in flight.

HOW BIG IS IT?

SPECIAL ADAPTATION

The Sanderling no longer has a hind toe (equivalent to our big toe), and this easily distinguishes it from other Sandpipers. This allows the bird to run more efficiently on sandy surfaces.

Dunlin

• ORDER • Charadriiformes • FAMILY • Scolopacidae • SPECIES • *Calidris alpina*

VITAL STATISTICS

WEIGHT	48g (1.7oz)
LENGTH	17–21cm (6.7–8.3in)
WINGSPAN	32–36cm (12.6–14.2in)
SEXUAL MATURITY	1 year
NUMBER OF EGGS	4 eggs
INCUBATION PERIOD	20–24 days
NUMBER OF BROODS	1, although another clutch may be laid if the first fails
TYPICAL DIET	Insects, small invertebrates; occasionally plants
LIFE SPAN	Typically 5 years

Dashing up and down the seashore like little, pot-bellied, wind-up toys, Dunlin are one of the most popular of all waders.

WHERE IN THE WORLD?

Dunlin prefer moors, marshes and estuaries. Northern European birds winter on African and Asian coastlines, while Canadian populations migrate to the coastlines of North America.

CREATURE COMPARISONS

There are numerous sub-species of Dunlin, which vary in coloration and bill size across their range. Those breeding in Greenland have the shortest bills and the palest red upper parts. Those breeding in the Arctic (shown) have the longest bills and the brightest red upper parts.

Adult of the Alpina race

BODY
In the winter, adult Dunlins shed their summer finery, and look rather plain, with brownish-grey upper parts and mainly white underparts.

BELLY
Adult Dunlin in full breeding plumage have distinctive black bellies. This helps to differentiate them from other coastal wading birds.

FEET
Dunlin have long toes. These splay out on soft mud, distributing the birds' weight more evenly, preventing them from sinking.

HOW BIG IS IT?

SPECIAL ADAPTATION

The long, downwards-curved bill of the Dunlin is designed specifically for rooting in the earth for food. Birds will often be seen making rapid probing motions in the soft mud, until they strike it lucky. Sensitive receptors in the bill help them to detect prey.

Red Knot

• **ORDER** • Charadriiformes • **FAMILY** • Scolopacidae • **SPECIES** • *Calidris canutus*

VITAL STATISTICS

WEIGHT	120–200g (4.2–7.1oz)
LENGTH	23–26cm (9.1–10.2in)
WINGSPAN	47–53cm (18.5–20.9in)
NUMBER OF EGGS	4 eggs
INCUBATION PERIOD	20–25 days
NUMBER OF BROODS	1 a year
TYPICAL DIET	Snails, mussels, worms and other small animals in the tidal zone
LIFE SPAN	Up to 17 years

The Red Knot is often seen in flocks, and during migrations these may number tens of thousands of birds.

WHERE IN THE WORLD?

The Red Knot is found along coastlines of the most northern parts of Europe, Canada and Russia. In winter, birds from North America migrate to Europe, and European birds migrate to Africa.

CREATURE COMPARISONS

In summer, the bird has a mottled grey and reddish-brown back and neck, whereas the face, throat, breast and belly are reddish-brown or cinnamon. The underside of the tail is pale. In winter, the plumage is much paler, and is greyish above and pale grey or off-white underneath. The eyes are red with a black iris. Males and females are similar.

BILL
The Red Knot has a long, pointed bill for probing in sand for worms, crustaceans and other small creatures.

WINGS
The wings are long and narrow, giving the Red Knot a fast flight, and the tips are usually darker than the rest of the wing.

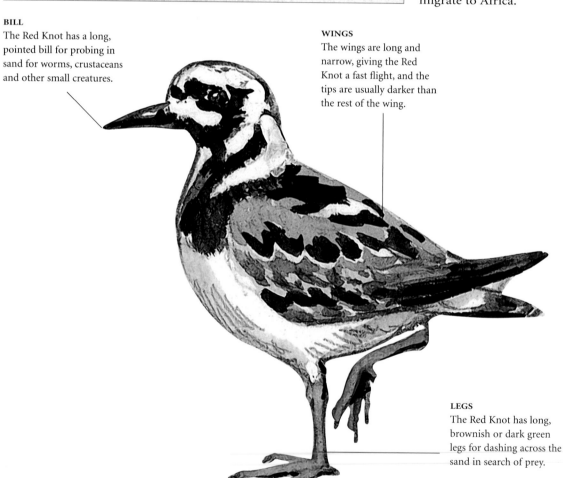

LEGS
The Red Knot has long, brownish or dark green legs for dashing across the sand in search of prey.

Summer Plumage

HOW BIG IS IT?

SPECIAL ADAPTATION
The Red Knot is a timid little bird, and it often associates with the Turnstone, which is a much more aggressive species. This ensures protection for the Red Knot's chicks.

Curlew Sandpiper

• **ORDER** • Charadriiformes • **FAMILY** • Scolopacidae • **SPECIES** • *Calidris ferruginea*

These exquisite waders may look fragile but, every year, they migrate thousands of kilometres from the cold north to the warmth of the Mediterranean – and back.

VITAL STATISTICS

WEIGHT	58g (2oz)
HEIGHT	19–21.5cm (7.5–8.5in)
WINGSPAN	44cm (17.3in)
SEXUAL MATURITY	2 years
INCUBATION PERIOD	19–20 days
FLEDGLING PERIOD	14–16 days
NUMBER OF EGGS	3–4 eggs
NUMBER OF BROODS	1 a year
TYPICAL DIET	Invertebrates
LIFE SPAN	Up to 12 years

WHERE IN THE WORLD?

Curlew Sandpipers breed in the far north of Arctic Siberia, but winter in the warmer regions of Africa, southern Asia and Australasia. Preferred habitats are marshes, wetlands and estuaries.

CREATURE COMPARISONS

In their everyday attire, Curlew Sandpipers look much like other waders. Yet during the course of the year they moult their winter plumage and, by June, have their new breeding plumage – predominantly black, white and red above, with a glorious brick red coloration (see right).

Winter plumage

BILL
The long, downwards-curved tip of the Sandpipers' bill is packed with sensitive receptors to feel for food in the mud.

BODY
In their grey and white winter plumage, Sandpiper Curlews look very similar to many other species of wader but shown here is the distinctive summer plumage.

RUMP
It has been suggested that the pure white rump helps Sandpipers to keep track of each other during long migrations.

HOW BIG IS IT?

SPECIAL ADAPTATION

The Curlew Sandpiper's long legs and bill offer a distinct advantage over other waders, enabling it to probe deeper waters and deeper mud for food that the waders cannot reach.

Purple Sandpiper

• **ORDER** • Charadriiformes • **FAMILY** • Scolopacidae • **SPECIES** • *Calidris maritima*

VITAL STATISTICS

WEIGHT	60–75g (2.1–2.6oz)
LENGTH	20–21cm (7.9–8.3in)
WINGSPAN	40–44cm (15.7–17.3in)
NUMBER OF EGGS	4 eggs
INCUBATION PERIOD	21–22 days
NUMBER OF BROODS	1 a year
TYPICAL DIET	Insects, worms, snails, water fleas and other small crustaceans
LIFE DPAN	Up to 10 years

The Purple Sandpiper often breeds in barren, inhospitable places, and has to fly to the coast to feed.

The Purple Sandpiper breeds on the tundra and in alpine areas across the Arctic, from northeastern Canada, through Greenland and Iceland, and eastwards along the northern coasts of Siberia.

CREATURE COMPARISONS

The Purple Sandpiper has a mottled plumage for camouflage in barren, open terrain. The upper side is charcoal-grey with dark spots and streaks, and the underside is pale grey or off-white with narrow dark stripes. The tail is short and wide, and is greyish in colour with a black stripe and white sides. Males and females are similar.

Purple Sandpiper

WINGS
The Purple Sandpiper has a distinctive, white band along the wing, visible only during flight.

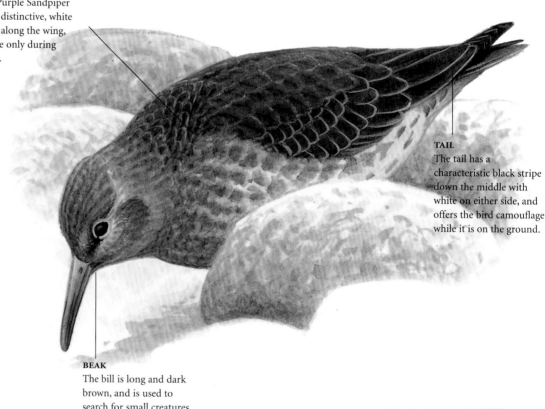

TAIL
The tail has a characteristic black stripe down the middle with white on either side, and offers the bird camouflage while it is on the ground.

BEAK
The bill is long and dark brown, and is used to search for small creatures in and on stony and sandy ground.

HOW BIG IS IT?

SPECIAL ADAPTATION

Male Sandpipers take care of the young. After hatching, he takes the chicks out to stony or sandy ground, where they learn how to hunt for food.

Pectoral Sandpiper

• **ORDER** • Charadriiformes • **FAMILY** • Scolopacidae • **SPECIES** • *Calidris melanotos*

VITAL STATISTICS

WEIGHT	40–50g (1.4–1.8oz)
LENGTH	22cm (8.7in)
WINGSPAN	43cm (16.9in)
INCUBATION PERIOD	21–23 days
FLEDGLING PERIOD	20–21 days
NUMBER OF EGGS	4 eggs
NUMBER OF BROODS	1 a year, although this varies as males and females mate with multiple partners
HABITS	Diurnal, migratory
TYPICAL DIET	Aquatic insects and plants
LIFE SPAN	Up to 10 years

CREATURE COMPARISONS

The Pectoral Sandpiper gets its common name from its most obvious physical feature, the pectoral band, which is the line on their bodies where the speckled breast meets the white belly. Unusually, birds of both sexes and of all ages have the same pectoral band.

Pectoral band

The Pectoral Sandpiper has an identity problem. Although technically a shorebird, it prefers wet grassland habitats, which is why it is also known as the Grass Snipe.

WHERE IN THE WORLD?

These handsome birds breed in the boggy tundra of North America and Siberia. In the winter, they migrate to freshwater regions of Latin America. A few make it to Australasia.

THROAT
Male Pectoral Sandpipers have a throat sac full of fat and fluid. In the summer, this swells, making them look bigger and more attractive to females.

BILL
A downward-curving bill makes it easier for Sandpipers to root in the sand or mud in search of prey.

BODY
These medium-sized birds are characterized by long necks, long, yellow legs, plump bodies and short, 'v'-shaped tails.

HOW BIG IS IT?

SPECIAL ADAPTATION

The hollow, hooting call of the Pectoral Sandpiper is produced by the throat sac of the male bird. The male inflates it and deflates it during courtship displays to attract a mate.

Spoon-billed Sandpiper

• **ORDER** • Charadriiformes • **FAMILY** • Scolopacidae • **SPECIES** • *Eurynorhynchus pygmeus*

VITAL STATISTICS

LENGTH	14–16cm (5.5–6.3in)
WINGSPAN	98cm–1.1m (38.6 in–3.6ft)
SEXUAL MATURITY	Males: 2 years. Females: Probably 1 year
INCUBATION PERIOD	Around 18–20 days
FLEDGLING PERIOD	15–20 days
NUMBER OF EGGS	4 eggs
NUMBER OF BROODS	1 a year, but a second clutch may be laid if the first is lost
HABITS	Diurnal, migratory
TYPICAL DIET	Insects, worms, molluscs, crustaceans and seeds
LIFE SPAN	Up to 10 years

CREATURE COMPARISONS

Spoon-Billed Sandpipers' may look handsome in their black- and-white winter plumage, but their red and brown summer plumage (shown) is much more appealing and eye-catching. This is deliberate, because attracting attention is the most important concern when trying to attract a mate.

Summer Plumage

Spoon-Billed Sandpipers are such specialists that they are found only in isolated regions. In fact, there may be fewer than 1000 remaining in the wild.

WHERE IN THE WORLD?

These rare birds need very specialized breeding habitats; usually lagoon spits, with low vegetation and nearby mudflats, as found on the coastlines of eastern Siberia. Populations winter in southern Asia.

HEAD
The Spoon-Billed Sandpipers' large, rounded head, is so muscular that the birds seem to lack a neck.

BILL
The Spoon-Bill Sandpipers' most obvious feature is its flattened, spatula-like bill. This is less apparent when the birds are in flight.

BODY
In common with many species of waders, the winter plumage of the Spoon-Billed Sandpiper (shown far right) is grey and white.

HOW BIG IS IT?

SPECIAL ADAPTATION
The spoon-shaped bill of this unique Sandpiper may look odd but it is actually a sophisticated tool. All Sandpipers have sensory cells in the tips of their bills to detect food, and this flat shape may allow the birds to find more food, more easily.

Snipe (Common)

• ORDER • Charadriiformes **• FAMILY •** Scolopacidae **• SPECIES •** *Gallinago gallinago*

It is the Common Snipe's zig-zagging flight that makes it so popular with hunters. In fact, especially skilled shots are known as snipers.

VITAL STATISTICS

WEIGHT	110g (3.9oz)
LENGTH	23–28cm (9–11in)
WINGSPAN	39–45cm (15.3–17.7in)
SEXUAL MATURITY	2 years
INCUBATION PERIOD	18–20 days
FLEDGLING PERIOD	19–20 days
NUMBER OF EGGS	4 eggs
NUMBER OF BROODS	1 a year
TYPICAL DIET	Invertebrates
LIFE SPAN	Typically 4 years

WHERE IN THE WORLD?

These elusive waders breed in wet meadows, marshes, bogs and wetlands in Europe, northern Asia and North America. Migrants tend to move south, to Central Africa, Central Asia and Latin America.

CREATURE COMPARISONS

In common with many species of wading bird, Common Snipe have an elongated bill, which is packed with touch-sensitive receptors. This incredible tool allows the birds to locate food by touch alone as they root around in the mud and shallow waters for invertebrates that are hidden below.

A Snipe searching for food

EYES
Eyes, set on the side of the Common Snipe's head, give the bird as wide a field of vision as possible.

BILL
The Common Snipes' elongated bill accounts for up to 7cm (2.7in) of the bird's entire body length.

BODY
Snipes are so well camouflaged that, until they move, they are almost impossible to see in their natural wetland habitats.

HOW BIG IS IT?

SPECIAL ADAPTATION

To attract a mate, male Common Snipes circle and dive through the air. The distinctive noise that accompanies their flight is made by the wind rushing through their outspread tail feathers.

85

Black-tailed Godwit

• **ORDER** • Charadriiformes • **FAMILY** • Scolopacidae • **SPECIES** • *Limosa limosa*

VITAL STATISTICS

WEIGHT	Males: 280g (9.9oz) Females: 340g (12oz)
LENGTH	37–42cm (14.6–16.5in)
WINGSPAN	63–74cm (24.8–29.1in)
SEXUAL MATURITY	1 year
INCUBATION PERIOD	22–24 days
FLEDGLING PERIOD	28–34 days
NUMBER OF EGGS	2–4 eggs
NUMBER OF BROODS	1 a year
TYPICAL DIET	Invertebrates, seeds and berries
LIFE SPAN	Typically 11 years

CREATURE COMPARISONS

The Black-Tailed Godwits' drab, winter plumage helps them blend in with their surroundings, as they feed on grey mudflats and marshes. However, come the summer, Godwits – males and females – change into more eye-catching attire, ready to attract a mate.

Winter plumage

Birdwatchers look out for the cruciform outline of the Black-Tailed Godwit in flight as these graceful birds pass by on their epic winter migrations.

WHERE IN THE WORLD?

These shorebirds breed on marshes and temperate wetlands in northern Europe and into northern Asia. Populations winter in southern Europe, southern Africa and southern Asia, as far as Australasia.

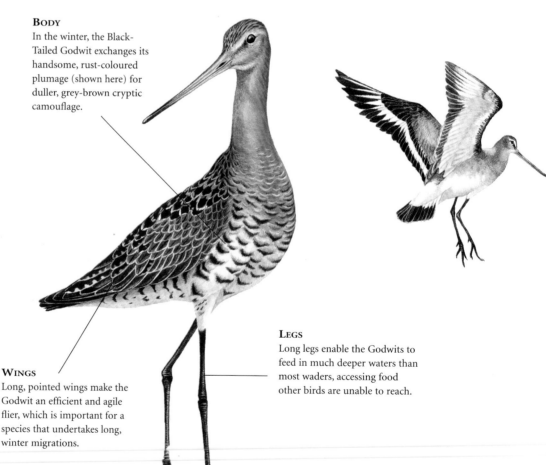

BODY
In the winter, the Black-Tailed Godwit exchanges its handsome, rust-coloured plumage (shown here) for duller, grey-brown cryptic camouflage.

LEGS
Long legs enable the Godwits to feed in much deeper waters than most waders, accessing food other birds are unable to reach.

WINGS
Long, pointed wings make the Godwit an efficient and agile flier, which is important for a species that undertakes long, winter migrations.

HOW BIG IS IT?

SPECIAL ADAPTATION

The Godwits' long, upwards-curved bill is more than just a handy tool for rooting in the mud. It is a very precise piece instrument packed with touch-sensitive receptors. The tip of the birds' bill enables them to find food, even if it is buried deep in the mud.

Whimbrel

• **ORDER** • Charadriiformes • **FAMILY** • Scolopacidae • **SPECIES** • *Numenius phaeopus*

Although Whimbrels are always a joy to watch, it is their plaintive cries that make them one of the most memorable of all wading birds.

Whimbrels breed in Eurasia and North America. Winters are spent in Africa, southern Asia, Australasia and the Americas, and they are often seen along coasts and in river estuaries hunting for food.

CREATURE COMPARISONS

Whimbrels and Curlews look very similar, so it is no surprise to learn that they also have similar habits and habitats. Marshes, mudflats and meadows are favoured by both species, meaning that both are a common sight along British and European coasts during the winter.

Male Whimbrel

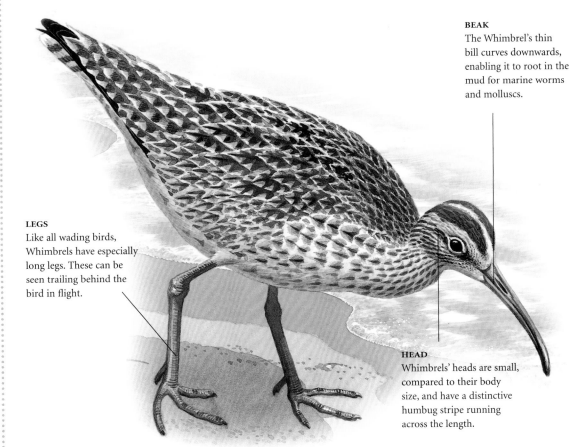

BEAK
The Whimbrel's thin bill curves downwards, enabling it to root in the mud for marine worms and molluscs.

LEGS
Like all wading birds, Whimbrels have especially long legs. These can be seen trailing behind the bird in flight.

HEAD
Whimbrels' heads are small, compared to their body size, and have a distinctive humbug stripe running across the length.

HOW BIG IS IT?

SPECIAL ADAPTATION
Although no one knows exactly why, ornithologists believe that the long, white wedge which extends from the Whimbrels' tail, up its back, is some type of marker. This may help individual birds to keep track of each other during their long, winter migrations.

Red-necked Phalarope

• **ORDER** • Charadriiformes • **FAMILY** • Scolopacidae • **SPECIES** • *Phalaropus lobatus*

VITAL STATISTICS

WEIGHT	36g (1.3oz)
LENGTH	17–19cm (6.7–7.5in)
WINGSPAN	30–34cm (11.8–13.4in)
SEXUAL MATURITY	1 year
INCUBATION PERIOD	17–21 days
FLEDGLING PERIOD	18–21 days
NUMBER OF EGGS	4 eggs per nest
NUMBER OF BROODS	Females may breed with 2 males and lay a clutch in each nest
TYPICAL DIET	Insects, freshwater crustaceans and plankton
LIFE SPAN	Up to 10 years

This species of Phalarope is one of the easiest to identify – simply look for the red neck that gives these birds their common name.

WHERE IN THE WORLD?

These widespread birds breed in North America and northern Europe, as far as Siberia in the east and Iceland in the north. Their preferred habitats are marshes, coasts and river estuaries.

CREATURE COMPARISONS

Red-Necked Phalarope belong to a group of birds known as waders. Despite the fact that this is a large and varied group, there are many traits that are recognized as typical of waders, including long legs, for wading and a long bill for rooting in mud.

Juvenile

BILL
A needle-like bill is used like a pair of tweezers to pluck small insects from the water with great accuracy.

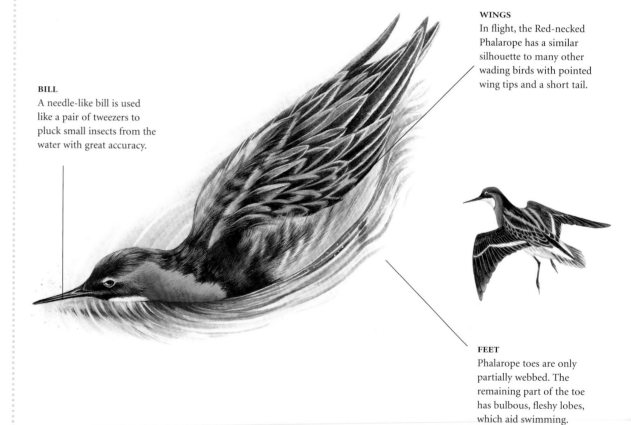

WINGS
In flight, the Red-necked Phalarope has a similar silhouette to many other wading birds with pointed wing tips and a short tail.

FEET
Phalarope toes are only partially webbed. The remaining part of the toe has bulbous, fleshy lobes, which aid swimming.

HOW BIG IS IT?

SPECIAL ADAPTATION

Red-necked Phalarope have an ingenious feeding technique. They swim in a circle, creating a mini whirlpool, which brings insects to the surface, ready to be eaten. They do not need to do this in the open sea because naturally turbulent waters have the same effect.

Ruff

With their extravagant and colourful neck collars, male Ruffs in their breeding plumage are not only an unmistakable sight but a truly spectacular one.

VITAL STATISTICS

WEIGHT MALES	180g (6.3oz). Females: 110g (3.9oz)
LENGTH MALES	29–32cm (11.4–12.6in). Females: 22–26cm (8.7–10.2in)
WINGSPAN	Males: 54–58cm (21.2–22.8in) Females: 48–53cm (18.9–20.9in)
SEXUAL MATURITY	At least 2 years
INCUBATION PERIOD	20–23 days
FLEDGLING PERIOD	25–28 days
NUMBER OF EGGS	4 eggs
NUMBER OF BROODS	1 a year
TYPICAL DIET	Invertebrates
LIFE SPAN	Up to 11 years

CREATURE COMPARISONS

Breeding males may look incredibly showy, but they sport their ruffs only between May to June. Once the mating season is over, they change into plainer attire (see below) and resemble the females (called reeves). However, as males are much larger, they are still easy to identify.

Winter plumage. Female (above), male (below)

WHERE IN THE WORLD?

These birds breed on marshes and in wetlands in northern Europe and Asia. They migrate in huge flocks, sometimes numbering millions, heading for warmer, southern regions.

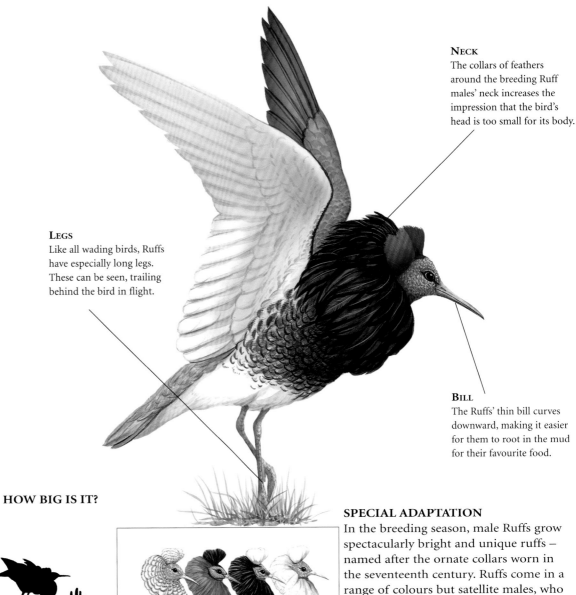

NECK
The collars of feathers around the breeding Ruff males' neck increases the impression that the bird's head is too small for its body.

LEGS
Like all wading birds, Ruffs have especially long legs. These can be seen, trailing behind the bird in flight.

BILL
The Ruffs' thin bill curves downward, making it easier for them to root in the mud for their favourite food.

HOW BIG IS IT?

SPECIAL ADAPTATION
In the breeding season, male Ruffs grow spectacularly bright and unique ruffs – named after the ornate collars worn in the seventeenth century. Ruffs come in a range of colours but satellite males, who do not display to females (but may mate with them secretly), have white ruffs.

89

Eurasian Woodcock

• **ORDER** • Charadriiformes • **FAMILY** • Scolopacidae • **SPECIES** • *Scolopax rusticola*

VITAL STATISTICS

LENGTH	33–38cm (13.0–15.0in)
WINGSPAN	55–65cm (21.7–25.6in)
NUMBER OF EGGS	4 eggs
INCUBATION PERIOD	20–24 days
NUMBER OF BROODS	1–2 a year
TYPICAL DIET	Mainly earthworms, insects, grubs and spiders, but also some plant matter
LIFE SPAN	Up to 12 years

The Eurasian Woodcock is well camouflaged among the leaf litter, but looks very striking when flying fast and low through the forest.

WHERE IN THE WORLD?

The Eurasian Woodcock is widespread across most of Europe, although not along the Mediterranean coasts. It extends eastwards across central Russia to the Sea of Okhotsk and is also found in Japan.

CREATURE COMPARISONS

The woodcock is extremely well camouflaged when lying on the forest floor, and is often seen only in flight. The upper side has a variety of brown and grey shades with a variety of spots, bars and stripes. The underside is greyish with pale dark patterns. The cheeks tend to be lighter in colour. The tail is very short and broad, with dark feathers with white tips. Males and females are similar.

Woodcock in flight

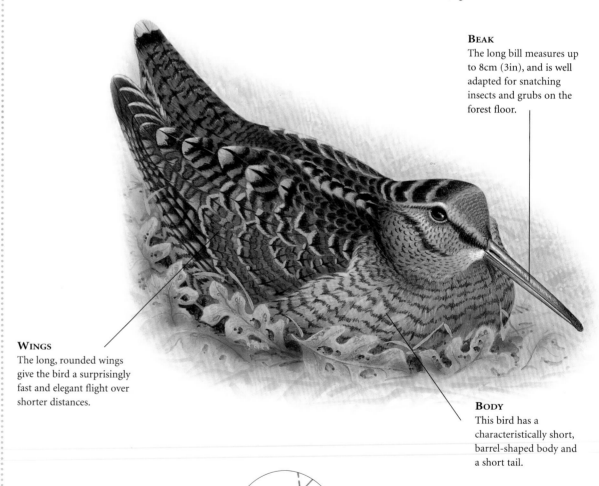

BEAK
The long bill measures up to 8cm (3in), and is well adapted for snatching insects and grubs on the forest floor.

WINGS
The long, rounded wings give the bird a surprisingly fast and elegant flight over shorter distances.

BODY
This bird has a characteristically short, barrel-shaped body and a short tail.

HOW BIG IS IT?

SPECIAL ADAPTATION
The eyes are set high on the head, giving the bird a wide field of vision. This allows the Eurasian Woodcock to see enemies approaching even when it is occupied probing for insects on the forest floor.

Greenshank

VITAL STATISTICS

WEIGHT	140–270g (4.9–9.5oz)
LENGTH	30–31.5cm (11.8–12.4in)
WINGSPAN	53–60cm (20.9–23.6in)
NUMBER OF EGGS	4 eggs
INCUBATION PERIOD	23–24 days
NUMBER OF BROODS	1 a year
TYPICAL DIET	Insects, worms, crayfish, snails, small fish
LIFE SPAN	Up to 12 years

The green legs of the Greenshank is the best way of distinguishing it from its close relative, the Redshank.

WHERE IN THE WORLD?

The Greenshank is found in northern Scotland, across northern Scandinavia and northern Asia. It spends the winter in Africa, southern Asia or even Australia.

CREATURE COMPARISONS

The back and upper side of the wings are mottled brown, and the head is dark grey or brownish. The throat is paler with brown stripes. The belly is white. There is a white stripe along the back, which is only visible during flight. Males and females are similar. The closely related Redshank looks similar, but has reddish legs, a shorter bill and is smaller.

WINGS
The Greenshank has long, narrow wings, and is quick to take to the air when it gets disturbed.

BEAK
The bill is very long and thin, and slightly upturned at the tip, and is well adapted for snatching small creatures.

LEGS
The legs and toes are long for fast running across sandy or stony surfaces near the coast.

The Greenshank (bottom) with the Common Redshank (top)

HOW BIG IS IT?

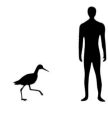

SPECIAL ADAPTATION

The Greenshank often returns to the same breeding ground every year, where a pair of birds will defend up to four different breeding territories by flying in a fast zig-zag mode.

Green Sandpiper

• ORDER • Charadriiformes **• FAMILY •** Scolopacidae **• SPECIES •** *Tringa ochropus*

VITAL STATISTICS

WEIGHT	70–90g (2.5–3.2oz)
LENGTH	22–24cm (8.7–9.4in)
WINGSPAN	41–46cm (16.1–18.1in)
NUMBER OF EGGS	4 eggs
INCUBATION PERIOD	20–23 days
NUMBER OF BROODS	1 a year
TYPICAL DIET	Insects, worms, snails, spiders
LIFE SPAN	Up to 10 years

The Green Sandpiper often lives in forested areas, and it usually prefers freshwater over saltwater.

WHERE IN THE WORLD?

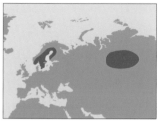

The Green Sandpiper is found across much of Scandinavia, except the high north, and across Siberia. It winters in southern Europe, southern Asia, and in Africa south of the Sahara.

CREATURE COMPARISONS

The upper side of the head, neck, back and are dark grey and mottled with white. The throat, breast and belly are white, as is the tail. Unusually, the underside of the wings is equally dark as the upper side. The legs and the long, narrow beak are dark olive-green. Males are similar to females. It may be confused with the Greenshank, but is darker overall.

Green Sandpiper

WINGS
The Green Sandpiper is easy to recognize in flight, because the wings are dark above and below.

BEAK
The olive-green bill is long and pointed, and is used to search out small creatures on the ground.

TAIL
The Green Sandpiper has an entirely white tail, which is clearly visible in flight.

HOW BIG IS IT?

SPECIAL ADAPTATION

Unlike most Sandpipers, the Green Sandpiper usually nests in trees, often using a nest abandoned by a Thrush. It is not a social species, although small flocks are sometimes seen.

Common Redshank

• **ORDER** • Charadriiformes • **FAMILY** • Scolopacidae • **SPECIES** • *Tringa totanus*

VITAL STATISTICS

WEIGHT	85–140g (3.0–4.9oz)
LENGTH	27–28cm (10.6–11.0in)
WINGSPAN	45–52cm (17.7–20.5in)
NUMBER OF EGGS	3–5 (usually 4)
INCUBATION PERIOD	23–24 days
NUMBER OF BROODS	1 a year
TYPICAL DIET	Insects, snails, crayfish, worms, small amphibians
LIFE SPAN	Up to 17 years

The Common Redshank is often seen in coastal areas, where the birds are busy finding food in the sand.

WHERE IN THE WORLD?

The Common Redshank widespread across much of Europe, although it is rare in central Europe, and across northern and central Asia. Birds from northern populations often migrate south for the winter.

CREATURE COMPARISONS

The Common Redshank has brownish mottled back and upper side of the wings, whereas the head, neck, breast and belly are greyish with faint dark stripes and spots. The upper and underside of the tail is white. Males and females are similar. It may be confused with the Greenshank, but this species has greenish legs and appears darker overall.

Common Redshank in flight

BILL
The long, pointed red bill with a black tip is adapted for probing for food in the ground.

WINGS
The wings are mottled brown but in flight a pearly white band along the hind-part of the wing becomes visible.

LEGS
The Common Redshank has long, reddish legs, and is a fast runner on the ground when chasing small prey.

HOW BIG IS IT?

SPECIAL ADAPTATION

The Common Redshank nests on stony ground. The eggs and chicks are beautifully camouflaged, and are often very difficult to spot, unless one stands almost next to a nest.

Great Skua

• **ORDER** • Charadriiformes • **FAMILY** • Stercorariidae • **SPECIES** • *Stercorarius skua*

VITAL STATISTICS

WEIGHT	1–1.8kg (2.2–4.0lb)
LENGTH	52–60cm (20.5–3.6in)
WINGSPAN	125–140cm (49.2–55.1in)
NUMBER OF EGGS	2 eggs
INCUBATION PERIOD	28–30 days
NUMBER OF BROODS	1 a year
TYPICAL DIET	Fish, squid, birds' eggs and chicks, small mammals, carrion
LIFE SPAN	Up to 30 years

This large, powerful bird is a real pirate, often bullying other seabirds to surrender their catch.

WHERE IN THE WORLD?

The Great Skua breeds on Iceland, the Faroe Islands, Scottish Islands and in Norway. It is migratory, and is widespread all over the Atlantic, reaching as far south as West Africa and Brazil.

CREATURE COMPARISONS

The Great Skua is rather drab in colour. Adults have a uniformly greyish-brown and streaked head, neck, body, tail and wings, except for a large band of pale white across the large wing feathers. The feet and the beak are also brownish. Males and females are similar, but females are usually larger. Juveniles are darker, and have fewer streaks in their plumage.

Juvenile

HOW BIG IS IT?

WINGS
The Great Skua has a wingspan of almost 1.5m (5ft), and will swoop down on any animal approaching its nest.

BEAK
The bill is very large, sturdy and has a hook at the end for attacking other birds and tearing into flesh.

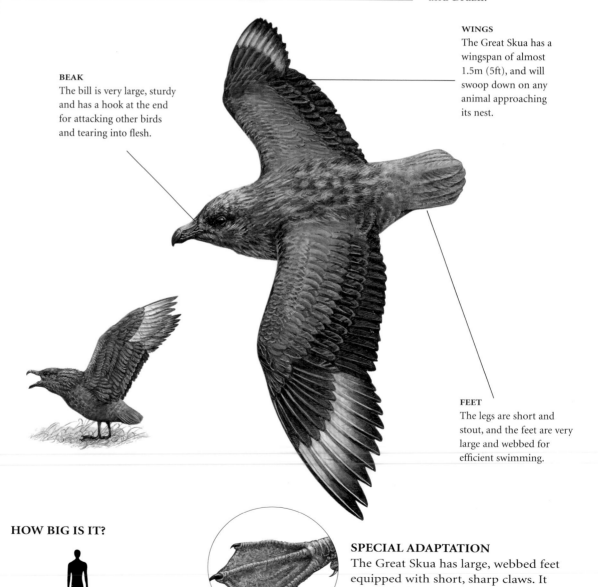

FEET
The legs are short and stout, and the feet are very large and webbed for efficient swimming.

SPECIAL ADAPTATION
The Great Skua has large, webbed feet equipped with short, sharp claws. It cannot hold prey in its feet like a bird of prey, but often uses its sharp claws in attacks on other birds.

Arctic Skua

• **ORDER** • Charadriiformes • **FAMILY** • Stercoraridae • **SPECIES** • *Stercorarius parasiticus*

VITAL STATISTICS

WEIGHT	450g (15.9oz)
LENGTH	37–44cm (14.6–17.3in)
WINGSPAN	1–1.2m (3.3–3.9ft)
SEXUAL MATURITY	3–4 years
INCUBATION PERIOD	25–28 days
FLEDGLING PERIOD	25–30 days
NUMBER OF EGGS	2 eggs
NUMBER OF BROODS	1 a year
TYPICAL DIET	Fish, birds, small mammals, insects, birds' eggs and carrion
LIFE SPAN	Up to 18 years

This avian thief is such a skilled flier that the British Royal Air Force's first dive-bomber, the Blackburn Skua, was named in its honour.

WHERE IN THE WORLD?

These elegant maritime birds breed all along the Arctic coastlines of North America, northern Europe and north Asia. Winters are spent at sea, in the warmer oceans of the Southern Hemisphere.

CREATURE COMPARISONS

Skua means gull in Old Norse and, at a distance, the species do look similar. In fact, trying to identify Arctic Skuas can be a real headache for bird-watchers. Not only do light, dark and intermediate coloured variations exist, but dark juveniles look like Pomarine Skuas.

Juvenile

FEET
The Arctic Skuas' webbed feet are tipped with sharp claws. These help birds grip onto slippery prey, such as fish.

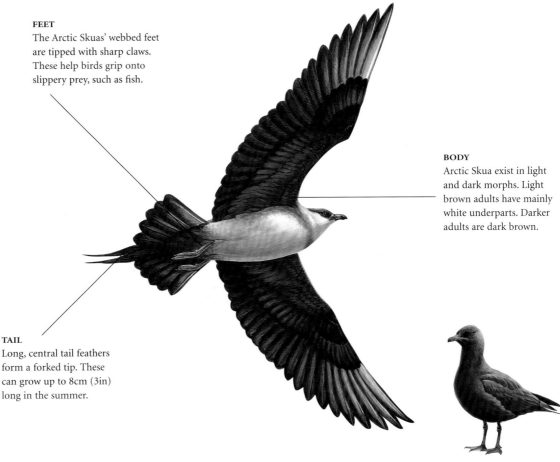

BODY
Arctic Skua exist in light and dark morphs. Light brown adults have mainly white underparts. Darker adults are dark brown.

TAIL
Long, central tail feathers form a forked tip. These can grow up to 8cm (3in) long in the summer.

HOW BIG IS IT?

SPECIAL ADAPTATION

Skuas are kleptoparasites, which means they regularly steal other birds' food. The shape of their wings enables them to both dive steeply and pursue their victims with great speed and agility. They strike their victims in mid-air, forcing them to drop their kills.

Black Tern

• ORDER • Charadriiformes **• FAMILY •** Sternidae **• SPECIES •** *Chlidonias niger*

With their streamlined, jet-black bodies, slate-grey wings and sharp, glossy bills, Black Terns make a handsome addition to the widespread Tern Family.

VITAL STATISTICS

WEIGHT	62g (2.2oz)
LENGTH	22–26cm (8.7–10.2in)
WINGSPAN	56–62cm (22–24.4in)
SEXUAL MATURITY	2–3 years
INCUBATION PERIOD	20–23 days
FLEDGLING PERIOD	19–25 days
NUMBER OF EGGS	2–4 eggs
NUMBER OF BROODS	1 a year
TYPICAL DIET	Insects; occasionally fish and amphibians
LIFE SPAN	Up to 17 years

WHERE IN THE WORLD?

Black Terns nest on floating rafts, or on the ground in European, central Asian and North American wetlands. Winter is spent on the coasts of Africa and tropical Latin America.

CREATURE COMPARISONS

In winter, adult Black Terns (shown) lose their dark breeding plumage and take on a paler, grey coloration, with a white breast and a black head. Juvenile birds look very similar, but have paler feet and darker patches on the side of their breast.

Adult Black Tern

BILL
Black Terns are such agile fliers that they can catch insects in mid-air. Slim bills are ideal tools for such precision work.

WINGS
There are three species of marsh terns. These can be distinguished from sea terns by their slower wing beats in flight.

TAIL
Black Terns have much shorter, broader wings and a less defined, forked tail than their sea tern relatives.

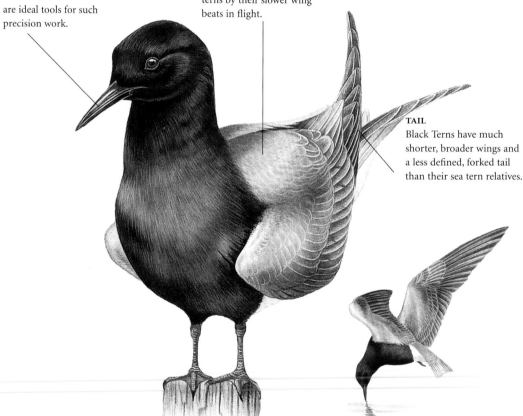

HOW BIG IS IT?

SPECIAL ADAPTATION

Every species of bird has their own special hunting techniques and Black Terns are no different. Flying low over water, they repeatedly dip down to pluck insects from the surface. They do this so quickly, and with such skill, that they rarely leave a ripple.

Sooty Tern

Colloquially, Sooty Terns are also known as Wide-awake Birds because of their almost non-stop 'ker-waky-wake' cries, which the birds make while in flight.

VITAL STATISTICS

LENGTH	42–45cm (16.4–17.7in)
WINGSPAN	72–80cm (28.3–31.5in)
SEXUAL MATURITY	6–8 years
INCUBATION PERIOD	26–33 days
FLEDGLING PERIOD	56–70 days
NUMBER OF EGGS	1 egg; occasionally 2
NUMBER OF BROODS	up to 3 a year are possible
HABITS	Diurnal/ nocturnal, migratory
TYPICAL DIET	Fish and squid; occasionally crustaceans
LIFE SPAN	Up to 32 years

WHERE IN THE WORLD?

These birds breed on rocky or coral islands, usually nesting on the ground. Found throughout the word's tropical and sub-tropical oceans, they number in the millions rather than the thousands.

CREATURE COMPARISONS

Not surprisingly, adult Sooty Terns have dark, sooty-black upper parts. Their underparts are white with a white patch on the forehead. Juveniles are paler, with sooty-grey bodies, whitish bellies and highly visible white barring on the upper body and tail. However, they lack the white forehead patch.

Juvenile

WINGS
Thanks to their slender streamlined bodies and narrow pointed wings, Sooty Terns are excellent fliers and superb aerial acrobats.

BELLY
White underparts help protect the birds from predators by making it harder for prey to spot them from the water.

TAIL
The Sooty Terns' long, forked tail streamers can grow up to 10cm (4in) long on an adult bird.

HOW BIG IS IT?

SPECIAL ADAPTATION

Terns are swift and agile in the air. They rarely come in to land, but feed and drink on the wing. They are such skilled fliers that they can dip their bills into the water without missing a wing beat.

Little Tern

• ORDER • Charadriiformes **• FAMILY •** Sternidae **• SPECIES •** *Sternula albifrons*

VITAL STATISTICS

WEIGHT	56g (2oz)
LENGTH	21–25cm (8.3–9.8in)
WINGSPAN	41–47cm (16.1–18.5in)
SEXUAL MATURITY	3 years
LAYS EGGS	From late May
INCUBATION PERIOD	21–24 days
NUMBER OF EGGS	2–3 eggs
NUMBER OF BROODS	1 a year
TYPICAL DIET	Sand eels, small fish, crustaceans; occasionally insects
LIFE SPAN	Up to 21 years

The smallest of the Terns is also one of the rarest, due to habitat loss, which has seen some European populations vanish entirely.

WHERE IN THE WORLD?

Little Terns breed on the coasts and waterways of Europe and Asia, but winter as far south as Australia. Their preferred habitats are shingle beaches, where they nest.

CREATURE COMPARISONS

Adult Terns are at their most attractive in the summer. For most of the year, their bills are black and their foreheads are white and grey. During the breeding season, however, their neat bills, turn yellow, providing a dramatic contrast to their darker, summer plumage.

Adult in the summer (top) and in the winter (bottom).

HEAD
Little Terns are the only adult Terns that have a white patch on their forehead during both summer and winter.

FEET
Many sea birds have large feet to propel them through the water. Terns have small feet, which are streamlined for diving.

BILL
The Little Tern's long narrow bill is ideal for eating a range of prey, from wriggling eels to small, flying insects.

HOW BIG IS IT?

SPECIAL ADAPTATION
Long, slender, wings enable Little Terns to fly with great speed and agility. In flight, these elegant birds are easy to spot because of their very rapid wing beats, and their habit of hovering for long periods before diving into the sea to catch fish.

Arctic Tern

VITAL STATISTICS

HEIGHT	110g (3.9oz)
LENGTH	33–39cm (13– 15.3in)
WINGSPAN	66–77cm (26–30.3in)
SEXUAL MATURITY	4 years.
INCUBATION PERIOD	20–27 days
FLEDGLING PERIOD	21–24 days
NUMBER OF EGGS	2–3 eggs
NUMBER OF BROODS	1 a year
TYPICAL DIET	Fish and crustaceans; occasionally insects
LIFE SPAN	Typically 13 years

Arctic Terns are real avian athletes. They regularly fly from Pole to Pole to enjoy the benefits of two summers a year.

WHERE IN THE WORLD?

These seabirds are a circumpolar species, and breed on lakes, rivers and tundra, from sub-Arctic North America to Arctic Siberia. Populations winter in the cold, grey oceans of the Antarctic.

CREATURE COMPARISONS

The most obvious difference between adult Arctic Terns and juveniles (shown below) is that, instead of the vivid red legs and bill, young birds have black legs and bill. During their first summer, their caps are also smaller, with more white on the crown.

Juveniles

TAIL
The Arctic Terns' elegant tail streamers may grow up to 11.5cm (4.5in) long during the summer.

BILL
During the breeding season the Arctic Terns' long, distinctive, blood red bill loses its black tip.

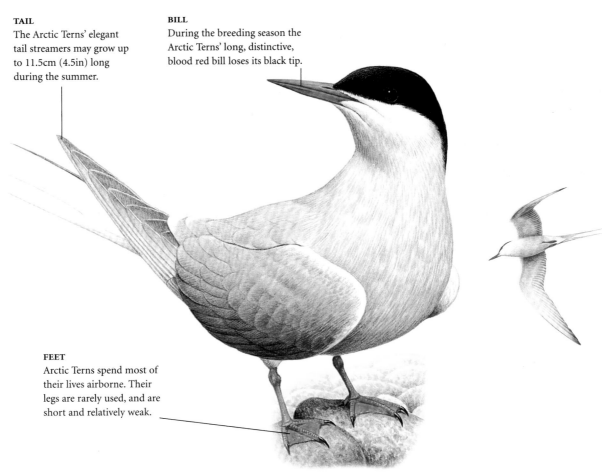

FEET
Arctic Terns spend most of their lives airborne. Their legs are rarely used, and are short and relatively weak.

HOW BIG IS IT?

SPECIAL ADAPTATION
The shape of the Arctic Terns' wings enables these amazing birds to be highly agile, fast and energy efficient in the air. They regularly make round trips of 50,000km (31,070 miles), so it is important to manoeuvre with precision and the minimum of effort.

Royal Tern

• **ORDER** • Charadriiformes • **FAMILY** • Sternidae • **SPECIES** • *Thalasseus maximus*

VITAL STATISTICS

WEIGHT	370g (13oz)
LENGTH	42–49cm (16.5–19.3in)
WINGSPAN	1.2–1.3m (3.9–4.3ft)
SEXUAL MATURITY	3–4 years
LAYS EGGS	May–June
INCUBATION PERIOD	25–31 days
NUMBER OF EGGS	1 egg; occasionally 2
NUMBER OF BROODS	1 a year
TYPICAL DIET	Fish and crabs
LIFE SPAN	Up to 17 years

Royal Terns make their nest on the ground of low lying islands. They defecate on the nest rim which eventually hardens and reinforces the nest against flooding.

WHERE IN THE WORLD?

Royal Terns build their nests on the ground. They breed along the coasts of North and Latin America but spend winter as far south as Argentina, with some populations migrating to West Africa.

CREATURE COMPARISONS

Many species of tern have distinctive black caps during the breeding season and, just like their relatives, the Royal Terns' headgear recedes as the year progresses. Eventually, by the winter, just a white fore crown, framed with a feathery crown of black, is visible.

Winter plumage

WINGS
Long pointed wings enable the Royal Tern to be fast and elegant in the air. A forked tail aids control and manoeuvrability.

FEET
Despite the fact that Terns hardly ever swim, they have webbed feet. These probably help spread their weight on soft sand.

BODY
When they are seen in profile, Royal Terns have oddly angular bodies, somewhere in size between Sandwich and Caspian Terns.

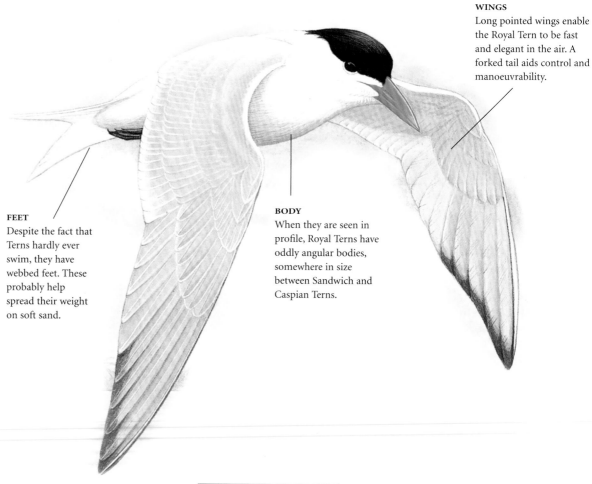

HOW BIG IS IT?

SPECIAL ADAPTATION
Royal Terns are superbly adapted for life spent almost entirely in the air. Their bodies are light and streamlined, kept airborne by long, powerful wings. They are precise, elegant fliers capable of hovering in mid-air before diving in pursuit of fish.

Great White Egret

• **ORDER** • Ciconiiformes • **FAMILY** • Ardeidae • **SPECIES** • *Ardea alba*

The snowy Great White Egret will wait patiently hours at a time by the water's edge for a tasty meal to pass by.

VITAL STATISTICS

WEIGHT	950g (33.5oz)
HEIGHT	1m (3.3ft)
WINGSPAN	1.3–1.4m (4.3–4.6ft)
LAYS EGGS	Breeding begins in April
SEXUAL MATURITY	2 years
INCUBATION PERIOD	23–24 days
NUMBER OF EGGS	2–3 eggs
NUMBER OF BROODS	1 a year
TYPICAL DIET	Insects, reptiles, amphibians and small mammals
LIFE SPAN	Up to 23 years

WHERE IN THE WORLD?

Egrets' ideal homes are near water, whether a mudflat or marsh. Populations are found in both the New World, from southern Canada to Australia, and the Old World of Europe, Africa and Asia.

CREATURE COMPARISONS

Great Egrets are the largest species of Old World Egret, as their name indicates. However, when it comes to the New World, the Great Blue Heron (*Ardea herodias*) which is found in the Americas, is actually larger, growing up to 1.2m (4ft) tall.

Great Egret

BILL
Great Egrets can be distinguished from other species of white Egrets by their yellow bill and black feet and legs.

BODY
Egrets fly with their necks in an 's'-shape. This distinguishes them from storks and cranes, which fly with their necks extended.

NECK
These skilled hunters use their extended neck and long bill to strike suddenly at their prey from a distance.

HOW BIG IS IT?

SPECIAL ADAPTATION

There is safety in numbers, which is why Great Egrets breed in colonies. Their nests are typically built in trees close to water, often near reedbeds, which are the birds' ideal hunting territories. From a distance, these nests usually look like nothing more than an untidy pile of sticks.

Grey Heron

• ORDER • Ciconiiformes • FAMILY • Ardeidae • SPECIES • *Ardea cinerea*

VITAL STATISTICS

WEIGHT	1.5kg (3.3lb)
HEIGHT	84cm–1m (33 in–3.3ft)
WINGSPAN	1.5–1.7m (4.9–5.6ft)
SEXUAL MATURITY	2–3 years
INCUBATION PERIOD	25–26 days
FLEDGLING PERIOD	45–55 days
NUMBER OF EGGS	1–5 in Europe, up to 10 elsewhere
NUMBER OF BROODS	1 a year
TYPICAL DIET	Fish, aquatic insects, small birds, reptiles and mammals
LIFE SPAN	Typically 5 years

Whether they are standing motionless, stalking their prey with, slow, deliberate movements, or striking at fish with lighting speed, Grey Herons always look immaculate.

WHERE IN THE WORLD?

Grey Herons breed in large colonies, nesting in trees, close to seashores, lakes or rivers, where there is plenty of food. Populations can be found across Europe, sub-Saharan Africa and Asia.

CREATURE COMPARISONS

Fully mature Grey Herons are the very image of elegance and grace. In comparison, juveniles look almost untidy. They not only lack the characteristic black head plume and stylish white chest ruffles worn by the adults, but their plumage can look distinctly tatty.

Juvenile

EYES
The Heron's yellow eyes are highlighted by bold black plumes, which start at the eyes and hang down the neck.

WINGS
In flight, these beautiful birds are very distinctive, with their long necks drawn into their shoulders, and slow, irregular wing beats.

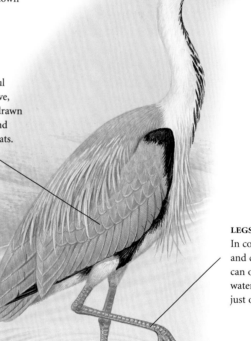

LEGS
In common with storks and cranes, Grey Herons can often be seen on the water's edge, resting on just one leg.

HOW BIG IS IT?

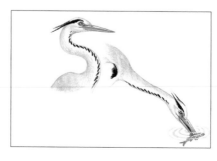

SPECIAL ADAPTATION

When hunting, Herons stand motionless for hours. However, once they have spotted prey, they shoot their heads forwards into the water with incredible speed. This is possible thanks to an elongated sixth vertebra, which allows them to extend their necks further than other species of long-necked birds.

Goliath Heron

VITAL STATISTICS

WEIGHT	4kg (8.8lb)
HEIGHT	1.4m (4.6ft)
WINGSPAN	2.1–2.3m (6.9–7.5ft)
SEXUAL MATURITY	2 years
LAYS EGGS	November–March
INCUBATION PERIOD	24–30 days
NUMBER OF EGGS	3–4 eggs
NUMBER OF BROODS	1 a year
TYPICAL DIET	Fish, some reptiles and mammals and carrion
HABITS	Diurnal, non-migratory

Taking their name from the famous Biblical giant, Goliath, these birds are the largest of all herons and one of Africa's most impressive wetland waders.

WHERE IN THE WORLD?

In the breeding season, these birds build large, stick nests in trees, bushes or on the ground, close to water. Populations are found in lakes, swamps and wetlands, in sub-Saharan Africa, Iraq and Iran.

CREATURE COMPARISONS

Extra long legs allow Goliath Herons to feed in much deeper waters than other waders. However, to reach down for food, Goliaths also need long necks. The result is a giant bird – standing up to 56cm (22in) taller than the Grey Heron.

BILL
Herons do not stab their prey with their long bills but catch it with their mandibles open.

WINGS
Deep chestnut-brown underparts are visible when the Herons are in flight. The birds' upper wings and tail are generally blue-grey.

LEGS
Long legs trail behind the body when the birds are in flight. This characteristic is typical of all Herons.

Juvenile

HOW BIG IS IT?

SPECIAL ADAPTATION
The sheer size and power of Goliath Herons gives them an incredible advantage. Not only are they able to catch and subdue prey that is too big for other birds to tackle, but their long legs give them access to food that smaller, wading birds can not reach.

Purple Heron

• **ORDER** • Ciconiiformes • **FAMILY** • Ardeidae • **SPECIES** • *Ardea purpurea*

VITAL STATISTICS

WEIGHT	800g (28.2oz)
LENGTH	90–97cm (35.4–38.2in)
WINGSPAN	1.1–1.4m (3.6–4.6ft)
SEXUAL MATURITY	1 year
INCUBATION PERIOD	25 days
NUMBER OF EGGS	2–5 eggs
CALL	A resonant 'kranck'
HABITS	Crepuscular, migratory
TYPICAL DIET	Fish and insects; occasionally reptiles, amphibians and small mammals
LIFE SPAN	Up to 23 years

Few fish can escape the lightning-fast reflexes and dagger-like bill of the Purple Heron, which shows enormous patience when hunting.

WHERE IN THE WORLD?

Purple Herons breed in southern and central Eurasia, wintering in southern Asia and tropical Africa. They roost in coastal mangroves, marshes and river estuaries, but feed on freshwater wetlands.

CREATURE COMPARISONS

Herons are patient predators, waiting motionless for prey to appear before striking, with lightning speed. Reddish Egrets (shown) have a slightly less elegant approach to catching a meal. They stagger from side to side with their wings outstretched. This casts a shadow and drives fish into shallower waters.

Feeding young

HEAD
In the breeding season, these normally shy birds will puff up their neck feathers and raise their crests to threaten rivals.

BILL
The Heron's bill may be slender but it is a surprisingly powerful tool easily capable of catching and killing large snakes.

NECK
The Purple Heron's distinctive, snake-like neck is usually folded back onto the bird's shoulder when in flight.

HOW BIG IS IT?

SPECIAL ADAPTATION
Referring to animal's in-built survival instincts, the poet Alfred Tennyson (1809–92) described nature as 'red in tooth and claw'. This is certainly true in the bird world, where older, bigger chicks will often take all the food, leaving their siblings to starve.

Bittern (Great)

Thanks to their excellent camouflage, Bitterns are rarely seen. However, the deep, foghorn-like booming call of the male is unlikely to be missed.

VITAL STATISTICS

WEIGHT	Males: 1.5kg (3.3lb). Females: 1kg (2.2lb)
LENGTH	69–81cm (27.2–31.9in)
WINGSPAN	1–1.3m (3.3–4.3ft)
SEXUAL MATURITY	1 year
INCUBATION PERIOD	25–26 days
FLEDGLING PERIOD	50–55 days
NUMBER OF EGGS	4–6 eggs
NUMBER OF BROODS	1 a year
TYPICAL DIET	Fish, aquatic insects, small reptiles, amphibians and mammals
LIFE SPAN	Up to 11 years

WHERE IN THE WORLD?

Bitterns are also called Eurasian Bitterns because they breed in reedbeds and wetlands in Europe, Asia and Africa. Populations in the milder south are resident, but northern birds migrate for the winter.

CREATURE COMPARISONS

Great Bitterns are slightly smaller than Grey Herons, with more compact bodies, a shorter neck and a distinctive hunched stance, in contrast to the Herons' upright posture. Juveniles (shown) are smaller still, with a browner crown and less obvious streaking on the neck.

Juvenile

HEAD
Every male Bittern has his own distinctive booming call, which can be heard over 1km (1.6 miles) away.

BILL
Bitterns are related to herons and have the same, dagger-like bill characteristic of this group of waders.

BODY
The Latin name for Bittern, *Botaurus stellaris,* means bull, referring to the birds' call, and starry, in reference to its plumage.

HOW BIG IS IT?

SPECIAL ADAPTATION
The Bittern's plumage, a form of cryptic camouflage, is almost the same colour as its surroundings. When it hides in the reeds with its head pointed upwards its plumage mimics the pattern formed by the reeds, making it almost invisible.

105

Cattle Egret

• **ORDER** • Ciconiiformes • **FAMILY** • Ardeidae • **SPECIES** • *Bubulcus ibis*

VITAL STATISTICS

WEIGHT	270–520g (9.5–18.3oz)
LENGTH	46–56cm (18.1–22.0in)
WINGSPAN	88–96cm (34.6–37.8in)
NUMBER OF EGGS	2–5 eggs
INCUBATION PERIOD	22–26 days
NUMBER OF BROODS	1 a year
TYPICAL DIET	Insects, spiders, earthworms, amphibians, lizards
LIFE SPAN	Up to 15 years

The Cattle Egret was originally found in southern Europe, but within the last century it has spread to most of the world.

The Cattle Egret comes from Portugal and southern Spain, but has spread to the southern USA, Central and South America, most of Africa and Madagascar, Southeast Asia, eastern Australia and New Zealand.

HEAD
The head is rounded and sits on a neck that is moderately long for an Egret.

BILL
The bill is large and is well adapted for snatching insects in the grass.

CREATURE COMPARISONS

Uniformly white in colour, the Cattle Egret usually has buff plumes on the head and breast during the breeding season. The bill and legs are usually yellow and the lower legs and large feet are black. During the breeding season, the bill and legs become reddish. Males and females are similar, but males tend to be larger.

WINGS
The large and wide wings give the Cattle Egret a slow flight, but allow it to soar on rising air currents.

Cattle Egret

HOW BIG IS IT?

SPECIAL ADAPTATION

This small bird spends most of its time in close proximity to cattle. This association with humans and their livestock may explain its geographical expansion during the twentieth century.

Little Egret

• ORDER • Ciconiiformes • FAMILY • Ardeidae • SPECIES • *Egretta garzetta*

VITAL STATISTICS

WEIGHT	450g (15.9oz)
LENGTH	55–65cm (21.6–25.6in)
WINGSPAN	88cm–1m (34.6 in–3.3ft)
SEXUAL MATURITY	1–2 years
INCUBATION PERIOD	21–25 days
FLEDGLING PERIOD	50–55 days
NUMBER OF EGGS	3–4 eggs
NUMBER OF BROODS	1 a year
TYPICAL DIET	Small fish, insects, amphibians and worms
LIFE SPAN	Typically 5 years

In Victorian times, the Egrets' beautiful feathers became a popular adornment on ladies' hats, and demand for the feathers almost led to the extinction of the species.

WHERE IN THE WORLD?

At least two sub-species, *Egretta garzetta* (Europe, Africa and Asia) and *Egretta garzetta nigripes* (Asia and Australasia) are known. The Australian Egret may be a separate species.

CREATURE COMPARISONS

Little Egret chicks are covered in white downy feathers. (Down is the fine, thermal layer lying beneath the tougher, outer feathers worn by adult birds.) As they mature, juvenile Egrets begin to look similar to non-breeding adults, with slightly duller legs and feet.

Non-breeding adult

BILL
The bare skin between the Little Egrets' bill and eyes is normally blue but becomes red during the breeding season.

NECK AND BACK
In the breeding season, adult Little Egrets have two long neck plumes and similar, elongated feathers along their backs.

BODY
Not all Egrets are pure white. The rare Slaty Egret is grey and the Reddish Egret has a rusty red head and neck.

HOW BIG IS IT?

SPECIAL ADAPTATION
Often it is only the males that moult into breeding plumage during the spring. However, both sexes of the Little Egret grow elongated display plumes on their head and across their backs.

Reddish Egret

• **ORDER** • Ciconiiformes • **FAMILY** • Ardeidae • **SPECIES** • *Egretta rufescens*

VITAL STATISTICS

WEIGHT	700–850g (24.7–30oz)
HEIGHT	66–81cm (26–31.9in)
WINGSPAN	1.1m (3.6ft)
SEXUAL MATURITY	2 years
INCUBATION PERIOD	25–26 days
FLEDGLING PERIOD	Around 45 days
NUMBER OF EGGS	2–7 eggs
NUMBER OF BROODS	1 a year
TYPICAL DIET	Small fish, crustaceans and amphibians
LIFE SPAN	Up to 12 years

Whatever Reddish Egrets do, they do with great gusto, whether they are practicing elaborate courtship dances or staggering around with enthusiasm hunting for fish.

WHERE IN THE WORLD?

These sociable birds breed along the coast of Mexico, Central Latin America and the Caribbean. Like other members of the Heron family, they nest in trees, on platforms made out of sticks.

CREATURE COMPARISONS

As adults, these appealing birds are generally slatey blue with a rust-coloured head and neck. Juveniles (shown below left) tend to be greyer. However, a white variation or morph (shown below right) also exists. These are white, both in their juvenile and their adult plumage.

Juveniles in grey plumage (left) and white plumage (right)

HEAD
As the start of the breeding season approaches, long, lacy plumes sprout from the Reddish Egrets' head and neck.

BILL
Herons are known for the loud clacking they make with their bills. Reddish Egrets make a similar noise during courtship displays.

FEET
Long feet help Egrets grip onto branches. They also help spread the birds' weight and stop them sinking in mud.

HOW BIG IS IT?

SPECIAL ADAPTATION

Herons are patient predators, waiting motionless for prey to appear before striking with lightning speed. Reddish Egrets have a slightly less elegant approach to catching a meal. They stagger from side to side with their wings outstretched. This casts a shadow and drives fish into shallower waters.

Little Bittern

• ORDER • Ciconiiformes • FAMILY • Ardeidae • SPECIES • Ixobrychus minutus

VITAL STATISTICS

WEIGHT	120–190g (4.2–6.7oz)
LENGTH	27–36cm (10.6–14.2in)
WINGSPAN	40–58cm (15.7–22.8in)
NUMBER OF EGGS	4–8 eggs (usually 4–6)
INCUBATION PERIOD	20–22 days
NUMBER OF BROODS	1–2 a year
TYPICAL DIET	Insects, worms, small fish, amphibians
LIFE SPAN	Up to 10 years

The Little Bittern is one of the smallest herons in the world, and lack the graceful build of most other herons.

WHERE IN THE WORLD?

The Little Bittern is widespread across central and southern Europe, across and western and southern Asia. Birds from Europe spend the winter in Africa south of the Sahara desert.

CREATURE COMPARISONS

This tiny heron has a dark brownish or black upper back and wings, with a large white area on each wing. The top of the head is also black. The sides of the head, neck, breast and belly are light brown or buff. The eyes are conspicuously red with a black pupil. Males and females are similar, but females are lighter brownish overall.

Juvenile Little Bittern

TAIL
The tail is short and wide, and is used for manoeuvring in the air and as a brake during landing.

NECK
The neck is quite short for a heron, and is often tucked in so the head appears to sit directly on the body.

BILL
The Little Bittern has a large, powerful bill for snatching small fish and frogs.

HOW BIG IS IT?

SPECIAL ADAPTATION

The Little Bittern builds a nest among the reeds, but waits until the reeds are tall enough to conceal it. It may defend its nest from intruders by spreading its wings to appear bigger.

African Open-billed Stork

• **ORDER** • Ciconiiformes • **FAMILY** • Ciconiidae • **SPECIES** • *Anastomus lamelligerus*

With their highly specialized, broad bills, the long-legged, long-necked African Open-billed Stork are among the most unusual members of the Stork family.

VITAL STATISTICS

LENGTH	80–90cm (31.5–37in)
SEXUAL MATURITY	3 years
INCUBATION PERIOD	25–30 days
FLEDGLING PERIOD	50–55 days
NUMBER OF EGGS	2–5 eggs
NUMBER OF BROODS	Usually 1 a year, although not all pairs breed every year
CALL	Loud croaks and honks
HABITS	Diurnal, migratory
TYPICAL DIET	Snails and mussels
LIFE SPAN	At least 10 years

WHERE IN THE WORLD?

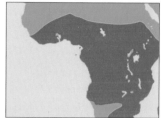

Storks tend to make their homes near freshwater lakes, marshes and swamps, where there is an abundant supply of food. African Open-billed Storks breed south of the equator, mainly in sub-Saharan Africa.

CREATURE COMPARISONS

African Open-billed Storks are not the only birds to have specialized bills. The flattened tip of the Spoonbills' bill is packed with touch-sensitive receptors. As they feed, Spoonbills keep their bill open, sweeping it from side to side, ready to snap shut on any food that they sense.

Stork in flight

WINGS
Although they are often seen to soar lazily on rising warm air currents, African Open-Billed Storks can be surprisingly acrobatic fliers.

BODY
Males and females look similar with black bodies and brownish bills. However, males tend to be slightly larger.

LEGS
Long, bare legs allow the birds to wade into deep water without getting waterlogged feathers, which would affect their ability to fly.

HOW BIG IS IT?

SPECIAL ADAPTATION

African Open-billed Storks have adapted a specialized way of feeding. The narrow tip of their upper mandible is used to hold prey still. Then, the sharp tip of the lower mandible is used to cut the muscle that holds the snail's body inside its shell.

White Stork

VITAL STATISTICS

WEIGHT	2.2–3.5kg (4.8–7.7lb)
LENGTH	95–105cm (37.4–41.3in)
WINGSPAN	150–170cm (59–67in)
NUMBER OF EGGS	3–5 eggs
INCUBATION PERIOD	32–34 days
NUMBER OF BROODS	1 a year
TYPICAL DIET	Amphibians, large insects, crayfish, worms, snails, fish
LIFE SPAN	Up to 30 years

The White Stork brings both good luck and babies according to folklore, but has become rare in many countries.

WHERE IN THE WORLD?

The White Stork is found in central Europe, Portugal and western Spain, as well as North Africa. It winters in Africa south of the Sahara and in southern Asia. It has declined in many countries.

CREATURE COMPARISONS

This bird is unmistakable owing to its large size and distinctive appearance. The overall colour of the neck, body and tail is white, but most of the large, wide wings are entirely black. The white stork has a long, straight, reddish or orange-red bill, and very long, stilt-like legs, which are also reddish in colour. Males and females are similar. The chicks are also white.

Long stiltlike legs

WINGS
The large broad wings allow the White Stork to soar efficiently on hot air currents during its long migration.

BILL
The long red bill is used for snatching or even stabbing prey but also for communication between the male and female in the nest.

LEGS
Long stiltlike legs are well adapted for wading through shallow water or walking through tall grass.

HOW BIG IS IT?

SPECIAL ADAPTATION

The White Stork has a very long, pointed bill, which is well adapted for snatching the wide variety of small animals on which it feeds from shallow water or in tall grass.

Black Stork

• **ORDER** • Ciconiiformes • **FAMILY** • Ciconiidae • **SPECIES** • *Ciconia nigra*

VITAL STATISTICS

WEIGHT	At least 3kg (6.6lb)
HEIGHT	98cm (38.5 in)
WINGSPAN	1.5–2m (5–6.6ft)
SEXUAL MATURITY	3 years
INCUBATION PERIOD	35–38 days
FLEDGLING PERIOD	63–71 days
NUMBER OF EGGS	2–6 eggs
NUMBER OF BROODS	1 a year
TYPICAL DIET	Fish, crustaceans and reptiles
LIFE SPAN	Up to 20 years

Standing gracefully at the water's edge, Black Storks are a picture of elegance. But despite appearances, these black waders are fearsome hunters.

WHERE IN THE WORLD?

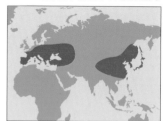

Black Storks breed in central and eastern Asia and central and southern Europe, especially the in Baltic republics. Populations in Spain are partly resident, but other birds overwinter in West Africa.

CREATURE COMPARISONS

Black Storks are most at home in marshy wetlands, where they build their voluminous nests. All Storks build impressive nests, usually in trees, although some also use hollows in cliffs or grass thickets. A Black Stork nest can reach 1.5m (4ft 6in) in diameter.

A Black Stork nest

BILL
The birds' long red bill and extended red legs make it difficult to confuse them with any other species of stork.

BODY
These large waders may look black but up close their plumage can be seen to shine with purples, greens and blues.

WINGS
Black Storks have broad wings that allow the birds to soar on rising air thermals during their long-distance migrations.

HOW BIG IS IT?

SPECIAL ADAPTATION

From bill to toe, Storks are built to hunt. Their long legs allow them to wade into deep waters in search of food. A lengthy neck allows them to stretch out to capture passing fish, while a big bill enables them to tackle large prey.

Marabou Stork

• **ORDER** • Ciconiiformes • **FAMILY** • Ciconiidae • **SPECIES** • *Leptoptilos crumeniferus*

VITAL STATISTICS

WEIGHT	9kg (20lb)
HEIGHT	1.5m (5ft)
WINGSPAN	3.2m (10.5ft)
SEXUAL MATURIT	4 years.
INCUBATION PERIOD	29–31 days
FLEDGLING PERIOD	95–115 days
NUMBER OF EGGS	2–3 eggs
NUMBER OF BROODS	1 a year
TYPICAL DIET	Small animals, birds' eggs and carrion.
LIFE SPAN	Up to 25 years

With their apparently hunched posture cloak-like black wings and fondness for corpses, it is no wonder that Marabou Storks are known colloquially as 'undertaker birds'.

WHERE IN THE WORLD?

Marabou Storks breed in sub-Saharan Africa. They prefer dry grasslands, and birds tend to leave areas once the rainy season arrives. They are often seen on rubbish tips looking for carrion.

CREATURE COMPARISONS

All storks build impressive nests, usually in large communal groups. Some storks use hollows in cliffs or grass thickets but most species, like the Marabou Stork, nest in trees. Here they construct immense platforms made out of layers and layers of dry sticks.

Marabou Storks nesting

WINGS
These storks have one of the largest wingspans of any land bird, beaten only by the Andean Condor.

NECK
Most Storks fly with their necks outstreached. However, Marabou Storks fly with their necks folded back into their body, as herons do.

LEGS
Marabou Storks' legs are grey-brown but look paler because of the birds' unsavoury habit of habit of squirting excrement over them.

HOW BIG IS IT?

SPECIAL ADAPTATION

Marabous have a taste for flesh. They are as likely to scavenge for carrion as hunt for fresh meat so, like vultures, they have bare heads. This prevents their feathers from becoming matted with blood, which would be difficult to clean.

Hammerkop

• **ORDER** • Ciconiiformes • **FAMILY** • Scopidae • **SPECIES** • *Scopus umbretta*

VITAL STATISTICS

LENGTH	50–56cm (19.7–22 in)
SEXUAL MATURITY	Unknown
INCUBATION PERIOD	28–32 days
FLEDGLING PERIOD	944–50 days
NUMBER OF EGGS	3–6 eggs
NUMBER OF BROODS	Several are possible but varies with local conditions
CALL	High-pitched 'yip' when in flight
HABITS	Diurnal, non-migratory
TYPICAL DIET	Fish, frogs and some crustaceans
LIFE SPAN	Up to 20 years

CREATURE COMPARISONS

Young Hammerkops take their first flight at around seven weeks old. However, they return home every evening, for at least another month. This gives the immature birds time to develop their adult bills, which they need when hunting. Until then they have a stubbier, brown version.

Juvenile Hammerkop

These unusual birds are the subject of many superstitions. In fact, people have been known to pull their homes down if a Hammerkop flies overhead.

WHERE IN THE WORLD?

Hammerkops are found in sub-Saharan Africa and south-west Arabia, where they roost close to water. Their enormous nests may house several Hammerkop generations as well as other animals.

HEAD
The Hammerkop is named after its thick, flat-topped crest. *Hammerkop* means hammer head in Dutch Afrikaans.

WINGS
Large, rounded wings, with long, finger-like primary feathers give Hammerkops a silhouette similar to that of a bird of prey.

FEET
The Hammerkop has partially webbed feet and long legs.

HOW BIG IS IT?

SPECIAL ADAPTATION
The Hammerkops' bill is highly versatile and able to cope with many different jobs. The narrow tip helps birds root among vegetation for food. The hooked end enables them to pick up small prey, while the blunt shape is ideal for stunning larger prey.

Scarlet Ibis

• **ORDER** • Ciconiiformes • **FAMILY** • Threskiornithidae • **SPECIES** • *Eudocimus ruber*

VITAL STATISTICS

WEIGHT	615 g (21.7oz)
LENGTH	66cm (26in)
WINGSPAN	54cm (21in)
LAYS EGGS	September–December
INCUBATION PERIOD	19–23 days
FLEDGLING PERIOD	35 days
NUMBER OF EGGS	3–5 eggs
NUMBER OF BROODS	1 a year
TYPICAL DIET	Crustaceans, aquatic insects and small fish
LIFE SPAN	Up to 33 years in captivity

Only wild Scarlet Ibis are truly scarlet. In captivity, these stunning birds have to be fed special supplements to keep their extraordinary colour.

WHERE IN THE WORLD?

Scarlet Ibis make their homes in Latin America's tropical wetlands. Populations range from Venezuela to eastern Brazil, and they are also found on Trinidad and Tobago.

CREATURE COMPARISONS

Young Scarlet Ibis are actually grey-brown in colour. Like flamingos, their colour is caused by the betacarotene in their diet. So, the juveniles' red plumage develops as the birds mature and eat more of the crustaceans that produce their scarlet coloration.

Juvenile Scarlet Ibis (behind)

BODY
All Ibis have long legs and a long neck. However, only Scarlet Ibis, both male and female, have the vivid red plumage and blue-black wing tips.

BILL
Male Scarlet Ibis tend to have a larger bill than the female.

FEET
Partially webbed feet allow Ibis to walk on mud without sinking, but do not give them the characteristic duck-like waddle of fully webbed birds.

HOW BIG IS IT?

SPECIAL ADAPTATION

There is safety in numbers, which is why Scarlet Ibis tend to build their nests very close together, sometimes several in just one tree. This helps the community look out for and defend themselves from predators and, ultimately, increases the survival rate of their young.

Spoonbill (Eurasian)

• **ORDER** • Ciconiiformes • **FAMILY** • Threskiornithidae • **SPECIES** • *Platalea leucorodia*

VITAL STATISTICS

LENGTH	70–80cm (27.5–31.5 in)
WINGSPAN	1.2–1.3m (3.9–4.3ft)
SEXUAL MATURITY	4 years
INCUBATION PERIOD	21–25 days
FLEDGLING PERIOD	45–50 days
NUMBER OF EGGS	3–4 eggs
NUMBER OF BROODS	1 a year
HABITS	Nocturnal, migratory
TYPICAL DIET	Aquatic insects and invertebrates, worms and small reptiles
LIFE SPAN	Up to 28 years

The Spoonbills' spatula-shaped bill may look big and cumbersome, but it is one of the reasons for this white wader's success as a hunter.

WHERE IN THE WORLD?

Mashy wetlands, lakes and mudflats are a Spoonbills' favourite habitat. These widespread birds make their nests in reeds, bushes and trees throughout Europe and Asia, usually wintering in North Africa.

CREATURE COMPARISONS

Juvenile Spoonbills have distinctive black wing tips and pinkish legs and bill. Despite this, it is easy to confuse them with Great Egrets. Not only are they a similar shape and body size, but young Spoonbills lack the long crest and black bill of their adult counterparts.

Juvenile Spoonbill

—

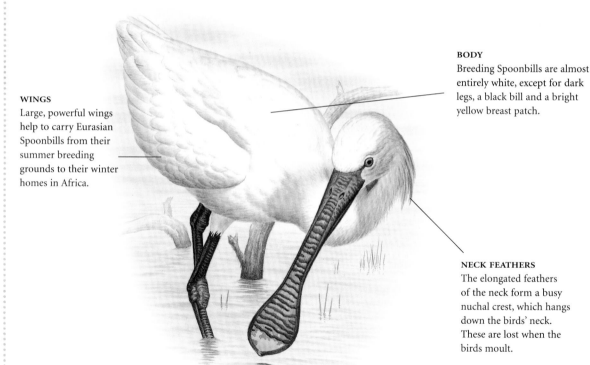

WINGS
Large, powerful wings help to carry Eurasian Spoonbills from their summer breeding grounds to their winter homes in Africa.

BODY
Breeding Spoonbills are almost entirely white, except for dark legs, a black bill and a bright yellow breast patch.

NECK FEATHERS
The elongated feathers of the neck form a busy nuchal crest, which hangs down the birds' neck. These are lost when the birds moult.

HOW BIG IS IT?

SPECIAL ADAPTATION

The Spoonbills bizarre bill is actually a highly specialized tool. The flattened tip is packed with touch-sensitive receptors. As the Spoonbills feed, they keep their bill open and sweep it from side to side, ready to snap shut on any food that they sense.

Feral Pigeon

• ORDER • Columbiformes **• FAMILY •** Columbidae **• SPECIES •** *Columba livia*

The Feral Pigeon is a familiar sight to all who live in larger cities, and is a descendent of the wild Rock Pigeon.

VITAL STATISTICS

Weight	200–300g (7.1–10.6oz)
Length	31–34cm (12.2–13.4in)
Wingspan	40–45cm (15.7–17.7in)
Number of Eggs	2 eggs
Incubation Period	16–18 days
Number of Broods	2–4 a year
Typical Diet	Mainly seeds, buds and fruit, but also snails and insects; in cities, often bread and other food scraps
Life Span	Up to 30 years

WHERE IN THE WORLD?

Found across the world, the Feral Pigeon is common in most large cities. It is widespread in coastal areas in Britain, southern Europe and northern Africa, as well as southwestern Asia.

CREATURE COMPARISONS

The body is bluish-grey with two distinct black bands along the wings. The neck and breast are colourful, especially in males, and have slightly metallic hues of green, red and purple. The feet are orange or reddish. Females are drabber and slightly smaller. The Stock Dove is similar to the Feral Dove, but the wing bands are thinner and less distinct.

Adult (top), juvenile (bottom)

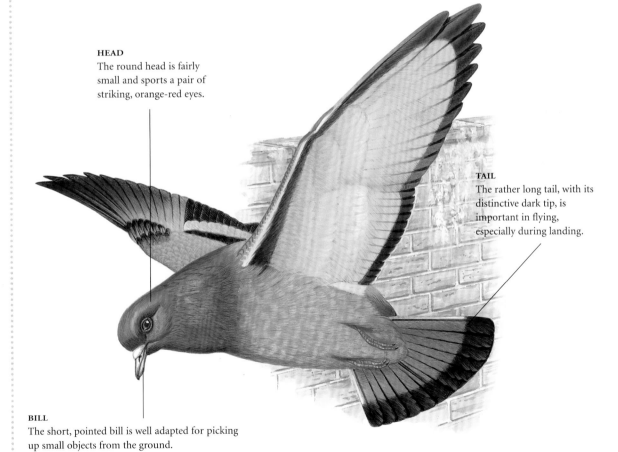

HEAD
The round head is fairly small and sports a pair of striking, orange-red eyes.

TAIL
The rather long tail, with its distinctive dark tip, is important in flying, especially during landing.

BILL
The short, pointed bill is well adapted for picking up small objects from the ground.

HOW BIG IS IT?

SPECIAL ADAPTATION
The Feral Pigeon is able to take off from level ground, often producing a distinctive clattering sound as the wings hit against each other above the bird's back as it lifts into the air.

Stock Dove

• **ORDER** • Columbiformes • **FAMILY** • Columbidae • **SPECIES** • *Columba oenas*

VITAL STATISTICS

WEIGHT	300g (10.6lb)
HLENGTH	28–32cm (11–12.6 in)
WINGSPAN	60–68cm (23.6–27 in)
SEXUAL MATURITY	1 year.
IINCUBATION PERIOD	21–23 days
FLEDGLING PERIOD	28–29 days
NUMBER OF EGGS	2 eggs
NUMBER OF BROODS	1–4 a year
TYPICAL DIET	Seeds, leaves; occasionally invertebrates.
LIFE SPAN	Up to 9 years

With their iridescent plumage and gentle cooing, Stock Doves are a class act, and very different from the tatty city-dwelling Feral Pigeons with which they are often confused.

WHERE IN THE WORLD?

Stock Doves are found in huge flocks in towns, woods and farmland throughout Europe, central Asia and northwest Africa. Northern and western populations migrate, but they are resident elsewhere.

CREATURE COMPARISONS

White doves are regarded as symbols of peace due to the tale of Noah and the great flood, which is told by Jews, Christians and Muslims. However, in real life, pure white doves are unusual and most commonly occur as a mutation of the Ring-necked Dove.

White Dove

BILL
Doves in general are unusual in that they can suck up water. Most birds have to tip up their heads to swallow liquid.

WINGS
Stock Doves often flock together with Wood Pigeons. They can be identified, in the air, by their faster, flicking wing beats.

FEET
The feet of the Stock Dove are typical of perching birds, with one short, backwards-facing toe and three forwards-facing toes.

HOW BIG IS IT?

SPECIAL ADAPTATION

Stock Doves make their home almost anywhere. A hole in a tree is preferable but they will use abandoned animal burrows, rock crevices and nest boxes, or even make a nest down in clumps of ivy.

Wood Pigeon

• ORDER • Columbiformes FAMILY • Columbidae • SPECIES • *Columba polumbus*

VITAL STATISTICS

WEIGHT	450–550g (16–19.4oz)
LENGTH	38–43cm (15.0–17in)
WINGSPAN	68–77cm (27–30.3in)
NUMBER OF EGGS	2 eggs
INCUBATION PERIOD	16–20 days
NUMBER OF BROODS	2–3 a year
TYPICAL DIET	Mainly plants, such as shoots, seedling, seeds, grain, berries, fruit; also snails and grubs
LIFE SPAN	Up to 20 years

This Wood Pigeon is found in woods and cities, and in parts of southern England it is known as the Culver.

The Wood Pigeon is widely distributed across most of Europe and into western Asia, parts of North Africa and the Middle East. Birds from northern areas migrate south for the winter.

CREATURE COMPARISONS

The Wood Pigeon looks very similar to the Rock Pigeon, but is larger. The head, upper part of the back and wings are bluish-grey or slate grey with white bars. The white patch on the throat, edged in dull green or purple, is also characteristic. The breast is pinkish, and the tail is grey with a darker tip. Juveniles lack the white spot on the side of the neck.

Adult (left), juvenile (right)

WINGS
The distinctive white bars on the wings are characteristic of the Wood Pigeon (along with the white throat patch).

TAIL
The Wood Pigeon can also be distinguished from its close relative, the Rock Pigeon, by its distinctly longer tail.

LEGS
The Wood Pigeon has short, powerful legs and feet with long toes for perching.

HOW BIG IS IT?

SPECIAL ADAPTATION
Although Wood Pigeons often breed in pairs, they sometimes form small colonies. This may give extra protection, because in spring the nests are often subjected to attacks by crows.

Luzon Bleeding-Heart

• ORDER • Columbiformes **• FAMILY •** Columbidae **• SPECIES •** *Gallicolumba luzonica*

VITAL STATISTICS

WEIGHT	184g (6.5oz)
LENGTH	30cm (12in)
WINGSPAN	38cm (15in)
SEXUAL MATURITY	1 year
LAYS EGGS	Mid-May
INCUBATION PERIOD	15–17 days
NUMBER OF EGGS	2 eggs
NUMBER OF BROODS	1 a year
TYPICAL DIET	Seeds, berries and insects
LIFE SPAN	Typically 15 years.

The Luzon Bleeding-Heart, a type of dove, is rarely seen. It gets its evocative name from the vivid splash of red on its breast.

WHERE IN THE WORLD?

As the name indicates, Luzon Bleeding-Hearts are found in Luzon and the smaller Philippine island of Polillo. These shy birds live in lowland forests, where they roost in low trees.

CREATURE COMPARISONS

Luzon Bleeding-Hearts are members of the dove family. However they spend most of their time on the forest floor feeding, which means that their bodies have adapted to resemble other ground-dwelling birds, like partridges. And, like partridges, they are able to fly, but prefer to walk.

Luzon Bleeding-Hearts spend most of their time feeding on the forest floor

EYES
It is hard to differentiate male and female Bleeding-Heart, although some bird-watchers claim females (shown) have purple rather than blue eyes.

BREAST
The red patch looks as if the bird has been injured and the impression is emphasized by the red patch being set in a grove in the bird's breast.

LEGS
Long legs enable the Luzon Bleeding-Heart to pick its way through the forest floor and avoid obstacles with ease.

HOW BIG IS IT?

SPECIAL ADAPTATION

Luzon Bleeding-Hearts have long legs and short wings, which enables them to weave through the undergrowth without getting their feathers tangled up in forest-floor debris. Short wings also give the birds the speed to escape predators.

Victoria Crowned Pigeon

• ORDER • Columbiformes **• FAMILY •** Columbidae **• SPECIES •** *Goura victoria*

VITAL STATISTICS

WEIGHT	2–2.5kg (4.4–5.5lb)
LENGTH	74cm (29in)
SEXUAL MATURITY	Around 15 months
SEXUAL MATURITY	4 years
INCUBATION PERIOD	28 days
FLEDGLING PERIOD	30 days
NUMBER OF EGGS	1 a year
CALL	A loud rumbling threat call
TYPICAL DIET	Fruit, seeds and invertebrates, especially snails
LIFE SPAN	Up to 25 years in captivity

CREATURE COMPARISONS

While the Victoria Crowned Pigeon is extremely rare, many other members of the pigeon family occur in huge numbers. This is especially true of the Collared Dove (shown below), which is so widespread that it is now considered to be a pest in many parts of the world.

A Victoria Crowned Pigeon (left) with a Collared Dove (right)

With its slatey blue plumage and spectacular crown, the turkey-sized Victoria Crowned Pigeon could not be more different from the Feral Pigeon of towns and cities.

WHERE IN THE WORLD?

The Victoria Crowned Pigeon is found in lowlands and marshy forests of northern New Guinea and its surrounding islands. Numbers are declining due to the loss of their natural habitats.

WINGS
These birds fly only when disturbed, and then, rest on low-level perches, which makes them an easy target for poachers.

BODY
Although they are the largest living species of pigeon, their extinct relatives, Dodos, grew to 1m (3ft 4in) tall.

FEET
Victoria Crowned Pigeons feed on the ground. Their strong feet and long toes are adapted for a mainly terrestrial lifestyle.

HOW BIG IS IT?

SPECIAL ADAPTATION

In the bird world, divorce is unusual and couples will break up only if they fail to breed. Courtship displays help to ensure the suitability of a mate. For Victoria Crowned Pigeons, these include the collecting of nesting materials by males, who present these to females.

Topknot Pigeon

• **ORDER** • Columbiformes • **FAMILY** • Columbidae • **SPECIES** • *Lopholaimus antarcticus*

VITAL STATISTICS

WEIGHT	525g (18.5oz)
LENGTH	40–45cm (15.7–17.7 in)
SEXUAL MATURITY	1 years
LAYS EGGS	August–December
IINCUBATION PERIOD	22–24 days
FLEDGLING PERIOD	22–26 days
NUMBER	1 egg
HABITS	Diurnal, non-migratory
TYPICAL DIET	Rainforest fruit and berries
LIFE SPAN	Up to 17 years

Topknot Pigeons, with their distinctive double head crest, are more at home in the rainforest than the concrete jungle.

WHERE IN THE WORLD?

The Topknot Pigeon is found in rainforests along the eastern coast of Australia. They tend to be nomadic, moving from coastal areas to highlands in the spring, following seasonal food sources.

CREATURE COMPARISONS

Adult male Topknot Pigeons have dark grey upper parts, light grey underparts and a characteristic two-toned head crest. Their tails are square-ended, with bands of black and white across the length. In comparison, juvenile Top-Knots resemble females, with browner heads and a noticeably smaller head crest.

Juveline Topknot Pigeon

HEAD
Topknot Pigeons have a unique double head crest, which is grey at the front and rusty red at the back. It is slightly larger in the male.

BILL
The orange-brown bill is strong, short and pointed. It is well adapted for plucking and eating fruit and berries.

FEET
Strong feet enable these birds to be surprisingly agile, allowing them to hang from branches while feeding on hard-to-reach fruit.

HOW BIG IS IT?

SPECIAL ADAPTATION

All Pigeons have a storage sac just above their gut, called a crop. Because Topknot Pigeons eat large fruit, their crops are bigger than those of other pigeons. This allows them to gorge on fruit when it is available, and then digest it later in smaller chunks.

Wompoo Fruit Dove

• ORDER • Columbiformes • FAMILY • Columbidae • SPECIES • *Ptilinopus magnificus*

Looking a little like a multi-coloured rain forest pigeon, Australia's spectacular Wompoo Fruit Dove well deserves its Latin species name, which means magnificent.

VITAL STATISTICS

LENGTH	29–45cm (11.4–17.7 in)
SEXUAL MATURITY	1–2 years
LAYS EGGS	Courtship begins in July but egg laying varies with local conditions
INCUBATION PERIOD	21 days
NUMBER OF EGGS	1 egg
NUMBER OF BROODS	1 a year although another egg may be laid if the first brood fails
CALL	A resonant 'wollack-a-woo' or a shorter, sudden 'boo'
TYPICAL DIET	Fruit, especially figs
HABITS	Diurnal, non-migratory
LIFE SPAN	Unknown

CREATURE COMPARISONS

Wompoos vary in size and colour across their range. Those in the north are larger with purple plumage around the neck, chest and upper belly, and have green underparts. In the south, especially in New Guinea (see below), they are smaller with a more ruddy, red breast.

A Woompoo Fruit Dove from northern New Guinea

WHERE IN THE WORLD?

The Wompoo Fruit Dove lives in lowland tropical rainforests along Australia's eastern coast, from central New South Wales to the Cape York peninsula. Populations are also present in New Guinea.

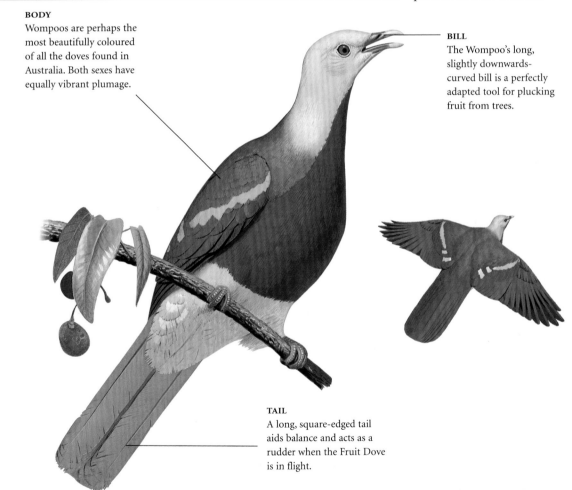

BODY
Wompoos are perhaps the most beautifully coloured of all the doves found in Australia. Both sexes have equally vibrant plumage.

BILL
The Wompoo's long, slightly downwards-curved bill is a perfectly adapted tool for plucking fruit from trees.

TAIL
A long, square-edged tail aids balance and acts as a rudder when the Fruit Dove is in flight.

HOW BIG IS IT?

SPECIAL ADAPTATION

Reaching food can be tricky but Wompoos are born acrobats and can crawl along branches using their tail and wings for balance like tightrope walkers. For those really hard-to-reach fruit, they may even hang upside-down.

Collared Dove

• **ORDER** • Columbiformes • **FAMILY** • Columbidae • **SPECIES** • *Streptopelia decaocto*

VITAL STATISTICS

WEIGHT	200g (7oz)
LENGTH	31–34cm (12.2–13.4 in)
WINGSPAN	48–56cm (19–22 in)
SEXUAL MATURITY	1 year
INCUBATION PERIOD	16–17 days
FLEDGLING PERIOD	17–19 days
NUMBER OF EGGS	2 eggs
NUMBER OF BROODS	3–6 a year
TYPICAL DIET	Cereal, seeds; invertebrates
LIFE SPAN	Typically 3 years

Collard Doves are superbly adapted for modern living, so much so that they are now considered to be pests in many parts of the world.

WHERE IN THE WORLD?

Collared Doves were originally only found in their natural homelands, in Turkey, the Middle East and southeastern Asia. Now they breed in northern Europe, North Africa and the USA.

CREATURE COMPARISONS

It is generally the job of the male bird to attract a mate. For some species, this means abandoning their everyday attire in favour of showy display plumage. Collared Doves, however, take a simpler approach by puffing up their chests, so that they look bigger and more impressive.

A Collared Dove puffing its chest during a display

HEAD
The 'decaocto' part of the Collared Doves' scientific name comes from the Greek for the birds' cooing call.

NECK
The black, half collar on the nape of the bird's neck gives it its common name.

FEET
The feet, typical of perching birds, have one short, backwards-facing toe and three forwards-facing toes.

HOW BIG IS IT?

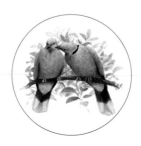

SPECIAL ADAPTATION
There were no Collared Doves in Britain before 1955. Since then numbers have rapidly increased. One of the reasons for this is their long breeding season, which extends from March to October, allowing them to raise up to six broods a year.

Black-bellied Sandgrouse

• **ORDER** • Columbiformes • **FAMILY** • Pteroclididae • **SPECIES** • *Pterocles orientalis*

The sturdy Black-bellied Sandgrouse may look big and clumsy but it is an amazingly skilful flier, a fact that hunters as well as bird-watchers appreciate.

VITAL STATISTICS

WEIGHT	Males: 400–550g (14–19.4oz). Females: 300–465g (10.6–16.4oz)
LENGTH	30–35cm (12–14 in)
LAYS EGGS	March–September, but varies across range
INCUBATION PERIOD	23–28 days
NUMBER OF EGGS	2 – 3 eggs
NUMBER OF BROODS	1 a year
HABITS	Diurnal/crepuscular; migratory
CALL	Light 'chowrr rrrr-rrrr'
TYPICAL DIET	Seeds; occasionally insects
LIFE SPAN	Unknown

WHERE IN THE WORLD?

Black-bellied Sandgrouse breed in North Africa, Iran, India, Pakistan, and parts of the Iberian Peninsula, from Turkey to Russia. Preferred habitats are steppe and semi-desert, seeded with grasses and shrubs.

CREATURE COMPARISONS

Females are a similar size to their male counterparts but have a very different coloration. Their upper parts are finely vermiculated, which means that they are covered in a black worm-like pattern. They also lack the characteristic rust-coloured neck patch of the male.

Male (front), female (back)

BODY
With their plump bodies and short necks, Black-bellied Sandgrouse resemble partridges, but are more closely related to pigeons.

WINGS
Long, pointed wings make the Black-bellied Sandgrouse a fast and powerful flier.

BELLY
The large black patch on the belly of the male and female gives this species its common name.

HOW BIG IS IT?

SPECIAL ADAPTATION

Male and female Sandgrouse take turns to incubate the eggs (females during the day and males at night), so they can feed themselves. Males also bring the new arrivals water by soaking their belly feathers for the chicks to suck.

Pallas's Sandgrouse

• **ORDER** • Columbiformes • **FAMILY** • Pteroclididae • **SPECIES** • *Syrrhaptes paradoxus*

VITAL STATISTICS

WEIGHT	150–500g (5.3–17.6oz)
LENGTH	30–41cm (12–16in)
WINGSPAN	45–60cm (17.7–23.6in)
NUMBER OF EGGS	2–3 eggs
INCUBATION PERIOD	26–29 days
NUMBER OF BROODS	2 a year
TYPICAL DIET	Seeds, green shoots and buds
LIFE SPAN	Unknown

The hardy Pallas's Sandgrouse is well adapted for life in scorching hot, dry regions, but it still needs to drink every day.

WHERE IN THE WORLD?

Pallas's Sandgrouse is found on dry steppes and similar areas in central Asia, from southern Russia and Kazakhstan across Mongolia to northern China.

CREATURE COMPARISONS

The head is yellowish with a dark stripe across the eye and a grey cheek. The neck and throat is grey. The body and wings are buff with dark markings. The breast is buff or yellowish-grey, and the belly is black. Males are similar to females but have a grey and dark breast band. It may be confused with the Tibetan Sandgrouse, which lacks a black belly.

Juvenile

HEAD
The head is small and pigeon-like, with a sturdy bill that is well adapted for eating hard seeds.

BODY
Loose, fluffy feathers along the belly can absorb large amounts of water.

TAIL
The long streamlined tail has two very long feathers, which are used in display.

HOW BIG IS IT?

SPECIAL ADAPTATION

Living in dry areas, adult birds fly long distances every morning to water holes, where they soak up water in their body feathers. They then fly back to the nest, where the chicks suck the moisture from the damp feathers.

Kingfisher

A flash of sapphire as the Kingfisher streaks downstream is all that you are likely to see of this most elusive of river-side hunters.

VITAL STATISTICS

WEIGHT	40g (1.4oz)
LENGTH	17–19.5cm (6.7–7.7in)
WINGSPAN	25cm (9.8in)
SEXUAL MATURITY	1 year
LAYS EGGS	April–August
INCUBATION PERIOD	19–21 days
NUMBER OF EGGS	5–7 eggs
NUMBER OF BROODS	2 a year
TYPICAL DIET	Freshwater fish and aquatic invertebrates
LIFE SPAN	Up to 15 years

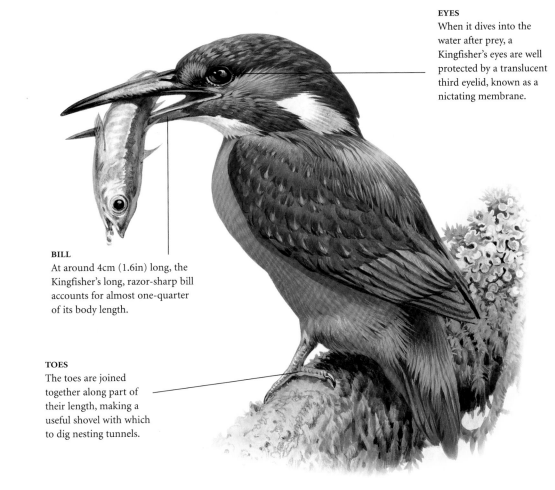

WHERE IN THE WORLD?

Kingfishers may look like an exotic resident of the Amazon, but they are more at home in Europe, North Africa and Asia. Being vulnerable to the cold, they rarely breed in the far north.

EYES
When it dives into the water after prey, a Kingfisher's eyes are well protected by a translucent third eyelid, known as a nictating membrane.

CREATURE COMPARISONS

Male and female Kingfishers are virtually identical, apart from a flash of pale orange that can be seen on the lower part of the female's bill. Juvenile Kingfishers are generally less colourful than the adults, with paler plumage and shorter bills.

Male (top), female (bottom)

BILL
At around 4cm (1.6in) long, the Kingfisher's long, razor-sharp bill accounts for almost one-quarter of its body length.

TOES
The toes are joined together along part of their length, making a useful shovel with which to dig nesting tunnels.

HOW BIG IS IT?

SPECIAL ADAPTATION
Kingfishers are adapted to be swift hunters. They sit, motionless, on a perch until they spot their prey, then attack at lightning speed. Their short, round wings and stubby tail make them fast and agile, and their short wings are also easier to fold back underwater when diving.

Southern Ground Hornbill

• ORDER • Coraciiformes • FAMILY • Bucerotidae • SPECIES • *Bucorvus leadbeateri*

VITAL STATISTICS

WEIGHT	Males: 3.2–6.2kg Females: 2.2–4.6kg
LENGTH	90cm–1.3m (35.4 in–4.3ft)
WINGSPAN	1–1.1m (3.3–3.6ft)
SEXUAL MATURITY	4 years
LAYS EGGSS	October–November
INCUBATION PERIOD	40–42 days
NUMBER OF EGGS	2 eggs
NUMBER OF BROODS	1 a year
TYPICAL DIET	Mammals, reptiles and insects
LIFE SPAN	Up to 40 years

These large and stately Southern Ground Hornbill lives in huge groups where the young are protected and cared for communally.

WHERE IN THE WORLD?

This heaviest of all Hornbills is found on southeastern Africa's woodlands, savannahs and open grasslands. The species is declining in numbers and is now mainly found in national parks and reserves.

CREATURE COMPARISONS

Head ornamentation helps differentiate male from female Hornbills. Males have a vivid, red neck pouch and face wattles. The females, which are smaller, look similar (see below), but have a purple neck patch. A juvenile's neck and wattles are greyish yellow.

Female (left), male (right)

NECK
Hornbills have an extra vertebra in their neck, which makes it easier for them to grab prey on the ground.

WINGS
Long, white, finger-like primary feathers are used in mating displays and provide a startling contrast to the Southern Ground Hornbills' black plumage.

FEET
They can fly, but Southern Ground Hornbills spend most of their time on the ground, walking with a slow stately gait.

HOW BIG IS IT?

SPECIAL ADAPTATION

A huge bill, hinged by powerful muscles, enables the Southern Ground Hornbill to eat a wide variety of foods. When hunting, the birds have a curious habit of putting all the food they have gathered on the ground, carefully arranging it, and then picking it all back up again.

Great Hornbill

• ORDER • Coraciiformes **• FAMILY •** Bucerotidae **• SPECIES •** *Buceros bicornis*

The huge Great Hornbill is the largest member of the hornbill family and is often exhibited in zoos and wildlife parks.

VITAL STATISTICS

WEIGHT	3–3.5kg (6.6–7.7lb)
LENGTH	120–140cm (47.2–55.1in)
WINGSPAN	150–170cm (59.1–66.9in)
NUMBER OF EGGS	1–2 eggs
INCUBATION PERIOD	38–40 days
NUMBER OF BROODS	1 a year
TYPICAL DIET	Mainly fruits and berries; also small mammals, amphibians, lizards and large insects
LIFE SPAN	Up to 50 years

CREATURE COMPARISONS

The Great Hornbill has a black head and an enormous yellow bill. The throat is yellow, forming a distinct contrast to the predominately black plumage on the body and wings, which are adorned with distinctive, white bars. The long tail is white with a wide black band. Females are similar to males, but are slightly smaller.

Great Hornbill

WHERE IN THE WORLD?

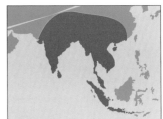

The Great Hornbill is found in forested areas in southeast Asia, in India, the Malay Peninsula, the island of Sumatra and on several Indonesian islands.

HEAD
Females and males look similar, but females have blue eyes, while males have bright red eyes.

TOP OF HEAD
The enormous growth on top of the bill is called a casque. Its exact purpose is still not known.

BILL
The bill can measure up to 35cm (14in) in a large male. However, it is hollow so it is quite light.

HOW BIG IS IT?

SPECIAL ADAPTATION
Despite its massive size, the huge bill is highly adapted for picking fruits. The yellow colour of its bill and wing feathers is actually due to a yellow oil from the preen gland.

129

Green Kingfisher

• **ORDER** • Coraciiformes • **FAMILY** • Cerylidae • **SPECIES** • *Chloroceryle americana*

VITAL STATISTICS

LENGTH	20cm (8in)
SEXUAL MATURITY	1 year
INCUBATION PERIOD	19–21 days
FLEDGLING PERIOD	22–26 days
NUMBER OF EGGS	4–5 eggs
NUMBER OF BROODS	1 a year
CALL	High-pitched rattle
HABITS	Diurnal, non-migratory
TYPICAL DIET	Small fish, crustaceans and insects
LIFE SPAN	Unknown

America's very own Green Kingfisher is smaller than other Kingfishers but they are every bit as agile and skilful.

WHERE IN THE WORLD?

Green Kingfishers belong to the Cerylidae Family of water Kingfishers, which are a group of specialist fish-eaters. Populations breed by rivers and lakes from Texas, in the USA, through to Latin America.

CREATURE COMPARISONS

Despite their dagger-like bills, Kingfishers do not spear their prey. That would be too dangerous because large fish could drown them. Nor do they eat live prey, which could injure them. Instead, all Kingfishers catch prey in their bills, stunning them with repeated blows before swallowing them whole.

PLUMAGE
Predominantly green plumage on the birds' upper body provides good camouflage among foliage.

BELLY
Pale underparts make it difficult for predators and prey to spot the Kingfisher when viewed from below.

FEET
Relatively strong but small feet are useful for perching but not powerful enough to lift prey from the water.

Green Kingfisher

HOW BIG IS IT?

SPECIAL ADAPTATION

The Kingfishers' bill is more than just a superb hunting tool. It is also used to excavate a nesting tunnel. This quickly wears down the outer edges of the bill. However, just like rodents' teeth, these parts of the bill constantly grow back.

European Roller

• ORDER • Coraciiformes • FAMILY • Coracidae • SPECIES • *Coracias garrulus*

VITAL STATISTICS

WEIGHT	140–170g (4.9–6.0oz)
LENGTH	29–32cm (11.4–12.6in)
WINGSPAN	52–58cm (20.5–22.8in)
NUMBER OF EGGS	4–6
INCUBATION PERIOD	19–20 days
NUMBER OF BROODS	1 a year
TYPICAL DIET	Insects, snails, lizards, frogs, earthworms
LIFE SPAN	Up to 10 years

The beautiful and exotic-looking European Roller is the only species from the Roller family to breed in Europe.

WHERE IN THE WORLD?

The European Roller is found in southern Spain and Portugal, across Eastern Europe and into the Middle East and central and southern Asia. It is also found in parts of North Africa.

CREATURE COMPARISONS

The European Roller has an orange or reddish-brown back and a blue or greenish-blue head. The neck, breast and belly are mottled off-white and pale blue, often with splashes of green. The tail is dark blue with paler blue sides. The wings are blue or greenish-blue with dark blue or almost black tips and dark hind part. Males and females are similar.

European Roller perching in a tree

WINGS
The wings are short and wide. During flight, their dark colouring provides a striking contrast to the blue body.

BILL
The short, powerful bill is well adapted for cracking the tough shells of large beetles, which form part of the bird's diet.

TAIL
The short square tail is important in manoeuvring in the air.

HOW BIG IS IT?

SPECIAL ADAPTATION

The European roller has a bounding flight like a jackdaw. The male uses a special kind of fluttering flight to attract the female during the breeding season.

131

Dollarbird

• ORDER • Coraciiformes • FAMILY • Coraciidae • SPECIES • *Eurystomus orientalis*

The large, conspicuous Dollarbird perching on a branch is a common sight in much of Southeast Asia and Australia.

VITAL STATISTICS

LENGTH	25–34cm (10–13.4in)
WINGSPAN	36–50cm (14.2–19.3in)
NUMBER OF EGGS	3–5 (usually 4)
INCUBATION PERIOD	Unknown
NUMBER OF BROODS	1 a year
TYPICAL DIET	Large flying insects, such as flower beetles and cicadas
LIFE SPAN	Unknown

WHERE IN THE WORLD?

The Dollarbird is widely distributed in Southeast Asia and along the Sunday Islands, Japan, Papua New Guinea, Borneo and the eastern part of Australia.

HEAD AND BILL
The large head sits on a short, stumpy neck. The heavy bill is well adapted for crushing the hard wingcases of beetles.

CREATURE COMPARISONS

The body and inner parts of the wings are bluish-green, while the rest of the wings are a deeper shade of blue. The head and the tail are darker, and the bill is strikingly orange. On each wing tip is a large pale area, which is only visible in flight. Juveniles have a dark bill, which turns orange when the bird matures.

WING
The wings each have a distinctive pale patch thought to resemble a silver dollar, hence the bird's name.

Australian species *pacificus*

TAIL
The short square tail is mainly used for manoeuvring during flight and landing.

HOW BIG IS IT?

SPECIAL ADAPTATION
The dollarbird has a predilection for flying insects. It uses its strong, powerful bill to crush the hard wingcases of insects, such as beetles.

Laughing Kookaburra

• ORDER • Coraciiformes • FAMILY • Halcyonidae • SPECIES • *Dacelo novaeguinae*

VITAL STATISTICS

WEIGHT	275–350g (10–12.3oz)
LENGTH	38–45cm (15–18in)
WINGSPAN	55–65cm (22–25.6in)
NUMBER OF EGGS	2–4
INCUBATION PERIOD	24–26 days
NUMBER OF BROODS	1 a year
TYPICAL DIET	Smaller animals such as lizards and snakes; large insects, worms, frogs, fish, rodents
LIFE SPAN	10–15 years

The Laughing Kookaburra, a large and eye-catching bird, is mainly known for its very loud, unusual call. It is unofficially regarded as Australia's national bird.

WHERE IN THE WORLD?

The Laughing Kookaburra is widely distributed throughout eastern Australia. It has been introduced into parts of western Australia and Tasmania, and to the North Island of New Zealand.

CREATURE COMPARISONS

The Laughing Kookaburra is a very large type of Kingfisher. It has white and dark feathers on top of its head, while the rest of the head, neck and body are largely white or cream. The back and wings are brownish with blue markings along the shoulders, and the tail is more reddish-brown. Females are usually larger than males and have fewer blue markings.

Laughing Kookaburra

BEAK
The very large, flattened beak is well adapted for snatching smaller animals.

HEAD
The large round head has a conspicuous dark stripe along the cheek.

WINGS
Short, stocky wings have distinctive white markings along the outer part of the primary feathers.

HOW BIG IS IT?

SPECIAL ADAPTATION
The Laughing Kookaburra has a large, pointed but flattened bill. This is a good adaptation for rummaging around on the ground looking for prey instead of spearing fish in the water.

Sacred Kingfisher

• **ORDER** • Coraciiformes • **FAMILY** • Halcyonidae • **SPECIES** • *Todiramphus sanctus*

VITAL STATISTICS

LENGTH	18–23cm (7–9in)
SEXUAL MATURITY	1 year
LAYS EGGS	September–December
INCUBATION PERIOD	18 days
FLEDGLING PERIOD	24–26 days
NUMBER OF EGGS	3–6 eggs
NUMBER OF BROODS	1–2 a year
CALL	Sharp 'kik-kik-kik'
HABITS	Diurnal, migratory
TYPICAL DIET	Crustaceans, small reptiles and mammals, insects; occasionally fish

CREATURE COMPARISONS

Sacred Kingfishers swallow their food whole. They later regurgitate any inedible bits (bones, skin or fur) in the form of pellets, which are formed in the birds' muscular gizzard. This is a common practice in the bird world, especially among birds of prey, such as owls.

Sacred Kingfisher hovering in the air

Sacred Kingfishers are the hunter-kings of Australia's woodlands, and are just as likely to make a meal of mice, frogs or spiders as catch fish.

WHERE IN THE WORLD?

The Sacred Kingfisher is found in mangrove forests and woodlands throughout Australia, New Zealand, New Caledonia and Indonesia. Australian birds migrate to northern coastal areas to breed.

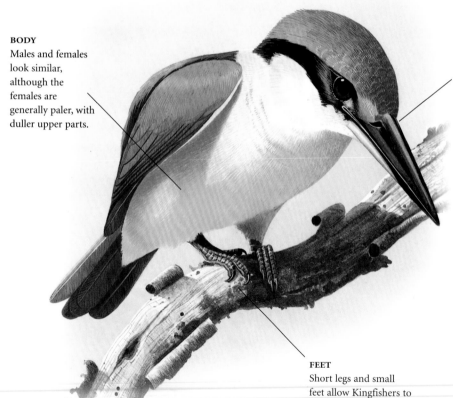

BODY
Males and females look similar, although the females are generally paler, with duller upper parts.

BILL
Long, flat bills are ideal for snapping insects from the air. Serrated edges on the upper mandible help grip wriggling prey.

FEET
Short legs and small feet allow Kingfishers to move about with ease in the confines of the nesting tunnel.

HOW BIG IS IT?

SPECIAL ADAPTATION

Kingfishers are famed for their fishing skills. However, Sacred Kingfishers have had to adapt to survive in a wide range of environments, so they also eat insects, which they catch in mid-air, as well as grabbing larger prey, like mice, directly off the ground.

European Bee-eater

• ORDER • Coraciiformes **• FAMILY •** Meropidae **• SPECIES •** *Merops apiaster*

VITAL STATISTICS

WEIGHT	44–78g (1.6–3oz)
LENGTH	27–29cm (10.6–11.4in)
WINGSPAN	44–49cm (17.3–19.3in)
NUMBER OF EGGS	5–8 (usually 5–6)
INCUBATION PERIOD	20–21 days
NUMBER OF BROODS	1 a year
TYPICAL DIET	Bees, wasps, hornets, flies and mosquitoes; butterflies, dragonflies
LIFE SPAN	Up to 9 years

The European Bee-eater possesses almost tropical beauty, and is a voracious predator of bees, wasps and even the fierce hornets.

WHERE IN THE WORLD?

The European Bee-eater is found in most of southern Europe, the Middle East and across southwestern Asia. It is also present in parts of North Africa.

CREATURE COMPARISONS

The European Bee-eater has a rich yellow and brown back and upper part of the head. There is a distinctive dark stripe across the face. The throat is bright yellow with a black collar. The breast and belly are blue or greenish-blue. The wings are greenish-blue with an orange-red and a green patch, and a black posterior edge. Males and females are similar.

European Bee-eaters

BILL
The long pointed bill is used to catch up to 250 bees or wasps every single day.

TAIL
The green-blue tail has two long green middle feathers extending further out than the others.

FEET
The feet have long toes adapted for perching. The short legs are usually greyish-brown.

HOW BIG IS IT?

SPECIAL ADAPTATION

European Bee-eaters nest in colonies. They excavate tunnels up to 2m (6ft 6in) long into a sandy ditch and then build a nest chamber at the end where the chicks are safe from predators.

Northern Carmine Bee-eater

• **ORDER** • Coraciiformes • **FAMILY** • Meropidae • **SPECIES** • *Merops nubicus*

VITAL STATISTICS

WEIGHT	42–56g (1.5–2oz)
LENGTH	35–38cm (14–15in)
WINGSPAN	28–32cm (11–12.25in)
LAYS EGGS	February–June, but varies with location
INCUBATION PERIOD	Around 20 days
FLEDGLING PERIOD	20–25 days
NUMBER OF EGGS	2 eggs
NUMBER OF BROODS	1 a year
CALL	Metallic 'took, took'
TTYPICAL DIET	Flying insects, especially bees and locusts

CREATURE COMPARISONS

While many birds keep watch for prey and predators perched in the tops of trees, Carmine Bee-Eaters choose more unusual places to roost, such as the backs of cattle or even large birds, like the Bustard (shown).

Northern Carmine Bee-eater perching on a Bustard

The Northern Carmine Bee-eater is a richly coloured, slender bird, predominantly carmine in colour, except for a greenish blue head and throat and distinctive black mask.

WHERE IN THE WORLD?

The Northern Carmine Bee-eater ranges over the northern region of sub-Saharan Africa in open woodlands, grasslands, mangrove swamps or beside lakes where there are suitable nesting sites.

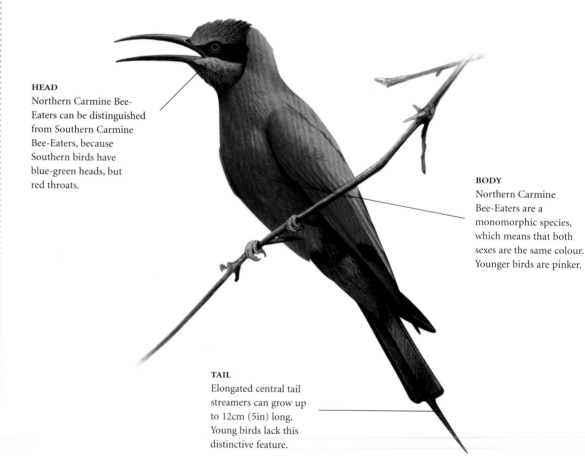

HEAD
Northern Carmine Bee-Eaters can be distinguished from Southern Carmine Bee-Eaters, because Southern birds have blue-green heads, but red throats.

BODY
Northern Carmine Bee-Eaters are a monomorphic species, which means that both sexes are the same colour. Younger birds are pinker.

TAIL
Elongated central tail streamers can grow up to 12cm (5in) long. Young birds lack this distinctive feature.

HOW BIG IS IT?

SPECIAL ADAPTATION

Choosing the right nest site is vital, but nest design is just as important. Carmine Bee-Eaters breed in colonies of as many as 10,000 couples. They design their nests as tunnels excavated into sandy river banks or cliff faces, which provides the colony with even greater security.

Jamaican Tody

VITAL STATISTICS

HEIGHT	11cm (4.3in)
SEXUAL MATURITY	1 year
INCUBATION PERIOD	21–22 days
FLEDGLING PERIOD	19–21 days
NUMBER OF EGGS	3–4
NUMBER OF BROODS	1 a year occasionally more
CALL	Unmusical buzzes and beeps
HABITS	Diurnal, non-migratory
TYPICAL DIET	Insects, spiders; occasionally small lizards and seeds
LIFE SPAN	Up to years

CREATURE COMPARISONS

Todies nest in tunnels in riverbanks or tree trunks. However, it is once the nest is built that the real hard work begins. These birds have an incredibly high metabolism and must feed their young up to 140 times a day, which is more than any other species of bird.

Jamaican Tody

These wonderfully vibrant Jamaican birds are the Caribbean island's equivalent of the Kingfisher, living their lives in multi-coloured blur of activity.

WHERE IN THE WORLD?

Jamaican Todies are found only on the Caribbean island of Jamaica, but members of the tody family are found in the forests of Puerto Rico, Jamaica and Cuba.

THROAT
The five known species of Tody all have green upper parts and all, except the Broad-Billed and Narrow-Billed, have a red throat patch.

WINGS
The wings produce a whirring rattle in flight, which may play a part in courtship or territorial displays.

PLUMAGE
Magnificent plumage indicates that these forest-dwellers belong to the Order Coraciiformes, which includes the equally colourful Kingfishers.

HOW BIG IS IT?

SPECIAL ADAPTATION
Like many fly-catchers, Jamaican Todies have specialized bills. Their long flat shape is ideal for snapping at insects in the air, while the sharp serrated edges on the upper mandible keep a grip on wriggling prey.

Hoopoe (Eurasian)

• ORDER • Coraciiformes **• FAMILY •** Upupidae **• SPECIES •** *Upupa epops*

VITAL STATISTICS

WEIGHT	68g (2.4oz)
LENGTH	25–29cm (10–11.4in)
WINGSPAN	44–48cm (17.3–19in)
LAYS EGGS	April–September, but varies across range
INCUBATION PERIOD	15–16 days
FLEDGLING PERIOD	26–29 days
NUMBER OF EGGS	7–8 eggs
NUMBER OF BROODS	1–2 a year
HABITS	Diurnal, migratory
TYPICAL DIET	Large insects; occasionally small reptiles

CREATURE COMPARISONS

Ornithologists disagree over exactly how many sub-species of Hoopoe there are. However, all share the same characteristics. They have long thin bills, broad wings, a square tail and moveable crests. The Eurasian Hoopoe became the national bird of Israel in 2008, beating the popular White Spectacled Bulbul.

The crest is raised when alarmed or excited (top)

Hoopoes create a dazzling aerial display by opening and closing their wings to reveal dramatic flashes of black and white.

Hoopoes are birds of the open steppe, farmyard and savannah. Birds breed in Europe, northwest Africa, the Middle East and central Asia. In the winter, populations migrate south to Africa and Asia.

CREST
The Hoopoe's dramatic crest is flat at rest but is raised when the bird is alarmed or excited.

BILL
The Hoopoe's downwards-curved bill can grow up to 5cm (almost 2in) long.

WINGS
Broad wings with round tips give better lift, allowing the Hoopoe to fly in tight circles.

HOW BIG IS IT?

SPECIAL ADAPTATION
Hoopoes often spread their feathers to allow the sun to 'cook' lice and other pests that may be attached to them, this also helps to keep the plumage clean.

Cuckoo

VITAL STATISTICS

WEIGHT	Males: 130g (4.6oz). Females: 110g (4oz)
LENGTH	32–36cm (12.6–14.2in)
WINGSPAN	54–60cm (21–23.6in)
SEXUAL MATURITY	2 years
LAYS EGGS	April–June
INCUBATION PERIOD	12–13 days
NUMBER OF EGGS	1 egg in each host nest
NUMBER OF BROODS	Dozens of eggs may be scattered around the Cuckoo's territory
TYPICAL DIET	Insects, especially caterpillars and beetles
LIFE SPAN	Up to 13 years

The call of the Cuckoo is one of the most eagerly awaited signs that winter is ending and spring is finally on its way.

WHERE IN THE WORLD?

Cuckoos prefer the temperate climates of Europe, Asia and North Africa in which to breed. In winter they migrate to regions, such as South Africa and southern Asia.

CREATURE COMPARISONS

Female Cuckoos lay their eggs in the nest of the species that raised them. Once these eggs hatch, the young Cuckoos (shown) dispose of their foster siblings. Instinct compels the parents to continue feeding the Cuckoo even though they look nothing like their own offspring.

Juvenile Cuckoo

BILL
A layer of soft bristles surrounds the Cuckoo's bill, protecting its eyes from damage when eating hairy caterpillars, their preferred prey.

BODY
Male and female Cuckoos generally look alike but some rare hepatic (liver-coloured) females are a ruddy brown in colour.

WINGS
Female Cuckoos spend a lot of time in the air looking for nests in which they will eventually deposit their own eggs.

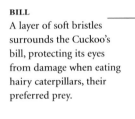

HOW BIG IS IT?

SPECIAL ADAPTATION

In flight, the Cuckoo's long, pointed wings give it the same silhouette as a small bird of prey, such as a kestrel. This may protect Cuckoos by making them appear more dangerous than they are.

Greater Roadrunner

• ORDER • Cuculiformes • FAMILY • Cuculidae • SPECIES • *Geococcyx californianus*

VITAL STATISTICS

WEIGHT	227–341g (8–12oz).
LENGTH	50–62cm (20–24.4in).
WINGSPAN	43–61cm (17–24in).
SEXUAL MATURITY	2–3 years
LAYS EGGS	May–September
INCUBATION PERIOD	17–20 days
NUMBER OF EGGS	2–8 eggs
NUMBER OF BROODS	1 or 2, depending on conditions
TYPICAL DIET	Reptiles, birds, insects, spiders; occasionally plants
LIFE SPAN	Typically 7–8 years

The Greater Roadrunners lives on the ground and is more likely to be seen sprinting around desert scrubland than flying through the air.

WHERE IN THE WORLD?

The Greater Roadrunner is a native of southwestern USA and Mexico. Its preferred habitat includes areas of dry desert, ideally with scattered bushes for cover and grassy scrub for foraging in.

CREATURE COMPARISONS

Despite differences in habits and habitat, Roadrunners are members of the cuckoo family. However, they do share similar physical characteristics, such as long slender bodies, a lengthy tail and strong legs. Cuckoos prefer the temperate climates of Europe, Asia and North Africa in which to breed.

Greater Roadrunner

TAIL
The tail is long and used like a rudder for steering and to aid balance. It is also raised during mating displays.

LEGS
Strong, long legs and flexible toes enable this bird to run at speeds of up to 27km/h (17mph).

HOW BIG IS IT?

SPECIAL ADAPTATION
To cope with freezing night-time temperatures of their desert habitat, Roadrunners begin the day by sunbathing. They spread out their wings to expose a bare patch of black skin that is adapted to absorb sunlight.

Grey Go-Away Bird

• ORDER • Cuculiformes **• FAMILY •** Musophagidae **• SPECIES •** *Corythaixoides concolor*

VITAL STATISTICS

Length	47–50cm (18.5–20in)
Sexual Maturity	1 year
Incubation Period	26–28 days
Number of Eggs	1–4
Number of Broods	1 a year
Call	A well-known 'g'waay' call
Habits	Diurnal, non-migratory
Typical Diet	Fruit, especially figs, flowers, nectar and insects
Life Span	Up to 9 years in captivity

Grey Go-Away Birds are the sentinels of the bird world, often warning other species that predators are near, with their famous 'go-away' call.

WHERE IN THE WORLD?

Grey Go-Away Birds are a common sight in southern Africa, from savannah grasslands to woodlands, and even urban parks and gardens. Populations nest near sources of water, often in large flocks.

CREATURE COMPARISONS

These unusual birds are one of the few species able to move their toes around as needed. Usually their three toes face forwards for perching. But they can point two toes forwards and two backwards, the way Woodpeckers do, when climbing.

Toes adapt for perching (top) and climbing (bottom)

HEAD
The conspicuous head crest can be raised even higher during courtship or territorial displays to make birds look more impressive.

BODY
The plumage is predominantly grey with a paler head and darker tail and wing tips.

WINGS
Grey Go-Away Birds are inelegant in flight but can clamber through the trees with incredible agility and speed.

HOW BIG IS IT?

SPECIAL ADAPTATION

Birds' bills are adapted to suit their individual habits and habitats. For example, waders have long bills for rooting in the mud while water fowl, such as Mergansers, have bills with serrated edges for holding fish. The Grey Go-Away Birds' bill is short and blunt, adapted for feeding on fruits and flowers.

141

Goshawk

• ORDER • Falconiformes **• FAMILY •** Accipitridae **• SPECIES •** *Accipiter gentilis*

VITAL STATISTICS

WEIGHT	600–2000g (21–71.6oz)
LENGTH	49–64cm (19.3–25in)
WINGSPAN	95–125cm (37.4–40in)
NUMBER OF EGGS	2–4 eggs
INCUBATION PERIOD	30–38 days
NUMBER OF BROODS	1 a year
TYPICAL DIET	Smaller mammals and birds, such as grouse, pigeons and even ducks; has been known to kill adult rabbits and hares
LIFE SPAN	Usually less than 10 years, but occasionally over 15

CREATURE COMPARISONS

The Goshawk is the largest member of the genus *Accipiter*. It is usually mottled grey, and males often have a bluish tint on the upper side, and are greyer on the underparts. Females are larger than males. The Goshawk will attack birds coming into its territory. It is sometimes confused with the Sparrow Hawk, which is much smaller.

Juvenile Goshawk

This lightning-fast Goshawk flies fast and silently, and stays low. This approach means that it is on top of its prey before it is detected.

WHERE IN THE WORLD?

The Goshawk is widely distributed across Europe, Russia, and North America. Though commonly seen across northern Asia, it has a patchy distribution in southern Asia. It appears on the flag of the Azores.

HEAD
The head carries a white stripe across the cheek on a background of grey head feathers.

BEAK
The strongly hooked beak is well adapted for tearing into flesh.

TAIL
The broad, fan-like tail is well adapted for manoeuvring, and is spread out wide when changing directions in mid-air or during landing.

HOW BIG IS IT?

SPECIAL ADAPTATION

The Goshawk has large, broad wings, which are well adapted for fast flight and fast manoeuvring in wooded areas and also for stealthy flight. This type of wing is also good for fast acceleration.

Sparrow Hawk

• ORDER • Falconiformes • FAMILY • Accipitridae • SPECIES • *Accipiter nisus*

The female Sparrow Hawk is much larger than the male, and therefore often takes much larger prey such as pigeons.

VITAL STATISTICS

WEIGHT	150–320g (5.3–11.3oz)
LENGTH	29–41cm (11.4–16in)
WINGSPAN	60–80cm (23.6–31.5in)
NUMBER OF EGGS	3–5
INCUBATION PERIOD	33–35 days
NUMBER OF BROODS	1 a year
TYPICAL DIET	Sparrows, finches and other small birds
LIFE SPAN	Up to 16 years

WHERE IN THE WORLD?

The Sparrow Hawk is widely distributed across much of Europe and Asia. Birds from northern populations migrate south for the winter as far as North Africa and southern Asia.

CREATURE COMPARISONS

Males of this small raptor have a dark grey or brown top of the head, neck, back and upper side of the wings. The underside is pale or off-white with distinctive reddish bars. The female is sometimes almost twice as large as the male, and has a grey underside with distinctive bars of dark grey. The feet are yellow with large, black talons.

Male Sparrow Hawk

BILL
The black bill is short and powerful with a markedly hooked tip for tearing into flesh.

WINGS
Short broad wings are adapted for a fast, powerful and agile flight.

TAIL
The long slender tail is important in manoeuvring when chasing small birds.

HOW BIG IS IT?

SPECIAL ADAPTATION

The Sparrow Hawk is a predator of smaller birds. In gardens, it will often hide in nearby trees and wait for small birds to come in to feed on bird tables, after which it strikes with great speed.

Black Vulture (Eurasian)

• **ORDER** • Falconiformes • **FAMILY** • Accipitridae • **SPECIES** •*Aegypius monachus*

VITAL STATISTICS

WEIGHT	9kg (19.8lb)
LENGTH	1–1.1m (3.3–3.6ft)
HEIGHT	1.5m (4.9ft)
WINGSPAN	2.8m (9.1ft)
SEXUAL MATURITY	4 years
INCUBATION PERIOD	50–62 days
FLEDGLING PERIOD	95–120 days
NUMBER OF EGGS	1 egg
NUMBER OF BROODS	1 a year
TYPICAL DIET	Carrion
HABITS	Diurnal, non-migratory
LIFE SPAN	Up to 39 years in captivity

CREATURE COMPARISONS

Despite their name, adult Eurasian Black Vultures are not really black. Seen up close, their plumage is more of a sooty brown colour. Juvenile plumage is much closer to the advertised black though, being much darker, and without the pale bands under the wing.

Juvenile

Soaring high over its mountain homelands, the Black Vulture is an impressive spectacle, with a wingspan larger than the height of an average adult.

WHERE IN THE WORLD?

These rare birds breed in the high mountains and lowland forests of Asia and southern Europe. Populations are resident all year round, although in cold weather, birds may winter in North Africa.

WINGS
To save energy, Black Vultures glide rather than actively fly, using occasional slow beats of their wings to stay in the air.

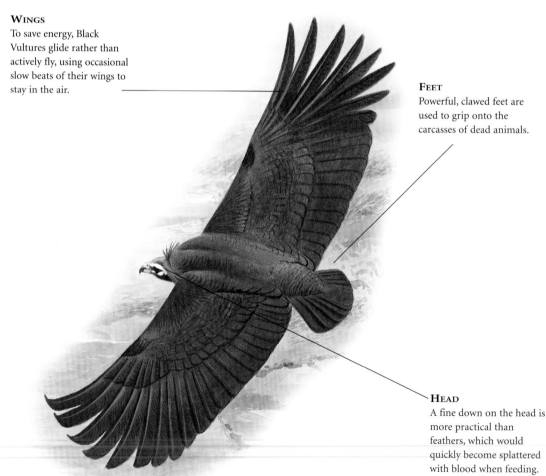

FEET
Powerful, clawed feet are used to grip onto the carcasses of dead animals.

HEAD
A fine down on the head is more practical than feathers, which would quickly become splattered with blood when feeding.

HOW BIG IS IT?

SPECIAL ADAPTATION

Black Vultures are one of the world's heaviest flying birds. To lift such a huge bulk in the air, long rectangular wings are vital. This shape provides the maximum possible surface area, which, in turn, provides the necessary lift to get the bird airborne.

Golden Eagle

• **ORDER** • Falconiformes • **FAMILY** • Accipitridae • **SPECIES** • *Aquila chrysaetositalic*

VITAL STATISTICS

WEIGHT	Males: 3.7kg (8lb). Females: 5.3kg (11.7lb)
LENGTH	80–93cm (31.5–36.6in)
WINGSPAN	1.9–2.2m (6.2–7.2ft)
SEXUAL MATURITY	3–4 years
LAYS EGGS	January–September, depending on location
INCUBATION PERIOD	43–45 days
NUMBER OF EGGS	2 eggs
NUMBER OF BROODS	1 a year
TYPICAL DIET	Mammals, reptiles, birds; occasionally carrion
LIFE SPAN	Up to 38 years

There are few birds in the world that can compare with the Golden Eagle in terms of majesty, beauty and sheer physical power.

WHERE IN THE WORLD?

Golden Eagles prefer moorlands, open forests and mountainous regions. Resident populations are found in North America, North Africa, northern Asia, the Middle East and parts of Europe.

CREATURE COMPARISONS

With their large eyes, deep, hooked bill, feathered legs and golden plumage, this massive raptor is unmistakable. Younger birds are equally distinctive, with all the features that mark them out as Golden Eagles. However, juveniles have patches of pure white on their wings and tail.

Juvenile

WINGS
Despite tales of Golden Eagles carrying off sheep, they are unlikely to fly carrying such a weight, even with such huge wings.

WING TIPS
Eagles' wings are tipped with long, finger-like primary feathers. These are splayed to reduce friction and give more control in the air.

EYES
A bony ridge protects the eyes from any accidental damage they may sustain when the bird captures struggling prey.

HOW BIG IS IT?

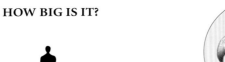

SPECIAL ADAPTATION

It is estimated that the vision of Golden Eagles' eyes is four to eight times better than that of humans. This means they can spot a hare on the ground, at a distance of over 3km (2 miles). Such remarkable eyesight enables them to capture a wide range of prey.

Spotted Eagle (Greater)

• **ORDER** • Falconiformes • **FAMILY** • Accipitridae • **SPECIES** • *Aquila clanga*

These large, dark eagles are becoming increasingly rare in the wild. Sadly, no amount of skill or power can replace their rapidly diminishing habitats.

VITAL STATISTICS

WEIGHT	Males: 2kg (4lb). Females: 2.4kg (5.3lb)
LENGTH	59–69cm (23.2–27.2in).
WINGSPAN	1.5–1.7m (5–5.5ft)
INCUBATION PERIOD	Around 42 days
FLEDGLING PERIOD	Around 42 days
NUMBER OF EGGS	1–3 eggs
NUMBER OF BROODS	1 a year
HABITS	Diurnal, migratory
CALL	A dog-like 'yip'
TYPICAL DIET	Small mammals, insects and carrion

WHERE IN THE WORLD?

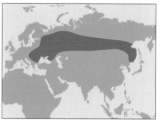

These large raptors breed from northern Europe into southeastern Asia. Populations winter in southeastern Europe, southern Asia and the Middle East.

CREATURE COMPARISONS

All eagle chicks need a lot of parental attention, to ensure that they survive into adulthood. In the case of Greater Spotted Eagles, both parents care for their young with the females keeping the chicks warm at night while the males provide food for them during the day.

Eagle chicks being fed

WINGS
Greater Spotted Eagles usually hunt on the wing, stooping (going into a sudden, deep dive) when prey is spotted.

BILL
In common with all raptors, Greater Spotted Eagles have hook-shaped bills, which they use for tearing the flesh off their prey.

FEET
A pair of large, powerful clawed feet, known as talons, are a typical raptor adaptation for grasping and killing prey.

HOW BIG IS IT?

SPECIAL ADAPTATION

Greater Spotted Eagles have a wide-ranging diet They prefer to catch mammals, but frogs, snakes, carrion and birds' eggs all form part of a rich diet, which prevents the birds from starving when their usual foods are in short supply.

Imperial Eagle (Eastern)

• ORDER • Falconiformes • FAMILY • Accipitridae • SPECIES • *Aquila heliaca*

Imperial Eagles are an impressive but increasingly rare sight in the wild, as numbers of these magnificent birds continue to fall across their range.

VITAL STATISTICS

LENGTH	70–83cm (27.5–32.7in)
WINGSPAN	1.7–2m (5.6–6.6ft)
SEXUAL MATURITY	At least 4 years
LAYS EGGS	March–April
INCUBATION PERIOD	43–44 days
FLEDGLING PERIOD	60–77 days
NUMBER OF EGGS	2 eggs
NUMBER OF BROODS	1 a year
TYPICAL DIET	Mammals and birds
LIFE SPAN	Up to 56 years in captivity

WHERE IN THE WORLD?

Eastern Imperial Eagles breed across central Europe and eastwards to Mongolia. The Spanish Imperial Eagle (*Aquila adalberti*), which breeds in Spain and Portugal, is now considered to be a separate species.

CREATURE COMPARISONS

The massive Imperial Eagle has a noble head, hooked bill, feathered legs and dark brown plumage. Juveniles are equally distinctive, with all the features that mark them out as Imperial Eagles. However, their plumage is yellow-brown, with darker flight feathers and white upper-wing bars.

Juvenile

BILL
A powerful, curved hook, at the end of the bill, is used to rip and tear prey into bite-sized chunks.

WINGS
Wings are tipped with finger-like primary feathers. These are splayed to reduce friction and give more control in flight.

FEET
A pair of large, powerful clawed feet, are a typical raptor adaptation for grasping and killing prey.

HOW BIG IS IT?

SPECIAL ADAPTATION

Eagles lay their eggs several days apart. This means that bigger, first-born chicks will often bully, or even kill their siblings to get the lion's share of the food. Imperial Eagles, therefore, diligently share food out among their brood to increase each chick's chance of survival.

Lesser Spotted Eagle

• ORDER • Falconiformes • FAMILY • Accipitridae • SPECIES • *Aquila pomarina*

VITAL STATISTICS

WEIGHT	1.2–2kg (2.6–4.4lb)
LENGTH	61–66cm (24–26in)
WINGSPAN	134–160cm (53–63in)
NUMBER OF EGGS	1–3 (usually 2)
INCUBATION PERIOD	50–55 days
NUMBER OF BROODS	1 a year
TYPICAL DIET	Rodents, frogs, lizards, snakes
LIFE SPAN	Up to 26 years

The Lesser Spotted Eagle looks very similar to the Greater Spotted Eagle, but can be distinguised by a white V on the rump.

WHERE IN THE WORLD?

The Lesser Spotted Eagle is found in parts of eastern-central Europe, extending southeastwards to Turkey. The birds spend the winter in Africa south of the Sahara Desert.

CREATURE COMPARISONS

The Lesser Spotted Eagle though largely similar to the Greater Spotted Eagle, has lighter plumage and is lighter in colour. The head and body are uniformly pale brown, and the wings are slightly darker brown, with lighter wing coverts. There is usually a white patch on the upper side of the wings. Males and females are similar, although females tend to be slightly larger.

Lesser Spotted Eagles

BILL
The bill is yellow with a black tip, and has a large hook at the end for tearing into the flesh of prey animals.

LEGS
The legs are covered in brown feathers, and the yellow feet have long, black talons for killing prey.

TAIL
The tail is brown above, but paler below, and is spread out as the eagle soars on rising air currents.

HOW BIG IS IT?

SPECIAL ADAPTATION
Unusually for eagles, the Lesser Spotted Eagle will often land and walk around on the ground in search of prey, which is how it often catches frogs, snakes and lizards.

Buzzard

• ORDER • Falconiformes • FAMILY • Accipitridae • SPECIES • *Buteo buteo*

The Buzzard, a large bird of prey, is still a common sight in much of Europe, probably because it can live in a wide variety of environments.

VITAL STATISTICS

WEIGHT	525–1000g (18.5–35.3oz)
LENGTH	50–58cm (19.7–23in)
WINGSPAN	110–135cm (43.3–53.1in)
NUMBER OF EGGS	2–4
INCUBATION PERIOD	28–35 days
NUMBER OF BROODS	1 a year
TYPICAL DIET	Mainly mice and other rodents, but also birds, large insects, earthworms and carrion
LIFE SPAN	Up to 25 years

WHERE IN THE WORLD?

The Buzzard is a common bird of prey throughout most of Europe, extending eastwards across central Asia to the Sea of Okhotsk, and in northern regions of North America. It winters in southern Africa.

CREATURE COMPARISONS

The Buzzard varies a lot in colour. Often, adults are various shades of brown, ranging from dark to pale brown with a lighter coloured underside. Some adults are much paler, and have a greyish-white upper side and white lower side. The feet are yellow, and the eyes range from yellow to light brown. Males and female are similar, but females are larger.

Two adults with different colourings

WINGS
The large, wide wings allow this bird to soar high above the ground on rising air currents for hours on end.

BILL
The bill is short and powerful with a distinct hook at the tip for tearing prey apart.

LEGS
The large feet are equipped with long, powerful toes and sharp, curved claws for killing prey.

HOW BIG IS IT?

SPECIAL ADAPTATION

The Buzzard often sits high on a perch, scanning the surroundings for prey, or soars slowly on outstretched wings high above the ground on rising air currents. In the wild, it can be recognized by this soaring behaviour.

Long-legged Buzzard

• ORDER • Falconiformes • FAMILY • Accipitridae • SPECIES • *Buteo rufinus*

VITAL STATISTICS

LENGTH	50–65cm (19.7–25.6in)
SEXUAL MATURITY	2–3 years
INCUBATION PERIOD	Around 30 days
NUMBER OF EGGS	2–4 eggs
NUMBER OF BROODS	1 a year
CALL	High, mournful 'me-ow' cry
HABITS	Diurnal, migratory
TYPICAL DIET	Small mammals, reptiles and insects
LIFE SPAN	Up to 30 years

Long-legged Buzzards are one of the most attractive and elegant members of the Buzzard family. In flight they resemble a miniature Golden Eagle.

WHERE IN THE WORLD?

These predators prefer dry, open landscapes in which to hunt. Populations are found throughout central Europe, central Asia and North Africa and in the mountainous woodlands of southeastern Europe.

CREATURE COMPARISONS

Birds of prey spend a long time in the air looking for food. Long, broad wings help save energy by allowing them to glide on rising air currents. Long-Legged Buzzards' wings are much larger than those of the Common Buzzard, so they use less energy hunting.

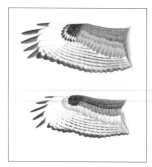

Long-legged Buzzard wings (top), Common Buzzard wing (bottom)

FEET
A pair of large, powerful clawed talons, are a typical raptor adaptation for grasping and killing prey.

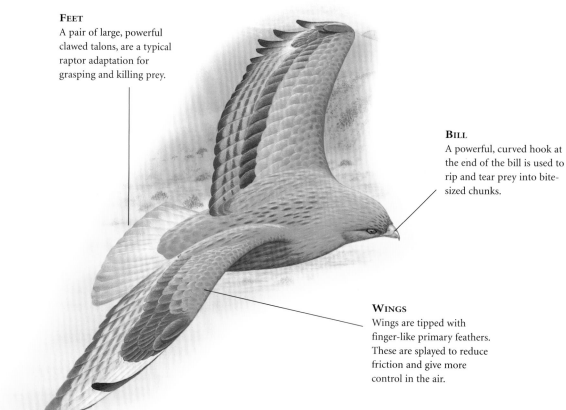

BILL
A powerful, curved hook at the end of the bill is used to rip and tear prey into bite-sized chunks.

WINGS
Wings are tipped with finger-like primary feathers. These are splayed to reduce friction and give more control in the air.

HOW BIG IS IT?

SPECIAL ADAPTATION

Sometimes a bird's survival can depend not on a natural adaptation but on skill and knowledge. Long-Legged Buzzards have learnt that smoke on the horizon means fire. So the bird flies towards the smoke, looking for fleeing animals, which provide an easy meal.

Western Marsh Harrier

• **ORDER** • Falconiformes • **FAMILY** • Accipitridae • **SPECIES** • *Circus aeruginosus*

VITAL STATISTICS

WEIGHT	Males: 540g (19oz) Females: 670g (23.6oz)
LENGTH	43-55 cm (16.9-21.6 in)
SEXUAL MATURITY	3 years
LAYS EGGS	Breeding begins March–May depending on location
IINCUBATION PERIOD	31–38 days
FLEDGLING PERIOD	35–40 days
NUMBER OF EGGS	3–8 eggs
NUMBER OF BROODS	1 a year per mate, but males may mate with several females
TYPICAL DIET	Marsh birds, mammals and amphibians.
LIFE SPAN	Typically 6 years

CREATURE COMPARISONS

Like owls, Western Marsh Harriers have a ruff of facial feathers that cover their large ears. However, unlike owls, Harriers are daylight hunters. They do not use their hearing to aid them on nocturnal hunting trips but to listen for prey in the long reeds and grass.

Western Marsh Harriers

When viewed from a distance, drifting, lazily over reed beds, it is easy to forget that the Western Marsh Harrier, though appealing, is a swift and skilful killer.

WHERE IN THE WORLD?

Western Marsh Harriers are also known as Eurasian Marsh Harriers because they breed across much of Europe and Asia. Winters tend to be spent in the warmer climates of southern Africa and Asia.

BODY
Female Marsh Harriers are dark brown with a creamy crown. Males are reddish-brown with a pale yellow head and breast.

HEAD
Marsh Harriers are known by many colloquial names, including Bald Buzzards and White-headed Harpies in a reference to their white heads.

WINGS
Marsh Harriers glide with their wings held in a 'v' shape, above the back.

HOW BIG IS IT?

SPECIAL ADAPTATION

During the breeding season, Western Marsh Harriers perform spectacular displays, with the male diving at the female as she rolls over and presents her talons. Such acrobatics are put to good use feeding hungry chicks, with males dropping food for the females to catch, in mid-air.

151

Hen Harrier

• **ORDER** • Falconiformes • **FAMILY** • Accipitridae • **SPECIES** • *Circus cyaneus*

VITAL STATISTICS

WEIGHT	Males: 350g (12.3oz). Females: 500g (17.6oz)
LENGTH	45–55cm (17.7–21.6in).
WINGSPAN	97cm–1.2m (38.2 in–3.9ft)
SEXUAL MATURITY	2–3 years
INCUBATION PERIOD	29–37 days
FLEDGLING PERIOD	29–38 days
NUMBER OF EGGS	3–6 eggs
NUMBER OF BROODS	1 a year
TYPICAL DIET	Small rodents, amphibians, birds and carrion
LIFE SPAN	Typically 7 years

In the past, the extraordinarily elegant Hen Harrier was persecuted by landowners for poaching their game. Luckily, they are now protected in much of their range.

WHERE IN THE WORLD?

These Hen Harrier breeds on moors and marshes in Europe, Asia and North America. Northern populations migrate south, to winter in North Africa, southern Asia and Central Latin America.

CREATURE COMPARISONS

Hen Harriers are famous for their ability to fly very low, making sudden, almost vertical, plunges after prey. It is in honour of them that the British Royal Air Force named its Harrier Jump Jet, renowned for its vertical take-offs and landings.

Juvenile

BILL
A stubby hooked bill, is used for tearing and ripping flesh.

WINGS
It is easy to recognize Hen Harriers in the air, as they fly with their long wings in a shallow 'V' shape.

LEGS
In flight, the long legs are fully extended, ready to grasp any unsuspecting prey, without having to land.

HOW BIG IS IT?

SPECIAL ADAPTATION

Hen Harriers are specialists in stealth. Long narrow wings enable them to glide almost silently, as they hug the ground in search of prey. Then, when prey is sighted they drop suddenly, surprising their victim before it has a chance to escape.

Montagu's Harrier

• **ORDER** • Falconiformes • **FAMILY** • Accipitridae • **SPECIES** • *Circus pygargus*

VITAL STATISTICS

WEIGHT	225–450g (7.9–15.9oz)
LENGTH	42–48cm (16.5–18.9in)
WINGSPAN	97–115cm (38.2–45.3in)
NUMBER OF EGGS	4–5 eggs
INCUBATION PERIOD	28–29 days
NUMBER OF BROODS	1 a year
TYPICAL DIET	Rodents, lizards, frogs, small birds, large insects
LIFE SPAN	Up to 16 years

Montagu's harrier is a medium-sized, long-winged bird of prey. Male and female Montagu Harriers have entirely differently coloured plumage.

WHERE IN THE WORLD?

Montagu's Harrier is widely distributed across much of Europe, from Finland in the north to Spain in the south, and across central and southern Asia to Kazakhstan in the east.

CREATURE COMPARISONS

The male has a slate-grey or pale bluish-grey back, head, neck and upper side of wings. The wingtips are black. The breast and belly are pale or off-white with reddish-brown bars. The female is distinctly larger than the male, and has a brown back, head, neck and upper wings, often with darker patterns. Females also have a light brown underside with darker bars.

Male (left), female (right)

WINGS
The wings are long and narrow giving a very graceful flight and powerful wing beats.

EYES
The eyes are strikingly yellow with a black pupil.

FEET
Montagu's Harrier has rather long, yellowish legs, and strong toes with very sharp but relatively short talons.

HOW BIG IS IT?

SPECIAL ADAPTATION
While the female broods the eggs, the male brings food to her in the nest around five to six times a day. When the chicks have hatched, they are usually fed 7–10 times a day.

Black-winged Kite

• ORDER • Falconiformes • FAMILY • Accipitridae • SPECIES • *Elanus caeruleus*

VITAL STATISTICS

LENGTH	30–35cm (12–13.7in)
WINGSPAN	71–85cm (28–33.5in)
INCUBATION PERIOD	25–33 days
FLEDGLING PERIOD	30–35 days
NUMBER OF EGGS	3–5 eggs
NUMBER OF BROODS	Usually 1 but Kites breed all year round, so several are possible
CALL	Occasional 'kree-ak' but mostly silent
HABITS	Diurnal, non-migratory
TYPICAL DIET	Small birds, mammals and insects. Carrion if food is scarce
LIFESPAN	Up to 10 years

CREATURE COMPARISONS

With their striking coral eyes, owl-like face and black and white mask, the hobby-sized Black-winged Kite is hard to miss. Younger birds are equally notable. However, their upper bodies are a darker grey, and their breasts are ruddy.

Juvenile

Black-winged Kites have all the best bird characteristics – they hover like a kestrel, soar like a harrier, hunt like an owl and fly like a tern.

WHERE IN THE WORLD?

These Black-winged Kite makes its home on the open plains and semi-deserts of sub-Saharan Africa and tropical Asia. They are rare in Europe but a small population is established in Spain.

HEAD
With their white head and a patch of dark feathers around the eye, Black-winged Kites look like they are wearing a black mask.

EYES
A protruding bony ridge protects the eyes from damage as the bird dives into foliage after prey.

TAIL
Long, narrow, wings give the Kite a falcon-like silhouette in the air and aid gliding.

HOW BIG IS IT?

SPECIAL ADAPTATION

Many birds have eyes on the side of their head. This gives them a wide field of vision and enables them to spot dangers more easily. Hunters' eyes point forwards. This binocular vision allows them to compare images from both eyes and so judge distances more accurately.

Lammergeier

VITAL STATISTICS

WEIGHT	5–7kg (11–15.4lb)
LENGTH	1–1.2m (3.3–3.9ft)
WINGSPAN	2.3–3m (7.5–9.2ft)
LAYS EGGS	December–February
INCUBATION PERIOD	53–58 days
FLEDGLING PERIOD	106–130 days
NUMBER OF EGGS	1–2 eggs
NUMBER OF BROODS	1 a year
TYPICAL DIET	Carrion and bone marrow
LIFE SPAN	Up to 40 years in captivity

CREATURE COMPARISONS

Vultures usually have bare skin around the head and face, to prevent their feathers becoming matted in blood as they feed. Lammergeier means lamb-vulture in German and, although they do not kill lambs, they are indeed vultures despite lacking that common vulture trait: the bare head.

Lemmergeier

These scavengers may be noble to look at but Lammergeiers have an unenviable reputation for killing lambs and even driving people off cliff edges.

WHERE IN THE WORLD?

Lammergeiers are rare in southern Europe, where less than 500 breeding pairs remain. However, they are relatively common across Asia and Africa, where they breed on mountains and craggy rock faces.

MOUSTACHE
Across much of their range, Lammergeiers are also known as Bearded Vultures, due to their prominent black moustache.

BODY
Adult Lammergeiers have a creamy yellow body and head. However, they often rub mud over themselves, resulting in rusty coloured plumage.

WINGS
The Lammergeiers' narrow wings and a wedge-shaped tail makes it easy to distinguish them from other vultures, in the air.

HOW BIG IS IT?

SPECIAL ADAPTATION
Rather than waiting around for animals to die, Lammergeiers have learnt to kill prey by dropping it from a great height. In fact, the Greek playwright Aeschylus (525–455 BCE) died when a Tortoise was dropped on his head by an eagle, probably a Lammergeier!

155

Griffon Vulture

• ORDER • Falconiformes • FAMILY • Accipitridae • SPECIES • *Gyps fulvus*

VITAL STATISTICS

WEIGHT	6–13kg (13.2–28.6lb)
LENGTH	95–110cm (37.4–43.3in)
WINGSPAN	230–265cm (7.5–8.7ft)
INCUBATION PERIOD	151–53 days
NUMBER OF BROODS	1 a year
TYPICAL DIET	Carrion of large animals, such as goats and sheep
LIFE SPAN	Up to 55 years

In former times, the huge, majestic Griffon Vulture could be seen in mountainous areas in Europe, but today it has become rare.

WHERE IN THE WORLD?

The Griffon Vulture is found in isolated pockets throughout parts of southern Europe, southern Asia, and northern Africa, but has been exterminated from most of its previous range.

CREATURE COMPARISONS

This is a huge vulture with a uniformly dark brown plumage on the body. The wings are also dark brown, but the posterior part is almost black. The head and neck are covered in short white feathers, and the face is often grey. There is a large collar of fluffy, off-white feathers around the base of the neck. Males and females are similar, although females are larger.

Griffon Vultures in flight

BILL
The bill is huge and powerful with a hooked tip to tear open the hide of dead animals to get at the flesh.

WINGS
The enormous wide wings, are used to soar on rising air currents for long periods at a time.

FEET
The legs are short and the feet are large. The bird often prefers to hop along the ground instead of walking.

HOW BIG IS IT?

SPECIAL ADAPTATION

The Griffon Vulture soars high above the ground, looking for carcasses to feed on. It has an incredibly sharp sight, and can spot a carcass from miles away.

White-tailed Eagle

• ORDER • Falconiformes **• FAMILY •** Accipitridae **• SPECIES •** *Haliaeetus albicilla*

The awe-inspiring White-tailed Eagle is also known as the Sea Eagle due to its skill in plucking fish – still live and wriggling – from the water.

VITAL STATISTICS

WEIGHT	Males: 4.3kg (9.5lb). Females: 5.5kg (12lb)
LENGTH	76–92cm (30–36.2in)
WINGSPAN	1.9–2.4m (6.2–8ft)
SEXUAL MATURITY	4–5 years
INCUBATION PERIOD	38 days
FLEDGLING PERIOD	70–75 days
NUMBER OF EGGS	2 eggs
NUMBER OF BROODS	1 a year
TYPICAL DIET	Fish, birds, small mammals, birds' eggs and carrion
LIFE SPAN	Up to 28 years

CREATURE COMPARISONS

Eagles typically build large nests, called eyries, on cliffs or in tall trees. These are usually huge constructions made from layers and layers of sticks. Once a nest has been established, generations of the same family may return there to breed, year after year.

White-tailed Eagle with chicks

WHERE IN THE WORLD?

These raptors breed in northern Europe and northern Asia. Populations are resident, although Scandinavian and Siberian birds may migrate for the winter. Preferred habitats are lakes and coastlines.

BODY
As is common with birds of prey, female White-Tails are larger and heavier than the males of the species.

WINGS
Long broad wings allow White-tailed Eagles to fly with the minimum of effort using shallow wingbeats and gliding on rising air currents.

FEET
A pair of powerful claws help the birds to keep a firm grip on any slippery or struggling prey.

HOW BIG IS IT?

SPECIAL ADAPTATION
To hunt effectively, predators need to be swift and silent. White-tailed Eagles are generally silent outside of the breeding season. However, once they have established a nest, couples (and males in particular) declare their ownership of a territory with raucous calls.

Bald Eagle

• **ORDER** • Falconiformes • **FAMILY** • Accipitridae • **SPECIES** • *Haliaeetus leucocephalus*

VITAL STATISTICS

WEIGHT	Males: 4kg (9lb). Females: 6kg (13lb)
LENGTH	71–96cm (28–38in)
WINGSPAN	1.7–2.4m (5.6–8ft)
SSEXUAL MATURITY	4–5 years
INCUBATION PERIOD	35 days
FLEDGLING PERIOD	70–920 days
NUMBER OF EGGS	1–3 eggs
NUMBER OF BROODS	1 a year
TYPICAL DIET	Fish, birds, small mammals, birds' eggs and carrion
LIFE SPAN	Up to 50 years in captivity

CREATURE COMPARISONS

Most eagles pair for life, so it is important to find a compatible mate. Courtship displays are part of this process and often involve elaborate aerial acrobatics. Bald Eagles' acrobatics are particularly impressive, culminating with the pair locking claws and spiralling towards the ground in free-fall.

A pair of Bald Eagles

It seems fitting that the Bald Eagle, the national symbol of the USA, should be one of the great superpowers of the bird world.

Bald Eagles are North America's only native species of Sea Eagle. The birds' preferred habitats are those close to open bodies of water and mature woodlands, where they can roost and nest.

HEAD
Bald Eagles are not, in fact, bald. Their name comes from the term piebald, which is applied to any black and white animal.

BODY
Male and female Bald Eagles have similar plumage and coloration. However, females are about one-quarter heavier than males.

TAIL
Bald Eagles are related to White-tailed Eagles. However, their bodies are darker brown, and the head and tail are white.

HOW BIG IS IT?

SPECIAL ADAPTATION
All Sea Eagles come equipped with a pair of powerful claws to grip struggling prey. Bald Eagles have an additional tool in their arsenal in the form of a highly developed hind toe. This is used to slice open prey, and reach the soft flesh inside.

African Fish–Eagle

• ORDER • Falconiformes **• FAMILY •** Accipitridae **• SPECIES •** *Haliaeetus vocifer*

VITAL STATISTICS

LENGTH	63–80cm (24.8–31.5in)
WINGSPAN	Males: 2m (6.6ft). Females: 2.4m (7.9ft)
SEXUAL MATURITY	5 years
INCUBATION PERIOD	42–45 days
FLEDGLING PERIOD	67–75 days
NUMBER OF EGGS	1–3 eggs
NUMBER OF BROODS	1 a year
TYPICAL DIET	Fish, especially catfish and lungfish; occasionally small birds
LIFE SPAN	Typically 12–15 years

CREATURE COMPARISONS

Large birds, especially birds of prey, have relatively long fledgling periods compared to other species of birds. It takes up to five years for juvenile Fish-Eagles (shown) to lose their brown and white mottled coloration and acquire the handsome plumage of adult birds.

Juvenile

The haunting, far-reaching call of the African Fish-Eagle is so well known that it is often referred to as the voice of Africa.

WHERE IN THE WORLD?

These large and impressive birds of prey are found throughout sub-Saharan Africa. Their preferred habitats are large rivers, lakes or dams, with nearby trees for them to build their nests in.

WINGS
Fish-Eagles do not fly while carrying especially heavy prey. Instead, they skim along the surface with it, until they reach the shore.

LEGS
The legs of the African Fish-Eagle are only partially feathered. This stops them from getting water-clogged, which would affect the bird's ability to fly.

FEET
The underside of a Fish-Eagle's foot is covered with tiny spines, which give the birds extra grip on wriggling, wet prey.

HOW BIG IS IT?

SPECIAL ADAPTATION

African Fish-Eagles have razor-sharp talons and formidable bills, which make these birds such efficient predators that many spend more time perching than hunting. Not that they can always be bothered to hunt. Sometimes they just steal from other birds.

Harpy Eagle (American)

• **ORDER** • Falconiformes • **FAMILY** • Accipitridae • **SPECIES** • *Harpia harpyja*

VITAL STATISTICS

WEIGHT	Males: 4–5kg (9–11lb) Females: 6.5–8kg (14.3–18lb)
LENGTH	Males: 89–120cm (35 in–47.3in). Females: 1–1.1m (3.3–3.6ft)
SEXUAL MATURITY	4–5 years
INCUBATION PERIOD	53–58 days
FLEDGLING PERIOD	Around 180 days
NUMBER OF EGGS	1–2 eggs. After the first egg hatches, the other egg is usually abandoned
NUMBER OF BROODS	1 every 2–3 years
CALL	Males make an eerie, wailing alarm call
HABITS	Diurnal, non-migratory
TYPICAL DIET	Tree-dwelling mammals, reptiles, occasionally birds

CREATURE COMPARISONS

It takes a big bird a long time to fully mature. In the case of the Harpy Eagle, it takes around four years for the juvenile (shown) to acquire the dramatic slate black feathers, white underparts and double head crest worn by adults.

Juvenile

The magnificent Harpy Eagle, a Latin American bird, is one of the largest members of the Eagle Family and the most powerful bird of prey in the world.

WHERE IN THE WORLD?

The awesome Harpy Eagle makes its home in the tropical lowland forests of Latin America, from southeastern Mexico into southern Brazil and down into the furthest reaches of northeastern Argentina.

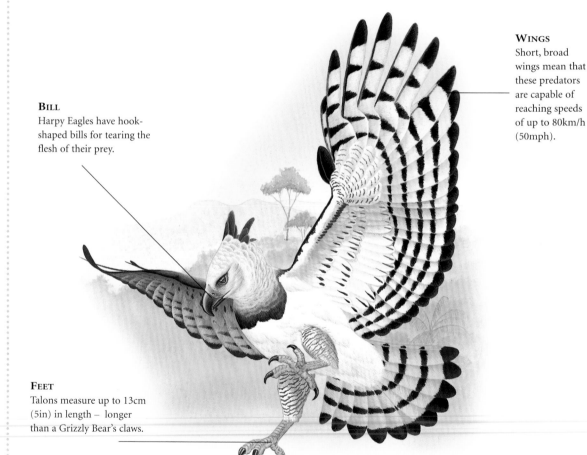

BILL
Harpy Eagles have hook-shaped bills for tearing the flesh of their prey.

FEET
Talons measure up to 13cm (5in) in length – longer than a Grizzly Bear's claws.

WINGS
Short, broad wings mean that these predators are capable of reaching speeds of up to 80km/h (50mph).

HOW BIG IS IT?

SPECIAL ADAPTATION

Harpy Eagles may have relatively short legs, but these are as thick as the wrist of a young child. This extreme design is necessary because the bird's legs act like huge shock absorbers, soaking up the force of impact as it slams into its prey.

Long-crested Eagle

• **ORDER** • Falconiformes • **FAMILY** • Accipitridae • **SPECIES** • *Lophaetus occipitalis*

This elegant Long-crested Eagle is the only member of its genus, and has a tall crown of feathers on top of its head.

VITAL STATISTICS

WEIGHT	g (oz)
LENGTH	53–58cm (21–23in)
WINGSPAN	1.2–1.5m (4–5ft)
NUMBER OF EGGS	1–2
INCUBATION PERIOD	40–43 days
NUMBER OF BROODS	1 a year
TYPICAL DIET	Rodents, especially rats, shrews, birds, reptiles and large insects
LIFE SPAN	15–20 years

CREATURE COMPARISONS

The body and upper side of the wings are uniformly brownish-black. The underside of the wings have strikingly white wing tips, and a pattern of pale patches forming long stripes along the inner parts of the wings. Males have strikingly yellow feet. Females are similar to males, but are usually larger and have brownish legs and feet. Both sexes have a large tuft of feathers on the head.

Male

WHERE IN THE WORLD?

The Long-crested Eagle is widely distributed in Africa south of the Sahara, though it is absent from the Horn of Africa and much of South Africa, where it is found only in coastal areas.

HEAD
The Long-crested Eagle has a crown of long feathers, which are raised when the bird is perching but are kept flat during flight.

WINGS
The long, slender wings are well adapted for soaring on currents of hot, rising air.

TAIL
The wide tail has three distinctive pale bars, which can be used to identify the bird during flight.

HOW BIG IS IT?

SPECIAL ADAPTATION
The short, powerful bill is strongly curved with a hook at the tip of the upper bill. This is a typical adaptation in birds of prey for tearing into flesh.

Black Kite

• **ORDER** • Falconiformes • **FAMILY** • Accipitridae • **SPECIES** • *Milvus migrans*

VITAL STATISTICS

WEIGHT	600–900g (21.2–31.7oz)
LENGTH	55–60cm (21.7–23.6in)
WINGSPAN	130–150cm (51.2–59.1in)
NUMBER OF EGGS	2–3 eggs
INCUBATION PERIOD	30–35 days
NUMBER OF BROODS	1 a year
TYPICAL DIET	All kinds of small vertebrates, carrion and dead fishes
LIFE SPAN	Up to 25 years

The large Black Kite is less shy than other large birds of prey, and is often seen soaring above the buildings in cities.

WHERE IN THE WORLD?

The Black Kite is widespread across much of Europe and Asia, and is also common in large parts of Africa south of the Sahara. It is also found in Australia and on the island of New Guinea.

CREATURE COMPARISONS

The plumage is mottled brownish with lighter upper parts of the wings and a more reddish-brown under side. The head is often more grey in colour. Males and females are similar, although females may be slightly larger. It can be distinguished in flight from its close relative, the Kite, by being of a darker overall colour, and by having a much less forked tail.

Black Kite

TAIL
A long tail with a shallow fork at the tip is a trait often used to identify the bird in flight.

BODY
Young adults have a spotted back, whereas older birds have a more uniformly brown back.

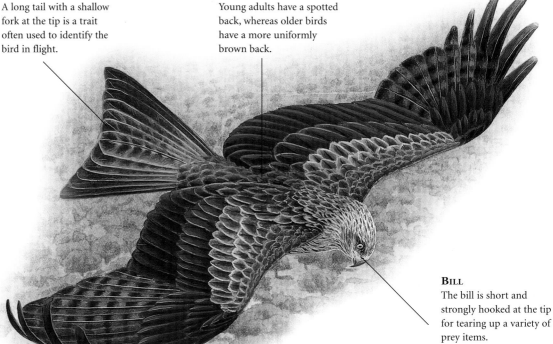

BILL
The bill is short and strongly hooked at the tip for tearing up a variety of prey items.

HOW BIG IS IT?

SPECIAL ADAPTATION
The Black Kite has a large geographical distribution. This is probably because it is able to feed on a wide variety of prey, even carrion.

Red Kite

• **ORDER** • Falconiformes • **FAMILY** • Accipitridae • **SPECIES** • *Milvus milvus*

VITAL STATISTICS

WEIGHT	Males: 1kg (2.2lb) Females: 1.2kg (2.6lb)
WINGSPAN	1.4–1.6m (4.6–5.2ft)
SEXUAL MATURITY	2–7 years
INCUBATION PERIOD	31–32 days
FLEDGLING PERIOD	50–60 days
NUMBER OF EGGS	2 eggs
NUMBER OF BROODS	1 a year
TYPICAL DIET	Carrion, some insects and small mammals
LIFE SPAN	Up to 26 years

In Shakespeare's time, Red Kites were so common they were considered pests. Nowadays, these rare raptors are welcome visitors wherever they are found.

WHERE IN THE WORLD?

These once common birds of prey are increasingly rare in their European homelands. Recent attempts to reintroduce the species to Britain and Ireland have, however, met with modest success.

CREATURE COMPARISONS

As is traditional for birds of prey, female Red Kites look like their male counterparts, but are generally bigger and heavier. Juvenile birds (shown below) resemble their parents, with red underparts, although these areas appear paler when seen from the air, as they are streaked with yellow.

Juvenile

WINGS
Kites are late risers and wait for the sun to warm up the air, so they can ride the rising currents.

BODY
The chest and belly are a deep red, giving this bird of prey its common name.

TAIL
In flight, the Red Kite's long forked tail can be seen to constantly twist and flex as the bird changes direction.

HOW BIG IS IT?

SPECIAL ADAPTATION

The reason Kites are such expert fliers is all down to aerodynamics. In aircraft, the left and right wings meet at an angle called the dihedral. This gives stability and prevents aircraft from rolling from side to side, in the air. The same principles work for Kites.

Egyptian Vulture

• **ORDER** • Falconiformes • **FAMILY** • Accipitridae • **SPECIES** • *Neophron percnopterus*

VITAL STATISTICS

WEIGHT	2.1kg (4.6lb)
LENGTH	60–70cm (23.6–27.5in)
WINGSPAN	1.5–1.8m (5–6ft)
SEXUAL MATURITY	4–5 years
INCUBATION PERIOD	Around 42 days
NUMBER OF EGGS	21–3 eggs
NUMBER OF BROODS	1 a year
TYPICAL DIET	Carrion and eggs
LIFE SPAN	Up to 37 years in captivity

Although, in modern times, Egyptian Vultures are sometimes mockingly referred to as Pharaoh's chickens', in the ancient world, they were considered divine.

WHERE IN THE WORLD?

Egyptian Vultures can be found in southern Europe, Africa, Asia and the Middle East. This adaptable species is increasingly abandoning natural habitats for urban areas, where they scavenge on rubbish dumps.

CREATURE COMPARISONS

With their fluffy pale plumage and yellow faces, adult Egyptian Vultures could hardly look more different from their offspring. Juveniles are dark brown, with contrasting ochre wing tips and belly. Their adult coloration gradually develops over a period of around five years as birds reach sexual maturity.

Juvenile

WINGS
With a comparatively light body and small wingspan, Egyptian Vultures need more wing beats to stay airborne than larger vultures.

BODY
Like Lammergeiers, Egyptian Vultures occasionally rub mud into their plumage using soil containing iron oxide, which turns their plumage a pinkish hue.

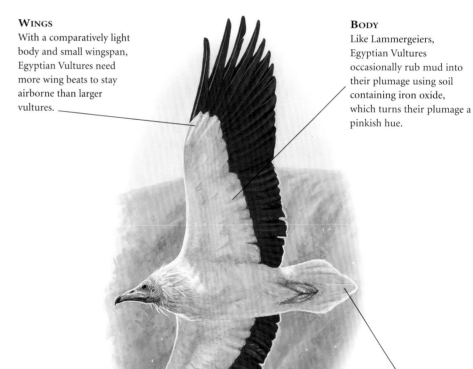

TAIL
With their distinctive, diamond-shaped tails, Egyptian Vultures are easy to distinguish from other members of the Vulture Family in flight.

HOW BIG IS IT?

SPECIAL ADAPTATION

Egyptian Vultures make up in brains what they lack in brawn. Their bills may be small compared to those of other vultures, but they are big enough to hold stones, which they use to smash open eggs. This behaviour is not instinctive – parents teach it to their young.

Honey Buzzard

• ORDER • Falconiformes • FAMILY •Accipitridae • SPECIES • *Pernis apivorus*

VITAL STATISTICS

WEIGHT	450–1000g (15.9–35.3oz)
LENGTH	52–60cm (20.5–23.6in)
WINGSPAN	120–150cm (47.2–59.1in)
NUMBER OF EGGS	1–4 (usually 2–3)
INCUBATION PERIOD	30–35 days
NUMBER OF BROODS	1 a year
TYPICAL DIET	Larvae, pupae and nests of social wasps, also frogs, lizards, rodents and birds

This medium-sized raptor is sometimes known as a Pern, and thrives on a very unusual type of diet.

WHERE IN THE WORLD?

The Honey Buzzard is found across most of Europe and into western and central Russia and western Asia. It is a migratory bird, and spends the winter in Africa south of the Sahara.

CREATURE COMPARISONS

The male has a grey head and a brownish body. The upper part of the wings are also brown with many darker markings. The underside of the body and wings are pale with distinctive dark bars, and a large dark patch anteriorly, and the tips of the wing feathers are dark brown. Females are larger than males with more brownish heads.

Male

TAIL
The wide, fan-like tail has two distinctive dark bands underneath, by which this bird can be identified during flight.

HEAD
The beady yellow eyes are small, but like most raptors, the Honey Buzzard has very keen eyesight.

WINGS
The underside of the wing is much more vividly patterned than the drab upper side.

HOW BIG IS IT?

SPECIAL ADAPTATION

Unlike its close relatives among the Kites, Honey Buzzard primarily eats the larvae and nests of social wasps, hornets and bees. It is believed that its feathers may contain a chemical deterrent protecting it from the bites of enraged insects.

Snail Kite

• **ORDER** • Falconiformes • **FAMILY** • Accipitridae • **SPECIES** • *Rostrhamus sociabilis*

VITAL STATISTICS

WEIGHT	453.5g (16oz)
LENGTH	40–45cm (15.7–17.7in)
WINGSPAN	1.2m (3.9ft)
SEXUAL MATURITY	1–3 years
LAYS EGGS	February–June, but varies with weather conditions
INCUBATION PERIOD	26–28 days
NUMBER OF EGGS	2–4 eggs
NUMBER OF BROODS	1 a year, possibly more as Snail Kites often have multiple partners
HABITS	Diurnal, non-migratory
TYPICAL DIET	Apple snails

CREATURE COMPARISONS

Snail Kites are sexually dimorphic meaning that males and females look different, both in terms of size and coloration. Males are traditionally slate grey, with bright orange legs. Females are dark brown with streaked underparts and yellowish legs. Young birds of both sexes resemble the females.

Juvenile

Snail Kites are one of the bird world's great specialist feeders, existing almost exclusively on a diet of small, freshwater apple snails.

WHERE IN THE WORLD?

Snail Kites are also known as Everglade Kites because they make their homes in swamps, marshes and everglades. Populations are resident in both South and Central America as well as Cuba.

WINGS
Large, broad wings and a slender, weak body make Snail Kites seem ungainly in the air compared to other Kites.

TAIL
The long-tail with a white rump makes a stark contrast to the dark upper bodies.

EYES
Male and female Snail Kites have red eyes. This helps distinguish them from Latin American Slender-Billed Kites, which they resemble.

HOW BIG IS IT?

SPECIAL ADAPTATION

To catch their preferred food, the apple snail, the Snail Kites swoop from the air and pluck them out of the water. Once on dry land, they use their curved bills to prise the snails out of their shells, holding them with one foot as they work.

Bateleur Eagle

• **ORDER** • Falconiformes • **FAMILY** • Accipitridae • **SPECIES** • *Terathopius ecaudatus*

VITAL STATISTICS

LENGTH	56–61cm (22–24in)
WINGSPAN	1.7m (5.7ft)
SEXUAL MATURITY	7 years
INCUBATION PERIOD	52–60 days
FLEDGLING PERIOD	93–194 days
NUMBER OF EGGS	1 egg
NUMBER OF BROODS	1 a year
HABITS	Diurnal, non-migratory
TYPICAL DIET	Snakes and other reptiles, birds, mammals, insects and carrion
LIFE SPAN	Up to 23 years

Africa's famous snake-eating eagles are named after French tightrope walkers in a reference to their side-to-side motion in the air, as though they are maintaining their balance.

WHERE IN THE WORLD?

The spectacular, boldly patterned Bateleur Eagle is found throughout much of sub-Saharan Africa. Their preferred habitats are open grasslands and savannah, with enough tall trees nearby in which to nest.

CREATURE COMPARISONS

Bird of prey chicks need a lot of care and attention. It takes 110 days until Bateleur Eagle chicks are strong enough to leave the nest, but they will return for food for another 100 days. Even with all this care, only a tiny number survive to adulthood.

Juvenile

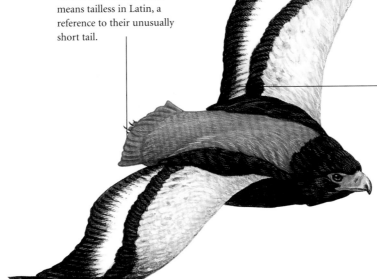

WINGS
The grey, inner layer of secondary feathers on the wings identifies this bird as the female of the species.

TAIL
The *ecaudatus* part of the Bateleurs' scientific name means tailless in Latin, a reference to their unusually short tail.

FEET
Bateleur Eagles feed on snakes. Tough, over-lapping scales on their feet protect them from bites.

HOW BIG IS IT?

SPECIAL ADAPTATION

To provide additional lift in the air, Bateleur Eagles have more secondary feathers (shown in grey) than most other birds of prey. Long, finger-like primary feathers give additional control and allow the bird to glide for hours, covering vast areas of territory effortlessly.

American Black Vulture

• **ORDER** • Falconiformes • **FAMILY** • Cathartidae • **SPECIES** • *Coragyps atratus*

VITAL STATISTICS

LENGTH	56–68cm (22.0–26.8in)
WINGSPAN	135–150cm (53.1–59.1in)
NUMBER OF EGGS	2
INCUBATION PERIOD	35–45 days
NUMBER OF BROODS	1 a year
TYPICAL DIET	Carrion, garbage, eggs and chicks from other birds, large insects, reptiles, amphibians, vegetable matter
LIFE SPAN	Unknown, but likely over 25 years

The American Black Vulture is often seen near cities. The vultures of America form their own group and are not related to vultures in Africa and Asia.

WHERE IN THE WORLD?

The American Black Vulture is found across most of the southern USA, through Central America and across most of South America, except in Patagonia and the Andes mountains.

CREATURE COMPARISONS

The American Black Vulture is uniformly jet black with few patterns other than some lighter streaks along several of the large flight feathers. The head is also black, but lacks feathers entirely, and is covered in wrinkly, greyish-black skin, which cools quickly to control body temperature. The legs are long, and the lower part of the legs is naked and is greyish in colour. Males and females are similar.

American Black Vulture

WINGS
Large, broad wings allow for efficient soaring on hot, rising air currents when searching for prey.

BEAK
Long, slightly curved beak is well adapted for tearing into carrion and garbage.

HEAD
The head is bald so that feathers will not get smeared with blood and grease or dirt during feeding.

HOW BIG IS IT?

SPECIAL ADAPTATION

The American Black Vulture may defecate on its own legs to cool itself off. As the liquid evaporates, it removes heat from the vulture's body. This habit is also found in many storks. Folds of skin on the vulture's head also help to cool the bird down.

California Condor

• **ORDER** • Falconiformes *(debated)* • **FAMILY** • Cathartidae • **SPECIES** • *Gymnogyps californianus*

VITAL STATISTICS

WEIGHT	8–9kg (17.6–20lb)
LENGTH	1.2–1.5m (4–5ft)
WINGSPAN	3m (9.2ft)
SEXUAL MATURITY	6 years
LAYS EGGS	February–April
INCUBATION PERIOD	55–60 days
NUMBER OF EGGS	1 egg
NUMBER OF BROODS	1 every 2 years
TYPICAL DIET	Carrion
LIFE SPAN	Up to 50 years

The majestic California Condor was once revered by ancient peoples. Now, sadly, its main claim to fame is that it is one of the world's rarest birds.

WHERE IN THE WORLD?

These New World vultures once ranged across the Pacific coastline of the USA. Today, small populations are found only around the Grand Canyon, Los Padres National Forest and Arizona.

CREATURE COMPARISONS

Juvenile Californian Condor bodies are as black. However, their heads are orange-brown rather than red, with mottled grey, rather than white, on the underside of their flight feathers. It takes around six years for them to develop the characteristic plumage of their adult counterparts.

Juvenile

WINGS
The wings of Condors are very long and broad across their length, giving the bird maximum lift.

BILL
The sharp, curved hook at the end of the bill is used to rip and tear prey into bite-sized chunks.

BODY
Usually, with birds of prey, the female of the species are bigger than the males. California Condor females are, however, smaller.

HOW BIG IS IT?

SPECIAL ADAPTATION

The wings of the Californian Condor are almost half as long again as Golden Eagles', and twice as broad.

King Vulture

• ORDER • Falconiformes **• FAMILY •** Cathartidae **• SPECIES •** *Sarcoramphus papa*

WEIGHT	3–4.5kg (6.6–10lb)
LENGTH	71–81cm (28–32in)
WINGSPAN	1.8–2m (6–6.6ft)
SEXUAL MATURITY	4 years
LAYS EGGS	Usually during the dry season, when food is plentiful
INCUBATION PERIOD	53–58 days
NUMBER OF EGGS	1 egg
NUMBER OF BROODS	1 every other year
TYPICAL DIET	Carrion
LLIFE SPAN	Up to 30 years in captivity

With its bold ruff and cream and black body, the King Vulture is unlikely to be mistaken for any of its smaller, duller relatives.

WHERE IN THE WORLD?

We know little about King Vultures partly because their preferred habitats are isolated tropical forests and grasslands. However, populations have been found in Central and southern America.

HEAD
King Vultures do not have a voice box. This means that, while they are not completely mute, they make only occasional croaking calls.

WINGS
Large wings are tipped with finger-like primary feathers. These are splayed to reduce friction and give more control in the air.

FEET
Vultures are scavengers, not hunters, so their talons are not strong enough to carry prey.

CREATURE COMPARISONS

Adult King Vultures may look dramatic, but juvenile birds are even more striking. Young King Vultures are entirely grey-black, and look a little like African Vultures, although they are not related to them. It takes around four years for the black plumage, ruff and face markings to develop.

Juvenile

HOW BIG IS IT?

SPECIAL ADAPTATION

It can be a messy business being a scavenger, which is why King Vultures have bare skin on their heads instead of feathers. During feeding, feathers would become clogged with blood which would be almost impossible for the bird to keep clean.

Andean Condor

• ORDER • Falconiformes **• FAMILY •** Cathartidae **SPECIES •** *Vultur gryphus*

It is thanks to its massive wingspan that the spectacular Andean Condor can claim the title of the largest flying land bird in the Western Hemisphere.

VITAL STATISTICS

WEIGHT	Males: 11–15kg (24.2–33.1lb). Females: 8–11kg (17.5–24lb)
LENGTH	1–1.3m (3.3–4.3ft)
WINGSPAN	3–3.2m (9.8–10.5ft)
SEXUAL MATURITY	5–6 years
INCUBATION PERIOD	54–58 days
FLEDGLING PERIOD	944–50 days
NUMBER OF EGGS	1–2 eggs
NUMBER OF BROODS	1 every 2 years. If a chick is lost, an egg will be laid to replace it
TYPICAL DIET	Carrion; occasionally small mammals and eggs
LIFE SPAN	Typically 50 years

WHERE IN THE WORLD?

These natives of the Andes Mountains were once numerous across the range, from Venezuela to Tierra del Fuego. However, they are now rare in areas like Columbia, where suitable habits are declining.

CREATURE COMPARISONS

Condor chicks start life covered with soft, grey feathery down. They do not start to develop adult plumage until they have grown almost as big as their parents. Even then, it takes until they are fully mature to develop the dramatic white ruff and wing panels of adult birds.

Juvenile

HEAD
Birds of the Carthartidae Family forage by smell and are able to detect the scent of decaying dead animals.

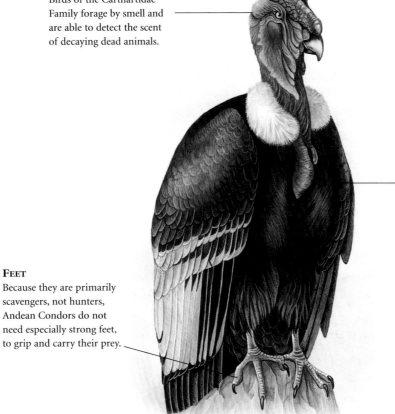

WINGS
A massive wing surface allows the bird to glide on rising air currents with ease, despite its great body weight.

FEET
Because they are primarily scavengers, not hunters, Andean Condors do not need especially strong feet, to grip and carry their prey.

HOW BIG IS IT?

SPECIAL ADAPTATION

With birds of prey, both sexes often look similar because females do not need protective camouflage – they are the ones doing the hunting! However, male Andean Condors do have impressive display head ornaments, which the females lack.

171

Northern Crested Caracara

• ORDER • Falconiformes • FAMILY • Falconidae • SPECIES • *Caracara cheriway*

LENGTH	49–58cm (19–23in)
WINGSPAN	1.2m (4ft)
LAYS EGGS	January–March
INCUBATION PERIOD	28–32 days
FLEDGLING PERIOD	At least 56 days
NUMBER OF EGGS	2–3 eggs
NUMBER OF BROODS	1–2 a year
CALL	Mostly silent
TYPICAL DIET	Small mammals, reptiles, amphibians and some carrion
LIFE SPAN	Unknown

Caracaras may be birds of prey but will also scavenge and steal from other birds, rather than hunt for themselves.

WHERE IN THE WORLD?

Crested Caracaras are divided into two species: northern and southern. Southern populations live south of the Amazon. Northern range as far as the US–Mexico boarder, from California to Texas.

HEAD
A shock of short feathers, from the base of the bill to the neck gives Caracaras their characteristic black crest.

CREATURE COMPARISONS

Caracaras often appear in the mythology of ancient Mexico, where they are referred to as Mexican Eagles. They also look similar to many species of hawk, due to their long legs. However, these beautiful birds of prey are neither eagles nor hawks but belong to the Falcon Family.

TAILS
The long tail has banded patterns with alternate black and white stripes, ending in a wide black band.

FEET
Caracaras have long strong legs. They are the most terrestrial of all falcons, and spend much of their time on the ground.

Northern Crested Caraca in flight.

HOW BIG IS IT?

SPECIAL ADAPTATION

Caracaras are opportunistic feeders that will eat almost anything. They are well known kleptoparasites, meaning they will steal food from other birds, although they are skilled hunters in their own right. They are also often seen feeding on carrion, among wakes (groups) of vultures.

Merlin

• **ORDER** • Falconiformes • **FAMILY** • Falconidae • **SPECIES** • *Falco columbarius*

The compact Merlin is justly famous for its beauty and hunting prowess. For many birdwatchers, just one glimpse of these graceful birds is truly magical.

VITAL STATISTICS

WEIGHT	Males: 180g (6.3oz). Females: 230g (8oz)
LENGTH	26–33cm (10.2–13in)
WINGSPAN	55–69cm (21.6–27.2in)
SEXUAL MATURITY	1–2 years
INCUBATION PERIOD	28–32 days
FLEDGLING PERIOD	25–27 days
NUMBER OF EGGS	3–5 eggs
OF EGGS	
NUMBER OF BROODS	1 a year
TYPICAL DIET	Small birds, especially meadow pippets
LIFE SPAN	Up to 12 years

WHERE IN THE WORLD?

These small birds of prey breed across northern Europe, Asia and North America. In the winter, they migrate south into warmer regions such as North Africa, southern China and parts of Latin America.

CREATURE COMPARISONS

Merlins are Europe's smallest species of Falcon. The females of the species are slightly larger and heavier than the males. They generally have browner upper parts and a pale breast, mottled with black.

Female Merlin

CALLS
Merlins are generally silent when hunting, but adults can occasionally be heard, on the nest, making sharp, rapid 'ki-ki-ki-ki' alarm calls.

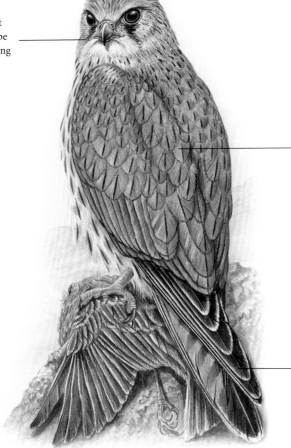

BODY
With their blue-grey upper bodies and rusty orange chest and throat, male Merlins are perhaps one of the most handsome of birds of prey.

WING AND TAIL
From the air, Merlins resemble small peregrines, as they have a similar wing shape and the same long, square tail.

HOW BIG IS IT?

SPECIAL ADAPTATION
Merlin prey includes skylarks which are famous for their courtship displays. This involves flying straight up, singing as they go, until they are out of sight. Despite this, Merlins can still catch them because their wing shape makes them faster in the air.

Eleonora's Falcon

• **ORDER** • Falconiformes • **FAMILY** • Falconidae • **SPECIES** • *Falco eleonorae*

VITAL STATISTICS

LENGTH	36–42cm (14.2–16.5in)
WINGSPAN	87cm–1m (34.2 in–3.3ft)
SEXUAL MATURITY	2–3 years
LAYS EGGS	July–August
INCUBATION PERIOD	28–30 days
FLEDGLING PERIOD	35–44 days
NUMBER OF EGGS	2–3 eggs
NUMBER OF BROODS	1 a year
TYPICAL DIET	Birds and large insects
LIFE SPAN	Unknown

Eleonora's Falcon takes its rather odd name from a Sardinian military commander who passed a law in the fourteenth century to protect birds of prey.

WHERE IN THE WORLD?

Eleonora's Falcon lives on rocky cliffs of the Mediterranean, particularly Greece, where two-thirds of the known population breed. These birds winter in Madagascar, East Africa and a few Indian islands.

CREATURE COMPARISONS

Unusually, for birds of prey, adult Eleonora's Falcons come in two distinct colour variations, or morphs. The dark brown version is perhaps the most dramatic. The paler, grey version has a ruddy breast and white cheeks, which makes it easy to confuse with a juvenile hobby.

Juvenile

TAIL
Long wings, a long tail and a streamlined body, all help to make Eleonora's Falcons skilled aerial hunters.

FEET
Strong, powerful feet are designed for catching birds in mid-air and holding them tightly while they struggle for freedom.

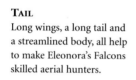

BODY
This sooty brown version of Eleonora's Falcon is a striking looking bird. A lighter morph, or colour variation, is more common.

HOW BIG IS IT?

SPECIAL ADAPTATION

In the air, it is surprisingly easy to confuse swifts and Eleonora's Falcons. In fact, in silhouette, swifts (shown left) look like small Falcons. The reason is that both birds hunt while they are in flight so they need long, swept back wings for speed and manoeuvrability.

Peregrine Falcon

VITAL STATISTICS

WEIGHT	Males: 670g (23.6oz) Females: 1kg (2.4lb)
LENGTH	Males: 38–45cm (15–17.7in). Females: 46–51cm (18–20in)
WINGSPAN	Males: 89cm–1m (35in–3.3ft) Females: 1–1.1m (3.3–3.6ft)
SEXUAL MATURITY	2–3 years
LAYS EGGS	Varies, depending on location
INCUBATION PERIOD	29–33 days
NUMBER OF EGGS	3–4 eggs
NUMBER OF BROODS	1 a year although another clutch may be laid if the first are lost
TYPICAL DIET	Birds; occasional mammals
LIFE SPAN	Typically 5 years.

CREATURE COMPARISONS

Juvenile Peregrines (known as eyas) can be distinguished from their parents thanks to a number of features. First, their legs tend to be blue-grey, rather than yellow. Secondly, their bodies are brown with heavy streaks on their underparts, rather than the bold barring visible on adults.

Juvenile, also known as eya

Reaching speeds of over 290km/h (180mph), a Peregrine in a hunting dive is one of the fastest creatures on Earth.

WHERE IN THE WORLD?

This Peregrine makes its home on moorlands, coasts, and even in cities, wherever a suitably isolated nesting site can be found. Populations are widespread, although rarely seen in great numbers.

EYES
A nictitating membrane (third eyelid) protects the eyes from dirt and damage, as the bird dives towards its prey.

WINGS
Once prey has been spotted, Peregrines begin their famous stoop, folding back their tail and wings to make themselves streamlined.

FEET
Sharp talons strike prey in mid-air, usually killing it instantly, before the bird adjusts direction to catch it as it falls.

HOW BIG IS IT?

SPECIAL ADAPTATION
One blow from a Peregrine in flight is usually enough to kill. However, if the victim survives the bird breaks the prey's neck using a special tooth in its upper mandible. The sharp, curved hook at the end of the bill tears prey into bite-sized chunks.

Eurasian Hobby

• **ORDER** • Falconiformes • **FAMILY** • Falconidae • **SPECIES** • *Falco subbuteo*

VITAL STATISTICS

WEIGHT	130–230g (4.6–8oz)
LENGTH	31–36cm (12.2–14.2in)
WINGSPAN	70–84cm (25.6–33in)
NUMBER OF EGGS	2–3 eggs
NCUBATION PERIOD	28–31 days
NUMBER OF BROODS	1 a year
TYPICAL DIET	Small birds, large flying insects, especially dragonflies
LIFE SPAN	Up to 15 years

The small, elegant Eurasian Hobby is fast and agile enough to be able to catch swallows and swifts in the air.

WHERE IN THE WORLD?

The Eurasian Hobby is widely distributed across most of Europe, except the high north, and across Russia to the Sea of Okhotsk in the east. It winters in Africa.

CREATURE COMPARISONS

The upper side of the head, neck, back and wings are slate-grey or brown. The throat is white, and the breast and belly are white with distinctive dark markings. The feathers along the upper part of the legs and underside of the tail are light brown or buff. Females are similar to males. Young birds appear more brownish, and lack the buff feathers along the legs and tail.

Eurasian Hobby

TAIL
The tail is long and wide, and is important in manoeuvring when the raptor is in high-speed pursuit of prey.

WINGS
The wings are long and streamlined for a very fast and manoeuvrable flight.

FEET
The Eurasian Hobby has large yellow feet and powerful toes armed with sharp, black talons for killing prey.

HOW BIG IS IT?

SPECIAL ADAPTATION
The Eurasian Hobby winters in sub-Saharan Africa, where they often take advantage of the abundance of flying termites, when these large insects come out to breed.

Kestrel (Common)

• **ORDER** • Falconiformes • **FAMILY** • Falconidae • **SPECIES** • *Falco tinnunculus*

Famous for its ability to hover while almost stationary in the air while hunting, the Kestrel deserves its reputation for grace and aerobatic skill.

VITAL STATISTICS

WEIGHT	Males: 155g (5.5oz). Females: 184g (6.5oz)
LENGTH	31–37cm (12.2–14.6in)
WINGSPAN	68–78cm (26.7–30.7in)
SEXUAL MATURITY	1 year
LAYS EGGS	April–May
INCUBATION PERIOD	28–29 days
NUMBER OF EGGS	3–6 eggs
NUMBER OF BROODS	1 a year
TYPICAL DIET	Small insects and mammals, especially beetles and voles
LIFE SPAN	Up to 16 years

CREATURE COMPARISONS

As these illustrations show, the female Kestrel is quite similar in appearance to the juvenile of the species. Both have a reddish-brown, barred back and tail feathers. In comparison, the adult males have a very noticeable blue-grey head and underparts.

Female (left) and juvenile (right)

WHERE IN THE WORLD?

These small birds of prey are common in Europe, Asia and southern and central Africa. Throughout its range, the species is known by a variety of local names, such as the Eurasian Kestrel.

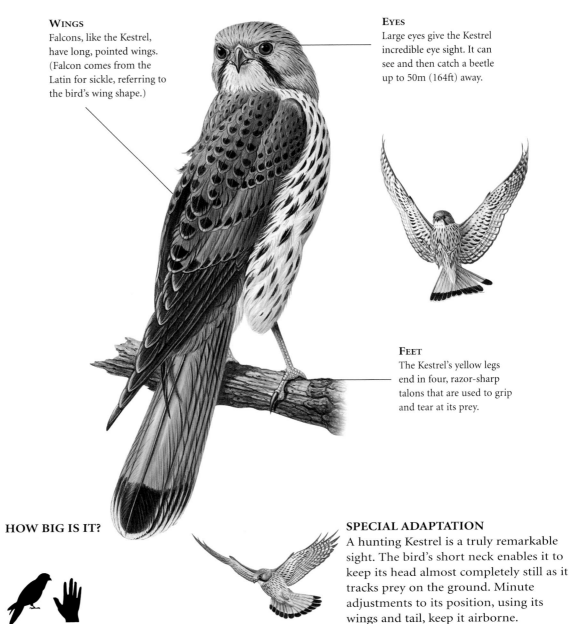

WINGS
Falcons, like the Kestrel, have long, pointed wings. (Falcon comes from the Latin for sickle, referring to the bird's wing shape.)

EYES
Large eyes give the Kestrel incredible eye sight. It can see and then catch a beetle up to 50m (164ft) away.

FEET
The Kestrel's yellow legs end in four, razor-sharp talons that are used to grip and tear at its prey.

HOW BIG IS IT?

SPECIAL ADAPTATION
A hunting Kestrel is a truly remarkable sight. The bird's short neck enables it to keep its head almost completely still as it tracks prey on the ground. Minute adjustments to its position, using its wings and tail, keep it airborne.

177

Laughing Falcon

• ORDER • Falconiformes **• FAMILY •** Falconidae **• SPECIES •** *Herpetotheres cachinnans*

VITAL STATISTICS

WEIGHT	Males: 410–680g (14.5–24oz). Females: 600–800g (21.2–28.2oz)
LENGTH	46–56cm (18.1–22in)
FLEDGLING PERIOD	Around 57 days
NUMBER OF EGGS	1–2 eggs
NUMBER OF BROODS	1 a year
HABITS	Migratory
NUMBER OF EGGS	1–2 eggs
NUMBER OF BROODS	1 a year
TYPICAL DIET	Snakes, some small reptiles and mammals
LIFE SPAN	Up to 14 years in captivity

CREATURE COMPARISONS

The *cachinnans* part of this species' Latin name means laughing out loud, which is a reference to their curious call used for communicating with their mates. Laughing Falcons are not the only birds with unusual calls, but theirs is one of the most amusing.

Laughing Falcon in flight

Judging by its name the Laughing Falcon may sound harmless but, Snake Hawk, its alternative name better highlights its skill and prowess as a hunter.

WHERE IN THE WORLD?

Laughing Falcons nest in rock crevices, holes in trees and, occasionally, nests abandoned by other birds of prey. Populations are most common in Latin America, from Mexico to northern Argentina.

HEAD
The bird's black mask may look dramatic but it has a practical purpose, making the eyes less of a target for snakes.

TAIL
There is a size difference between male and female Laughing Falcons, although females have a slightly longer tail and are heavier.

WINGS
When pursuing snakes, agility is more important than speed, so Laughing Falcons have short wings, designed for flying in tight spaces.

HOW BIG IS IT?

Many birds of prey specialize in aerial combat, but Laughing Falcons are patient predators that hide in treetops, waiting to swoop down on passing snakes. However, venomous prey can be dangerous, so the Falcons' feet are protected from bites by a layer of tough, scales.

Osprey

• ORDER • Falconiformes • FAMILY • Pandionidae • SPECIES • *Pandion haliaetus*

The unique and specialized Osprey is also known as the Sea Hawk, Fish Hawk or Fish Eagle, names that celebrate the birds' superb fishing skills.

VITAL STATISTICS

WEIGHT	1.5 kg (3.3lb)
LENGTH	52–60cm (20.5–23.6in)
WINGSPAN	1.5–1.7m (4.9–5.6ft)
SEXUAL MATURITY	3 years
INCUBATION PERIOD	44–59 days
FLEDGLING PERIOD	44–59 days
NUMBER OF EGGS	1–4 eggs
NUMBER OF BROODS	1 a year
TYPICAL DIET	Fish, some small mammals, amphibians and reptiles
LLIFE SPAN	Typically 8 years

CREATURE COMPARISONS

Male and female Ospreys look very similar in size and coloration, although males have slimmer bodies and narrower wings. Juveniles (shown) have lighter upper parts, with white-tipped feathers. They also have more distinct bars on the wings, which makes them easier to identify in flight.

Juvenile

WHERE IN THE WORLD?

There is nothing more impressive than the sight of an Osprey diving to catch a meal. Fortunately, it is one many bird watchers can enjoy since populations are found on every continent, except Antarctica.

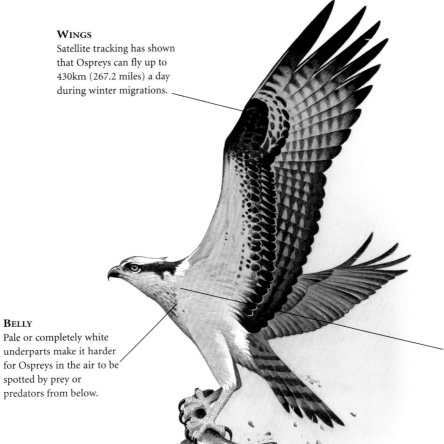

WINGS
Satellite tracking has shown that Ospreys can fly up to 430km (267.2 miles) a day during winter migrations.

BELLY
Pale or completely white underparts make it harder for Ospreys in the air to be spotted by prey or predators from below.

RUFF
A ruff of feathers on the back of the head may be raised in anger to make the Osprey look larger.

HOW BIG IS IT?

SPECIAL ADAPTATION
Osprey are the only birds of prey with a reversible outer toe, allowing them to firmly grasp prey with two toes in front and two behind. Such a strong, flexible grip is important because the birds regularly catch fish that are much heavier than themselves.

Secretary Bird

• **ORDER** • Falconiformes • **FAMILY** • Sagittariidae • **SPECIES** • *Sagittarius serpentarius*

VITAL STATISTICS

WEIGHT	3.3kg (7.3lb)
HEIGHT	1.2m (3.9ft)
WINGSPAN	2m (6.6ft)
SEXUAL MATURITY	2–3 years
INCUBATION PERIOD	42–46 days
FLEDGLING PERIOD	70–100 days
NUMBER OF EGGS	1–3 eggs
NUMBER OF BROODS	1–2 a year
HABITS	Diurnal, non-migratory
TYPICAL DIET	Insects; occasionally birds and reptiles, particularly snakes

With the head of an eagle and the thin, long legs of a crane, the Secretary Bird could almost be some strange, mythical beast.

WHERE IN THE WORLD?

Secretary Birds prefer the open grasslands and savannahs of sub-Saharan Africa, from Senegal to South Africa. They do not migrate but will travel long distances following their favourite foods.

CREATURE COMPARISONS

During the breeding season, Secretary Birds perform elaborate courtship displays, chasing each other with their wings raised in a similar way to which they chase their prey. Their long, quill-like crest may be raised during such displays. Ordinarily, these feathers hang down the neck.

Adult with its long crest raised during a courtship display

HEAD
Secretary Birds get their name from their crest of quill-like feathers, which look as if they have been tucked behind their ear, the way secretaries once did.

BILL
These curious birds have a short, downwards-curved bill, which is backed by an area of bare red and yellow skin.

FEET
Although they can fly, Secretary Birds are largely terrestrial, and one of the few birds of prey to habitually hunt on foot.

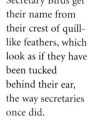

HOW BIG IS IT?

SPECIAL ADAPTATION

The long legs of the Secretary Bird are adapted to a life spent largely on the ground – walking up to 12km (20 miles) a day. This hunter is partial to snakes and uses its clawed toes to grasp them and beat them to death with their bill.

Plain Chachalaca

• ORDER • Galliformes **• FAMILY •** Cracidae **• SPECIES •** *Ortalis vetula*

These over-sized American chickens get their unique name from the loud, rhythmic and raucous calls that form part of the birds' dawn chorus.

VITAL STATISTICS

WEIGHT	300–685g (10.6–24.2oz)
LENGTH	48–58cm (19–23in)
SEXUAL MATURITY	1–2 years
INCUBATION PERIOD	22–27 days
NUMBER OF EGGS	2–4 eggs
NUMBER OF BROODS	1 a year
CALL	Repeated 'cha-cha-lac-a'
HABITS	Diurnal, non-migratory
TYPICAL DIET	Fruit, foliage and twigs
LIFE SPAN	Up to 10 years

WHERE IN THE WORLD?

Plain Chachalacas breed in sub-tropical forests and scrublands along the Eastern coastline of the Gulf of Mexico, from the Rio Grande River in Texas, to the northeastern seaboard of Costa Rica.

CREATURE COMPARISONS

Plain Chachalacas belong to the Cracidae Family, the same bird group as guans and curassows. These large birds are said to resemble ground-dwelling turkeys. However, most Cracids, apart from the smaller Chachalacas, are arboreal, and spend their time roosting, nesting and feeding in trees.

The different races vary in colour

HEAD
A patch of bare skin on the male Chachalaca's throat turns a blush red during the breeding season.

BODY
Chachalacas are surprisingly acrobatic and are often seen hanging, precariously, from branches to reach food or drink from an upturned leaf.

LEGS
A pair of strong, powerful legs are useful for climbing, perching and running through the undergrowth to escape danger.

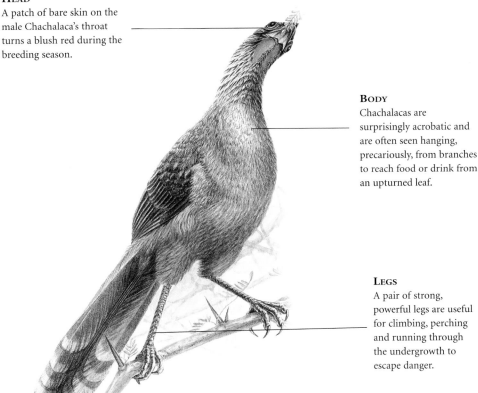

HOW BIG IS IT?

SPECIAL ADAPTATION
To avoid danger, Chachalacas do not take to the air, which may be difficult in thick foliage. Instead, they half-run, half-glide through the undergrowth. Their long tails are thought to help them steer as they bound over vegetation.

Malleefowl

• **ORDER** • Galliformes • **FAMILY** • Megapodiidae • **SPECIES** • *Leipoa ocellata*

The large ground-dwelling Malleefowl leaves its eggs to incubate in the soil. The chicks are able to fly only a few hours after hatching.

VITAL STATISTICS

WEIGHT	1–3kg (35.3–106oz; 2.2–6.6lb)
LENGTH	55–60cm (21.7–23.6in)
WINGSPAN	70–90cm (27.6–35.4in)
NUMBER OF EGGS	2–35 eggs (usually 15–18)
INCUBATION PERIOD	50–90 days (usually 62–64)
NUMBER OF BROODS	1 a year
TYPICAL DIET	Shoots, flowers, seeds, fruit, berries, insects and other invertebrates
LIFE SPAN	Unknown, probably over 10 years

WHERE IN THE WORLD?

The malleefowl is found in dry areas of mallee-shrub in southern and south-western Australia. It has been reduced to three separate wild populations, which are not in contact with each other.

CREATURE COMPARISONS

The Malleefowl has a greyish upper side and flanks, with greyish wing feathers adorned with large eye-like patches in golden-brown hues. The underside is creamy or buff and the legs are greyish. It has a distinctive long, dark stripe running down the breast. The throat is pale yellow. Males and females are similar, although females are smaller and drabber overall.

Male Malleefowl

BILL
The male uses its sensitive bill as a thermometer to check the temperature of the nesting mound.

WINGS
Malleefowl have short, rounded wings. They rarely fly unless an emergency arises. Even then they often prefer to run from danger.

FEET AND LEGS
The legs are powerful and the feet are large and used for scraping and digging in the ground when building a nesting mound.

HOW BIG IS IT?

SPECIAL ADAPTATION

The male scrapes a large depression in sandy soil, and begins building a large mound of leaves, twigs and earth. The female lays her eggs inside an egg chamber, and the heat from the rotting vegetation incubates the eggs.

Wild Turkey

VITAL STATISTICS

WEIGHT	2.5–10kg (5.5–22.0lb)
LENGTH	100–130cm (39.4–51.2in)
WINGSPAN	130–155cm (51.2–61.0in)
NUMBER OF EGGS	8–15 eggs
INCUBATION PERIOD	25–30 days
NUMBER OF BROODS	1 a year
TYPICAL DIET	Shoots, leaves, seeds, acorns, fruits, insects and other invertebrates
LIFE SPAN	Up to 12 years

There are only two species of Wild Turkey in the world, one of which is found in North America, and the other in Mexico.

WHERE IN THE WORLD?

The Wild Turkey was once widely distributed in North America. This is still true in southern Canada, the USA and parts of northern Mexico, but it has been exterminated from many of its former habitats.

CREATURE COMPARISONS

The Wild Turkey is a large, heavy bird The largest recorded wild specimen was reported as weighing 17.2kg (38lb). The plumage of the male is glossy dark brown-black with distinct bronze areas along the back and upper side of the wings. The tail is yellow with brown stripes and bars, and a white rim. The head is naked and strikingly red. Females are much smaller and drabber with a pale head.

Female

HEAD
Male turkeys have a distinctive caruncle, or fleshy growth, on the head, which can become very large and worm-like.

WINGS
The wide, rounded wings have distinct white markings on the upper side, creating a beautiful pattern.

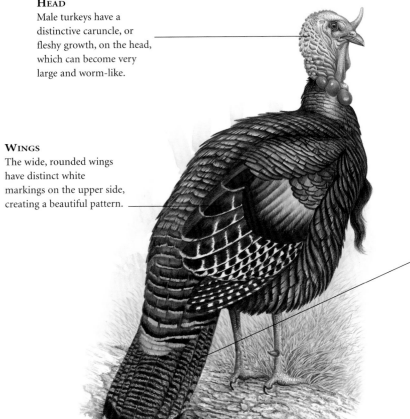

TAIL
The large, wide tail is important for efficient steering when these large, heavy birds take flight.

HOW BIG IS IT?

SPECIAL ADAPTATION

Turkeys are massive birds, and often prefer to flee from enemies by running. They are reportedly able to reach speeds of 50km/h (31mph). However, despite their size, they can fly very well.

Helmeted Guineafowl

• ORDER • Galliformes **• FAMILY •** Numididae **• SPECIES •** *Numida meleagris*

Guineafowl may not look that exotic, but they have royal ancestry. According to Greek mythology, the sisters of Prince Meleagros were magically transformed into Guineafowl.

VITAL STATISTICS

WEIGHT	1.3 kg (3lb)
LENGTH	58–68cm (22.8–27in)
SEXUAL MATURITY	Around 2 years
LAYS EGGS	Just after the rainy season
INCUBATION PERIOD	26–28 days
FLEDGLING PERIOD	Around 70 days
NUMBER OF EGGS	20–30 eggs, but up to 50 are recorded
CALL	A stuttering 'keerrrr' sound
TYPICAL DIET	Seeds, roots, insects, small reptiles and amphibians
LIFE SPAN	Up to 15 years

WHERE IN THE WORLD?

Helmeted Guineafowl are natives of sub-Saharan Africa's dry grasslands. Populations have been introduced to Europe and the United States, where the birds are farmed for their meat and eggs.

CREATURE COMPARISONS

Guineafowl belong to the same Order (Galliformes) as turkeys and pheasants, and all three species have similar characteristics. However, while turkeys and partridges display strong sexual dimorphism (the males and females look different), Guineafowl are monomorphic and monochromatic, meaning males and females sexes look and act alike.

It is hard to distinguish between a male and a female

WINGS
Guineafowl have short, broad wings. They can fly, but do so only occasionally, usually taking to the air when trouble strikes.

LEGS
Long spurs on the back of the legs are used in fights with rival males over territory or mates.

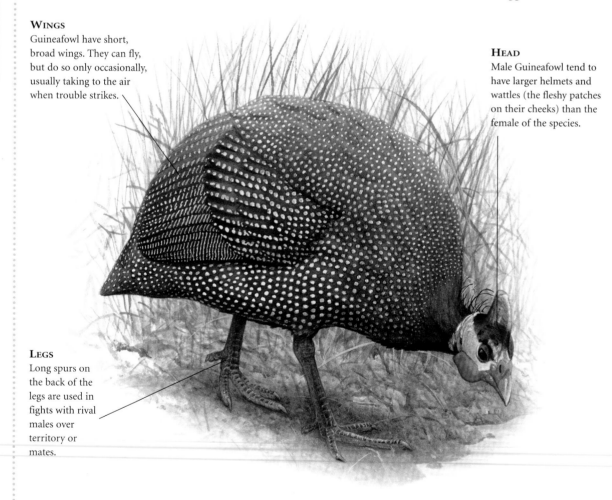

HEAD
Male Guineafowl tend to have larger helmets and wattles (the fleshy patches on their cheeks) than the female of the species.

HOW BIG IS IT?

SPECIAL ADAPTATION
These plump birds nest on the ground because their bodies and habits have adapted to a terrestrial existence. They are strong fliers but are more likely to use their powerful legs to walk. They can cover up to 10km (6 miles) a day in search of food.

Rock Partridge

• **ORDER** • Galliformes • **FAMILY** • Phasianidae • **SPECIES** • *Alectoris graeca*

VITAL STATISTICS

WEIGHT	400–500g (14.1–17.6oz)
LENGTH	32–35cm (12.6–14in)
WINGSPAN	55–65cm (21.7–25.6in)
NUMBER OF EGGS	5–21 eggs (usually 9–14)
INCUBATION PERIOD	24–26 days
NUMBER OF BROODS	1 a year
TYPICAL DIET	Shoots, buds, leaves, berries, fruit, seeds, insects
LIFE SPAN	Up to 10 years

The Rock Partridge is a popular gamebird, able to lay many eggs and breed quickly, thus replenishing lost stock.

WHERE IN THE WORLD?

The Rock Partridge is found in open and often hilly areas in southeastern Europe, across parts of the Middle East and across many parts of southwestern Asia.

CREATURE COMPARISONS

The Rock Partridge is a compact bird with a light brown or greyish-brown back, a grey head, breast and belly, and a white throat edged in black. The eye is surrounded by a distinct red ring. The wings are grey above, but paler below. Along the flank is a conspicuous area of pinkish-white and dark streaks. Males and females are similar.

Males and females are similar

BILL
The bill is short and stout, and is well adapted for all-purpose feeding on plant and animal matter.

WINGS
The wings are short and round. The Rock Partridge is not a particularly good flier.

LEGS
The legs and large feet, which are red, are well adapted for walking and running along the ground.

HOW BIG IS IT?

SPECIAL ADAPTATION
Rock Partridges lay many eggs but often do so in two separate scrape-nests in the ground. The male then broods on one batch of eggs, and the female broods on the other.

185

Galliformes

Golden Pheasant

• **ORDER** • Galliformes • **FAMILY** • Phasianidae • **SPECIES** • *Chrysolophus pictus*

With their patchwork plumage and dazzling displays, Golden Pheasants bring a splash of eastern exoticism with them wherever populations are found.

VITAL STATISTICS

WEIGHT	630g (22.2oz)
LENGTH	Males: 90cm–1m (35.4 in–3.3ft). Females: 60–80cm (23.6–31.5in)
WINGSPAN	70cm (27.5in)
SEXUAL MATURITY	1–2 years
INCUBATION PERIOD	22–23 days
FLEDGLING PERIOD	12–14 days
NUMBER OF EGGS	5–12 eggs
NUMBER OF BROODS	1 a year
TYPICAL DIET	Leaves, seeds and invertebrates
LIFE SPAN	Typically 1 year

CREATURE COMPARISONS

Golden Pheasant hens (the females) lack the dramatic, multi-coloured plumage of their male counterparts. However, while their tails may be less colourful, they are still extremely long – growing up to 35cm (14in) in length, which is over half the length of the females' body.

Female Golden Pheasant

WHERE IN THE WORLD?

The Golden Pheasant is found in the mountain woodlands of central and southern China. They have also been introduced into Europe and the USA, where feral populations now exist.

BODY
Despite their amazing plumage, male Golden Pheasants can be surprisingly difficult to see among the foliage of their natural woodland habitat.

TAIL
The male Golden Pheasant's spectacularly showy tail accounts for up to two-thirds of the bird's entire body length.

WINGS
They may be ground-feeders, but Golden Pheasants can fly, using sudden bursts of speed to propel them into the air.

HOW BIG IS IT?

SPECIAL ADAPTATION
The male Golden Pheasant carries a distinctive black and orange cape that lies over its shoulders. This can be fanned out during breeding displays, to cover the birds' entire face, except for a single, bright yellow eye.

Red-necked Francolin

• ORDER • Galliformes **• FAMILY •** Phasianidae **• SPECIES •** *Francolinus afer*

The secretive Red-necked Francolin is a relative of pheasants. Scientists have divided it into seven sub-species, which differ a lot in size.

VITAL STATISTICS

WEIGHT	300–1000g (10.6–35.3oz)
LENGTH	30–42cm (12–16.5in)
WINGSPAN	45–60cm (17.7–23.6in)
NUMBER OF EGGS	3–9 eggs
INCUBATION PERIOD	220–25 days
NUMBER OF BROODS	1 a year
TYPICAL DIET	Shoots, seeds, fruits, tubers, roots, and insects and other invertebrates
LIFE SPAN	Unknown but probably around 7–8 years

WHERE IN THE WORLD?

The Red-necked Francolin is widely distributed in Africa south of the Equator. In Tanzania and South Africa it is usually confined to the eastern coastal areas.

CREATURE COMPARISONS

The upper side and wings are mottled brownish-grey with short, dark stripes. The underside is brownish, either with or without a blue tint, and also bears darker markings. The tail is brown. The bill, the naked part of the face and the legs are bright red. There is also a bright red patch on the throat. Females are similar to males but drabber, and have much shorter leg-spurs.

The seven sub-species differ in size, head pattern and colouring of underparts

BODY
Like most pheasants, the Red-necked Francolin has a long, heavy body.

WINGS
The short, round wings are used only for emergency purposes, as Red-necked Francolins do not fly often. They prefer to hide or run away when danger approaches.

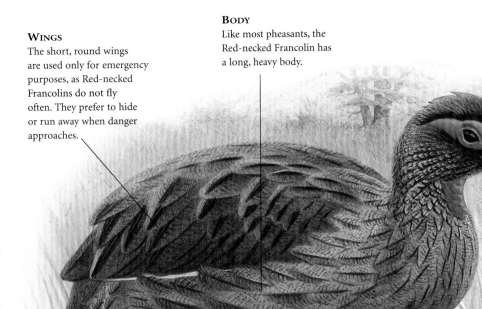

LEGS
Short strong legs are well adapted for scratching in the ground when looking for food.

HOW BIG IS IT?

SPECIAL ADAPTATION

Red-necked Francolins usually hide in tall grass or dense shrub. It lives in pairs or smaller flocks, and both the chicks and the adults rely on their mottled plumage for camouflage.

Chicken (Domestic)

• **ORDER** • Galliformes • **FAMILY** • Phasianidae • **SPECIES** • *Gallus gallus*

VITAL STATISTICS

WEIGHT	Varies with breed
LENGTH	Varies with breed
WINGSPAN	Varies with breed
SEXUAL MATURITY	18–20 weeks
INCUBATION PERIOD	Around 21 days, but varies with breed
FLEDGLING PERIOD	Around 14 days, but varies with breed
NUMBER OF EGGS	1 at a time clutch is complete (clutch sizes vary)
NUMBER OF BROODS	Farmed breeds may lay continually
TYPICAL DIET	Seeds, insects; occasionally small reptiles and mammals
LIFE SPAN	Typically 6 weeks when farmed, but up to 15 years is possible

CREATURE COMPARISONS

Hens lay an egg a day until their clutch is complete. Then, they will stop laying to incubate their eggs. As this is not efficient, many domestic breeds have been selectively bred so that they do not brood and continue laying instead. Incubation is achieved by artificial methods.

A female incubating her eggs

The chicken has been part of human history since our ancestors first learnt to farm, arriving in Europe around the seventh century BCE.

WHERE IN THE WORLD?

There are more chickens than any others species of bird. They are descended from India's Red Junglefowl, and hundreds of breeds are now found across much of the world, excluding the Poles.

BODY
Due to their weight, chickens cannot fly over long distances, but they can make short flights to escape danger.

LEGS
Domestic chickens, bred for eating, are heavier than they would be in the wild. This can give them problems walking.

HEAD
Many chicken breeds have a red comb on their heads and a pair of fleshy cheek flaps called wattles.

HOW BIG IS IT?

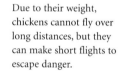

SPECIAL ADAPTATION

In the wild and on some free-range farms chickens live together in large flocks. To avoid conflict within the group, birds establish a pecking order in which more dominant birds are allowed access to the best food and nesting sites than the less dominant flock members.

Red Junglefowl

• ORDER • Galliformes **• FAMILY •** Phasianidae **• SPECIES •** *Gallus gallus*

Seeing this handsome, tropical pheasant in its natural habitat makes it hard to believe that it is the ancestor of our own humble, farmyard chicken.

VITAL STATISTICS

LENGTH	Males: 65–75cm (25.6–29.5in). Females: 42–46cm (16.5–18in)
SEXUAL MATURITY	1 year
INCUBATION PERIOD	18–21 days
FLEDGLING PERIOD	Around 12 days
NUMBER OF EGGS	4–9 eggs
NUMBER OF BROODS	1 a year
CALL	Like domestic chickens, males make a loud 'cock-a-doodle-doo' cry
HABITS	Diurnal, non-migratory
TYPICAL DIET	Seeds, grains, grasses and worms
LIFE SPAN	Up to 10 years

CREATURE COMPARISONS

Junglefowl are strongly sexually dimorphic, meaning males and females look very different from each another. The smaller females have dull brown plumage, a form of cryptic camouflage, which enables them to stay hidden from predators as they incubate their eggs.

Female

WHERE IN THE WORLD?

Red Junglefowl live in the lush forests of southern Asia, from northeastern India to Java. Although they are shy, they can often be spotted in forest clearings scratching for food in the bare earth.

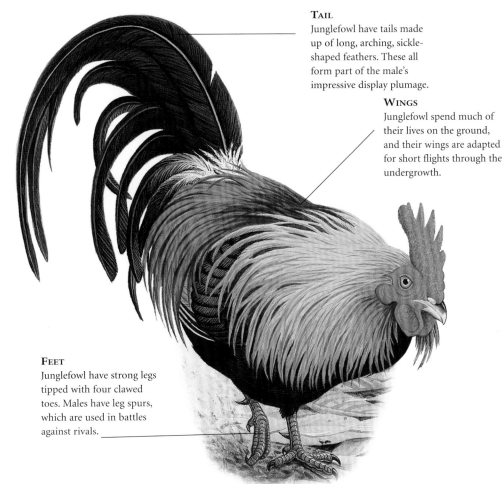

TAIL
Junglefowl have tails made up of long, arching, sickle-shaped feathers. These all form part of the male's impressive display plumage.

WINGS
Junglefowl spend much of their lives on the ground, and their wings are adapted for short flights through the undergrowth.

FEET
Junglefowl have strong legs tipped with four clawed toes. Males have leg spurs, which are used in battles against rivals.

HOW BIG IS IT?

SPECIAL ADAPTATION
With long, ornamental feathers (called hackles) on his neck, a pair of inflatable fleshy, wattles and a scarlet crown, there is no doubt that the regal head of the male Junglefowl is designed to impress both rival males or interested females.

189

Indian Peafowl

• **ORDER** • Galliformes • **FAMILY** • Phasianidae • **SPECIES** • *Pavo cristatus*

VITAL STATISTICS

WEIGHT	Males: 4–6 kg (8.8–13.2lb). Females: 2.5–4 kg (5.5–9lb)
LENGTH	Males: 2.3m (7.5ft) with tail, in breeding season. Females: 86cm (34in)
WINGSPAN	Males: 1.4–1.6m (4.6–5.2ft)
SEXUAL MATURITY1	2–3 years
INCUBATION PERIOD	28–30 days
FLEDGLING PERIOD	21 days
NUMBER OF EGGS	4–8 eggs
NUMBER OF BROODS	Depends on the male, who may mate with up to 6 hens
TYPICAL DIET	Insects, small mammals, fruit, berries and cereal crops
LIFE SPAN	Typically 20 years

CREATURE COMPARISONS

With her brown body and white belly, the female Indian Peafowl, known as a Peahen, is much less showy than the multi-coloured male. Her only ornamentation is a head crest and green neck feathers. Although females weigh almost as much as males, they are rarely longer than 1m (3.3ft).

Female

Many ornamental gardens keep male Indian Peafowl, called Peacocks, for their beauty. Originally, however, they were valued for their ear-shattering cries, which made them the excellent watchmen.

WHERE IN THE WORLD?

As their name suggests, these birds are from India. However, their popularity in Europe and the Americas means that escaped feral populations can now be found in these regions too.

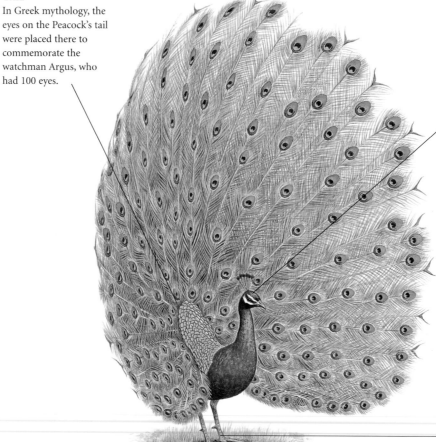

TAIL
In Greek mythology, the eyes on the Peacock's tail were placed there to commemorate the watchman Argus, who had 100 eyes.

HEAD
Indian Peafowl have always been considered to be royal birds, so it is appropriate that the male, known as the peacock, has his own fan-like crown.

FEET
Indian Peafowl belong to the Phasianidae Family of birds, which includes pheasants. Like Pheasants, male Peacocks also have spurs on their legs.

HOW BIG IS IT?

SPECIAL ADAPTATION

The Peacock's most famous feature is its trail formed from elongated upper body feathers which is grown during the breeding season. This adaptation is believed to be the result of sexual selection, as females mate with males that make the most dramatic displays.

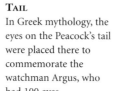

Grey Partridge

• ORDER • Galliformes **• FAMILY •** Phasianidae **• SPECIES •** *Perdix perdix*

The Grey Partridge has declined dramatically throughout much of its European range because humans have cultivated much of its natural habitat.

VITAL STATISTICS

WEIGHT	300–450g (10.6–16oz)
LENGTH	28–32cm (11.0–12.6in)
WINGSPAN	44–55cm (17.3–21.7in)
NUMBER OF EGGS	10–20 eggs (up to 29)
INCUBATION PERIOD	23–25 days
NUMBER OF BROODS	1 a year
TYPICAL DIET	Seeds, shoots, leaves, and also insects, grubs and worms
LIFE SPAN	Up to 10 years

WHERE IN THE WORLD?

The Grey Partridge is found in Europe extending into central Russia, but is absent from most of the Iberian Peninsula and northern Scandinavia. It has been introduced into the northern USA.

CREATURE COMPARISONS

The plumage is greyish with reddish-brown patterns on the upper side, wings and flanks. The breast and throat are more uniformly grey, and the face is pale orange. Males are larger than females and have a horseshoe-shaped brownish or reddish-brown patch on the breast. The plumage is mottled to provide camouflage on the ground.

BILL
A short, slightly curved bill is used for picking up seeds and tearing off leaves.

WINGS
Short round wings give the bird a powerful but rather uneven flight.

LEGS
Short legs and stout feet are well adapted for scratching in the ground after food.

Juvenile

HOW BIG IS IT?

SPECIAL ADAPTATION

This has been a favourite gamebird for centuries, but the rapid decline in many European countries is due to intensive farming, which robs the bird of large, open grasslands where it has adapted to feed on plants and seeds.

Pheasant (Common)

• **ORDER** • Galliformes • **FAMILY** • Phasianidae • **SPECIES** • *Phasianus colchicus*

VITAL STATISTICS

WEIGHT	Males: 1.4 kg (3lb). Females: 975g (43.4lb)
LENGTH	Males: 70–90cm (27.5–35.4in). Females: 55–70cm (21.6–27.5in)
WINGSPAN	80cm (31.5in)
SEXUAL MATURITY	First Spring
LAYS EGGS	April–June
INCUBATION PERIOD	23–28 days
NUMBER OF EGGS	6–15 eggs
NUMBER OF BROODS	Will continue laying until a successful brood has been raised
TYPICAL DIET	Seeds and grains; occasionally small insects
LIFE SPAN	Typically less than 1 year

The whirring flight and explosive speed of the Common Pheasant ensures that, for every bird shot, some will always escape to boost wild populations.

WHERE IN THE WORLD?

Common Pheasants are one of the world's most hunted birds. Originally natives of Asia, these game birds are so popular that they have been introduced throughout Europe and North America.

CREATURE COMPARISONS

Female Pheasants need to stay safely hidden on the nest while they incubate their eggs. So, unlike males, who become even more showy in the breeding season, they are well camouflaged. Their mottled white, grey and brown plumage allows them to blend in well with their surroundings.

Female

NECK
Common Pheasants are also known as Ring-Necked Pheasants because some males have a distinctive white neck collar.

TAIL
In a breeding male, almost 50cm (20in) of its body length is comprised of a spectacular fan-like tail.

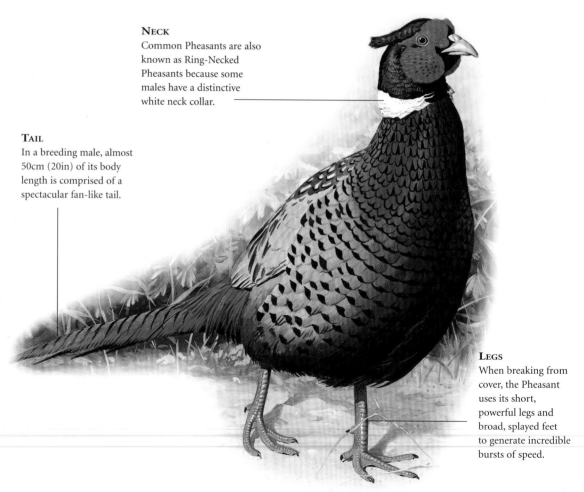

LEGS
When breaking from cover, the Pheasant uses its short, powerful legs and broad, splayed feet to generate incredible bursts of speed.

HOW BIG IS IT?

SPECIAL ADAPTATION
The male Pheasant is perhaps the most handsome of game birds, thanks to a shimmering, dark green head, flanked by a pair of bright scarlet wattles. These cheek pouches are inflated during breeding displays to impress females or warn off rival males.

Himalayan Snowcock

• **ORDER** • Galliformes • **FAMILY** • Phasianidae • **SPECIES** • *Tetraogallus himalayensis*

Snowcocks may look like oversized chickens but these birds have adapted to live in the Himalayas, one of the world's most inhospitable environments.

VITAL STATISTICS

WEIGHT	Up to 3kg (6.6lb)
LENGTH	50–70cm (20–27.5in)
SEXUAL MATURITY	Unknown
INCUBATION PERIOD	27–30 days
NUMBER OF EGGS	5–10 eggs
NUMBER OF BROODS	1 a year
CALL	Repeated 'kuk-kuk'
HABITS	Diurnal, non-migratory
TYPICAL DIET	Roots and grasses
LIFE SPAN	Unknown

WHERE IN THE WORLD?

These hardy birds make their homes in the Himalayas, nesting on the ground in shallow scrapes. Small numbers have also been introduced into the Ruby and Humboldt ranges in Nevada, USA.

CREATURE COMPARISONS

Most male Snowcocks engage in dawn and dusk choruses, cackling loudly at the rising and setting sun. These calls allow birds to announce themselves to rivals or mates.

BILL
The Snowcock's powerful bill curves downwards, making it easy for the bird to dig in the earth for roots and tubers.

BODY
The bird's brownish plumage looks grey from a distance, enabling it to blend in with the bare Himalayan rock faces.

FEET
Snowcocks are diurnal, so feed during the day. Generally, adults fly downhill to feed in the mornings and walk back uphill.

Himalayan Snowcock in flight

HOW BIG IS IT?

SPECIAL ADAPTATION

Snowcocks are swift and agile birds. This is partly due to their broad rounded tails. The tail feathers are specially adapted for helping Snowcocks steer around obstacles in the same way as the rudder on a ship.

Temminck's Tragopan

• ORDER • Galliformes • FAMILY • Phasianidae • SPECIES • *Tragopan temminckii*

VITAL STATISTICS

LENGTH	58–64cm (22.8–25.2in)
SEXUAL MATURITY	Males: 2 years. Females: 1 year
INCUBATION PERIOD	26–28 days
NUMBER OF EGGS	3–5 eggs
NUMBER OF BROODS	1 a year
CALL	Mournful 'waaa' call
HABITS	Diurnal, non-migratory
TYPICAL DIET	Seeds, grasses, fruit and berries; occasionally insects
LIFE SPAN	Unknown

Despite its dazzling, colourful plumage, Temminck's Tragopan is a shy and secretive species that lives hidden away in the dense forest canopy of its Himalayan home.

WHERE IN THE WORLD?

Temminck's Tragopan lives in dense forests in the Eastern Himalayas, from northwestern India to China. Populations are under threat from habitat loss and attempts at captive breeding are being made.

CREATURE COMPARISONS

Temminck's Tragopan is related to the Common Pheasant. In fact, both species originate in the same part of the world. While the Pheasant, like many game birds, nests on the ground, Temminck's Tragopan nests in trees, which allows it to stay safely hidden among the dense foliage.

WINGS
Temminck's Tragopan has short rounded wings. This design is ideal for rapid take-offs and landings among dense forest foliage.

BILL
The bird feeds on a variety of vegetation. Its short strong bill is adapted for tearing and grasping plants.

FEET
Strong, wide feet enable Temminck's Tragopan to perch on tree branches.

Temminck's Tragopan in flight

HOW BIG IS IT?

SPECIAL ADAPTATION

The remarkable courtship display of the male Tragopan is rarely seen. Below the male's throat is a blue patch, called a lappet, which inflates during displays to create a vivid azure beard. A set of horns, which are usually invisible, add to this amazing spectacle.

Hazel Grouse

The intricately patterned Hazel Grouse is about the same size as a Jackdaw, which makes it one of the smallest and most appealing species of Grouse.

VITAL STATISTICS

LENGTH	34–39cm (13.4–15.4in)
LAYS EGGS	May–June, but varies depending on location
SEXUAL MATURITY	Around 10 months
INCUBATION PERIOD	23–25 days
NUMBER OF EGGS	3–6 eggs
NUMBER OF BROODS	1 a year
CALL	Males make a high-pitched 'ti-ti-ti-ti-ti' call
HABITS	Diurnal, non-migratory
TYPICAL DIET	Leaves, seeds; occasionally insects
LIFE SPAN	Typically 1 year

CREATURE COMPARISONS

Gamebirds have always been eaten and much ceremony surrounds the start of the Grouse hunting season which, in the UK, is referred to as the Glorious Twelfth. However, as Grouse nest on the ground, they are also vulnerable to more traditional predators such as foxes.

Hazel Grouse are vulnerable to predators

WHERE IN THE WORLD?

The speckled Hazel Grouse breeds across Europe and Asia, from Scandinavia to Siberia. Their preferred habitats are damp, mixed woodlands, with plenty of dense undergrowth for nesting.

HEAD
Male Hazel Grouse have prominent red eyebrows and a short head crest they can raise and lower during courtship displays.

BODY
Hazel Grouse have short, plump bodies and a small, rounded head.

THROAT
Male birds have a white-bordered black throat. In comparison, females have a brown throat, which is flecked with white.

HOW BIG IS IT?

SPECIAL ADAPTATION
To be successful, a species must survive long enough to breed. Camouflage plays an important role in this, keeping both chicks and mature birds safe. Many birds, including the Hazel Grouse, lay eggs that also have cryptic camouflage in order to blend in with the background.

Willow Grouse

• **ORDER** • Galliformes • **FAMILY** • Tetraonidae • **SPECIES** • *Lagopus lagopus*

VITAL STATISTICS

WEIGHT	430–810g (15.2oz)
LENGTH	35–43cm (14–17in)
WINGSPAN	60–65cm (23.6–25.6in)
LAYS EGGS	April–July, but varies depending on location
SEXUAL MATURITY	First winter
INCUBATION PERIOD	21 days
NUMBER OF EGGS	7–10 eggs
NUMBER OF BROODS	1 a year
TYPICAL DIET	Leaves, berries, seeds and insects
LIFE SPAN	Typically 1 year

CREATURE COMPARISONS

The British sub-species of the Willow Grouse (*Lapogus lapogus scoticus*) is known, appropriately enough, as the Red Grouse. This is because, unlike their more exotic cousins, these rusty coloured birds do not change their colouring in the winter, but remain red all year round.

Spring Plumage

Willow Grouse may look like little more than moorland chickens, but in Lapland they are honoured in legend as symbols of purity and messengers of God.

WHERE IN THE WORLD?

Willow Grouse are found in northern parts of Europe, Asia, Canada and Alaska, where they are known as Willow Ptarmigans. Birds nest in hollows on the ground, often in meadows or open woodlands.

TAIL
During the breeding season, male Willow Grouse fan out their black tail feathers to make themselves look more impressive to potential mates.

BODY
In common with other members of the Grouse Family, these stout-bodied birds have a small head and short, rounded tail.

LEGS
The Willow Grouse's scientific name, *Lagopus lagopus,* comes from the Greek word for 'hare foot', referring to the birds' heavily feathered legs.

HOW BIG IS IT?

SPECIAL ADAPTATION

Willow Grouse camouflage changes through the year. Winter birds are completely white, to blend in with the snow. As spring arrives, birds develop a ruddy head and neck, with brown and white bodies (top). By the middle of summer, their upper parts are almost entirely brown with white underparts.

Red Grouse

• ORDER • Galliformes **• FAMILY •** Tetraonidae **• SPECIES •** *Lagopus lagopus scoticus*

VITAL STATISTICS

WEIGHT	600g (21.2oz)
LENGTH	33–38cm (13–15in)
WINGSPAN	60cm (23.6in)
SEXUAL MATURITY	1 year
LAYS EGGS	April–May
INCUBATION PERIOD	19–25 days
NUMBER OF EGGS	6–11 eggs
NUMBER OF BROODS	1 a year
TYPICAL DIET	Heather, seeds and berries
LIFESPAN	Up to 8 years

Survival is a major problem for the Red Grouse. If bad weather and lack of food does not kill them, then hunters almost certainly will.

WHERE IN THE WORLD?

Whether the Red Grouse is a British sub-species of the Willow Grouse or a species in its own right is debatable. However, these famous game birds are found exclusively in the British Isles.

CREATURE COMPARISONS

During the breeding season, the female Grouse develops yellow markings on her plumage, which make her virtually invisible on the nest. Juveniles have a similar pattern and, when danger threatens, they instinctively freeze, making it even harder for predators to spot them.

Female Red Grouse

HOW BIG IS IT?

WINGS
Grouse are a popular game bird because they are capable of incredible bursts of speed, making them a challenging target for hunters.

FEET
The long feathered feet of the Red Grouse act like snowshoes, helping them walk on top of, rather than sink into, snow.

TAIL
A sooty tail helps to differentiate Red Grouse from another moorland inhabitant, the partridge, which has a characteristic reddish tail.

SPECIAL ADAPTATION

Grouse make their nest on the ground, so good camouflage is vital for the survival of parents and chicks. Outside its natural habitat, the bird's brown and red plumage may seem showy, but among the heather of its moorland home, it is the ideal colour to blend in.

Rock Ptarmigan

• ORDER • Galliformes • FAMILY • Tetraonidae • SPECIES • *Lagopus muta*

VITAL STATISTICS

LENGTH	31–36cm (12.2–14.2in)
WINGSPAN	47–60cm (18.5–23.6in)
NUMBER OF EGGS	6–10 eggs
INCUBATION PERIOD	21–24 days
NUMBER OF BROODS	1 a year
TYPICAL DIET	A variety of tundra and alpine plants, seeds, insects and worms
LIFE SPAN	Up to 20 years

This Rock ptarmigan, an Arctic bird, also breeds in mainland Europe in high mountainous areas above the tree limit.

WHERE IN THE WORLD?

The Rock Ptarmigan is widespread across the Arctic from North America and across Eurasia. Isolated populations are also found in the Pyrenees, the Alps, the Urals and the Altai Mountains.

CREATURE COMPARISONS

In summer, the upper part of the male Rock Ptarmigan's wing is mottled greyish or brownish mottled, as is the back, with a slightly darker neck and breast. The sides of the wings and the belly are white. Females are also mottled, but appear more yellowish-brown, and are smaller than males. In winter, both sexes change into a uniformly, snowy white plumage.

Rock Ptarmigan and predator

BILL
The very short, stout bill is well adapted for plucking buds and catkins from willows and other trees.

WINGS
The wings are short and wide. Males perform a low mating flight to attract females.

FEET
The feet are large and strong for walking and running on the ground, and are covered in short, white feathers.

HOW BIG IS IT?

SPECIAL ADAPTATION

The Ptarmigan is well camouflaged for all seasons. In summer, its mottled plumage allows it to hide in shrubland. In winter the white plumage blends in with the snow.

Black Grouse

• **ORDER** • Galliformes • **FAMILY** • Tetraonidae • **SPECIES** • *Tetrao tetrix*

The impressive large Black Grouse used to be common on moorland across much of northern Europe but its numbers have declined heavily.

VITAL STATISTICS

WEIGHT	750–1400g (26.5–49.4oz)
LENGTH	49–55cm (19.3–21.7in)
WINGSPAN	65–80cm (25.6–31.5in)
NUMBER OF EGGS	6–11 eggs
INCUBATION PERIOD	25–27 days
NUMBER OF BROODS	1 a year
TYPICAL DIET	Green plants, shoots, berries, seeds, insects
LIFE SPAN	Up to 20 years

WHERE IN THE WORLD?

The Black Grouse is found throughout eastern and northern Europe, and across much of central and northern Russia. It is sedentary, and does not migrate south in winter.

CREATURE COMPARISONS

The head, neck, and body of the male is uniformly black or bluish-black with a metallic hue, apart from a bright red crest on top of the head. The wings are dark-brown or brownish-black with a white bar. The tail is large and lyre-shaped with striking, white feathers. Females are distinctly smaller, and are mottled brown or greyish-brown with a normal tail.

Male (front, female (back)

HEAD
The male has a striking red crest on top of its head, which is used to attract females.

TAIL
The wide, lyre-shaped tail is distinctly forked when the male flies, and the white plumes are indistinct.

FEET
The feet are small but powerful, and are well adapted for walking and running on the ground. The legs are also short.

HOW BIG IS IT?

SPECIAL ADAPTATION

In spring, males perform a spectacular display to attract females during the breeding season. They gather each morning in special open areas, called leks, where they dance and call out.

Capercaillie

• **ORDER** • Galliformes • **FAMILY** • Tetraonidae • **SPECIES** • *Tetrao urogallus*

VITAL STATISTICS

WEIGHT	Males: 4.3kg (9.5Ib) Females: 2kg (4.4Ib)
LENGTH	Males: 70–90cm (27.5–35.4in). Females: 54–63cm (21.2–25in)
WINGSPAN	1m (3.3ft)
SEXUAL MATURITY	Males: 2–3 years Females: 1 year
LAYS EGGS	April–May, depending on location
INCUBATION PERIOD	24–26 days
NUMBER OF EGGS	5–11 eggs
NUMBER OF BROODS	1 a year
TYPICAL DIET	Pine needles and seeds in winter; grasses and fruit, especially blueberries, in summer.

CREATURE COMPARISONS

In the bird world, it is the males that dress up to attract a mate. Females generally incubate the eggs, so they need to be as inconspicuous as possible to avoid predators. Female Capercaillie (shown) therefore lack the dark dramatic plumage that make males look so striking.

Female

Nothing looks – or sounds – quite like a Capercaillie. In fact, their common name comes from the Gaelic *capull coille,* meaning horse of the woods.

WHERE IN THE WORLD?

The largest members of the Grouse Family, Capercaillie are found across northern Europe and Asia, especially in mature conifer forests. They were extinct in Scotland but have now been reintroduced.

BODY
It is easy to differentiate male and female Capercaillie, as they are quite different in size and colour.

LEGS
Because they live in the cooler regions of northern Europe, Capercaillie have feathered legs to protect them against the cold.

FEET
The feet are covered in rows of small, elongated horns, which give them good grip.

HOW BIG IS IT?

SPECIAL ADAPTATION

Pine needles, grass and leaves are not easy to digest. Capercaillie have adapted especially long digestive tracts, which allow fibrous plants to be broken down and the nourishment extracted. They also swallow gastroliths, or small stones, which help to grind up tough plants in the gut.

Greater Prairie Chicken

• **ORDER** • Galliformes • **FAMILY** • Tetraonidae • **SPECIES** • *Tympanuchus cupido*

With their elaborate mating dances and dramatic display plumage, the rare and beautiful Prairie Chicken could not be more different from its domestic counterpart.

VITAL STATISTICS

WEIGHT	700–1200g (24.7–42.3oz)
LENGTH	47cm (18.5in)
SEXUAL MATURITY	1 year
LAYS EGGS	Breeding starts late March
INCUBATION PERIOD	23–24 days
NUMBER OF EGGS	5–17 eggs
NUMBER OF BROODS	1 per nest but males mate with many females
CALL	Male makes booming 'whooo-doo-dooh'
TYPICAL DIET	Seeds, fruit and insects
LIFE SPAN	Typically 2–3 years

WHERE IN THE WORLD?

The Greater Prairie Chicken was once common throughout the North American Prairie. Much of this land is now farmed and the species survives only in isolated patches of managed land.

CREATURE COMPARISONS

Female Prairie Chickens are dedicated mothers. Yet whole broods can be lost because ring-necked pheasants lay their eggs in the Chickens' nests. The pheasants' eggs hatch first and the mother Chicken assumes that it is her young which have hatched, and abandons the nest.

Mother and brood

HOW BIG IS IT?

HEAD
Adult females have shorter head feathers and lack the males' distinctive orange eyebrows and the circular patches on the neck.

EARS
During breeding displays, males will raise their elongated, ear-like feathers, above their heads, to make themselves look more impressive to mates.

NECK
Large orange patches on the side of the male Prairie Chickens' neck can be inflated during breeding displays.

SPECIAL ADAPTATION

Among Prairie Chickens, only the males that have struggled for and won dominance mate. Males gather together in communal display areas, called leks, to strut. The longer a male displays, the stronger he proves himself to be, and the greater number of mates he will attract.

201

Great Northern Diver

• **ORDER** • Gaviiformes • **FAMILY** • Gaviidae • **SPECIES** • *Gavia immer*

VITAL STATISTICS

WEIGHT	4kg (9Ib)
LENGTH	73–88cm (28.7–34.6in)
WINGSPAN	1.2–1.5m (4–5ft)
SEXUAL MATURITY	2–3 years
INCUBATION PERIOD	24–25 days
FLEDGLING PERIOD	70–77 days
NUMBER OF EGGS	1–3 eggs
NUMBER OF BROODS	1 a year
TYPICAL DIET	Fish, large invertebrates and amphibians
LIFE SPAN	Up to 20 years

In North America, Great Northern Divers are known as Loons because of the haunting, yodelling calls these birds make during the breeding season.

WHERE IN THE WORLD?

The Great Northern Diver breeds in Canada, parts of Alaska, Greenland and Iceland, where they make nests from hollows in the earth. They winter on the coasts of Canada and northern Europe.

CREATURE COMPARISONS

In their winter plumage, adult male Northern Divers are primarily dark brown, with almost completely white underparts. In the breeding season, they take on a spectacular, black and white coloration, which is said to resemble the pattern on a chess board.

Juvenile

WINGS
Great Northern Divers live mainly on the water, and take to the air only during the breeding season. However, they are remarkably strong fliers.

BELLY
When the bird comes in to land, it does a belly flop, skimming along the water on its belly to slow its descent.

LEGS
The legs of Great Northern Divers are positioned well back on the body. This is ideal for diving, but does make them clumsy on land.

HOW BIG IS IT?

SPECIAL ADAPTATION

Great Northern Divers' bills are tailor-made for catching fish. As their name implies, Divers hunt by diving, sometimes to depths of 60m (197ft), in search of prey. Occasionally they use their heavy bills to crush large fish, making them easier to swallow.

Sunbittern

• **ORDER** • Gruiformes *(under review)* • **FAMILY** • Eurypygidae • **SPECIES** • *Eurypyga helias*

VITAL STATISTICS

LENGTH	43–48cm (17–19in)
SEXUAL MATURITY	2–3 years
INCUBATION PERIOD	30 days
FLEDGLING PERIOD	20–22 days
NUMBER OF EGGS	1–2 eggs
NUMBER OF BROODS	1–2 a year
TYPICAL DIET	Spiders, insects, small reptiles and amphibians
CALL	'Kak-kak-kak-kak'
HABITS	Diurnal, non-migratory
LIFE SPAN	Up to 30 years in captivity

CREATURE COMPARISONS

Unusually, there is little variation between Sunbittern males, females or juveniles. However, the species does vary in appearance across its range, to such an extent that there were once thought to be two species, *E. helias* from the Amazon Basin and *E. major* of Central America (shown).

Adult

Sunbitterns are great bluffers. When trouble comes, they open their wings to reveal a pair of giant eyes, much to the alarm of predators.

WHERE IN THE WORLD?

Sunbitterns favour the tropical woodlands of southern and Central Latin America. They live near fast-moving streams, ponds and swamps, at 100–1200m (300–4000ft) above sea level.

WINGS
Sunbitterns rarely take to the air, but when they do, their broad, heavily feathered wings allow them to fly almost silently.

TOES
Three long forwards-facing toes and one short toe give stability on the ground and enable Sunbitterns to grip branches.

LEGS
A pair of long legs enable Sunbitterns to wade easily through rock pools, rivers and streams in search of prey.

HOW BIG IS IT?

SPECIAL ADAPTATION
When danger strikes, the normally camouflaged Sunbittern holds both wings up like a shield. In this position, the chestnut patterns on the wings look like two large eyes or sunspots. Such natural adaptations are designed to scare off potential predators.

Black Crowned Crane

• ORDER • Gruiformes • FAMILY • Gruidae • SPECIES • *Balearica pavonina*

VITAL STATISTICS

WEIGHT	3.6kg (8lb)
LENGTH	1–1.5m (3.3–5ft)
WINGSPAN	1.87m (6ft)
SEXUAL MATURITY	2–5 years
INCUBATION PERIOD	28–32 days
FLEDGLING PERIOD	60–100 days
NUMBER OF EGGS	2–5 eggs
NUMBER OF BROODS	1 a year
TYPICAL DIET	Seeds, insects; occasionally reptiles
LIFE SPAN	Up to 28 years

With their shimmering, tinsel-like crowns, the Black Crowned Crane makes a welcome addition to the marshy grasslands of their tropical African home.

WHERE IN THE WORLD?

Black Crowned Cranes are found in the savannahs of Sahel and Sudan, Africa. There are two sub-species: the West African Crowned Crane and the Sudan Crowned Crane, whose names reflect their location.

WINGS
Long, broad wings allow Cranes to fly with slow, leisurely wing beats and soar lazily on rising air currents.

CREATURE COMPARISONS

Many of these elegant birds produce surprisingly inelegant noises, such as the loud bugling calls produced by the Eurasian Common Crane. Black Crowned Cranes have longer wind pipes and so make louder honks, which are distinctly different from the calls of other species of Crane.

BILL
Cranes prefer to eat seeds and grasses, but they are omnivores and are capable of killing reptiles or crabs for food.

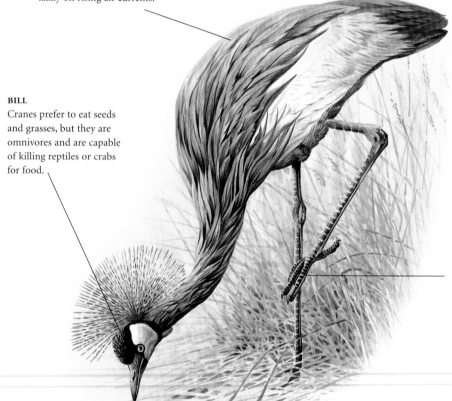

FEET
The toes of the Black Crowned Crane curl up tightly even when the bird relaxes, allowing it to keep a secure grip on a branch while it sleeps.

Black Crowned Crane in flight

HOW BIG IS IT?

SPECIAL ADAPTATION

These long-necked, long-legged birds can be found on every continent except Antarctica and Latin America. Yet only the Black and Grey Crowned Cranes are able to roost in trees. This is because their feet are especially adapted with an extra long hind toe to grip a branch.

Grey Crowned Crane

• **ORDER** • Gruiformes • **FAMILY** • Gruidae • **SPECIES** • *Balearica regulorum*

VITAL STATISTICS

WEIGHT	3.5kg (7.7lb)
HEIGHT	1.6m (5.2ft)
SEXUAL MATURITY	Around 3 years
LAYS EGGS	November–December
INCUBATION PERIOD	30 days
FLEDGLING PERIOD	50–90 days
NUMBER OF EGGS	2–3 eggs
NUMBER OF BROODS	1 a year
TYPICAL DIET	Grasses, seeds, invertebrates and small vertebrates
LIFE SPAN	Up to 22 years

With their elaborately layered, grey and russet plumage and striking golden crown, it would be hard to mistake these remarkable-looking Cranes for any other bird.

CREATURE COMPARISONS

All Crane species are famous for their spectacular dance, which involve a complex mix of leaps, bows and fluttering of the wings. Although such displays are most common during the breeding season, they may take place at any time, with adults and juveniles all showing the same behaviour.

Grey Crowned Crane dance

WHERE IN THE WORLD?

Grey Crowned Cranes inhabit the dry savannah. There are two sub-species, the East African Crested Crane and the South African Crowned Crane, which are found through much of sub-Saharan Africa.

HEAD
Sub-species can be identified by the red skin above the cheek. East African birds have more red than South African.

NECK
The bright red patch on the Grey Crowned Crane's throat is a sac that can be inflated during courtship displays.

LEGS
A pair of long legs, as well as a long neck and superb peripheral vision, helps Cranes to spot predators in the tall grass.

HOW BIG IS IT?

SPECIAL ADAPTATION

Grey Crowned Cranes are unusual in that they not only nest but also roost in trees, thanks to an elongated hind toe that is adapted for gripping a branch. This nesting adaptation gives the birds added security and helps them avoid unwanted encounters with predators.

Whooping Crane

• **ORDER** • Gruiformes • **FAMILY** • Gruidae • **SPECIES** • *Grus americana*

VITAL STATISTICS

WEIGHT	6kg (2.7lb)
HEIGHT	1.5m (5ft)
WINGSPAN	2.1–2.4m (7–8ft)
LAYS EGGS	April–May
INCUBATION PERIOD	29–30 days
FLEDGLING PERIOD	80–90 days
NUMBER OF EGGS	2 eggs
NUMBER OF BROODS	1 a year
CALL	Loud 'kar-r-r-o-o-o'
TYPICAL DIET	Crustaceans, insects, small fish, amphibians and reptiles

Whooping Cranes get their unusual name from the complex, colourful and highly co-ordinated whooping calls used by mating couples.

WHERE IN THE WORLD?

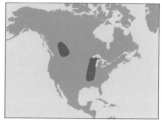

Native to North America, Whooping Cranes once ranged throughout the Midwest. Now very rare, they are scattered through National Parks in Arkansas and Wisconsin, USA, and Alberta, Canada.

CREATURE COMPARISONS

Adult Whooping Cranes have pure white bodies, with a black moustache, black wing tips and a patch of vivid red on their crown. Juveniles grow whiter as they reach maturity, but initially have large, rust-coloured markings all over their body, head and neck.

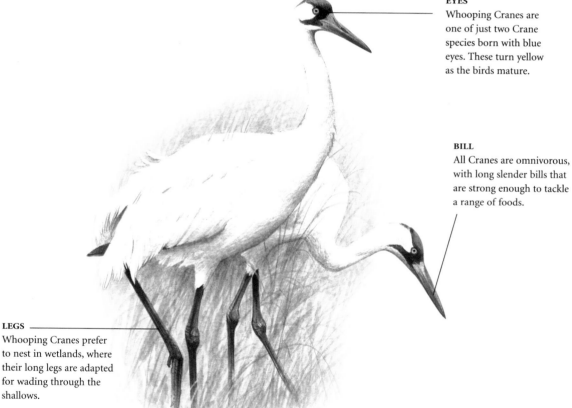

EYES
Whooping Cranes are one of just two Crane species born with blue eyes. These turn yellow as the birds mature.

BILL
All Cranes are omnivorous, with long slender bills that are strong enough to tackle a range of foods.

LEGS
Whooping Cranes prefer to nest in wetlands, where their long legs are adapted for wading through the shallows.

Adult (top), juvenile (bottom)

HOW BIG IS IT?

SPECIAL ADAPTATION

All Cranes dance. While such acrobatics are usually part of mating displays, Cranes of all ages dance, and at all times of the year. It is believed that this evolved as a way for birds to develop and refine their motor skills, as well as to deflect their aggression.

Eurasian Crane

The Eurasian Crane is one of the few cranes to occur naturally in Europe. It is easily distinguished from herons, which it resembles, by the drooping tail feathers.

VITAL STATISTICS

WEIGHT	4.0–7.0kg (9–15.4lbs)
HEIGHT	115–120cm (3.8–4ft)
WINGSPAN	200–225cm (6.6–7.4feet)
NUMBER OF EGGS	1–2 eggs
INCUBATION PERIOD	28–31 days
NUMBER OF BROODS	1 a year
TYPICAL DIET	Frogs, newts, crustaceans, snails, large insects, seeds, berries
LIFE SPAN	Up to 15 years

WHERE IN THE WORLD?

The Eurasian Crane is found across southern and eastern Europe, and across northern and central Russia.

CREATURE COMPARISONS

The Eurasian Crane has a greyish-blue or grey body plumage. The wings are also greyish-blue or grey, but the large wing feathers and the back edge of the wing are black. The tail is short and wide and similar in colour to the body. The neck is dark underneath, but is entirely white along the sides. The top of the head is red and the forehead is black. Males and females are similar.

Eurasian Cranes

WINGS
The Eurasian Crane has large, wide wings, and is able to migrate long distances between its summer and winter habitats.

BEAK
The long, pointed, yellow bill is adapted for catching small animals and picking up seeds and berries.

LEGS
The legs are very long and stilt-like, and are well adapted for walking around in tall grass or reeds.

HOW BIG IS IT?

SPECIAL ADAPTATION

Male and female cranes often perform spectacular dances during courtship, during which they leap up in the air, flap their huge wings and give out a loud trumpeting call.

Great Bustard

• **ORDER** • Gruiformes • **FAMILY** • Otidae • **SPECIES** • *Otis tarda*

VITAL STATISTICS

WEIGHT	Males: 8–16kg (17.6–35.3Ib) Females: 3.5–5kg (7.7–11Ib)
LENGTH	Males: 90–100cm (35.4–39.4in). Females: 75–85cm (29.5–33.5in)
WINGSPAN	Males: 2.1–2.4m (7–8ft). Females: 1.7–2m (5.6–6.2ft)
SEXUAL MATURITY	Males: around 5 years
LAYS EGGS	Breeding begins in March
INCUBATION PERIOD	Around 28 days
NUMBER OF EGGS	2–3 eggs
NUMBER OF BROODS	1 per nest but males may mate with up to 5 females
TYPICAL DIET	Plants and invertebrates
LIFE SPAN	10 years

CREATURE COMPARISONS

Male Great Bustards put on a flamboyant display when the breeding season arrives. Their plumage becomes more vivid and they puff themselves up, flashing their white underparts to attract the attention of potential mates.

Male Great Bustard

Male Bustards may look like over-grown turkeys, but they have the distinction of being the heaviest bird capable of getting airborne.

WHERE IN THE WORLD?

These huge birds breed in southern and central Europe, and the more temperate parts of Asia. Populations in Europe tend to be residents, while the Asian birds migrate south for the winter.

HEAD
During the breeding season, male Great Bustards grow large moustaches, which can reach 20cm (8in) in length.

BODY
Bustards exhibit a huge difference in size between the sexes. Some males are 50 per cent larger than females.

WINGS
Despite their size, Bustards are fast fliers, able to reach speeds of up to 60km/h (37.3mph).

HOW BIG IS IT?

SPECIAL ADAPTATION

To be successful, a species must survive long enough to breed. Camouflage plays an important role in this, keeping both chicks and mature birds safe. Many birds, including the Great Bustard, also lay eggs that have cryptic camouflage to blend in with the background.

Corn Crake

• ORDER • Gruiformes • FAMILY • Rallidae • SPECIES • *Crex crex*

The Corn Crake is a small, shy and timid bird that is heard more often than seen. They spend most of their time hidden in tall vegetation.

VITAL STATISTICS

WEIGHT	125–210g (4.4–7.4oz)
LENGTH	22–25cm (8.7–10in)
WINGSPAN	46–53cm (18.1–21in)
NUMBER OF EGGS	8–12 eggs
INCUBATION PERIOD	19–20 days
NUMBER OF BROODS	1 a year
TYPICAL DIET	Insects, worms, snails, spiders, seeds
LIFE SPAN	Up to 15 years

WHERE IN THE WORLD?

The Corn Crake is found in much of Europe, except the high north and the Iberian Peninsula, and also across western Asia. They migrate to Africa during winter.

CREATURE COMPARISONS

The Corn Crake has a greyish-brown or bluish-grey upper parts adorned with a vivid pattern of dark spots and bars. The head and neck are also brown with a paler stripe above the eye. The flanks are more reddish-brown and have faint streaks. The wings are distinctly reddish-brown or chestnut. Males and females are similar.

Corn Crake

BILL
The short, stout bill is yellowish-brown and used to catch small creatures as well as to pick seeds.

WINGS
The wings are large and wide, and the bird is a poor flyer, often preferring to hide instead of flying away.

FEET
The legs are long and the feet are large, and well adapted for walking in tall grass, where the bird will also hide.

HOW BIG IS IT?

SPECIAL ADAPTATION

Most birds are active during the day, but Corn Crakes are mostly active during the night, when they go out in search of food. They hide and sleep during the day.

Coot (Eurasian)

VITAL STATISTICS

WEIGHT	800g (28.2oz)
LENGTH	36–42cm (14.1–16.5in)
WINGSPAN	75cm (29.5in)
SEXUAL MATURITY	1–2 years
INCUBATION PERIOD	21–26 days
FLEDGLING PERIOD	55–60 days
NUMBER OF EGGS	5–10 eggs but adults often kill their own young if they have too many to feed
NUMBER OF BROODS	1–2 a year
TYPICAL DIET	Aquatic plants and insects; occasionally small amphibians and birds' eggs
LIFE SPAN	Typically 5 years

Coots are raucous, quarrelsome and always ready for a fight, whether it is over territory, food or a mate.

WHERE IN THE WORLD?

Species of Coot are found all over Europe, North Africa, Asia and Australasia. Populations that breed in milder climates are mainly resident, making their nests on freshwater lakes, reservoirs and rivers.

CREATURE COMPARISONS

Coot chicks (shown) do not share their parents aggressive and territorial nature. However, these black and red balls of fluff can be just as noisy as their parents, especially when they are begging for food, with loud, plaintiff and incessant 'uh-lif' calls.

Juvenile

WINGS
Although they appear to be completely black, the wings of Coots have a pale band across their secondary feathers, which is visible in flight.

BILL
From a distance, Coots are often be mistaken for moorhens. However, moorhens have a red head shield and yellow bill.

HEAD
The Coot's white head shield is believed to have given rise to the phrase 'as bald as a Coot.'

HOW BIG IS IT?

SPECIAL ADAPTATION

Coots belong to the same family as other wetland birds such as Rails and Crakes, which means their bodies are adapted for swimming and walking on mud. None of this group have webbed feet, but Coots have fleshy lobes around the toes, which serve a similar purpose to webbing.

Giant Coot

• ORDER • Gruiformes **• FAMILY •** Rallidae **• SPECIES •** *Fulica gigantea*

The Giant Coot, which is the largest of the world's Coots, lives in such isolated regions that few but the hardiest mountaineers have ever seen them in the wild.

VITAL STATISTICS

LENGTH	48–49cm (19–19.3in)
SEXUAL MATURITY	1 year
INCUBATION PERIOD	No accurate data, but at least 25 days
FLEDGLING PERIOD	44–59 days
NUMBER OF EGGS	3–7 eggs
CALL	Males make a loud, gobbling call
HABITS	Diurnal, non-migratory
TYPICAL DIET	Aquatic plants and algae
LIFE SPAN	Unknown

WHERE IN THE WORLD?

Giant Coots are found in the high, dry puna zone of the Andes, from Central Peru to northwest Argentina. Populations normally nest at 3100–5000m (10,170–16,404ft) above sea level.

CREATURE COMPARISONS

Fully grown adult Giant Coots are so large they are unable to fly. Young birds, however, are small and light enough to get airborne. In fact, the juveniles, who also lack the bold black, red and yellow coloration of the adult, could almost belong to a different species.

Juvenile

BODY
Giant Coots are around twice as big as Common Coots. Such large bodies may help them survive the extremes of Andean winters.

HEAD
Adult Giant Coots have a bony ridge on either side of their head, which forms a distinct bulge over the eyes.

FEET
The feet are broad and lobed rather than webbed, which makes them good swimmers and waders.

HOW BIG IS IT?

SPECIAL ADAPTATION

Giant Coots build bulky nests using aquatic vegetation. These impressive raft-like structures can reach 20–25cm (8–10in) above the height of the water. The heat generated as the vegetation begins to decompose is thought to help in the incubation of the birds' eggs.

Weka

VITAL STATISTICS

WEIGHT	Males: 1kg (2.2lb) Females: 700g (24.7oz)
LENGTH	Males: 50–60cm (19.7–23.6in). Females: 46–50cm (18–19.7in)
SEXUAL MATURITY	1 year
LAYS EGGS	August–January, but varies depending on food supplies
INCUBATION PERIOD	26–28 days
FLEDGLING PERIOD	Around 28 days
NUMBER OF EGGS	2–3 eggs
NUMBER OF BROODS	Up to 4 a year are possible
TYPICAL DIET	Insects, invertebrates, small mammals, reptiles; birds, fruit and seeds
LIFE SPAN	Up to 15 years

CREATURE COMPARISONS

There are four sub-species of Weka. North Island Weka are greyish in colour. Western Weka are chestnut, except in Fiordland, where a dark form is found. Buff Weka are the lightest in colour, while Stewart Island Weka come in two morphs: chestnut and black.

South Island Weka

Unfortunately, immigration has brought more than people to New Zealand. It has also brought animals that predate on the ground-nesting Weka.

WHERE IN THE WORLD?

These flightless birds are natives of New Zealand. Sadly, they have now vanished from large parts of their traditional range and work is underway to re-establish them on safer, off-shore islands.

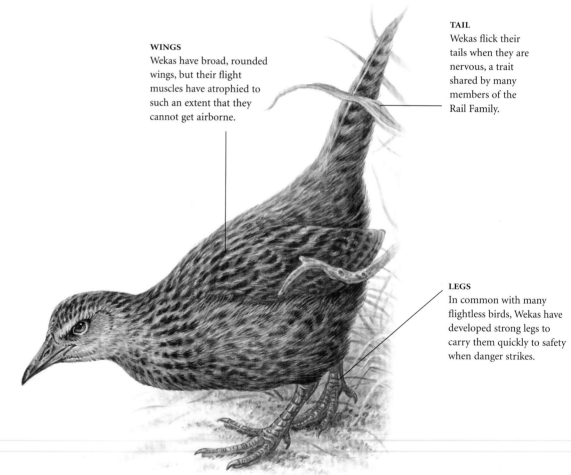

WINGS
Wekas have broad, rounded wings, but their flight muscles have atrophied to such an extent that they cannot get airborne.

TAIL
Wekas flick their tails when they are nervous, a trait shared by many members of the Rail Family.

LEGS
In common with many flightless birds, Wekas have developed strong legs to carry them quickly to safety when danger strikes.

HOW BIG IS IT?

SPECIAL ADAPTATION

The reddish-brown bills of Wekas make formidable weapons. They grow to about 5cm (2in) long and have numerous uses, such as rooting through the earth in search of worms, removing tree bark to look for insects, breaking open eggs or even stunning rats with a hammer-like blow.

Spotted Crake

• **ORDER** • Gruiformes • **FAMILY** • Rallidae • **SPECIES** • *Porzana porzana*

The wary little Spotted Crake is a water bird and, though quite common throughout much of its range, it is rarely seen.

VITAL STATISTICS

WEIGHT	65–130g (2.3–4.6oz)
LENGTH	22–24cm (8.7–9.4in)
WINGSPAN	40–45cm (15.7–17.7in)
NUMBER OF EGGS	6–15 eggs (usually 7–12)
INCUBATION PERIOD	19–22 days
NUMBER OF BROODS	2 a year
TYPICAL DIET	Small insects, worms, snails, some seeds
LIFE SPAN	Unknown

WHERE IN THE WORLD?

The Spotted Crake is widely distributed in much of Europe (except the high north and most of the Iberian Peninsula), and across temperate Asia. It winters in Africa and southern Asia.

CREATURE COMPARISONS

The Spotted Crake has a brownish-grey head and neck with small dark brown markings forming fine lines. The back is brown with fine dark lines. The breast is greyish or bluish-grey and mottled with white. The belly is white with brown stripes along the flanks. The wings are wide, and the inner parts are brownish-grey at the front, with darker brown hind parts.

Spotted Crake

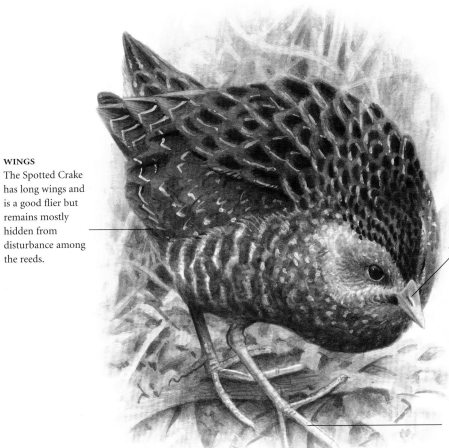

WINGS
The Spotted Crake has long wings and is a good flier but remains mostly hidden from disturbance among the reeds.

BILL
The Spotted Crake may be easily distinguished from the Water Rail, which it resembles, by its short, yellow bill with its red base.

FEET
Long greenish legs and large feet are well adapted for walking across water lilies and other plants on the water's surface.

HOW BIG IS IT?

SPECIAL ADAPTATION

The Spotted Crake has an elongated streamlined body, which makes moving among reeds easier. During the breeding season, it is very secretive, and is often heard rather than seen.

Water Rail

• **ORDER** • Gruiformes • **FAMILY** • Rallidae • **SPECIES** • *Rallus aquaticus*

VITAL STATISTICS

WEIGHT	Males: 140g (5oz) Females: 110g (4oz)
LENGTH	23–26cm (9–10.2in)
WINGSPAN	42cm (16.5in)
SEXUAL MATURITY	1 year
LAYS EGGS	April–July, depending on location
INCUBATION PERIOD	19–22 days
NUMBER OF EGGS	5–11 eggs
NUMBER OF BROODS	2 a year
TYPICAL DIET	Aquatic insects and other small vertebrates
LIFE SPAN	Up to 6 years

The elusive Water Rail may be difficult to spot, but there is no mistaking their eerie calls, which have been described as sounding like a pig being slaughtered.

WHERE IN THE WORLD?

Water Rails breed in swamps and reedbeds throughout Europe and central Asia. The populations of western Europe tend to be resident, but northern and eastern birds migrate to Africa and Asia for winter.

CREATURE COMPARISONS

Male and female Water Rails have similar plumage, with mottled brown upper parts, blue-grey underparts and a red bill. Juveniles are paler, with a white throat and breast, rather than the adult grey coloration. Their legs are usually paler, with less obvious red on the bill.

Juvenile

LEGS
A pair of long legs allow Water Rails to wade through pools and muddy reed beds in search of prey.

TOES
Three long, forwards-facing toes and one short toe give stability on the ground and stop Water Rails from sinking into the mud.

TAIL
Mottled brown plumage provides perfect camouflage in reed beds. Yet a flash of white, from beneath the tail, often gives their location away.

HOW BIG IS IT?

SPECIAL ADAPTATION

The Water Rail's body is ideally adapted for life among the reeds. Its slim profile is due to an especially narrow breast bone. This helps the bird to squeeze through tight gaps in the undergrowth, without having to break cover, which might reveal its location to predators.

Kagu

• **ORDER** • Gruiformes *(under review)* • **FAMILY** • Rhynochetidae • **SPECIES** • *Rhynochetos jubatus*

So little is known about the shy, secretive, chicken-sized Kagu that they have earned the nickname 'the ghosts of the forest' on their native island.

VITAL STATISTICS

LENGTH	55cm (21.6in)
SEXUAL MATURITY	2 years
INCUBATION PERIOD	33–37 days
FLEDGLING PERIOD	Around 98 days
NUMBER OF EGGS	1 egg
NUMBER OF BROODS	1 a year
CALL	'Goo-goo-goo' dog-like bark
HABITS	Diurnal, non-migratory
TYPICAL DIET	Worms, snails, lizards
LIFE SPAN	Up to 31 years in captivity

WHERE IN THE WORLD?

Kagu are endemic to New Caledonia, which means that they are found only on this remote Australasian Island. Their preferred habitat is isolated mountain woodlands.

CREATURE COMPARISONS

The Kagu is a real oddity. It lacks any recognizable camouflage and has binocular vision, which is usually reserved for birds of prey. But its blood is a real mystery because it contains just one-third of the red blood cells of other birds but three times the haemoglobin.

Kagu in flight

CREST
A crest of long elongated feathers is raised and lowered as part of breeding displays to attract a mate.

LEGS
When hunting, the Kagu may use one foot to move leaf litter about to flush out insects.

HOW BIG IS IT?

SPECIAL ADAPTATION

This mysterious bird get its species name, *Rhynochetos jubatus,* from the Greek for *rhis*, meaning nose, and *chetos*, meaning corn. This refers to the flaps of skin that closes over the bird's nostrils as it roots around for food beneath the leaf litter.

215

Hoatzin

• **ORDER** • Opisthocomiformes *(under review)* • **FAMILY** • Opisthocomidae • **SPECIES** • *Opisthocomus hoazin*

Hoatzin may be curiously primitive-looking birds, but they are more famous for their smell than their appearance. In Guyana, they are known as 'stink birds'.

VITAL STATISTICS

WEIGHT	816g (29oz)
LENGTH	61–66cm (24–26in)
SEXUAL MATURITY	3 years
INCUBATION PERIOD	28 days
FLEDGLING PERIOD	Around 60 days
NUMBER OF EGGS	2–5 eggs
NUMBER OF BROODS	1 a year
CALL	Described as sounding like a smokers' wheezing rasp
TYPICAL DIET	Leaves and fruit
LIFE SPAN	Up to 8 years

CREATURE COMPARISONS

It was once believed that Hoatzin were related to the earliest of all birds, the Archaeopteryx, although this theory has now been dismissed. However, to date, very little is known about this curious species. It is not even known for certain who their closest relatives are.

Hoatzin

WHERE IN THE WORLD?

These chicken-sized birds live in densely packed territories of up to 30 nests in one tree. Their natural home is among the swamps and mangrove forests of South America's Amazon and Orinoco Basins.

HEAD
The bird's spiky crest gives it its scientific name, *Opisthocomus hoazin*, which comes from the Greek for 'wearing long hair behind'.

BREAST
A large, rubbery mound on the breastbone acts like a tripod and stops the Hoatzin falling over when its stomach is full.

BODY
For birds, Hoatzins have a unique digestive system. They ferment vegetation in the front of the gut, just as cows do.

HOW BIG IS IT?

SPECIAL ADAPTATION
Young Hoatzin have two large claws on each wing. These are used to grip onto branches, and they fall off as the birds mature. Even then, Hoatzin are poor fliers and more likely to use their wings to keep their balance when perching, than for flying.

Rifleman

• ORDER • Passeriformes **• FAMILY •** Acanthisittidae **• SPECIES •** *Acanthisitta chloris*

VITAL STATISTICS

WEIGHT	6g (0.2oz)
LENGTH	8cm (3.1in)
SEXUAL MATURITY	As early as 9 months
INCUBATION PERIOD	19–20 days
FLEDGLING PERIOD	23–25 days
NUMBER OF EGGS	2–5 eggs
NUMBER OF BROODS	2 a year
TYPICAL DIET	Insects; occasionally fruit
LIFE SPAN	Up to 6 years

The tiny woodland Rifleman gets its unusual name from its characteristic, high-pitched call, which sounds just like a rifle being fired.

WHERE IN THE WORLD?

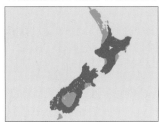

Riflemen are endemic to New Zealand, which means that this species are found nowhere else naturally. Preferred habitats are woodlands but this varies across the species' range depending on availability.

CREATURE COMPARISONS

Both male and female Riflemen have a patch of white plumage beneath their head and a white brow stripe across the eyes. However, males are bright green on their upper parts while the females are more sombre, with brownish upper parts. Juveniles look similar, but have streaked breasts.

Juvenile

BODY
Riflemen are New Zealand's smallest-known species of native bird. As a rule, females are slightly heavier than the males.

WINGS
Short, rounded wings and a tiny, stubby tail enable Riflemen to flit easily through the dense vegetation in woodland homes.

BILL
The long, thin, slightly up-turned bill is an ideal tool for rooting among leaf litter or probing in bark for insects.

HOW BIG IS IT?

SPECIAL ADAPTATION
Riflemen have a very unusual way of climbing trees. They make their way up the trunk in a series of tiny hops, using their long and exceptionally sharp feet to grip on to the bark. This is similar to the technique used by European Treecreepers.

Long-tailed Tit

• ORDER • Passeriformes • FAMILY • Aegithalidae • SPECIES • *Aegithalos caudatus*

VITAL STATISTICS

WEIGHT	7–9g (0.2–0.3oz)
LENGTH	13–15cm (5–6in)
WINGSPAN	16–19cm (6.3–7.5in)
NUMBER OF EGGS	7–12 eggs
INCUBATION PERIOD	13–14 days
NUMBER OF BROODS	1 a year
TYPICAL DIET	Insects, especially beetles, spiders, caterpillars; seeds in winter
LIFE SPAN	Unknown

CREATURE COMPARISONS

This tiny handsome bird has an almost entirely white body, while the upper back is pinkish-brown with a black central stripe. The wings are blackish with white markings, and the tail is very long. Females and males are similar. The northern race has an entirely white head, while the southern race has a distinct black stripe across the eye.

Southern species (top), Northern species (bottom)

Despite its name the Long-tailed Tit is not a true Tit. A tiny bird, it is often seen in small, twittering flocks during the winter.

WHERE IN THE WORLD?

The Long-tailed Tit is found in much of Europe (except northern Scandinavia), in parts of the Middle East, across western Russia, and as far east as parts of China and Japan.

BODY
The body of the Long-tailed Tit is short and round, which means that the large head looks like it sits directly on the body.

BILL
The bill is very short and pointed, and is well adapted for picking up small insects.

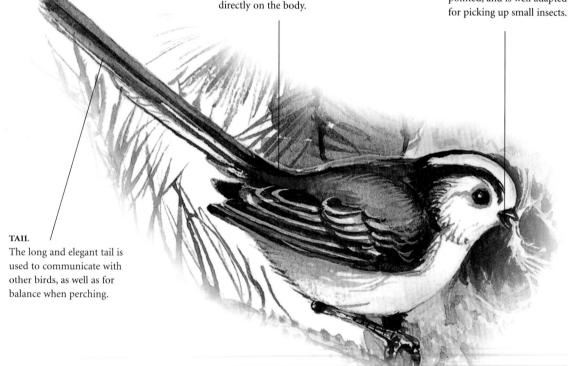

TAIL
The long and elegant tail is used to communicate with other birds, as well as for balance when perching.

HOW BIG IS IT?

SPECIAL ADAPTATION
On cold nights, these sociable little birds will fluff up their body feathers and huddle closely together for warmth in preferred sleeping places.

Bushtit

• ORDER • Passeriformes • FAMILY • Aegithalidae • SPECIES • *Psaltriparus minimus*

VITAL STATISTICS

WEIGHT	5–8g (0.2–0.3oz)
LENGTH	9–11cm (3.5–4.3in)
WINGSPAN	15–18cm (5.9–6.7in)
INCUBATION PERIOD	11–12 days
NUMBER OF BROODS	2 a year
TYPICAL DIET	Small insects, caterpillars, spiders, some seeds and berries
LIFE SPAN	4–5 years (usually shorter)

The Bushtit is one of the smallest Tits in the North America, and it is the only member of its family to be found there.

WHERE IN THE WORLD?

The Bushtit is found in western North America, from southwestern British Columbia to California, and in highland areas in Mexico. It extends eastwards to northwestern Texas.

CREATURE COMPARISONS

The Bushtit is very plain, and in the field the bird is often identified by a combination of its size, call and behaviour. The upper side is uniformly greyish, and the underside is lighter greyish-white. The head, which has a light brown top, is large and the neck is short, but the tail is very long. Males and females are similar, but males have dark eyes, while those of females are yellow.

Mexican species has black cheek patches

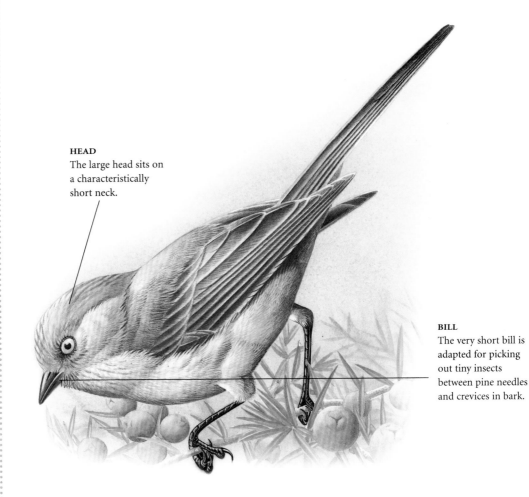

HEAD
The large head sits on a characteristically short neck.

BILL
The very short bill is adapted for picking out tiny insects between pine needles and crevices in bark.

HOW BIG IS IT?

SPECIAL ADAPTATION

The Bushtit lives in flocks of 10–40 birds. It builds a round nest that encloses both the adult birds and their eggs or young. In flight, the birds utter short, ticking calls to each other constantly.

Skylark

• **ORDER** • Passeriformes • **FAMILY** • Alaudidae • **SPECIES** • *Alauda arvensis*

VITAL STATISTICS

WEIGHT:	33–45g (1.2–1.6oz)
LENGTH	16–18cm (6.3–7in)
WINGSPAN	30–36cm (12–14.2in)
NUMBER OF EGGS	2–5 eggs (usually 3–4)
INCUBATION PERIOD	11–14 days
NUMBER OF BROODS	2–3 a year (occasionally 4)
TYPICAL DIET	Seeds, leaves, insects, worms, some berries
LIFE SPAN	Up to 7 years

A familiar and popular songbird, the Skylark has unfortunately become much rarer in the last 30 years in many countries.

CREATURE COMPARISONS

The upper side is earthy to yellowish brown with dark longitudinal stripes forming a mottled pattern, which provides camouflage on open farmland and heaths. The head is lighter in colour, and bears a brownish cheek patch. The long brown tail also has longitudinal stripes but with white feathers along the sides. Females are smaller than males and have more slender wings.

Juvenile

WHERE IN THE WORLD?

The Skylark is found throughout Europe, except the far north, across much of central Russia to the Sea of Okhotsk, in parts of Asia and the Middle East; and along the Mediterranean coasts of Africa.

HEAD
The crest of short feathers on top of the head can be lowered and raised, and is used for communication.

TAIL
The short V-shaped tail is used for manoeuvring and hovering during flight, and is fanned out during landing.

LEGS
The short sturdy legs are well adapted for hopping around on the ground.

HOW BIG IS IT?

SPECIAL ADAPTATION
The Skylark sings its loud, beautiful, trilling song high in the air, and has often been associated with daybreak in rural areas.

Shore Lark

• ORDER • Passeriformes **• FAMILY •** Alaudidae **• SPECIES •** *Eremophila alpestris*

VITAL STATISTICS

WEIGHT	37g (1.3oz)
LENGTH	16–19cm (6.3– 7.5in)
WINGSPAN	32cm (12.6in)
SEXUAL MATURITY	1 year
INCUBATION PERIOD	10–11 days
FLEDGLING PERIOD	16–18 days
NUMBER OF EGGS	2–4 eggs
NUMBER OF BROODS	1 a year
TYPICAL DIET	Seeds, especially in the winter, and insects
LIFE SPAN	Up to 7 years

The hardy Shore Lark makes its home in some of the bleakest locations, flourishing among Arctic tundra and barren, high mountains.

WHERE IN THE WORLD?

Tundra, barren grasslands and wind-blown shorelines are where you are most likely to spot Shore Larks. Populations can be found in North America, Asia, North Africa and parts of Europe.

CREATURE COMPARISONS

Birdsong may sound melodic, but it serves a serious purpose. In some cases, it allows males to declare themselves to mates or rivals. However, male and female Shore Larks also rely on appearance to impress, sprouting a pair of horns that make them look bigger and more aggressive.

HEAD
In the summer, male Shore Larks sport feathered tufts, which give the species its American name, the Horned Lark.

BILL
A distinctive black stripe starts at the Shore Larks' bill and runs through the eye, down either side of the head.

BODY
Female Shore Larks are generally smaller and paler than the males, with grey instead of black in some areas.

Feathered tufts can be raised and lowered

HOW BIG IS IT?

SPECIAL ADAPTATION
Shore Larks have three forwards-facing toes and one extra long, hind toe, which is tipped with a straight claw. This spur is a common characteristic of birds in the Lark Family and is used, offensively and defensively, during fights for mates or territory.

Woodlark

VITAL STATISTICS

WEIGHT	30g (1oz)
LENGTH	15cm (6in)
WINGSPAN	28cm (11in)
SEXUAL MATURITY	1 year
INCUBATION PERIOD	14 days
FLEDGLING PERIOD	11–13 days
NUMBER OF EGGS	3–6 eggs
NUMBER OF BROODS	2–3 a year
TYPICAL DIE	Seeds and insects during the breeding season
LIFE SPAN	Up to 4 years

All members of the Lark family sing beautifully, but the soft, melancholy song of the Woodlark is perhaps the most appealing of all.

WHERE IN THE WORLD?

Woodlarks breed over most of Europe, Asia, the Middle East and North Africa. Populations tend to be resident in the west, but migratory in the east, moving south for winter.

CREATURE COMPARISONS

Most birds will aggressively defend their nest from predators. Even so, Woodlarks are surprisingly fearsome for such small birds. They have been known to drive off even the most determined predators, bolting from their nests to assault their attackers with noisy alarm calls and out-stretched wings.

A Woodlark defending its nest

HEAD
Woodlarks, like many larks, have a head crest. This is not always obvious, but can be seen when raised during displays.

FEET
Woodlarks have three forward-facing toes and one extra long, hind toe, which is tipped with a straight claw.

HOW BIG IS IT?

SPECIAL ADAPTATION
The Woodlarks' melodic song is usually delivered while the bird is in flight, often at dawn or dusk.

Pied Currawong

• **ORDER** • Passeriformes • **FAMILY** • Artamidae • **SPECIES** • *Strepera graculina*

VITAL STATISTICS

WEIGHT	270–300g (9.5–10.6oz)
LENGTH	42–50cm (16.5–19.7in)
WINGSPAN	65–80cm (25.6–31.5in)
NUMBER OF EGGS	3 eggs
INCUBATION PERIOD	20–23 days
NUMBER OF BROODS	1 a year
TYPICAL DIET	Insects, small reptiles, amphibians, seeds, fruit, carrion
LIFE SPAN	Up to 15 years

Although resembling the Crow, the Pied Currawong is only distantly related to them and is more closely related to the Magpie.

WHERE IN THE WORLD?

The Pied Currawong is found in eastern Australia from Cape York to western Victoria. It is also found on Lord Howe Island. It is often found in gardens, parks and rural woodlands.

CREATURE COMPARISONS

The head, neck and body are uniformly black. The wings are also black, but sport a large crescent-shaped white patch towards the tip. The base and much of the tip of the tail is black, but the central part of the tail and the outermost tip are both white. The handsome eyes have a bright yellow iris, and a dark pupil. Females and males are similar.

Pied Currawong in flight

BEAK
The bill is large and heavy, like a crow's, and enables the Pied Currawong to feed on both plant and animal matter.

WINGS
The bright white spots on the wings may be used for identification when flying in flocks.

TAIL
The long tail can be fanned ou, and is important for steering and manoeuvring.

HOW BIG IS IT?

SPECIAL ADAPTATION

The Pied Currawong was originally a forest bird, but it has adapted well to human settlement. The long bill and hooked tip make is easy for probing lawns for grubs and worms and for plucking berries from bushes.

Waxwing (Bohemian)

• **ORDER** • Passeriformes • **FAMILY** • Bombycillidae • **SPECIES** • *Bombycilla garrulusa*

VITAL STATISTICS

WEIGHT	63g (2.2oz)
LENGTH	18cm (7in)
WINGSPAN	34cm (13.4in)
SEXUAL MATURITY	1 year
INCUBATION PERIOD	13–14 days
FLEDGLING PERIOD	15–17 days
NUMBER OF EGGS	5 eggs
NUMBER OF BROODS	1 a year
TYPICAL DIET	Insects in the summer. Fruit in the winter.

Waxwings are named after their bright red wing tips, which are said to look like drops of freshly melted wax running down their feathers.

WHERE IN THE WORLD?

Waxwings are found throughout the northernmost parts of Europe, Asia and western North America. Favouring coniferous forests and woodlands, they often build their nests in pine trees.

CREATURE COMPARISONS

In flight, Waxwings can easily be mistaken for starlings. Both species have a similar profile, with a short tail and pointed wings. They also both fly with quick, undulating movements. However, Waxwings have white wing bars (shown), which help bird-watchers to differentiate between them.

HEAD
The Waxwing's large chestnut head crest, black bib and mask makes it almost impossible to confuse the bird with other species.

BODY
Bohemian Waxwings are larger and than their close relatives the cedar waxwings, which are found only in North America.

TAIL
Bombycilla, part of the Waxwing's scientific name, means silk tail in Latin, a reference to the bird's soft plumage.

Waxwing in flight

HOW BIG IS IT?

SPECIAL ADAPTATION

The right nest site is vital, but nest design is just as important. Birds instinctively know how to build nests, and each species has its own preferred design for camouflage and safety. The Waxwing builds a cup-shaped nest (shown) in a tree, and line it with moss.

Yellow-billed Oxpecker

• **ORDER** • Passeriformes • **FAMILY** • Sturnidae • **SPECIES** • *Buphagus africanus*

Oxpeckers feed on ticks that infest herding animals. However, this relationship is not always good for the host because Oxpeckers also have a taste for blood.

VITAL STATISTICS

WEIGHT	60g (2oz)
LENGTH	20cm (8in)
SEXUAL MATURITY	1 years
INCUBATION PERIOD	Around 12 days
NUMBER OF EGGS	2–3 eggs
NUMBER OF BROODS	1 a year
CALL	Hissing 'krisss' cry
HABITS	Diurnal, non-migratory
TYPICAL DIET	Ticks and the blood of its hosts
LIFE SPAN	Unknown

WHERE IN THE WORLD?

Yellow-billed Oxpeckers are natives of sub-Saharan Africa, from Senegal to Sudan. They tend to lose territory and food to red-billed oxpeckers, so are less common in the east, where the species overlap.

CREATURE COMPARISONS

Although Red-billed Oxpeckers look very similar to their Yellow-billed relatives, there are two obvious differences between the species. Yellow-bills have yellow at the base of their bills but they do not have a yellow ring around each eye, as the red-bill does. Yellow-bills are also less common.

Red-billed Oxpecker (right), Yellow-billed Oxpecker (left)

EYE
Male and female Yellow-billed Oxpeckers look alike, with light brown upper parts, pale underparts and a red circle around the eye.

BILL
Oxpeckers use their specially adapted, scissor-shaped bills to dig ticks and parasites out of the hides of grazing animals.

BODY
Oxpeckers belong to the same family as Starlings and are around the same size, although their bodies tend to be more stocky.

HOW BIG IS IT?

SPECIAL ADAPTATION
Oxpeckers are adapted for life on the move. Long, stiff tail feathers help them to keep their balance as they perch on their host's back to feed. Short legs and feet, tipped with sharp claws, also ensure that they have a good, strong grip.

Saddleback

• **ORDER** • Passeriformes • **FAMILY** • Callaeidae • **SPECIES** • *Philesturnus carunculatus*

VITAL STATISTICS

WEIGHT	60–75g (2.1–2.6oz)
LENGTH	24–25cm (9.4–10in)
WINGSPAN	45–50cm (17.7–19.7in)
NUMBER OF EGGS	1–4 eggs (usually 2–3)
INCUBATION PERIOD	18–20 days
NUMBER OF BROODS	1–2 a year
TYPICAL DIET	Insects, grubs, caterpillars, spiders, worms, fruit; sometimes nectar
LIFE SPAN	Up to 20 years

The Saddleback is only one of two remaining species of wattlebird left in New Zealand, and is endangered because of introduced pests such as rats.

WHERE IN THE WORLD?

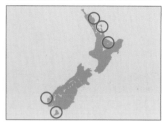

The Saddleback is found only in the forests of New Zealand, and almost became extinct. Today, several populations have been successfully re-established on both the North and South Islands.

CREATURE COMPARISONS

The Saddleback has a uniformly jet-black head, neck and body. The back and front part of the wings are vividly chestnut in colour, as is the base of the tail. However, the long tail feathers, legs and feet are black. There is a reddish fleshy outgrowth at the base of the bill, known as a wattle. Females and males are similar.

Juvenile of South Island species

HEAD
The head is jet black, but spots a pair of wobbly, bright orange or red wattles at its base.

BILL
The bill is large and slightly curved. It is very strong, and is often used to tear bark off dead trees.

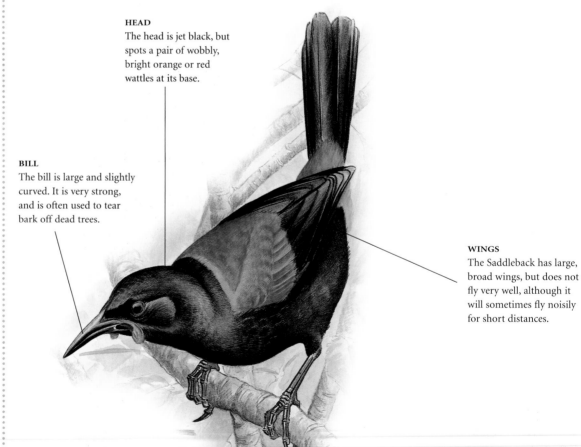

WINGS
The Saddleback has large, broad wings, but does not fly very well, although it will sometimes fly noisily for short distances.

HOW BIG IS IT?

SPECIAL ADAPTATION

Like its close relative, the Kokako, the Saddleback does not fly much, and usually only bounds from branch to branch. It often nests near the ground, and defends its territory by singing.

Red-crowned Ant Tanager

• **ORDER** • Passeriformes • **FAMILY** • Cardinalidae *(under review)* • **SPECIES** • *Habia rubica*

VITAL STATISTICS

WEIGHT	Males: 34g (1.2oz). Females: 31g (1oz)
LENGTH	17–19cm (6.7–7.5in)
SEXUAL MATURITY	1 years
INCUBATION PERIOD	13–14 days
FLEDGLING PERIOD	10 days
NUMBER OF EGGS	2–3 eggs
NUMBER OF BROODS	1 a year
HABITS	Diurnal, non-migratory
TYPICAL DIET	Insects and fruit
LIFE SPAN	Up to 7 years

Flocks of chattering Ant Tanagers are found throughout Latin America's tropical forests. Hundreds of species are known, many of which share the Red-crowns' vivid plumage.

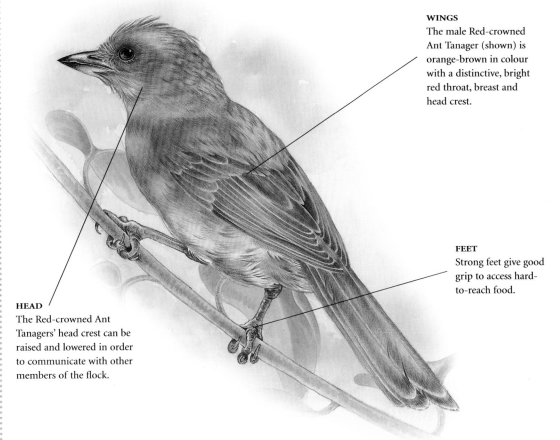

WHERE IN THE WORLD?

These tropical birds live in the lush forests of Latin America. Populations are found in Mexico and throughout central and southern regions of the continent. Populations are also found in Trinidad.

CREATURE COMPARISONS

Genetic testing has made it possible to group birds more accurately than before, so many species have new classifications. This is why Red-crowned Ant-Tanagers are also known as Red-crowned Habias. They used to be part of the Tanager Family (Thraupidae), but are now classed as Cardinals (Cardinalidae).

WINGS
The male Red-crowned Ant Tanager (shown) is orange-brown in colour with a distinctive, bright red throat, breast and head crest.

HEAD
The Red-crowned Ant Tanagers' head crest can be raised and lowered in order to communicate with other members of the flock.

FEET
Strong feet give good grip to access hard-to-reach food.

Female

HOW BIG IS IT?

SPECIAL ADAPTATION
Despite their name, Ant-Tanagers eat more than just ants. In fact, their bills are strong enough to tackle even hard-bodied insects, like beetles, which they hack into bits before eating. They also eat berries, using their narrow bills to nibble the flesh from seed.

Golden-fronted Leafbird

• ORDER • Passeriformes • FAMILY • Chloropseidae • SPECIES • *Chloropsis aurifrons*

VITAL STATISTICS

WEIGHT	40–70g (1.4–2.5 oz)
LENGTH	18–20cm (7–8in)
WINGSPAN	25–35cm (10–14in)
NUMBER OF EGGS	2–3 eggs
INCUBATION PERIOD	Unknown
NUMBER OF BROODS	1
TYPICAL DIET	Fruits, nectar, pollen and insects
LIFE SPAN	Unknown, but probably only a few years

The strikingly beautiful Golden-fronted Leafbird is quite common throughout its range, but hides in the treetops and is seldom seen.

WHERE IN THE WORLD?

The Golden-fronted Leafbird is found in India and Sri Lanka, Burma and Thailand. There are also populations on the island of Sumatra, but scientists are unsure if they are also part of this species.

CREATURE COMPARISONS

The Golden-fronted Leafbird has a strikingly bright green plumage. The side of the face is black and the throat is blue. Adult males have a yellow band extending from the forehead and along the throat. Females are similar to males, but lack a yellow throat-band. Immature birds can easily be identified by having a green head.

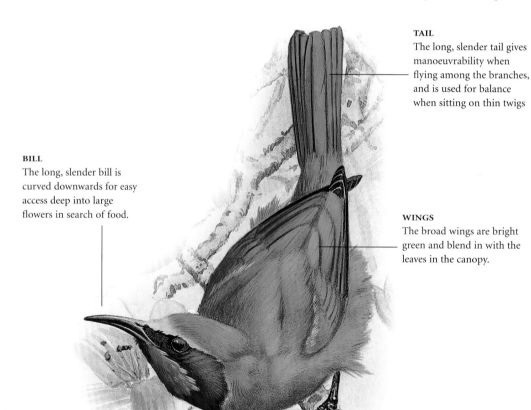

TAIL
The long, slender tail gives manoeuvrability when flying among the branches, and is used for balance when sitting on thin twigs

BILL
The long, slender bill is curved downwards for easy access deep into large flowers in search of food.

WINGS
The broad wings are bright green and blend in with the leaves in the canopy.

Male

HOW BIG IS IT?

SPECIAL ADAPTATION

These small, active birds spend much of their time fluttering around in the crown of trees looking for food. They are often targeted by birds of prey. However, if parts of the plumage are grabbed by a predator, their feathers easily pull out, allowing the bird to escape.

Dipper (White Throated)

• ORDER • Passeriformes • FAMILY • Cinclidae • SPECIES • *Cinclus cinclus*

VITAL STATISTICS

WEIGHT	64g (2.2oz)
LENGTH	17–20cm (6.7–7.8in)
WINGSPAN	28cm (11in)
SEXUAL MATURITY	1 year
LAYS EGGS	April–May, depending on location
INCUBATION PERIOD	15–18 days
NUMBER OF EGGS	3–6 eggs
NUMBER OF BROODS	2 a year
TYPICAL DIET	Aquatic invertebrates, especially caddis worms and shrimps; occasionally small fish
LIFE SPAN	Typically 3 years

The perky Dipper is one of the bird world's true oddities, spending most of its life in or beside fast-flowing water.

WHERE IN THE WORLD?

The Dipper (White-Throated) is also called the European Dipper because it makes its home primarily beside Europe's fast-flowing rivers and streams. Smaller populations are also found in North Africa and Asia.

CREATURE COMPARISONS

Dippers have a habit of bobbing spasmodically while they are perched. It is from these sudden dips that they get their name. Several sub-species are known, and each one is classified according to the colour of its plumage. As the name suggests, the Northern European Black-Bellied Dipper (shown) has a black rather than chestnut belly.

Northern European Black-Bellied Dipper

HEAD
While underwater, Dippers hold their heads well down and their bodies against the water flow, to give a more streamlined shape.

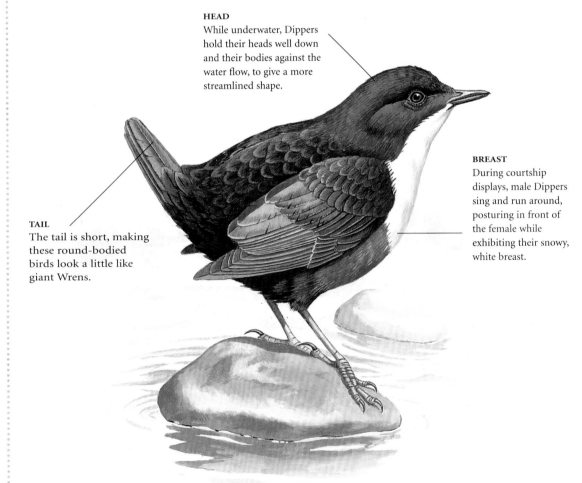

BREAST
During courtship displays, male Dippers sing and run around, posturing in front of the female while exhibiting their snowy, white breast.

TAIL
The tail is short, making these round-bodied birds look a little like giant Wrens.

HOW BIG IS IT?

SPECIAL ADAPTATION

Dippers have developed a rather unusual hunting technique. They deliberately submerge themselves in the water and, gripping the rocks with their strong feet, use their wings to paddle along the bottom. This enables them to secure food that other birds are unable to reach.

Bananaquit

• **ORDER** • Charadriiformes • **FAMILY** •Coerebidae • **SPECIES** • *Coereba flaveola*

VITAL STATISTICS

WEIGHT	8–10g (0.3–0.4 oz)
LENGTH	10.5–11cm (4.1–4.3in)
WINGSPAN	24–30cm (9.4–12in)
NUMBER OF EGGS	2–3 eggs
INCUBATION PERIOD	12–13 days
NUMBER OF BROODS	2–3 a year
TYPICAL DIET	Mainly nectar and pollen, but also fruit, berries, insects, and grubs
LIFE SPAN	Unknown

The brightly coloured Bananaquit is common in gardens in South America. It does not feed on bananas but has a bright yellow banana-coloured breast.

WHERE IN THE WORLD?

The Bananaquit is found in southern Central America, the Caribbean, and in the northern and eastern parts of South America. It is sometimes found in south Florida. It is absent from dense rainforest tracts.

CREATURE COMPARISONS

The Bananaquit is vividly coloured. The top of the head and the face are black, with a distinctive large, white stripe above the eye. The lower part of the face and the throat are greyish in colour. The breast and upper and lower part of the tail are strikingly yellow. Males and females are similar, but females tend to be drabber in colour.

BEAK
Long, slender bill is well adapted for probing deep into flowers for nectar.

HEAD
The Bananaquit has a black head with a distinct white stripe above the eyes.

WINGS
White spots on wings appear like flashes of light when the bird flies and may confuse predators.

Juvenile

HOW BIG IS IT?

SPECIAL ADAPTATION

As well as a long slim bill, the Bananaquit's lengthy slender tongue is well adapted for probing deep into flowers. It uses the brush-like tip of the tongue for collecting nectar and pollen from flowers.

Florida Scrub Jay

• **ORDER** • Passeriformes • **FAMILY** • Corvidae • **SPECIES** • *Aphelocoma coerulescens*

Scrub Jays are one of the bird world's most sociable species, living in communal family groups that work together to help the breeding pair.

VITAL STATISTICS

WEIGHT	77g (3oz)
LENGTH	25–30cm (10–12in)
WINGSPAN	43cm (17in)
SEXUAL MATURITY	1 year
LAYS EGGS	March–June
INCUBATION PERIOD	16–19 days
NUMBER OF EGGS	1–5 eggs
NUMBER OF BROODS	1 a year
TYPICAL DIET	Insects and small invertebrates; seeds and nuts in the winter
LIFE SPAN	Typically 4–5 years

WHERE IN THE WORLD?

Florida Scrub Jays make their homes in the scrublands of southwestern USA and Mexico. This habitat is, however, increasingly under threat, and thus the species is too.

CREATURE COMPARISONS

Birds are often classified as belonging to either the Old World (Europe, Asia and Africa) or the New World (the Americas and Australasia). Florida Scrub Jays are New World blue jays, a group that includes around 36 species. Old World species include Brown Jays and Grey jays.

BILL
Long, multi-purpose bills are perfect for crushing seeds and rooting in the earth. Stiff bristles, beneath the bill, protect the eyes.

BODY
Male and female Florida Scrub Jays tend to resemble each other, although males' bodies tend to be slightly larger.

FEET
Strong, dextrous feet enable Scrub Jays to grip and manipulate food easily. Their long legs are ideal for hopping and perching.

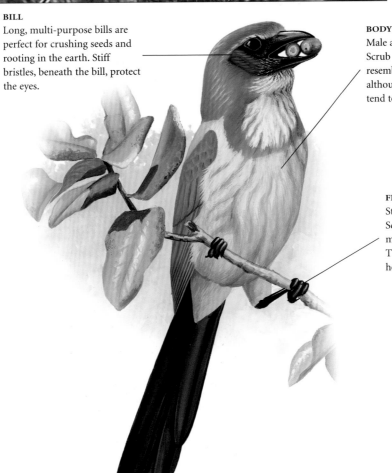

Florida Scrub Jay in flight

HOW BIG IS IT?

SPECIAL ADAPTATION

For birds who spend much of their time foraging among the tangled scrub, it is important to be as agile as possible. Its short rounded wings are therefore ideal for manoeuvring in a confined space. The bird's long tail aids balance and acts as a rudder.

231

Raven (Common)

• **ORDER** • Passeriformes • **FAMILY** • Corvidae • **SPECIES** • *Corvus corax*

VITAL STATISTICS

WEIGHT	Males: 1.3 kg (3lb) Females: 1.1 kg (2.4lb)
LENGTH	54–67cm (21.2–26.4in)
WINGSPAN	1–1.3m (3.6–4.2ft)
SEXUAL MATURITY	2–6 years
INCUBATION PERIOD	20–22 days
FLEDGLING PERIOD	35–39 days
NUMBER OF EGGS	4–6 eggs
NUMBER OF BROODS	1 a year
TYPICAL DIET	Carrion and human food scraps; occasionally small animals, seeds and fruit
LIFE SPAN	Up to 29 years in captivity

CREATURE COMPARISONS

Juvenile Ravens begin to court potential mates from a young age, although they may not bond with a partner for two or three years. Once they have paired up, birds will stay together for life, and can often be seen flying side by side over their territory.

Juvenile

The Raven has an all-black plumage and a habit of feeding on corpses, so it is no wonder that some associate this bird with death and misfortune

WHERE IN THE WORLD?

The Raven is found in woodlands or on rockfaces, wherever there is a ready supply of food. Populations can be found across Europe, Asia and northern America.

BILL
A long, curved bill is a useful, multi-purpose tool: equally good at plucking flesh from carcasses, or rooting through rubbish.

HEAD
Common Ravens are well known for their intelligence. In fact, they have one of the largest brain-body ratios of any bird.

BODY
Ravens can be distinguished from their crow cousins thanks to their larger and heavier bills, shaggy throat and wedge-shaped tail.

HOW BIG IS IT?

SPECIAL ADAPTATION

Success is all about timing. Most species time their breeding to coincide with the warm weather, when there is plenty of food. Some populations of Raven, however, breed early, when poor weather is a disadavantages to other species, thus ensuring a ready supply of carrion.

Hooded Crow

VITAL STATISTICS

WEIGHT	540–600g (19.0–21.2oz)
LENGTH	42–47cm (16.5–18.5in)
WINGSPAN	90–100cm (35.4–39.4in)
NUMBER OF EGGS	3–6 eggs (usually 4–5)
INCUBATION PERIOD	17–19 days
NUMBER OF BROODS	1 a year
YPICAL DIET	Insects, worms, grubs, small lizards, snakes and amphibians, seeds, fruit, berries, carrion
LIFE SPAN	Up to 19 years

CREATURE COMPARISONS

As far as size, appearance and habits are concerned, the Hooded Crow is very similar to the Carrion Crow. However, they may easily be distinguished by the colour of the plumage. The Hooded Crow has a black head and throat, and black wings. The breast, belly and upper part of the back are greyish. Males and females look similar.

Hooded Crows in flight

Until 2002, the Hooded Crow was considered to be a variant of the Carrion Crow, but now scientists think they are different species.

WHERE IN THE WORLD?

The Hooded Crow is found throughout eastern Europe and across Asia to the Sea of Okhotsk. It does not extend into western Europe, which is populated by the carrion crow.

WINGS
Large, broad wings allow the bird to fly relatively fast and also to soar on rising air currents.

HEAD
Sensitive bristles around the eyes and along the bill are used as touch receptors during feeding.

BEAK
The beak is long and strong. It is used for feeding on a wide-ranging diet and for fighting.

HOW BIG IS IT?

SPECIAL ADAPTATION

Crows are intelligent birds, and breeding pairs often cooperate in finding food. The strong bill is used for all purposes, pecking small objects, probing in soil, tearing larger things apart and as a wedge for breaking into solid structures.

Carrion Crow

• ORDER • Passeriformes • FAMILY • Corvidae • SPECIES • *Corvus corone*

VITAL STATISTICS

WEIGHT	450–550g (16–19.4oz)
LENGTH	42–47cm (16.5–18.5in)
WINGSPAN	90–100cm (35.4–39.4in)
NUMBER OF EGGS	3–6 eggs (usually 4–5)
INCUBATION PERIOD	17–18 days
NUMBER OF BROODS	1 a year
TYPICAL DIET	Insects, worms, grubs, small lizards, snakes and amphibians; seeds, fruit, berries, carrion
LIFE SPAN	Up to 18 years

The Carrion Crow is a common crow of western Europe, and is most easily distinguished from a Raven by its smaller size.

WHERE IN THE WORLD?

The Carrion Crow is found in western Europe, from the Iberian Peninsula, across France, Belgium, the Netherlands and Germany, as well as in Great Britain and across Asia.

CREATURE COMPARISONS

The entire head, back, throat, breast, belly, wings and tail of the Carrion Crow are uniformly black. The plumage usually has a distinctive greenish or purplish sheen, giving the bird a glossy appearance. Males and females are similar. The Carrion Crow looks very similar to the Rook, but usually has a distinctly more greenish shine.

BILL
The bill of the Carrion Crow is stouter than that of the Rook, which it resembles, and the nostrils are covered in stiff bristles.

TAIL
The tail is sturdy and wide and is important for manoeuvring in the air and during landing.

LEGS
The black legs are short and sturdy, and the feet have long toes for perching and for hopping around on the ground.

Carrion Crow in flight

HOW BIG IS IT?

SPECIAL ADAPTATION

It was once believed that the Carrion Crow and Hooded Crow were two variants of the same species. They are not, but they do overlap in central Europe, and often interbreed.

Jackdaw

VITAL STATISTICS

WEIGHT	220–270g (7.8–9.5oz)
LENGTH	33–37cm (13.6–14.6in)
WINGSPAN	65–75cm (25.6–29.5in)
NUMBER OF EGGS	3–8 eggs (usually 4–5)
INCUBATION PERIOD	17–19 days
NUMBER OF BROODS	1 a year
TYPICAL DIET	Insects, worms, spiders, seeds, grain, carrion, dead fish
LIFE SPAN	Up to 14 years

CREATURE COMPARISONS

Like most Crows, the Jackdaw is dark. The face, wings, belly and tail are black, sometimes with a bluish tint, while the cheeks, neck and breast are greyish. Males are similar to females, although the male is larger. It can be distinguished from other European crows because of its pigeon-like size, and because it has a silvery iris. Juveniles are darker in colour, and have a bluish iris.

Adult Jackdaw

The familiar Jackdaw is a species of Crow. It is one of the smallest in the Crow Family, and is curious and intelligent.

WHERE IN THE WORLD?

The Jackdaw is found in most of Europe, with the exception of the high north, and across much of Asia and the Middle East. Birds from northern areas migrate south for the winter.

HEAD
The head is rather small for a Crow, and is grey with a characteristically black face and shiny, silvery eye.

BILL
The bill is short and strong, and is used to collect a wide variety of foods, from small animals to carrion.

WINGS
The Jackdaw has smaller and more narrow wings than other species of Crow, and cannot soar on rising air currents.

HOW BIG IS IT?

SPECIAL ADAPTATION

The Jackdaw is a sociable bird. Males and females form a strong pair bond, and birds living in the same area establish a pecking order.

Fish Crow

• **ORDER** • Passeriformes • **FAMILY** • Corvidae • **SPECIES** • *Corvus ossifragus*

VITAL STATISTICS

WEIGHT	195–330g (6.8–11.6oz)
LENGTH	36–41cm (14.2–16.1in)
SEXUAL MATURITY	1 year
INCUBATION PERIOD	16–18 days
FLEDGLING PERIOD	21–28 days
NUMBER OF EGGS	4–5 eggs
NUMBER OF BROODS	1 a year
CALL	A nasal 'kwo'k' and two-toned 'wah-wah'
HABITS	Diurnal, non-migratory
TYPICAL DIET	Crustaceans, aquatic invertebrates; fruit and seeds; carrion and scraps
LIFE SPAN	Unknown

CREATURE COMPARISONS

Crows are intelligent enough to take advantage of any habitat. Carrion Crows, for example, have learned to break open shellfish by dropping them from the air, a technique they have probably learnt from Gulls. Fish Crows know the same trick, but are greater seafood specialists.

Fish Crow in flight

The glossy black Fish Crow combs the beach for food using its expertise in the air to hover and dive for food on the seashore.

WHERE IN THE WORLD?

The Fish Crow is found along the Atlantic coast of the USA, from Rhode Island to the northern part of the Gulf of Mexico. Some northern birds may migrate south in winter.

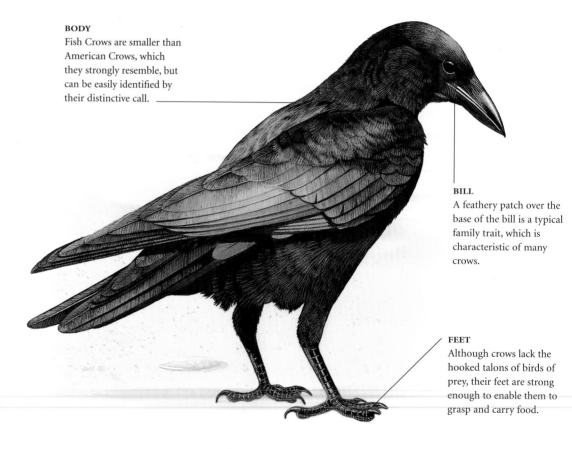

BODY
Fish Crows are smaller than American Crows, which they strongly resemble, but can be easily identified by their distinctive call.

BILL
A feathery patch over the base of the bill is a typical family trait, which is characteristic of many crows.

FEET
Although crows lack the hooked talons of birds of prey, their feet are strong enough to enable them to grasp and carry food.

HOW BIG IS IT?

SPECIAL ADAPTATION

Fish Crows are such accomplished fliers that they can stop and turn in flight, and even scoop up food from the surface of the water. This aerial skill enables them to take food that may be exposed by the tide for only a few moments.

House Crow

• **ORDER** • Passeriformes • **FAMILY** • Corvidae • **SPECIES** • *Corvus splendens*

VITAL STATISTICS

WEIGHT	250–350g (8.8–12.3oz)
LENGTH	40–43cm (15.7–17in)
SEXUAL MATURITY	2 years
LAYS EGGS	March–July
INCUBATION PERIOD	15–18 days
FLEDGLING PERIOD	27–28 days
NUMBER OF EGGS	2–5 eggs
NUMBER OF BROODS	1 a year but 2 are possible
CALL	Loud, raucous, 'ka-ka'
HABITS	Diurnal, non-migratory
TYPICAL DIET	Insects, plants; carrion and human food scraps

CREATURE COMPARISONS

House Crows are so numerous that it is difficult to be certain how many sub-species exist. Up to five are recognized, and these vary in both the thickness of their bills and the colour of their plumage. The Southern Chinese sub-species (shown below) is the darkest.

Southern Chinese sub-species

In many Asian cities the House Crow is a real nuisance, dive bombing school children in order to steal their lunches.

WHERE IN THE WORLD?

These widespread birds are natives of Asia, where populations exist in most towns and cities. The species has been introduced into East Africa, and also Australia, where it has been exterminated as a pest.

WINGS
A pair of long, broad wings enable House Crows to be both powerful and acrobatic in the air.

BILL
The House Crow's long bill can be used for rooting in the earth for insects, for picking through carrion or tearing up vegetation.

FEET
Strong feet with long toes allow these omnivorous birds to hang upside down to reach the trickiest food sources.

HOW BIG IS IT?

SPECIAL ADAPTATION

Crows are often found in towns and cities, where this adaptable and intelligent species enjoys rich pickings, taking advantage of all the food waste left in bins and tips. Crows make use of pylons and telegraph poles as a handy alternative to trees for perching on.

Blue Jay

• **ORDER** • Passeriformes • **FAMILY** • Corvidae • **SPECIES** • *Cyanocitta cristata*

VITAL STATISTICS

WEIGHT	70–100g (2.5–3.5oz)
LENGTH	22–30cm (8.7–12in)
WINGSPAN	34–43cm (13.4–7in)
NUMBER OF EGGS	3–6 eggs (usually 4–5)
INCUBATION PERIOD	16–18 days
NUMBER OF BROODS	2 a year
TYPICAL DIET	Acorns, nuts, seeds, fruit, berries, insects, snails, grubs
LIFE SPAN	Unknown

The Blue Jay is a member of the Crow Family, and is not closely related to other Jays.

WHERE IN THE WORLD?

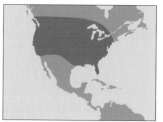

The Blue Jay is found across much of eastern and central North America, from southern Canada to southern Florida and northeastern Texas. Northern birds migrate south for the winter.

BILL
The sturdy bill is black, and is used as an all-purpose tool for gathering a wide range of different foods.

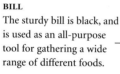

CREATURE COMPARISONS

The head, throat and breast are white, and there is a thin black collar around the throat. The black collar extends around the back of the head, forming a border between the white head and distinctive blue crest on its head. The back, wings and tail are a strong shade of blue. Females are similar to males, but are slightly smaller.

WINGS
The Blue Jay has short wide wings. It is not a strong flier, although it is able to migrate considerable distances.

TAIL
The blue tail is long and graceful, adorned with black cross-bars along its length.

Blue Jay

HOW BIG IS IT?

SPECIAL ADAPTATION

A male and female Blue Jay will mate for life. They will build a nest, collect food, and rear the chicks together. The female broods the eggs herself, however, and is fed by the male.

Green Jay

• ORDER • Passeriformes • FAMILY • Corvidae • SPECIES • *Cyanocorax yncas*

VITAL STATISTICS

WEIGHT	65–110g (2.3–3.9oz)
LENGTH	25–28cm (9.0–11.0in)
WINGSPAN	45–55cm (17.7–21.7in)
NUMBER OF EGGS	3 eggs
INCUBATION PERIOD	18–24 days
NUMBER OF BROODS	1 a year
TYPICAL DIE	Insects and other small creatures, acorns, seeds, eggs, carrion
LIFE SPAN	Unknown

Despite its stunning colouring, it is often easier to hear this bird in the treetops than to spot it because its plumage camouflages it so well.

WHERE IN THE WORLD?

The Green Jay has two populations, which are not connected. One is found from southern Texas, through Mexico and into Central America; the other in Colombia, Venezuela, Ecuador, Peru and Bolivia.

CREATURE COMPARISONS

This colourful jay has a yellow breast and underside, and a rich green upper side. The tail is green from above but yellow from below. The sides of the face are black with a blue stripe. The northern population has a blue head with a black mask, and the blue bristles above the beak are small. Birds of the southern population are usually larger, and have yellowish-white feathers on top of the head, and long blue bristle above the beak.

Northern species

HEAD
The large blue bristles are used as display to other birds, but are much less prominent in northern birds.

WINGS
The short wide wings give great manoeuvrability when flying among branches.

TAIL
The sides of the tail appear yellow when viewed from above, but this is due to the lower, yellow feathers being visible besides the green ones.

HOW BIG IS IT?

SPECIAL ADAPTATION

Unlike most animals, the Green Jay will not flee an area where there has been a forest fire. Instead, it will often to bathe in the smoke from smouldering trees. This unusual behaviour is believed to rid the plumage of unwanted pests.

239

Jay (Eurasian)

• ORDER • Passeriformes **• FAMILY •** Corvidae **• SPECIES •** *Garrulus glandarius*

With their elegant pinkish plumage and brilliant blue wing panels, Eurasian Jays are one of the most handsome members of the widespread Crow Family.

VITAL STATISTICS

WEIGHT	170g (6oz)
LENGTH	32–35cm (12.6–14in)
WINGSPAN	54–58cm (21.2–23in)
SEXUAL MATURITY	1–2 years
INCUBATION PERIOD	16–17 days
FLEDGLING PERIOD	21–22 days
NUMBER OF EGGS	4–6 eggs
NUMBER OF BROODS	1 a year
TYPICAL DIET	Nuts, seeds, especially acorns; invertebrates; birds' eggs; small mammals and carrion
LIFE SPAN	Up to 18 years

CREATURE COMPARISONS

In Europe, Eurasian Jays are simply known as Jays, as other species are rare visitors. However, several races exist and all look different. This means that identifying individuals is difficult, especially as the juvenile (shown) also varies, being redder and less streaked than adults.

WHERE IN THE WORLD?

These adaptable members of the Crow Family can be found wherever there is a plentiful supply of food. Populations are usually resident in western Europe and central and southeastern Asia.

HEAD
The Jay's black and white, streaked crest can be raised or dropped in reflection of the bird's mood.

BILL
Although they can be shy around humans, Jays are noisy neighbours and are often heard long before they are seen.

TAIL
Jays can be difficult to spot, but a flash of the birds' distinctive white rump is a good indicator.

Juvenile

HOW BIG IS IT?

SPECIAL ADAPTATION

Members of the Crow Family are highly protective of their young and it is not unusual to see individuals or flocks of birds mobbing birds of prey to drive them away from the nest. Ironically, though, Jays will habitually steal eggs from other birds' nests.

Nutcracker (Spotted)

• ORDER • Passeriformes • FAMILY • Corvidae • SPECIES • *Nucifraga caryocatactes*

The slender-bodied Spotted Nutcracker does not look like a typical member of the Crow Family. Yet, as soon as their raucous screams are heard, their heritage becomes apparent.

VITAL STATISTICS

WEIGHT	160g (5.6oz)
LENGTH	32–35cm (12.6–14in)
WINGSPAN	49–53cm (19.3–21in)
LAYS EGGS	March–May
INCUBATION PERIOD	18 days
FLEDGLING PERIOD	23 days
NUMBER OF EGGS	2–4 eggs
CALL	Like Eurasian Jay ('kraak-kraak-kraak-kraak')
HABITS	Diurnal, non-migratory
TYPICAL DIET	Seeds, especially pine nuts; insects, birds' eggs and carrion

WHERE IN THE WORLD?

Spotted Nutcrackers make their homes across Europe, from Scandinavia in the west to Siberia in the east, and into eastern Asia as far as Japan. Nests are typically built in high mountainous woodlands.

CREATURE COMPARISONS

All birds play a valuable part in the ecology of the planet, but the positive impact of Nutcrackers has been well documented. These birds often store seeds for later use, but do not always eat them. This has helped re-establish Swiss Pine in areas previously cleared by people.

BODY
As would be expected from its name, the Spotted Nutcracker's chocolate brown body is liberally sprinkled with white spots.

BILL
Nucifraga, the Nutcracker's scientific name, can be translated as 'to shatter nuts', in reference to its seed-cracking bill.

FEET
Nutcrackers are passerine birds, which is the name given to species that perch, the shape of the feet being adapted to this purpose.

Spotted Nutcracker in flight

HOW BIG IS IT?

SPECIAL ADAPTATION

The more flexible a species is, the more successful it is likely to be. Nutcrackers are growing in numbers because they are opportunists and, when seeds are scarce, they will look for other foods. They prefer seeds but will eat anything, from insects to leftovers.

241

Magpie (Common)

• ORDER • Passeriformes **• FAMILY •** Corvidae **• SPECIES •** *Pica pica*

VITAL STATISTICS

WEIGHT	Males: 240g (8.5oz) Females: 200g (7oz)
LENGTH	40–51cm (15.7–20in)
WINGSPAN	52–60cm (20.5–23.6in)
SEXUAL MATURITY	2 years
LAYS EGGS	April–May
INCUBATION PERIOD	20–21 days
NUMBER OF EGGS	4–7 eggs
NUMBER OF BROODS	1 a year
TYPICAL DIET	Insects, seeds, fruit and carrion
LIFE SPAN	Typically 5 years

Magpies are intelligent, sociable birds. Thanks to their dramatic black and white plumage, they are also one of the easiest to identify.

WHERE IN THE WORLD?

Magpies prefer open woods, scrubland and farmland. However, this adaptable species is now increasingly found in urban areas throughout Europe, Asia and western North America.

CREATURE COMPARISONS

Magpies leave the nest around 30 days after hatching, but are fed by their parents for a further four weeks. After this, juveniles form loose flocks with other young birds. These are easily identified because the birds have duller plumage and shorter tails than adults.

Adult Magpie

BILL
This powerful, curved bill is the perfect multi-purpose tool for an opportunist prepared to make a meal out of almost anything.

BODY
Seen up close, Magpies are not actually black and white (pied). Their plumage has an iridescent sheen, like a beetle's shell.

FEET
Magpies' feet have have three toes pointing forwards and one pointing backwards. This gives them a jerky, uneven motion when walking.

HOW BIG IS IT?

SPECIAL ADAPTATION
When it comes to choosing a mate, female Magpies know what they like. Over thousands of years, sexual selection by females has favoured males with the longest, most impressive tails. In fact, the tails of male Magpies can be up to half their body length.

Alpine Chough

• **ORDER** • Passeriformes • **FAMILY** • Corvidae • **SPECIES** • *Pyrrhocorax graculus*

The Alpine Chough is also known as the Yellow-billed Chough, and breeds high up in the mountains.

VITAL STATISTICS

WEIGHT	300–350g (10.6–12.3oz)
LENGTH	36–39cm (14.2–15.4in)
WINGSPAN	65–74cm (25.6–29in)
NUMBER OF EGGS	3–5 eggs
INCUBATION PERIOD	21–22 days
NUMBER OF BROODS	1 a year
TYPICAL DIET	Insects, worms, snails, spiders, seeds, berries
LIFE SPAN	Up to 20 years

WHERE IN THE WORLD?

The Alpine Chough is found locally in high mountainous areas in southern Europe, and across parts of the Middle East and parts of central and southern Asia.

CREATURE COMPARISONS

The head, neck, body and tail of the Alpine Chough are uniformly glossy black with a metallic lustre. The bill is short and yellow, and the legs are long and red. Males and females are similar. The Alpine Chough looks very similar to the closely related Red-billed Chough, which has a distinctly larger, curved red bill.

Alpine Choughs

WINGS
The wings are large and wide, enabling the Alpine Chough to glide around on rising air currents.

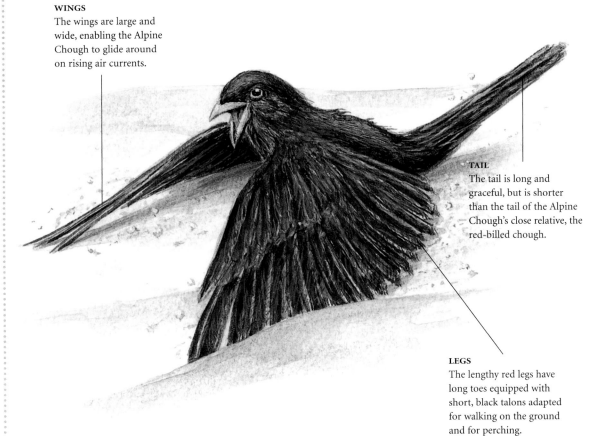

TAIL
The tail is long and graceful, but is shorter than the tail of the Alpine Chough's close relative, the red-billed chough.

LEGS
The lengthy red legs have long toes equipped with short, black talons adapted for walking on the ground and for perching.

HOW BIG IS IT?

SPECIAL ADAPTATION

The males perform a special mating dance to attract the females. A male will raise its head and walk around on stiff legs while scraping the tail along the ground.

Chough (Red-billed)

• ORDER • Passeriformes • FAMILY • Corvidae • SPECIES • *Pyrrhocorax pyrrhocorax*

VITAL STATISTICS

Weight	310g (11oz)
Length	39–40cm (15.3–15.7in)
Wingspan	68–80cm (26.8–31.5in)
Sexual Maturity	2–4 years
Lays Eggs	April–May
Incubation Period	17–21 days
Number of Eggs	3–6 eggs
Number of Broods	1 a year
Typical Diet	Worms, insects; some seeds and grains in winter
Life Span	Up to 16 years

Choughs are spectacular aerial performers, diving with their wings almost closed, and turning mid-air somersaults, with an ease we associate with birds of prey.

WHERE IN THE WORLD?

The Red-billed Chough is increasingly rare in the UK, but larger populations of are found in Europe and across central Asia. It prefers open mountainous regions with inaccessible cliffs for nesting.

CREATURE COMPARISONS

Many birds are sexually dimorphic, meaning the sexes look different. However, both male and female Choughs have the same glossy black coloration, long, curved red bills and red legs. In comparison, juveniles, during their first year, tend to have orange-yellow bills, pink legs and less shiny plumage.

Juvenile

BODY
Although Choughs may look completely black, their plumage has a distinct sheen, which is green-blue on the wings and purple on the body.

HEAD
Before species numbers began to plummet, the ringing 'ki'chuf' call of the Chough was once a familiar cry in Britain.

WINGS
Choughs are acrobatic fliers and can often be seen soaring over the wind-battered cliffs where they make their homes.

HOW BIG IS IT?

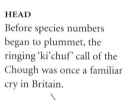

SPECIAL ADAPTATION

Choughs belong to the Crow Family, a group of opportunists that will make a meal of almost anything. However, unlike crows, Choughs have long, downwards-curved bills. These are adapted to probe the earth for insects, which provide an additional food source in winter.

Andean Cock-of-the-Rock

• **ORDER** • Passeriformes • **FAMILY** • Cotingidae • **SPECIES** • *Rupicola peruviana*

VITAL STATISTICS

WEIGHT	275–350g (9.7–12.3oz)
LENGTH	30–32cm (12–12.6in)
WINGSPAN	60–65cm (23.6–25.6in)
NUMBER OF EGGS	2 eggs
INCUBATION PERIOD	22–28 days
NUMBER OF BROODS	1 a year
TYPICAL DIET	A variety of fruits, berries, some seeds and insects
LIFE SPAN	Unknown

The Andean Cock-of-the-Rock is one of the most colourful birds in South America, and the national bird of Peru.

WHERE IN THE WORLD?

The Andean Cock-of-the-Rock lives in the cloud forests on the eastern slopes of the Andes Mountains, and is found in Venezuela, Columbia, Ecuador, Bolivia and Peru.

CREATURE COMPARISONS

Males are most beautiful, and have a bright scarlet-red or orange head, neck, back, breast and belly. The wings are black with a large white patch on the upper side. The tail is also black. The eyes are bright yellow with a black center. Females are much drabber and are greenish or olive-brown overall, and they are also slightly smaller than the males.

Female

BILL
The bill is short and strongly hooked, somewhat resembling a chicken's bill, and is used to gather a variety of fruits.

HEAD
Both sexes have a large, conspicuous crest on top of the head, but the crest is much larger in the colourful males.

WINGS
The wings are wide and strong, giving the bird the manoeuvrability needed for flying around in the canopy.

HOW BIG IS IT?

SPECIAL ADAPTATION

Males gather in special areas in the trees, called leks, where they dance and perform displays to attract females. Despite the colourful plumage, the birds are not often seen, however.

Mistletoebird

• **ORDER** • Passeriformes • **FAMILY** • Dicaeidae • **SPECIES** • *Dicaeum hirundinaceum*

VITAL STATISTICS

WEIGHT	10–12g (0.4oz)
LENGTH	10–12cm (3.9–4.7in)
WINGSPAN	20–25cm (8–10in)
NUMBER OF EGGS	3 eggs
INCUBATION PERIOD	3–16 days
NUMBER OF BROODS	1 a year
TYPICAL DIET	Mainly mistletoe berries; nectar, pollen, insects
LIFE SPAN	Unknown but probably only a few years

This bird can be found wherever mistletoe grows throughout parts of Australasia, and it has adapted an intimate relationship with this plant.

WHERE IN THE WORLD?

The Mistletoebird is found throughout Australia, although it does not live in the drier parts of the country or in Tasmania. It is also found on Papua New Guinea and parts of eastern Indonesia.

CREATURE COMPARISONS

Adult males have a bluish upper side and a striking red throat and breast. The rest of the chest is whitish with a dark stripe. The female is much drabber. A female has a greyish upper side and a whitish underside. The lower part of the base of the tail is pinkish in both sexes. Juvenile birds look similar to females but have an orange beak instead of black.

Female

WINGS
The wings are short, broad and powerful. The Mistletoe bird is a fast flier, darting about in the treetops.

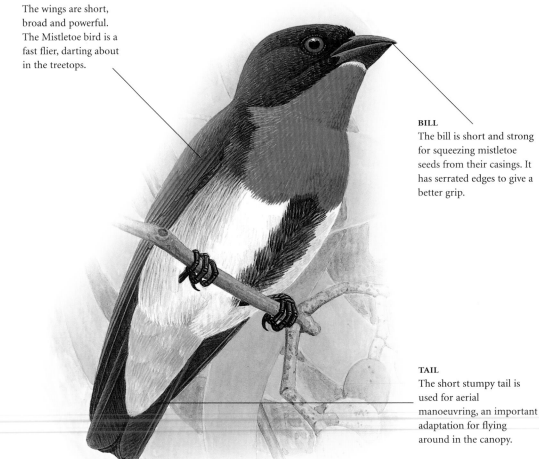

BILL
The bill is short and strong for squeezing mistletoe seeds from their casings. It has serrated edges to give a better grip.

TAIL
The short stumpy tail is used for aerial manoeuvring, an important adaptation for flying around in the canopy.

HOW BIG IS IT?

SPECIAL ADAPTATION

The Mistletoebird's digestive system is able to digest berries quickly. The food passes quickly through the stomach and into the intestines, where the flesh is digested, while the seeds are excreted after only 15–20 minutes.

Magpie-Lark

• **ORDER** • Passeriformes • **FAMILY** • Dicruridae • **SPECIES** • *Grallina cyanoleuca*

Magpie-Larks may look harmless enough, but looks can be deceptive. In the breeding season, it is so aggressive that it will attack its own reflection.

VITAL STATISTICS

WEIGHT	92g (3.2oz)
LENGTH	26–30cm (10.2–12in)
SEXUAL MATURITY	1 year
LAYS EGGS	August–February, but varies with local conditions
INCUBATION PERIOD	17–18 days
FLEDGLING PERIOD	18–23 days
NUMBER OF EGGS	3–5 eggs
NUMBER OF BROODS	2 a year, but 4 are possible
TYPICAL DIET	Insects and small animals
HABITS	Diurnal, non-migratory

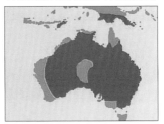

WHERE IN THE WORLD?

Magpie-Larks are a highly adaptable and successful species. Having spread across much of Australia, they are now found in most rural and urban areas, excluding the inland desert and Tasmania.

CREATURE COMPARISONS

Although male and female Magpie-Larks look similar at first glance, they are easy to tell apart. Females have a white throat, while males have a black throat and white eyebrow. Juveniles have the female's white throat and the male's eyebrow.

Juvenile (left), female (right).

BILL
The Magpie-Lark's sharp, narrow bill is a handy multi-purpose tool, useful for both catching insects and building nests.

WINGS
These distinctive birds have a rather unusual method of getting airborne. They leap, vertically, from the ground, flapping wildly.

BODY
Despite their name (given by European settlers), these birds are neither Magpies nor Larks but are related to Drongos, which they resemble.

HOW BIG IS IT?

SPECIAL ADAPTATION
The more flexible a species is, the more successful it will be. Magpie-Larks are successful because they are opportunists with a very wide-ranging diet. Their habitat requirements are simple too, including a tree to nest in and mud for making the nest.

Lark Bunting

• **ORDER** • Passeriformes • **FAMILY** • Emberizidae • **SPECIES** • *Calamospiza melanocorys*

VITAL STATISTICS

WEIGHT	30–51g (1–2oz)
LENGTH	18cm (7.1in)
WINGSPAN	28cm (11in)
SEXUAL MATURITY	1–2 years
INCUBATION PERIOD	11–12 days
FLEDGLING PERIOD	9 days
NUMBER OF EGGS	4–5 eggs
NUMBER OF BROODS	1 a year
TYPICAL DIET	Seeds in winter and insects in summer
LIFE SPAN	Up to 10 years

In common with their namesakes, the Larks, Lark Buntings are famous for their rich repertoire of musical songs, whistles, rattles and trilling calls.

WHERE IN THE WORLD?

The traditional home of the Lark Bunting is on the prairie grasslands of central Canada and Midwestern USA. However, numbers are declining due to the loss of their natural habitat to urban development.

CREATURE COMPARISONS

In their pied plumage, male breeding Lark Buntings may be dramatic, but the paler females look more like typical buntings. Their upper parts are a dull grey-brown with buff underparts, and heavy striping on the back and breast. Wings are edged with dark brown.

Female

WINGS
Bright white patches in the middle of each wing help make the males more visible to any potential mates.

BODY
Male Lark Buntings typically fly over their territory singing as they descend to declare their ownership of an area.

BILL
Wedge-shaped bills are usually associated with seed-eating birds, like finches, to which buntings are related. However, Lark Buntings also eat insects.

HOW BIG IS IT?

SPECIAL ADAPTATION

Although songs and verbal calls are an important part of the male Lark Bunting's breeding display, so too is its plumage. The bold black and white coloration is designed to make the birds visible from a distance, an important consideration when trying attract a mate.

Rock Bunting

• ORDER • Passeriformes **• FAMILY •** Emberizidae **• SPECIES •** *Emberiza cia*

VITAL STATISTICS

WEIGHT	22–27g (0.7–1.0oz)
LENGTH	15–16cm (6–6.3in)
WINGSPAN	30–35cm (12–14in)
NUMBER OF EGGS	3–5 eggs
INCUBATION PERIOD	12–13 days
NUMBER OF BROODS	1 a year
TYPICAL DIET	Seeds, insects
LIFE SPAN	Up to 8 years

The Rock Bunting is a common bird but it is rarely seen because it hides among twigs and branches.

WHERE IN THE WORLD?

The Rock Bunting is most often found in mountainous areas across southern Europe and parts of North Africa, extending eastwards across central Asia and the Himalayas.

CREATURE COMPARISONS

The male has a brownish or chestnut back and upper neck, while the wings are brown or chestnut with distinctive dark stripes. The head and throat are pale grey, with dark facial markings. The breast and belly are buff. The tail is long and brown. Females are similar to males, but are usually slightly drabber in colour.

Male

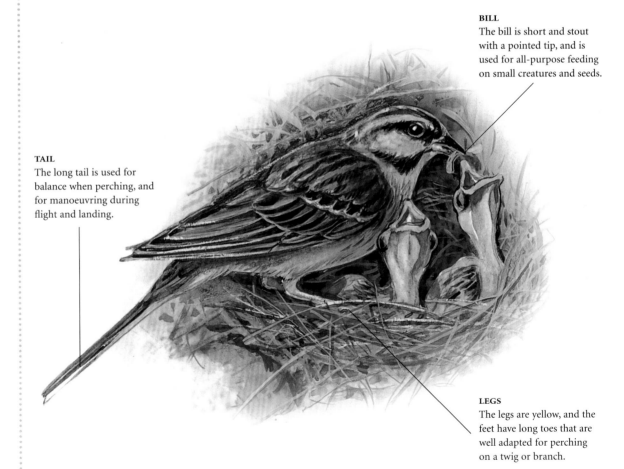

TAIL
The long tail is used for balance when perching, and for manoeuvring during flight and landing.

BILL
The bill is short and stout with a pointed tip, and is used for all-purpose feeding on small creatures and seeds.

LEGS
The legs are yellow, and the feet have long toes that are well adapted for perching on a twig or branch.

HOW BIG IS IT?

SPECIAL ADAPTATION
The Rock Bunting is able to snatch spiders from their webs. It hovers in front of the web, and quickly snatches the spider without getting entangled in the sticky silk.

Yellowhammer

VITAL STATISTICS

WEIGHT	31g (1oz)
LENGTH	15.5–17cm (6.1–6.7in)
WINGSPAN	26cm (10.2in)
SEXUAL MATURITY	1 year
INCUBATION PERIOD	13–14 days
FLEDGLING PERIOD	13–16 days
NUMBER OF EGGS	3–6 eggs
NUMBER OF BROODS	2–3 a year
TYPICAL DIET	Seeds and cereals; insects during the breeding season
LIFE SPAN	Typically 3 years

CREATURE COMPARISONS

In the bird world, it is common for chicks to be raised by their mothers alone. However, Yellowhammers share the job of raising their young. The female builds the cup-shaped nest and incubates the eggs, while the male helps out with the feeding duties.

The female builds the nest

The children's author Enid Blyton (1897–1968) gave bird-watchers an unforgettable way of recalling the Yellowhammers' song: 'little bit of bread and no cheese'.

WHERE IN THE WORLD?

Grassland and farms, where there is a plentiful supply of seeds, are the preferred haunts of Yellowhammers. Birds breed across Europe, western and Central Asia and New Zealand where the species was introduced.

BODY
The male Yellowhammer has a yellow head and underparts. Its back is browner, with speckled black streaks.

BILL
A thick, wedge-shaped bill is usually associated with seed-eating birds, like Finches and Buntings. Yellowhammers belong to the Bunting Family.

FEET
The feet of the Yellowhammer are typical of perching birds, with one short, backwards-facing toe and two forwards-facing toes.

HOW BIG IS IT?

SPECIAL ADAPTATION

Camouflage plays an important role, keeping both chicks and mature birds safe from predators. Many birds, including the Yellowhammer, have also adapted to lay eggs that have their own form of so-called cryptic camouflage, which blends in with the surroundings.

Ortolan Bunting

• **ORDER** • Passeriformes • **FAMILY** • Emberizidae • **SPECIES** • *Emberiza hortulana*

In the French countryside, the Ortolan Bunting is celebrated for its flavour. Traditionally, diners drape a linen napkin over their head while eating the bird to preserve the aromas.

VITAL STATISTICS

WEIGHT	20–25g (0.7–0.9oz)
LENGTH	16cm (6.3in)
WINGSPAN	26 (10.2in)
INCUBATION PERIOD	11–12 days
FLEDGLING PERIOD	12–13 days
NUMBER OF EGGS	4–5 eggs
NUMBER OF BROODS	1 a year
TYPICAL DIET	Seeds and cereals; insects during the breeding season
LIFE SPAN	2–3 years

WHERE IN THE WORLD?

These shy birds can be found in most of Europe and western regions of Asia. Populations typically migrate south to Africa in the winter, and return only at the start of spring.

CREATURE COMPARISONS

All birds have been eaten at some point in human history. However, Ortolans have the distinction of being gourmet food in France. Here, birds used to meet a grisly end, having been force-fed all their life, and then drowned in Armagnac.

Ortolans Buntings

EYES
Eyes, set on the side of the Ortolan's head, give the bird as wide a field of vision as possible.

BILL
The Ortolan's bill is slightly longer than that of most Buntings, but retains the wedge shape that is common in seed-eaters.

THROAT
Ortolans can easily be mistaken for the slightly smaller Cretzschmar Bunting. However, Ortolans have a yellowish throat. The neck of the Cretzschmar is rusty red.

HOW BIG IS IT?

SPECIAL ADAPTATION

Once Ortolan Buntings have established a nest, males declare their ownership of the site by circling over their territory, singing as they go. This may seem like a waste of energy, but it is a very practical development that helps to avoid more serious confrontations later.

Reed Bunting (Common)

• ORDER • Passeriformes • FAMILY • Emberizidae • SPECIES • *Emberiza schoeniclus*

The appealing and widespread Common Reed Bunting looks similar to many other little brown birds, but every male's mating song is unique.

VITAL STATISTICS

WEIGHT	21g (0.7oz)
LENGTH	13.5–16cm (5.3–6.3in)
WINGSPAN	24cm (9.4in)
SEXUAL MATURITY	1 year
LAYS EGGS	April–June
INCUBATION PERIOD	12–15 days
NUMBER OF EGGS	4–5 eggs
NUMBER OF BROODS	2 a year, occasionally 3
TYPICAL DIET	Insects when feeding young, otherwise seeds
LIFE SPAN	Typically 3 years

WHERE IN THE WORLD?

As the name suggests, Reed Buntings are often found in reedbeds, although some now breed in farms and gardens. Populations are found across Europe and temperate regions of northern Asia.

CREATURE COMPARISONS

When they sing, male Reed Buntings can usually be seen perching on top of a reed head or bush. The female Reed Bunting has a much duller, browner plumage than the male. This adaptation is a form of cryptic camouflage that blends in with the environment and keeps the nesting birds and their eggs safe from danger.

Female

HEAD
In their breeding plumage, the male Reed Bunting has a black head with a white collar.

WINGS
Buntings will divert predators away from the nest by shuffling along the ground as though they have a broken wing.

TAIL
Buntings are sparrow-sized but slightly slimmer in the body, and with a long, notched tail that trails behind them in flight.

HOW BIG IS IT?

SPECIAL ADAPTATION

Reed Buntings that breed in the north of their range have smaller, less bulbous bills, which are suitable for eating seeds and small insects. Those from southeastern Europe have sturdier bills to cope with tougher seeds and a more varied diet.

Red-billed Firefinch

• **ORDER** • Passeriformes • **FAMILY** • Estrildidae *(under review)* • **SPECIES** •*Lagonosticta senegalaitalic*

VITAL STATISTICS

WEIGHT	8.3g (0.3oz)
LENGTH	9–12cm (3.5–4.7in)
SEXUAL MATURITY	1 year
INCUBATION PERIOD	11–14 days
FLEDGLING PERIOD	14–20 days
NUMBER OF EGGS	1–6 eggs
NUMBER OF BROODS	Up to 5 a year are possible
CALL	Soft 'queet-queet'
HABITS	Diurnal, non-migratory
TYPICAL DIET	Seeds; occasionally insects

The vividly coloured Red-billed Firefinch is a common sight all over sub-Saharan Africa, where urban birds are often kept as colourful – and tuneful – pets.

WHERE IN THE WORLD?

This small gregarious bird can be found in most regions of sub-Saharan Africa. Populations tend to be resident although birds may be nomadic, moving to follow seasonal food within their own region.

CREATURE COMPARISONS

Adult male Red-billed Firefinches have scarlet bodies and brown wings. Females (shown below) are brown all over, with a characteristic red patch in front of each eye. This patch helps bird-watchers to distinguish females from the juvenile birds, which look very similar, but lack the red mark.

Female

WINGS
Male Red-billed Firefinches have brown wings, though the body is scarlet.

BILL
All Finches have short, thick bills. These work like a pair of miniature nutcrackers to split open seed cases.

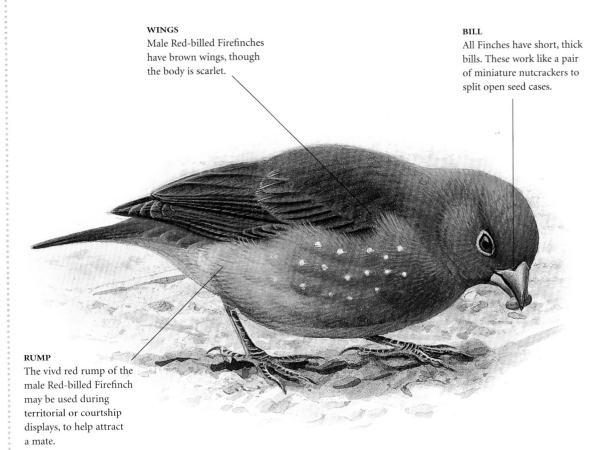

RUMP
The vivd red rump of the male Red-billed Firefinch may be used during territorial or courtship displays, to help attract a mate.

HOW BIG IS IT?

SPECIAL ADAPTATION

Most birds preen not only themselves, but family members too. This has a practical purpose because partners can groom areas that birds cannot reach for themselves. Such close contact is also important socially because it helps maintain a bond between mated couples.

Zebra Finch

• **ORDER** • Passeriformes • **FAMILY** • Estrildidae • **SPECIES** • *Taeniopygia guttata*

VITAL STATISTICS

WEIGHT	12g (0.4oz)
LENGTH	10–12cm (4–4.7in)
LAYS EGGS	October–April, but varies with rainfall
SEXUAL MATURITY	70–80 days after hatching.
INCUBATION PERIOD	14 days
FLEDGLING PERIOD	21 days
NUMBER OF EGGS	3–12 eggs
NUMBER OF BROODS	1 a year
TYPICAL DIET	Seeds; occasionally fruit and insects
LIFE SPAN	Typically 5 years.

CREATURE COMPARISONS

Most male birds sing, especially during the breeding season, when they use their songs to attract a mate or defend territory. Songs vary, but they often begin as unconnected notes and get more elaborate as birds experiment, eventually copying the songs their fathers made.

A singing Zebra Finch

With its plump, rounded body and bulky, seed-cracking bill, the Australian Zebra Finch is perhaps one of the most Finch-like of all Finches.

WHERE IN THE WORLD?

These sociable birds can be found in large flocks on Timor, the Lesser Sunda Islands and throughout Australia, with the exception of the Cape York Peninsula and some coastal regions.

CHEEKS
Zebra Finches are also known as Chestnut-Eared Finches because males have rusty-brown cheek patches. Females lack this characteristic.

BODY
Zebra Finches get their common name from the distinctive, black-and-white zebra-style barring around their neck, rump and tail.

BILL
The colourful Zebra Finch can always be identified by its bulky bill.

HOW BIG IS IT?

SPECIAL ADAPTATION

Some birds take a new partner each season. Others have multiple partners. Most, including Zebra Finches, mate for life, choosing a new partner only when the previous one dies. This is a sensible strategy because established pairs raise more young than inexperienced couples.

Lesser Green Broadbill

• **ORDER** • Passeriformes • **FAMILY** • Eurylaimidae • **SPECIES** • *Calyptomena viridis*

VITAL STATISTICS

LENGTH	14–17cm (5.5–6.7in)
SEXUAL MATURITY	Unknown
INCUBATION PERIOD	Around 17 days
FLEDGLING PERIOD	22–23 days
NUMBER OF EGGS	2–3 eggs
NUMBER OF BROODS	1 a year, but another clutch may be laid if the first fails
CALL	Quiet, bubbling 'toi-toi-oi-oi-oi-oick'
HABITS	Diurnal, non-migratory
TYPICAL DIET	Fruit, especially figs
LIFE SPAN	Up to 19 years in captivity

CREATURE COMPARISONS

These curious-looking birds are sexually dimorphic, which means that the males and females of the species differ in appearance. Males have black bands across their wings and a distinct, black spot behind each eye. Females and juveniles tend to have duller green plumage.

Female

With their dark green, camouflaged bodies and bills designed for eating forest fruits, Lesser Green Broadbills are perfectly adapted for life among the trees.

WHERE IN THE WORLD?

Lesser Green Broadbills make their homes in the evergreen forests of Thailand, Malaysia, Sumatra, Borneo and Indonesia. Sadly, numbers are falling rapidly due to loss of suitable habitats.

BILL
A crest of short feathers sits above the bird's bill. It is so thick it and almost covers the bill. —

BODY
Dark green plumage is the ideal camouflage for a species that lives among the leaves and vegetation of an evergreen forest. —

WINGS
Bands of black and pale green on the wings help to differentiate the males from the females.

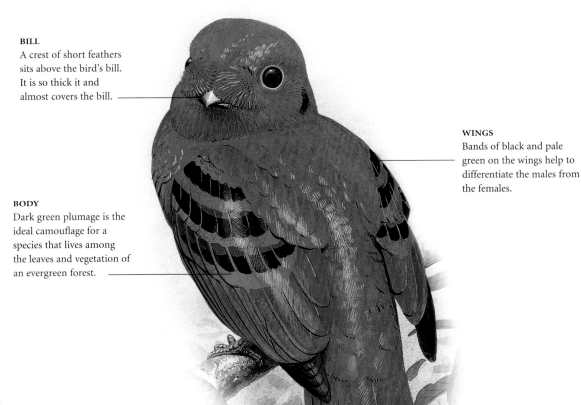

HOW BIG IS IT?

SPECIAL ADAPTATION

These birds may have broad bills, but they lack the sharp cutting edges other broad-billed species have. This is because soft fruits can be eaten without cracking open shells or seeds. Additionally, Lesser Green Broadbills have such wide mouths they can eat large fruit whole.

Redpoll (Common)

• **ORDER** • Passeriformes • **FAMILY** • Fringillidae • **SPECIES** • *Carduelis flammea*

VITAL STATISTICS

WEIGHT	14g (0.5oz)
LENGTH	11.5–14cm (4.5–5.5in)
WINGSPAN	23cm (9in)
SEXUAL MATURITY	1 year
INCUBATION PERIOD	10–12 days
FLEDGLING PERIOD	11–14 days
NUMBER OF EGGS	4–6 eggs
NUMBER OF BROODS	2 a year
TYPICAL DIET	Seeds, especially conifer seeds
LIFE SPAN	Up to 7 years

Thanks to the growing number of commercially managed woodlands, the future of the Common Redpoll is looking almost as rosy as its red cap.

WHERE IN THE WORLD?

These finches breed all over northern Europe, northern Asia, Alaska, Canada and Greenland. They can tolerate cold weather and tend to move locally in search of food rather than migrating.

CREATURE COMPARISONS

Members of the Finch Family come in all shapes and sizes, but none are more gloriously attired than the Goldfinch. Like the Redpoll, it has distinctive red markings, although these form a large, dark red mask that extends (in the males) to just behind the eye.

Juvenile (left), female (centre), male (right)

HEAD
It is the vibrant, red cap that gives this species its common name. It is present on both males and females.

BILL
The Redpoll belongs to the large and varied Finch Family, members of which can be identified by their characteristically bulky bill.

FEET
The Redpoll is a passerine, which is a term used to describe perching birds. Like all perching birds, its feet are designed to grip branches.

HOW BIG IS IT?

SPECIAL ADAPTATION
Like all successful species, Redpoll are always ready to adapt their diet to accommodate any new and plentiful food source. Fortunately, they are ideally equipped for the job, with such strong feet that they can reach most seeds with ease, even if it means hanging upside-down.

Linnet (Common)

VITAL STATISTICS

WEIGHT	19g (0.8oz)
LENGTH	12.5–14cm (4.9–5.5in)
WINGSPAN	24cm (9.4in)
SEXUAL MATURITY	1 year
INCUBATION PERIOD	13–14 days
FLEDGLING PERIOD	13–14 days
NUMBER OF EGGS	4–5 eggs
NUMBER OF BROODS	2 a year
TYPICAL DIET	Seeds
LIFE SPAN	Typically 2 years

British Linnets were once kept as songbirds, a fact celebrated by famous music hall song 'My Old Man', in which the singer has an 'old cock Linnet'.

WHERE IN THE WORLD?

These tuneful birds are found in Europe, North Africa and western and central parts of Asia. Their ideal homes are in open countryside, where there is a plentiful supply of seeds to eat.

CREATURE COMPARISONS

Outside of the breeding season, Linnets, in common with other members of the Finch Family, are generally gregarious birds, migrating and feeding in large flocks. However, their sociability is not limited to their own kind. They are often seen in mixed groups with other species.

Linnets often mix with other birds

BODY
Linnets are related to Redpolls, Siskins and Goldfinches. Although these birds vary in colouration, their stocky bodies are characteristically finch-like.

BILL
The bill is pointed and flattened for extracting small tree seeds.

FEET
Like all perching birds, their feet are designed to grip a branch.

HOW BIG IS IT?

SPECIAL ADAPTATION
It is usually the job of male birds to attract a mate, so most have adapted to be bigger and more colourful. This is why male Linnets (shown left) have a red breast and cap, while females (far left) are camouflaged, to keep safe while brooding their young.

Goldfinch

• ORDER • Passeriformes • FAMILY • Fringillidae • SPECIES • *Carduelis carduelis*

VITAL STATISTICS

WEIGHT	14–19g (0.5–0.7oz)
LENGTH	12cm (4.7in)
WINGSPAN	22–25cm (9–10in)
NUMBER OF EGGS	4–6 eggs
INCUBATION PERIOD	24–25 days
NUMBER OF BROODS	2 a year sometimes 3
TYPICAL DIET	Seeds, in particular thistle seeds; insects, spiders, worms and grubs
LIFE SPAN	Up to 10 years

Twittering flocks of this exquisite little bird are often seen in open country, but have declined in numbers in recent years.

WHERE IN THE WORLD?

The Goldfinch is found throughout Europe, except most of Sweden, Norway, and Finland. It is found too in parts of eastern and central Asia, northern Africa and the Middle East.

CREATURE COMPARISONS

The Goldfinch has wings with a black upper side interrupted by a wide, yellow band, and a black tail with a white tail-base. The throat is white and the chest is pale brown to buff. Males have a bright red head and white cheeks and a black eye-stripe, while females have a pale brownish head and are drabber overall.

Juvenile

BILL
The narrow, pointed, brownish bill is wide at the base but tapers rapidly towards the tip.

WINGS
The narrow black wings with their bright yellow bands are characteristic of the Goldfinch.

TAIL
The long tail is black and white with a fork at the tip.

HOW BIG IS IT?

SPECIAL ADAPTATION

The Goldfinch has a short, almost triangular bill with a very pointed tip. This makes it a precision tool for picking seeds directly from such plants as thistles and teasels.

Greenfinch

• **ORDER** • Passeriformes • **FAMILY** • Fringillidae • **SPECIES** • *Carduelis chloris*

The Greenfinch is less colourful than its relative the Goldfinch, but it is more commonly found in gardens and woodlands than the Goldfinch.

VITAL STATISTICS

WEIGHT	25–34g (0.9–1.2oz)
LENGTH	14–15cm (5.5–6in)
WINGSPAN	25–30cm (10–12in)
NUMBER OF EGGS	5–6 eggs
INCUBATION PERIOD	13–14 days
FLEDGLING PERIOD	44–59 days
NUMBER OF EGGS	5–6 eggs
NUMBER OF BROODS	2–3 a year
TYPICAL DIET	Mainly seeds, but also berries, and insects
LIFE SPAN	Up to 12 years

CREATURE COMPARISONS

True to its name, the Greenfinch is an olive-greenish bird and has more greyish wings with a large, distinct yellow patch on the outer part of the wing surface. The underside is yellowish-green, becoming whiter towards the base of the tail. Females are more greyish and drabber in colour overall, and have less yellow on the wings.

Adult (top), juvenile (bottom)

WHERE IN THE WORLD?

The Greenfinch is found in Europe (except the north), the eastern part of central Asia, the Middle East and northern Africa. It has been introduced into South America, Australia and New Zealand.

HEAD
The Greenfinch's large head is set on a short, stout neck, which has strong muscles for operating the bill.

BILL
The short and powerful bill is well adapted for cracking seeds.

TAIL
The short tail has bright yellow markings and a forked tip.

HOW BIG IS IT?

SPECIAL ADAPTATION
The Greenfinch has a large stout bill that is well adapted for cracking seeds. The upper part of the bill has a groove that holds the seed in place, while the lower bill moves towards the upper one, cracking the seed.

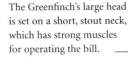

Citril Finch

• ORDER • Passeriformes • FAMILY • Fringillidae • SPECIES • *Carduelis citrinella*

VITAL STATISTICS

WEIGHT	4–15g (0.5oz)
LENGTH	12–13cm (4.7–5.1in)
WINGSPAN	22–26cm (8.7–10.2in)
NUMBER OF EGGS	4–5 eggs
INCUBATION PERIOD	13–15 days
NUMBER OF BROODS	1 a year
TYPICAL DIET	Seeds, insects, worms, spiders
LIFE SPAN	Up to 5 years

This small songbird breeds in Alpine forests, and is found across only a small range. The song of the Citril Finch is metallic and melancholic.

WHERE IN THE WORLD?

The Citril Finch is found only in mountainous parts of Spain, France and northern Italy. The most northern populations are found in the Black Forest of southern Germany.

CREATURE COMPARISONS

The Citril Finch has a greyish back, often with a brown hue, and darker stripes. The head and flanks are mousy grey with a darker facial ring. The wings are dark brown or black with distinctive yellow markings. The throat, breast and belly are yellow. Males and females are similar, although young females may have a greyish-yellow underside.

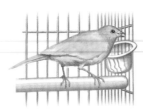

Citril Finch

BILL
The bill is short and stout, and is used not only to collect and crack seeds, but also to catch small creatures.

FEET
The short legs are yellowish-brown, and the toes are long and well adapted for perching on small branches and twigs.

TAIL
The tail is yellow at the base, with dark brown or black feathers. It is distinctly forked at the tip.

HOW BIG IS IT?

SPECIAL ADAPTATION

The Citril Finch prefers to nest in conifer trees such as pine or spruce. It builds a round nest of leaves and grasses, and coats it with down or hairs to keep the chicks warm.

Twite

VITAL STATISTICS

WEIGHT	16g (0.6oz)
LENGTH	12.5–15cm (5–6in)
WINGSPAN	23cm (9in)
SEXUAL MATURITY	1 year
INCUBATION PERIOD	12–13 days
FLEDGLING PERIOD	10–15 days
NUMBER OF EGGS	3–7 eggs
NUMBER OF BROODS	1–2 a year
TYPICAL DIET	Seeds; occasionally insects
LIFE SPAN	Up to 6 year

Twites are a surprisingly hardy breed, making their homes along the wild coastlines of northern Europe and on the windswept mountainsides of Scandinavia.

WHERE IN THE WORLD?

Twites can be found in two separate ranges: northwestern Europe and central Asia. Favourite habitats are treeless moors and coastal heathlands, where the bird nests in low bushes or shrubs.

CREATURE COMPARISONS

Seeds can make a challenging meal for a small bird. Fortunately Twites, like all Finches, have bills designed for just such a diet. Holding seeds in place with their tongue, they apply pressure to the sides of the seed case, until it splits open.

BILL
In the winter, the male Twite's bill is brown-grey. In the breeding season, it is yellow, with a dark tip.

TAIL
Twites are similar in size and shape to Linnets but can be identified due to their longer, more deeply forked tails.

BODY
Male Twites have brownish upper parts that are heavily streaked with black. Their rumps feature a highly visible pink patch.

Twite in flight

HOW BIG IS IT?

SPECIAL ADAPTATION

Twites make their homes in regions where food can be scarce. Therefore, they have learnt the value of opportunistic feeding. The shape of their bills tell us that they are natural seed-eaters but they are adaptable enough to eat insects and even forage for food on rubbish tips.

Eurasian Siskin

• ORDER • Passeriformes **• FAMILY •** Fringillidae **• SPECIES •** *Carduelis spinus*

VITAL STATISTICS

WEIGHT	10–14g (0.4–0.5oz)
LENGTH	11.5–12cm (4.5–4.7in)
WINGSPAN	20–23cm (8–9in)
NUMBER OF EGGS	2–6 eggs (usually 4–5)
INCUBATION PERIOD	12–13 days
NUMBER OF BROODS	2 a year
TYPICAL DIET	Seeds, especially spruce-seeds, small insects
LIFE SPAN	Up to 8 years

The Eurasian Siskin is a small finch that is common throughout much of Europe. There is also a separate population in eastern Asia.

WHERE IN THE WORLD?

The Eurasian Siskin is found in conifer forests across central, northern and eastern Europe, and extends eastwards across central Russia and into parts of northern Japan.

CREATURE COMPARISONS

The Eurasian Siskin has a greyish-green back, upper neck and head, with darker stripes along the back. The wings are yellow and black, the belly is off-white, often with dark streaks. Males have a yellow head, throat and breast, and a black head-cap. Females are drabber overall, and have a greyish-green head and no cap.

Female (left), male (right)

HEAD
A black cap on top of the head and a small black spot on the throat instantly identifies a Siskin as male.

WINGS
The wide greenish wings display two distinct yellow bands in flight.

TAIL
Distinctly forked at the tip, the short tail is used in manoeuvring during flight.

HOW BIG IS IT?

SPECIAL ADAPTATION

The Eurasian Siskin prefers to nest in spruce trees. It often builds its nest at the tip of a branch well hidden from view. This makes it more difficult for predators to find and reach.

Hawfinch

• ORDER • Passeriformes **• FAMILY •** Fringillidae **• SPECIES •** *Coccothraustes coccothraustes*

The Hawfinch is also often called the Crossbeak. It uses its extremely powerful bill to feed on hard-shelled seeds.

VITAL STATISTICS

WEIGHT	48–62g (1.7–2.2oz)
LENGTH	16.5–18cm (6.5–7in)
WINGSPAN	29–33cm (11.4–13in)
NUMBER OF EGGS	2–7 eggs (usually 3–6)
INCUBATION PERIOD	12–13 days
NUMBER OF BROODS	1 a year
TYPICAL DIET	Fruits, such as cherries, various seeds
LIFE SPAN	Up to 11 years

WHERE IN THE WORLD?

The Hawfinch is found across much of Europe (except northern Scandinavia), parts of North Africa and across much of central Asia to the Pacific Ocean.

CREATURE COMPARISONS

This little bird has a brown back, while the throat, breast, and belly are buff or greyish-orange. The head is orange-brown, and the cheek has an orangey patch. The wings are dark brown or black, with two distinctive white bands. Females are similar to males, but are drabber overall, and often lack the male's black face mask.

Hawfinches

HEAD
The head is characteristically large and round. Muscles in the head are specially adapted to exert a huge pressure on the beak.

BILL
The huge bill is dark in summer but becomes paler in winter, and is well adapted for cracking hard seeds.

TAIL
The tail is wide and very short. When the Hawfinch is in flight the tail sometimes seems to disappear altogether.

HOW BIG IS IT?

SPECIAL ADAPTATION

Although the Hawfinch is a tiny bird, it has an enormously powerful bill. Experiments have indicated that when closing the bill, it is able to exert a pressure of about 36.25kg (80lb).

Evening Grosbeak

• **ORDER** • Passeriformes • **FAMILY** • Fringillidae • **SPECIES** • *Coccothraustes vespertinus*

The Evening Grosbeak gets its common name from the loud chirruping calls that it is said to sing only as the sun begins to set.

VITAL STATISTICS

WEIGHT	53–74g (2–2.6oz).
LENGTH	16–18cm (6.3–7in)
WINGSPAN	30–36cm (12–14.2in)
SEXUAL MATURITY	1 year
INCUBATION PERIOD	11–14 days
FLEDGLING PERIOD	13–14 days
NUMBER OF EGGS	3–4 eggs
NUMBER OF BROODS	Possibly 2 a year
TYPICAL DIET	Fruit, nuts, seeds and insects
LIFE SPAN	Typically 8 years

WHERE IN THE WORLD?

This brightly coloured member of the Finch Family is found in coniferous woodlands across Canada, the USA and parts of Mexico. Typically it builds its nest in the fork of a tree.

CREATURE COMPARISONS

Adult male Evening Grosbeaks have brown bodies that are dotted with a patchwork of white and yellow splashes. In comparison, the females (shown) have paler, olive-brown bodies with white blotches on their wings. Younger, juvenile birds resemble the females, but tend to be browner.

Female

HEAD
Evening Grosbeaks have large heads. These house the muscles needed to transfer enough power into the bill to crush seeds and nuts.

WINGS
The large, bright white wing patches are used by male Evening Grosbeaks during breeding displays to find a mate.

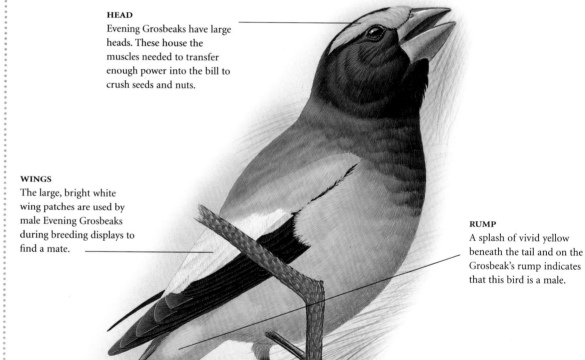

RUMP
A splash of vivid yellow beneath the tail and on the Grosbeak's rump indicates that this bird is a male.

HOW BIG IS IT?

SPECIAL ADAPTATION

Grosbeaks can crack even the toughest nuts, thanks to grooves on the sides of the upper mandibles (the top part of the bill). These hold nuts in place while the tough, outer husks are stripped off.

Chaffinch (Common)

• ORDER • Passeriformes **• FAMILY •** Fringillidae **• SPECIES •** *Fringilla coelebs*

VITAL STATISTICS

WEIGHT	24g (0.8oz)
LENGTH	14–16cm (5.5–6.3in)
WINGSPAN	26cm (10.2in)
SEXUAL MATURITY	1 year
LAYS EGGS	April–June
INCUBATION PERIOD	12–14 days
NUMBER OF EGGS	3–6 eggs
NUMBER OF BROODS	2 a year
TYPICAL DIET	Seeds; occasionally small invertebrates
LIFE SPAN	Typically 3 years

Considered to be a chatterbox, the Common Chaffinch is often heard in woodlands and gardens long before it is seen.

WHERE IN THE WORLD?

The Common Chaffinch breeds throughout Europe, North Africa and northwest Asia. It has been introduced into South Africa and New Zealand, where resident populations are swollen by flocks migrating for winter.

CREATURE COMPARISONS

It is very easy to confuse Common Chaffinches with that other common garden visitor, the House Sparrow. Female Chaffinches are about the same size as Sparrows and have similar plumage. The main difference is the bold stripes on the female Chaffinch's back, which the House Sparrow lacks.

Female

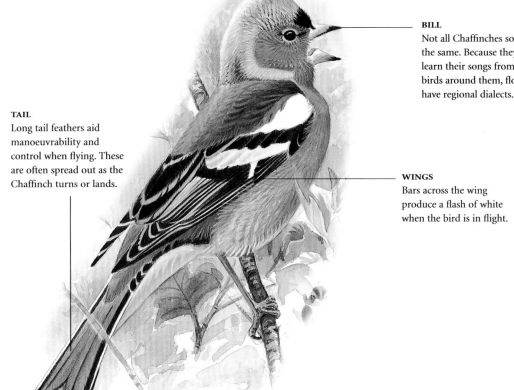

TAIL
Long tail feathers aid manoeuvrability and control when flying. These are often spread out as the Chaffinch turns or lands.

BILL
Not all Chaffinches sound the same. Because they learn their songs from the birds around them, flocks have regional dialects.

WINGS
Bars across the wing produce a flash of white when the bird is in flight.

HOW BIG IS IT?

SPECIAL ADAPTATION

Wedge-shaped bills that crush seeds and shells make finches the nutcrackers of the bird world. The bills of Chaffinches are finer than those of other finches, enabling them to eat a great variety of food.

265

Common Crossbill

• **ORDER** • Passeriformes • **FAMILY** • Fringillidae • **SPECIES** • *Loxia curvirostra*

The Common Crossbill is aptly named, and is perfectly adapted for survival in conifer forests on a diet that would be impossible for most other birds.

VITAL STATISTICS

WEIGHT	21–27g (0.7–0.9oz)
LENGTH	14–17cm (5.5–6.7in)
WINGSPAN	24–29cm (9.4–11.4in)
NUMBER OF EGGS	3–5 eggs (usually 4)
INCUBATION PERIOD	12–15 days
NUMBER OF BROODS	1 a year
TYPICAL DIET	Seeds from the cones of spruce and pine
LIFE SPAN	Usually 2–3 years, but up to 5 years

WHERE IN THE WORLD?

The Common Crossbill is widely distributed in conifer forests in the eastern part of Europe, across northern Russia and parts of central and eastern Asia, and in the northern parts of North America.

BILL
The short bill is very powerful and has distinctly crossed tips, which can be used to identify the Crossbill from other finches.

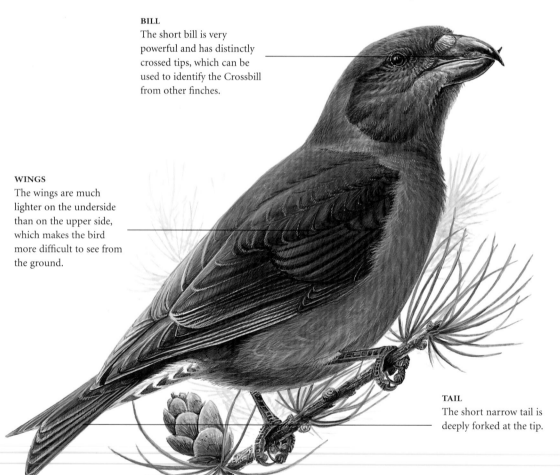

WINGS
The wings are much lighter on the underside than on the upper side, which makes the bird more difficult to see from the ground.

TAIL
The short narrow tail is deeply forked at the tip.

CREATURE COMPARISONS

The colour of adult birds shows much variation. Typically, the body and head of males are orange in colour, with dark brownish wings and tip of tail. The wings are pale underneath. Females look very different and have a greenish-yellow body and dark wings. Immature birds have greyish-brown upper sides and greyish-white undersides with heavy streaking.

Female

HOW BIG IS IT?

SPECIAL ADAPTATION

The Common Crossbill has a powerful, peculiar-looking beak. The tips of the upper and lower bill are crossed, acting like a pair of crossed scissors. This allows it to extract seeds from pinecones.

Bullfinch

• ORDER • Passeriformes **• FAMILY •** Fringillidae **• SPECIES •** *Pyrrhula pyrrhula*

VITAL STATISTICS

WEIGHT	21–27g (0.7–0.9oz)
LENGTH	14.5–17cm (5.7–6.7in)
WINGSPAN	20–25cm (8–10in)
NUMBER OF EGGS	4–5 eggs
INCUBATION PERIOD	12–14 days
NUMBER OF BROODS	2 a year (sometimes 3)
TYPICAL DIET	Seeds, buds from a variety of trees and bushes
LIFE SPAN	Up to 12 years

The Bullfinch is one of the most colourful finches in Europe, and is a familiar sight in many gardens.

WHERE IN THE WORLD?

The Bullfinch is found throughout much of Europe, but is absent in most of Greece, Portugal and Spain. It extends eastwards across central Russia to the Sea of Okhotsk and Japan.

CREATURE COMPARISONS

This is a large, powerfully built finch. Males have a red chest and a bluish-grey back. The top of the head is black or blackish-blue. The female is much drabber, and has a greyish or pinkish-brown upper side and buff underside. Both sexes have blackish wings with white bars and a blackish tail and beak. The birds utter a sad, squeaky, wheezy warbling call.

Female

HEAD
A large round head and a short neck gives the bird a bull-necked appearance, hence its common name.

BILL
The short, very powerful bill is well adapted for cracking even tough seeds.

WINGS
The short broad wings are dark with a contrasting pattern of white bars.

HOW BIG IS IT?

SPECIAL ADAPTATION
During the breeding season, adults develop cheek pouches. This allows them to collect large amounts of food at one time, meaning that they need to leave the nest less often.

Trumpeter Finch

• ORDER • Passeriformes • FAMILY • Fringillidae • SPECIES • *Rhodopechys githaginea*

VITAL STATISTICS

WEIGHT	22g (0.7oz)
LENGTH	11.5–13cm (4.5–5in)
WINGSPAN	26cm (10.2in)
EXUAL MATURITY	1 year
INCUBATION PERIOD	13–14 days
FLEDGLING PERIOD	13–14 days
NUMBER OF EGGS	4–6 eggs
NUMBER OF BROODS	1–2 a year
HABITS	Diurnal/ nocturnal, non-migratory
TYPICAL DIET	Seeds; occasionally insects

The curious call of the Trumpeter Finch, which sounds just like a child's toy trumpet, gives this species its unusual name.

WHERE IN THE WORLD?

Finches are on the increase, and the non-migratory Trumpeter Finch (which usually inhabits the dry, open countryside of southern Eurasia and North Africa) has been seen as far north as the UK.

CREATURE COMPARISONS

The Finch group is a large and varied family of birds, which includes species as different from one another as Bramblings and Crossbills. However, all members share certain physical characteristics that cause them to be grouped together, most noticeably their stubby, seed-cracking bills.

Female

WINGS
Rhodopechys, the Trumpeter Finch's scientific name, means 'rosy forearm', an appropriate term to describe the pink coloration of the Trumpeter Finch.

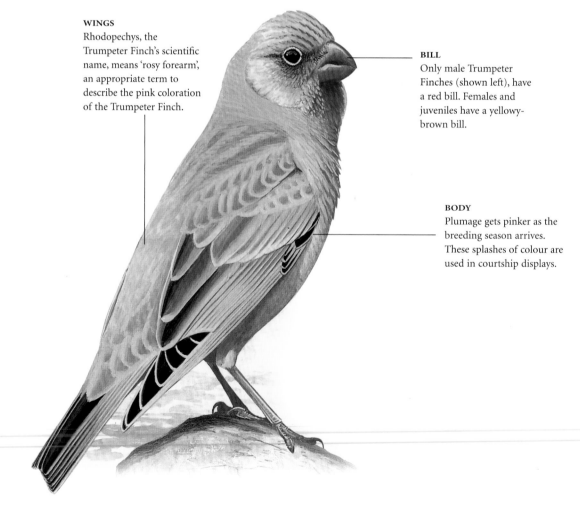

BILL
Only male Trumpeter Finches (shown left), have a red bill. Females and juveniles have a yellowy-brown bill.

BODY
Plumage gets pinker as the breeding season arrives. These splashes of colour are used in courtship displays.

HOW BIG IS IT?

SPECIAL ADAPTATION

Trumpeter Finches live in parched, semi-desert regions. Adapted to the hot days and cold nights, they often feed before dawn, when it is cooler, and thus have developed good night vision.

Canary (Common)

• ORDER • Passeriformes **• FAMILY •** Fringillidae **• SPECIES •** *Serinus canaria*

VITAL STATISTICS

WEIGHT	15–20g (0.5–0.7oz)
LENGTH	12.5cm (5in)
WINGSPAN	20–23cm (8.7–9in)
LAYS EGGS	January–June, but varies depending on location
INCUBATION PERIOD	13–14 days
FLEDGLING PERIOD	14–12 days
NUMBER OF EGGS	2–5 eggs
CALL	Silvery 'tvi-vi-vi' call
TYPICAL DIET	Seeds; occasionally insects
LIFE SPAN	Up to 15 years in captivity

CREATURE COMPARISONS

Canaries were first bred in captivity during the 1600s, when breeding pairs of these colourful birds were brought to Europe by sailors. Since then, the Domestic Canary has become a popular pet, with many varieties in different colours and sizes being produced by enthusiastic breeders.

Canary

Canaries were one of the earliest songbirds to be bred commercially. They were brought to Europe from their native islands in the seventeenth century and admired ever since.

WHERE IN THE WORLD?

These well known birds are named after the Canary Islands where the species was first discovered. Birds are also found in the Azores and Madeira, with introduced populations in Hawaii and Puerto Rico.

WINGS
Canaries have short wings with rounded tips designed for flying in tight spaces, such as the pine woodlands in their native homes.

BODY
Naturally occurring male Canaries, which have not been selectively bred, tend to have a yellow-green head, and underparts with grey-green upperparts.

TAIL
The relatively short, straight-edged tail helps the Common Canary to balance and manoeuvre in flight.

HOW BIG IS IT?

SPECIAL ADAPTATION

Some adaptations occur as a result not of evolution but of selective breeding to enhance particular traits. The Harz Roller Canary, for example (shown left), has been bred for its singing ability.

House Martin

• **ORDER** • Passeriformes • **FAMILY** • Hirundinidae • **SPECIES** • *Delichon urbica*

VITAL STATISTICS

WEIGHT	15–21g (0.5–0.7oz)
LENGTH	12–14cm (4.7–5.5in)
WINGSPAN	25–30cm (10–12in)
NUMBER OF EGGS	4–5 eggs
INCUBATION PERIOD	13–15 days
NUMBER OF BROODS	2–3
TYPICAL DIET	Insects, mainly flies and mosquitoes, but even large butterflies
LIFE SPAN	Up to 14 years

Related to swallows, the House Martin is a small bird that has adapted well to living in an urban environment.

WHERE IN THE WORLD?

The House Martin is common throughout most of Europe, North Africa and Central Asia, extending east to the Sea of Okhotsk. It winters in Africa south of the Sahara, in India and in parts of southeast Asia.

CREATURE COMPARISONS

The top of the head and upper side of the back are bluish-black. This colour extends onto the anterior inner part of the wings, while the rest of the wing is more dull black. The underside is white. Males and females are similar. The House Martin can be distinguished from other Martins by the white upper part of the rump.

House Martin

BILL
A very short, pointed bill and wide mouth are perfect for snatching insects in the air.

WINGS
Long narrow wings gives the House Martin a fast, agile flight. It often performs breakneck aerial manoeuvres.

BODY
The distinctive white rump is characteristic of this species of Martin.

HOW BIG IS IT?

SPECIAL ADAPTATION

The House Martin has small feet with very sharp claws. These are well adapted for clinging onto rough vertical surfaces, allowing the bird access to its nesting sites.

Blue Swallow

The Blue Swallow is one of the world's rarest swallows, surviving only in isolated mountain regions of its African homeland.

VITAL STATISTICS

WEIGHT	12–15g (0.4–0.5oz)
LENGTH	20cm (8in), plus 11cm (4.3in) for tail
SEXUAL MATURITY	1 year
LAYS EGGS	September–October
INCUBATION PERIOD	14–16 days
FLEDGLING PERIOD	20–26 days
NUMBER OF EGGS	2–3 eggs
NUMBER OF BROODS	2 a year
CALL	High pitched 'peeps'
HABITS	Diurnal, migratory
TYPICAL DIET	Insects, mainly tiny flies

CREATURE COMPARISONS

One sure way of telling male Blue Swallows from the female of the species is that the females have smaller tails. Juveniles lack the trailing tail and have a sooty plumage, rather than the blue coloration that gives the species its name.

Juvenile (left), female (right)

WHERE IN THE WORLD?

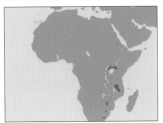

The natural habitat of the Blue Swallow is also ideal for growing timber, which is why species numbers have fallen so rapidly. Populations now survive in a few upland regions of Southern Africa.

BILL
Swallows are extremely graceful fliers, skimming just above the ground, with their broad bills perpetually open to catch insects.

BODY
Swallows are designed for a life in the air, with streamlined bodies and curved wings for speed and economy of movement.

TAIL
The long forked tail is characteristic of members of the Swift Family. Long, trailing outer feathers help the bird steer.

HOW BIG IS IT?

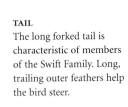

SPECIAL ADAPTATION

Unlike their European counterparts, Blue Swallows nest on the ground, using disused animal burrows (especially those of the Aardvark), which they cement together with mud, grass and saliva.

Swallow

• ORDER • Passeriformes **• FAMILY •** Hirundinidae **• SPECIES •** *Hirundo rustica*

The fast-flying Swallow is familiar to most people in Europe and North America, and is often heralded as the harbinger of summer.

VITAL STATISTICS

WEIGHT	30–35g (1.1–1.2oz)
LENGTH	17–19cm (6.7–7.5in)
WINGSPAN	35–44cm (14–17.3in)
NUMBER OF EGGS	3–6 eggs (usually 4–5)
NUMBER OF BROODS	2–3 a year
TYPICAL DIET	Flying insects, in particular flies, mosquitoes, and bees
LIFE SPAN	Up to 16 years

WHERE IN THE WORLD?

The Swallow is found across most of Europe and Asia and the Indonesian islands, and also in North America. North American birds winter in South America, while European birds migrate to Africa.

BILL
The bill is small but the mouth is wide, and is held open as the bird chases insects in the air.

CREATURE COMPARISONS

The upper side is uniformly shiny blackish or bluish-black, with a collar around the throat, and the underside is white. The wings are more dull black with paler edges along the large wing feathers. Males have a reddish throat, while it is yellowish in females. The tail is short, but has two very long feathers in males, while they are much shorter in females.

WINGS
Elongated narrow wings give the Swallow a fast flight and superb agility.

TAIL
The tail is short and broad in female birds, but has two very long and elegant outer feathers in males.

Female

HOW BIG IS IT?

SPECIAL ADAPTATION
The male Swallow uses its two extra long tail feathers, called streamers, to perform aerial manoeuvres, and as a display to attract females.

Sand Martin

• **ORDER** • Passeriformes • **FAMILY** • Hirundinidae • **SPECIES** • *Riparia riparia*

VITAL STATISTICS

WEIGHT	12–18g (0.4–0.6oz)
LENGTH	11.5–12cm (4.5–4.7in)
WINGSPAN	26.5–29cm (10.4–11.4in)
NUMBER OF EGGS	4–5 eggs
INCUBATION PERIOD	14–15 days
NUMBER OF BROODS	2 a year
TYPICAL DIET	Flying insects, spiders
LIFE SPAN	Up to 8 years

The small Sand Martin arrives at its breeding grounds earlier than other swallows, feeding on the insects of early spring.

WHERE IN THE WORLD?

In summer, the Sand Martin is widely distributed across virtually all of Europe, northern and Central Asia, and North America, except northern Canada.

CREATURE COMPARISONS

This elegant little swallow has a uniformly brown upper side of the wings, back, neck and head. The throat, breast and belly are uniformly white, and there is a distinct brown collar around the throat.
The tail is short and forked at the tip and is uniformly brown above but darker below, and often has a pale white stripe across. Males and females are similar.

Sand Martin

BILL
The bill is very short and pointed, and is well adapted for catching tiny flying insects in flight.

WINGS
The wings are long and narrow, and are held in a V-shape when the bird glides swiftly through the air.

FEET
The legs are short and the feet are small, and are tucked into the plumage during flight.

HOW BIG IS IT?

SPECIAL ADAPTATION
The Sand Martin has an unusual way of breeding. It breeds in flocks that can number hundreds, and digs long tunnels into sandy ditches and overhangs, where it builds its nest.

Tree Swallow

• **ORDER** • Passeriformes • **FAMILY** • Hirundinidae • **SPECIES** • *Tachycineta bicolor*

VITAL STATISTICS

WEIGHT	19g (0.7oz)
LENGTH	14cm (5.5in)
SEXUAL MATURITY	1 year
LAYS EGGS	May–September
INCUBATION PERIOD	11–16 days
NUMBER OF EGGS	2–8 eggs
NUMBER OF BROODS	1 a year although a second clutch may be laid if the first fails
HABITS	Diurnal, migratory
TYPICAL DIET	Insects, berries and seeds in the winter
LIFE SPAN	Up to 11 years

Tree Swallows are graceful in the air but on the ground, whether they are fighting for territory or a mate, they are quarrelsome and aggressive.

WHERE IN THE WORLD?

Tree Swallows nest in any cavity, from holes in dead trees to the eves of houses. Populations breed in North America and winter in Latin America and the Caribbean.

CREATURE COMPARISONS

Only male Tree Swallows sing, but both sexes use calls and body language to communicate a wide range of messages. Juvenile Tree Swallows are similar in body size and shape to adult birds. However, unlike the vibrantly coloured adults, juveniles are grey-brown in colour. They also have a faint band across their breast.

Juvenile

BILL
Swallows typically fly with their short stubby bills wide open, snapping up insects while in flight.

BODY
Adult Tree Swallows have an iridescent blue-green plumage in dramatic contrast to their white underparts.

WINGS
These small birds are excellent fliers. The bulk of their diet consists of flying insects, which they catch in mid-air.

HOW BIG IS IT?

SPECIAL ADAPTATION

Tree Swallows have learnt that sharing body heat can help them to survive when cold weather strikes. They are also able to lower their body temperature to further save energy.

Red-backed Shrike

• **ORDER** • Passeriformes • **FAMILY** • Laniidae • **SPECIES** • *Lanius collurio*

There are over 30 known species of shrike, spread over four continents, excluding Australasia. Red-backed Shrike are one of the 'Old World' species.

VITAL STATISTICS

WEIGH	30g (1oz)
LENGTH	16–18cm (6.3–7.1in)
WINGSPAN	26cm (10.2in)
INCUBATION PERIOD	14 days
FLEDGLING PERIOD	14–15 days
NUMBER OF EGGS	4–6 eggs
NUMBER OF BROODS	1 a year but a second clutch may be laid if the first fails
TYPICAL DIET	Insects, especially beetles; small mammals, birds and reptiles
LIFE SPAN	Typically 3 years

WHERE IN THE WORLD?

Red-backed Shrikes breed across most of Europe and into western Asia. In the winter, populations tend to migrate south, heading for the warmer climates to be found in tropical Southern Africa.

CREATURE COMPARISONS

It is important to find a compatible mate, so all birds engage in courtship displays, which help them to choose a partner. During displays, males present food to the female. Both birds wag their tails, possibly, in the case of the female, to signal their acceptance of the gift.

Red-backed Shrike courtship display

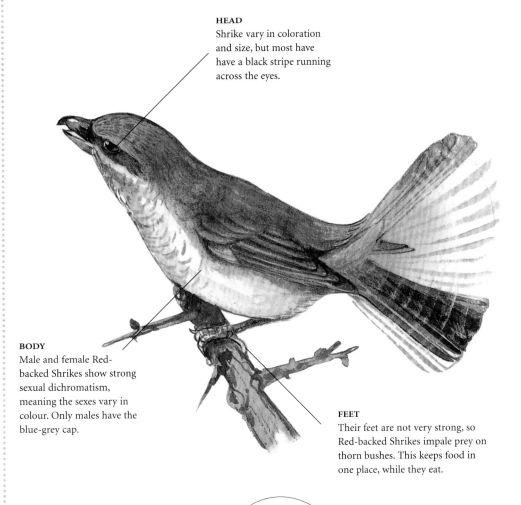

HEAD
Shrike vary in coloration and size, but most have have a black stripe running across the eyes.

BODY
Male and female Red-backed Shrikes show strong sexual dichromatism, meaning the sexes vary in colour. Only males have the blue-grey cap.

FEET
Their feet are not very strong, so Red-backed Shrikes impale prey on thorn bushes. This keeps food in one place, while they eat.

HOW BIG IS IT?

SPECIAL ADAPTATION
The Red-backed Shrike has a diet that consists mainly of insects. The bird has evolved a set of bristles at the base of its bill to protect its eyes from flailing legs or stings.

Great Grey Shrike

• ORDER • Passeriformes **• FAMILY •** Laniidae **• SPECIES •** *Lanius excubitor*

VITAL STATISTICS

WEIGHT	68g (2.4oz)
LENGTH	22–26cm (8.6–10.2in)
WINGSPAN	32cm (12.6in)
SEXUAL MATURITY	1 years
INCUBATION PERIOD	15–17 days
FLEDGLING PERIOD	15–18 days
NUMBER OF EGGS	4–7 eggs
NUMBER OF BROODS	1–2 a year
TYPICAL DIET	Birds, small mammals and insects
LIFE SPAN	Up to 10 years

Shrike are commonly known as Butcher Birds, thanks to their gruesome habit of impaling the bodies of their victims on thorn bushes.

WHERE IN THE WORLD?

Shrikes are birds of tundra and open country. They breed in northern Europe, Asia and North America, but winter in warmer areas of southern Europe, central Asia and southwestern USA.

CREATURE COMPARISONS

Great Grey Shrike are surprisingly good mimics and will cunningly imitate the call of other birds to lure them from cover. Physically, their white underparts contrast dramatically with their black tail, wing tips and face markings. In comparison, juveniles (shown below) are greyish brown above, with distinct barring on their underparts.

Juvenile

BODY
Great Grey Shrikes have large, grey stocky bodies with white underparts. are surprisingly good mimics and will imitate the calls of other birds to lure them from cover.

FEET
Their feet enable Shrike to hold on to small prey such as insects, but they are too weak to grip larger prey.

EYES
Shrike like to hunt from on high, swooping down on prey from the air. Excellent eyesight makes this possible.

HOW BIG IS IT?

SPECIAL ADAPTATION
Shrike may be accomplished hunters but they do not have the strength to hold large prey down. Instead, they impale it on a sharp barb, then tear it apart with their Hawk-like bill.

Splendid Fairy Wren

• **ORDER** • Passeriformes • **FAMILY** • Maluridae • **SPECIES** • *Malurus splendens*

The richly coloured Splendid Fairy Wren is related to the Sparrow. Males are polygamous, meaning that they have several breeding partners.

VITAL STATISTICS

WEIGHT	7.5–11.5g (0.3–0.4oz)
LENGTH	13–15cm (5.1–6in)
WINGSPAN	30–35cm (12–14in)
NUMBER OF EGGS	2–4 eggs
INCUBATION PERIOD	14–15 days
NUMBER OF BROODS	1 –2 a year
TYPICAL DIET	Insects, grubs, worms, snails; some seeds, fruit and flowers
LIFE SPAN	Unknown

WHERE IN THE WORLD?

The Splendid Fairy Wren is found in dry habitats, even deserts, across large parts of western and central Australia, but it is also found in some parts of eastern Australia.

CREATURE COMPARISONS

During the breeding season, the male is most attractive. His head is turquoise blue with a black stripe across the eye. His body, wings and tail are deep blue. The upper part of his wings is pale blue, and there is a distinctive black collar around the breast. Females and non-breeding males look very different, and have a predominately greyish-brown plumage.

Male (top), female (bottom)

BILL
The long pointed bill is well adapted for snatching insects, such as ants and grasshoppers.

TAIL
The tail is very long and graceful, and is usually held upright. It is important for balancing while the bird hops around on the ground.

LEGS
The legs of the Splendid Fairy Wren are long, with feet that are adapted both for perching and for hopping around on the ground.

HOW BIG IS IT?

SPECIAL ADAPTATION

When the chicks are fully grown, most stay with their parents and help to care for and feed future broods. This ensures that the parent birds can rear more young.

Noisy Friarbird

• **ORDER** • Passeriformes • **FAMILY** • Meliphagidae • **SPECIES** • *Philemon corniculatus*

A loud and aggressive bird, the Noisy Friarbird may look like a miniaturized vulture, but it feeds on nectar rather than cutting up carrion.

VITAL STATISTICS

WEIGHT	117g (4.1oz)
LENGTH	31–35cm (12.2–14in)
LAYS EGGS	August–March
INCUBATION PERIOD	18 days
FLEDGLING PERIOD	18 days
NUMBER OF EGGS	2–4 eggs
NUMBER OF BROODS	1–2 a year
CALL	Cries sound like 'tobacco' or 'four o'clock'
HABITS	Diurnal, migratory
TYPICAL DIET	Nectar, fruit and insects

WHERE IN THE WORLD?

The Noisy Friarbird can be found in eastern and southeastern Australia and southern New Guinea. It tolerates a range of habitats from scrublands, to heaths, wetlands and dry forests.

BILL
The Friarbird's most distinctive characteristic is its long black bill, which has a prominent casque, or bump, near the base.

CREATURE COMPARISONS

Noisy Friarbirds are the largest member of the Friarbird Family. This additional bulk (and their naturally combative nature) enables the birds to keep the best, nectar-rich plants for themselves. Smaller species, like the Silver-Crowned Friarbird, must make do with smaller blossoms.

Juvenile

NECK
A ruff of cream-coloured feathers around the Noisy Friarbird's neck emphasizes its friar-like bald head.

TAIL
Long tails may help the Noisy Friarbird to balance on a branch while it feeds. White tips help to distinguish it from other species.

HOW BIG IS IT?

SPECIAL ADAPTATION

A bald head is usually associated with scavengers like vultures, and serves the same purpose for the Noisy Friarbird by preventing its feathers from becoming matted as it feeds, in this case, on sticky nectar.

Superb Lyrebird

• ORDER • Passeriformes • FAMILY • Menuridae • SPECIES • *Menura novaehollandiae*

VITAL STATISTICS

WEIGHT	800–1100g (38.2–39oz)
LENGTH	74–100cm (29.2–39.4in)
WINGSPAN	68–76cm (27–30in)
NUMBER OF EGGS	1 egg
INCUBATION PERIOD	50–60 days
NUMBER OF BROODS	1 a year
TYPICAL DIET	Insects, spiders, worms; some seeds and plants
LIFE SPAN	Unknown

CREATURE COMPARISONS

The Superb Lyrebird is able to mimic a wide range of sounds, from bird calls to the click of a camera shutter. Its spectacular tail has two outer feathers, which are shaped like a lyre, and are striped with yellowish-green or yellow and dark brown, followed by two cover feathers, and 12 fine lacy feathers. Females are similar but lack the extravagant tail.

Superb Lyrebird

The Superb Lyrebird is famous for its fanciful plumage and ability to mimic all sorts of sounds and noises.

The Superb Lyrebird is found only in forested areas of southeastern Australia: in Victoria, New South Wales and Queensland. The bird was introduced to Tasmania in the nineteenth century.

BODY
The male has a rather drab plumage on its body and head, which is brown or greyish-brown. It resembles a pheasant in shape.

TAIL
The tail of the male Lyrebird contains 16 feathers, and is held over its body and head during courtship.

LEGS
The legs of the Superb Lyrebird are short and stout, and are used to scrape earth and plant matter into a large nesting mound.

HOW BIG IS IT?

SPECIAL ADAPTATION

The male maintains an open area for courtship display, and calls to attract females. If one arrives, he will perform a spectacular dance using his beautiful tail to impress the female.

Blue Flycatcher

• **ORDER** • Passeriformes • **FAMILY** • Monarchidae • **SPECIES** • *Elminia longicauda*

VITAL STATISTICS

WEIGHT	15–18g (0.5–0.6oz)
LENGTH	13cm (5.1in)
WINGSPAN	20–25cm (8–10in)
NUMBER OF EGGS	1–2 eggs
INCUBATION PERIOD	14–16 days
NUMBER OF BROODS	1 a year
TYPICAL DIET	Insects, in particular small wasps and flies, bees, moths, and beetles
LIFE SPAN	Unknown

Many small insects hide in crevices in bark on the trunks of trees, but the Blue Flycatcher dances to scare them out.

WHERE IN THE WORLD?

The Blue Flycatcher is found in western Africa from Senegal in the east to Kenya in the west, and south to Angola and Zaire. It is found in various types of wooded areas, from plantations to rainforests.

CREATURE COMPARISONS

The upper side in the male is a uniformly striking blue, and there is a small feather crest on top of the head. The hind part of the body and underside of the tail are pale grey or white. The tail feathers are conspicuously long. Females are more blue-greenish in colour with a paler throat, and shorter tail. Juveniles are drabber with a greyish upper side and brownish bars on the wings and upper side.

Juvenile

HEAD
Short stiff bristles around the base of the bill protect eyes from fluttering insect wings and are also touch-sensitive.

BILL
The Blue Flycatcher has a short pointed bill for picking up insects hiding in the crack and crevices of bark.

TAIL
The very long sumptuous tail feathers are used for display. In addition, by sweeping the feathers across tree bark, the bird flushes out insects hiding in the crevices.

HOW BIG IS IT?

SPECIAL ADAPTATION
The Blue Flycatcher jumps around from branch to branch, flicking its tail from side to side along the bark. This scares out any insects hiding among crevices in the bark. Then the bird turns round to snatch them up in its bill.

Meadow Pipit

VITAL STATISTICS

WEIGHT	19g (0.7oz)
LENGTH	14–15.5cm (5.5–6in)
WINGSPAN	24cm (9.4in)
SEXUAL MATURITY	1 year
INCUBATION PERIOD	13–15 days
FLEDGLING PERIOD	12–14 days
NUMBER OF EGGS	4–5 eggs
NUMBER OF BROODS	2 a year
TYPICAL DIET	Insects and some seeds in winter
LIFE SPAN	Typically 3 years

The Meadow Pipit has a tough life. When it is not fighting to find food or nesting sites, it may be playing host to a cuckoo chick.

WHERE IN THE WORLD?

Meadow Pipits inhabit heaths, moors and meadows. They breed across much of northern Europe and Asia. Migrating birds winter in southern Europe, North Africa and southern Asia.

CREATURE COMPARISONS

Meadow Pipits can raise up to five chicks. However, the Cuckoo often lays its egg in a Meadow Pipit's nest and, once this hatches, the young Cuckoo disposes of the other eggs. Instinct compels the Meadow Pipit to feed the Cuckoo chick, although it looks nothing like its own offspring.

Meadow Pipit with chick

PLUMAGE
Typically, the Meadow Pipits' plumage consists of olive-brown upper parts, which are pattered with dark streaks, and mainly olive-buff underparts.

BODY
Male and female Meadow Pipits look alike, both in terms of their body size and the colour of their plumage.

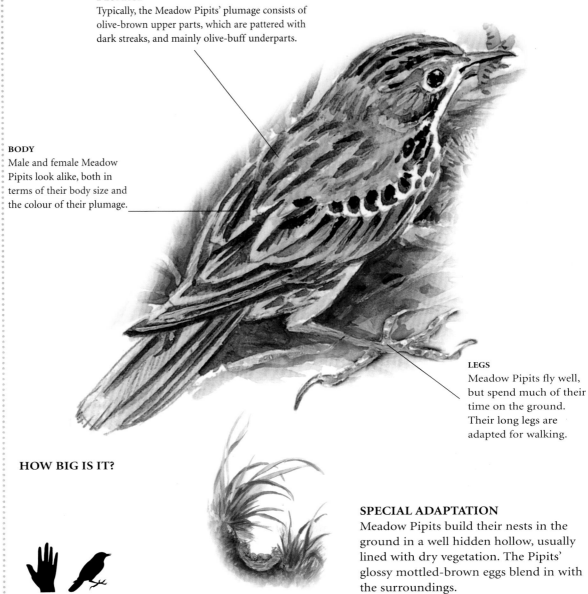

LEGS
Meadow Pipits fly well, but spend much of their time on the ground. Their long legs are adapted for walking.

HOW BIG IS IT?

SPECIAL ADAPTATION
Meadow Pipits build their nests in the ground in a well hidden hollow, usually lined with dry vegetation. The Pipits' glossy mottled-brown eggs blend in with the surroundings.

Water Pipit

• **ORDER** • Passeriformes • **FAMILY** • Motacillidae • **SPECIES** • *Anthus spinoletta*

VITAL STATISTICS

WEIGHT	22–26g (0.8–0.9oz)
LENGTH	16.5–17cm (6.5–6.7in)
WINGSPAN	35–37cm (14–14.6in)
NUMBER OF EGGS	4–5 eggs
INCUBATION PERIOD	14–16 days
NUMBER OF BROODS	2 a year
TYPICAL DIET	Insects, worms, caterpillars, spiders
LIFE SPAN	Up to 9 years

Some populations of Water Pipit migrate north in winter to the UK because of the mild coastal climate in parts of Britain.

WHERE IN THE WORLD?

The Water Pipit breeds in mountainous areas in southern and central Europe, across southern temperate Asia eastwards to China. It is not resident north of the Alps.

CREATURE COMPARISONS

A slender long-limbed type of Pipit, the Water Pipit in winter has brownish upper parts of the wings and back with darker stripes, and a greyish-brown head. The underside is greyish off-white or buff with dark stripes. Males and females are similar. During the summer breeding season, the breast feathers are pale orange or pinkish.

Water Pipit

WINGS
The wide wings of the Water Pipit are brown above, but are paler below, making the bird harder to see from the ground.

BILL
The bill is brown with a darker tip. Long and pointed, it is well adapted for catching small animals.

LEGS
The brown legs of the Water Pipit are long. The feet are adapted for perching as well as running on the ground.

HOW BIG IS IT?

SPECIAL ADAPTATION

In early spring, the Water Pipit often finds much of its food on the snow. Dead insects often drop on the snow or get carried there by the wind, and make an easy meal.

Tree Pipit

• ORDER • Passeriformes **• FAMILY •** Motacillidae **• SPECIES •** *Anthus trivialis*

The Tree Pipit looks almost identical to the Meadow Pipit, but can be distinguished by its trilling song, and slight physical differences.

VITAL STATISTICS

WEIGHT	20–25g (0.7–1oz)
LENGTH	14–15cm (5.5–6in)
WINGSPAN	25–27cm (10–10.6in)
NUMBER OF EGGS	4–6 eggs
INCUBATION PERIOD	12–14 days
NUMBER OF BROODS	1–2 a year
TYPICAL DIET	Insects, worms, grubs; seeds in winter
LIFE SPAN	Up to 8 years

WHERE IN THE WORLD?

The Tree Pipit breeds across most of Europe and across central Asia. In winter, central Asian birds migrate to southern Asia, and European birds migrate to regions of Africa south of the Sahara.

CREATURE COMPARISONS

The plumage of the Tree Pipit serves as a camouflage in bushes and shrub. The upper part of the head, neck, back and wings are brown or olive-brown with darker streaks. The throat and belly are pale off-white, while the breast is buff with dark spots and streaks. The tail is long and dark brown. Males and females are similar.

Tree Pipits

BILL
The Tree Pipit has a slightly larger and stouter bill than its close relative, the Meadow Pipit.

WINGS
With wings that are strong and rounded, the Tree Pipit has a fast flight and is able to migrate long distances.

FEET
The yellowish-brown legs are long. The feet are adapted for perching on a twig or a long leaf of grass.

HOW BIG IS IT?

SPECIAL ADAPTATION
The male Tree Pipit defends his territory, and tries to attract females, by taking off from a twig and performing a short looping flight while loudly singing.

Pied Wagtail

• **ORDER** • Passeriformes • **FAMILY** • Motacillidae • **SPECIES** • *Motacilla alba*

VITAL STATISTICS

WEIGHT	21g (0.7oz)
LENGTH	16.5–19cm (6.5–7.5in)
WINGSPAN	28cm (11in)
SEXUAL MATURITY	1 year
INCUBATION PERIOD	12–14 days
FLEDGLING PERIOD	14–15 days
NUMBER OF EGGS	4–6 eggs
NUMBER OF BROODS	2 a year
TYPICAL DIET	Small invertebrates
LIFE SPAN	Typically 2 years

Despite their name, Wagtails do not wag their tails. Instead, they bob them up and down, making them an easy species for bird-watchers to recognize.

WHERE IN THE WORLD?

This common species is found throughout Europe, North Africa and Asia. Populations are resident in much of their range, but some northern birds migrate south to warmer regions for the winter.

CREATURE COMPARISONS

In continental Europe, *Motacilla alba* is known as the White Wagtail (*alba* means white). It is the British sub-species *Motacilla alba yarrellii* that is usually referred to as Pied, because it tends to be black and white. *Motacilla alba* is black and white with a grey back.

Juvenile

TAIL
A long tail helps the bird to balance when it is on the ground, and to manoeuvre when they are in flight.

WINGS
All birds' wings are adapted to suit their needs. The wings of Wagtails are short and rounded for agility in the air.

FEET
Wagtails spend much of their time feeding on the ground, so they have strong legs and long toes for running.

HOW BIG IS IT?

SPECIAL ADAPTATION

No one knows why Wagtails bob their tails up and down. It has been suggested that the long tail acts like a counterweight, to help the birds regain their balance when they stop or change direction while chasing prey.

Grey Wagtail

• ORDER • Passeriformes • FAMILY • Motacillidae • SPECIES • *Motacilla cinerea*

VITAL STATISTICS

WEIGHT	15–23g (0.5–0.8oz)
LENGTH1	7–18cm (6.7–7in)
WINGSPAN	25–27cm (10–10.6in)
NUMBER OF EGGS	4–6 eggs
INCUBATION PERIOD	12–14 days
NUMBER OF BROODS	2 a year
TYPICAL DIET	Insects, aquatic insects and insect larvae, caterpillars, worms, spiders
LIFE SPAN	Up to 9 years

The Grey Wagtail often lives in mountainous areas, near running water. It is the longest tailed of the European Wagtails.

WHERE IN THE WORLD?

The Grey Wagtail is found across much of Europe (except northern Scandinavia), North Africa, the Middle East and Central Asia all the way to the coast of the Pacific Ocean.

CREATURE COMPARISONS

Males of the Grey Wagtail have a grey back, and the upper part of the neck and top of the head are also grey. The upper side of the wings are grey, but the large wing feathers are bluish-black. The underside is yellow. During the breeding season, the male has a black throat patch. Females are similar to males, but are drabber overall, with a pale yellow underside.

Grey Wagtails

HEAD
The Grey Wagtail has a grey head. Females have a pale throat, while breeding males have a black throat.

TAIL
The dark tail of the Grey Wagtail is even longer than that of its close relative, the Yellow Wagtail.

TOES
The large toes are equipped with small, blunt claws for walking and hopping on the ground.

HOW BIG IS IT?

SPECIAL ADAPTATION
The Grey Wagtail prefers to nest close to streams or rivers. It usually nests between rocks or boulders, but today the bird often takes advantage of man-made structures, such as dams.

Yellow Wagtail

• ORDER • Passeriformes **• FAMILY •** Motacillidae **• SPECIES •** *Motacilla flava*

VITAL STATISTICS

WEIGHT	16–22g (0.6–0.8oz)
LENGTH	15–17cm (6–6.7in)
WINGSPAN	30–35cm (12–14in)
NUMBER OF EGGS	4–6 eggs
INCUBATION PERIOD	12–14 days
NUMBER OF BROODS	1 a year
TYPICAL DIET	Insects, but also worms and grubs
LIFE SPAN	Up to 10 years

True to the name, the familiar Yellow Wagtail often bobs its long tail up and down when searching for food on the ground.

WHERE IN THE WORLD?

The Yellow Wagtail breeds throughout most of Europe and northern and Central Asia, and spends the winter in southern Asia and in Africa south of the Sahara desert.

CREATURE COMPARISONS

The Yellow Wagtail has a pale greenish upper side with a dark band across the wing and a bright yellow underside. Females are drabber than males and have a more brownish back and whitish breast. There are a variety of geographical races, mainly distinguished by the head colour of the male. Some have a yellow head. Others have a black and white stripe on the cheek, while still others have a black head.

Juvenile

HEAD
The colour of the head in males varies according to where they come from.

BEAK
The long, slender beak is adapted for catching insects.

TAIL
The long dark tail with white outer feathers is rarely still, and is probably used for communication with other Wagtails.

HOW BIG IS IT?

SPECIAL ADAPTATION
The Yellow Wagtail uses its long tail as a rudder when hunting insects in the air. The tail gives the bird great manoeuvrability, allowing it to twist and roll while hunting insects on the wing.

Nightingale

• ORDER • Passeriformes **• FAMILY •** Muscicapidae **SPECIES •** *Luscinia megarhynchos*

The familiar and ever popular Nightingale makes up for its drab colour with its singing ability.

VITAL STATISTICS

WEIGHT	22–33g (0.8–1.2oz)
LENGTH	15–17cm (6–6.7in)
WINGSPAN	25–30cm (10–12in)
NUMBER OF EGGS	4–6 eggs
INCUBATION PERIOD	12–15 days
NUMBER OF BROODS	1 in the north but often 2 in the south
TYPICAL DIET	Insects, also fruit and berries
LIFE SPAN	6–8 years

WHERE IN THE WORLD?

The Nightingale is widely distributed across southern Europe, northwestern Africa and into the Middle East. It is also found in parts of western Asia.

CREATURE COMPARISONS

The Nightingale is related to flycatchers. The upper side is uniformly brown with few markings, and the upper side of the tail tends to be more of a rusty brown. The underside of the body and tail are whitish or creamy. Males are similar to females. Immature birds resemble the adults, but have many distinct spots along the underside.

Juvenile

WINGS
The Nightingale's long wings have rounded wing tips, and are adapted for long-distance flying during migration.

BILL
The sharp pointed bill is well adapted for catching small insects.

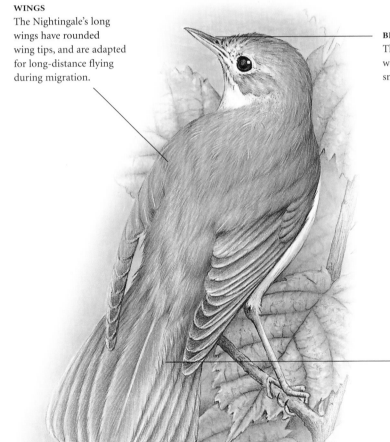

TAIL
The long tail is used to communicate with other Nightingales and also for steering in flight.

HOW BIG IS IT?

SPECIAL ADAPTATION

The song of the Nightingale has been admired by poets and writers, and the name of the bird itself means 'night songstress.' However, it is the male that sings, by day as well as night.

Isabelline Wheatear

• **ORDER** • Passeriformes • **FAMILY** • Muscicapidae • **SPECIES** • *Oenanthe isabellina*

VITAL STATISTICS

WEIGHT	31g (1oz)
LENGTH	15–16.5cm (6–6.5in)
WINGSPAN	29cm (11.4in)
SEXUAL MATURITY	1 year
INCUBATION PERIOD	Around 12 days
FLEDGLING PERIOD	13–15 days
NUMBER OF EGGS	4–7 eggs
NUMBER OF BROODS	1–2 a year, but up to 3 are possible in the south of the range
HABITS	Diurnal, migratory
TYPICAL DIET	Insects, especially ants and beetles

CREATURE COMPARISONS

The Isabelline Wheatear nests underground, safe from the attentions of bird-eating predators. In common with other burrowing species, like burrowing owls, Wheatears do not excavate their own nests because their feet are not up to the task. Instead, they take over abandoned burrows or naturally occurring tunnels.

Isabelline Wheatear

The Isabelline Wheatear can be tricky to spot because it blends in perfectly with the buff and brown of the barren grasslands upon which it nests.

WHERE IN THE WORLD?

The Isabelline Wheatear lives in open meadows, coastal grasslands and farmland. Populations breed across southern Eurasia but spend winter in sub-Saharan Africa, Arabia and India.

WINGS
The Isabelline Wheatear runs more often than flies but, once airborne, it propels itself forwards with strong, slow wing beats.

LEGS
Long legs give Isabelline Wheatears the height they need to see over long distances while hunting or looking out for predators.

BILL
The bird's long, slightly downwards-curved bill is adapted for seizing insects or prying them out of tight rock crevices.

HOW BIG IS IT?

SPECIAL ADAPTATION

The Isabelline Wheatear is an accomplished mimic. This ability seems to play a part in mating displays. Studies have shown that females prefer males with a large, varied repertoire of calls.

Black Wheatear

• ORDER • Passeriformes **• FAMILY •** Muscicapidae *(under review)* **• SPECIES •** *Oenanthe leucura*

VITAL STATISTICS

WEIGHT	35g (1.2oz)
LENGTH	16–18cm (6.3–7in)
WINGSPAN	28cm (11in)
SEXUAL MATURITY	1 year
INCUBATION PERIOD	14–18 days
FLEDGLING PERIOD	14–15 days
NUMBER OF EGGS	3–5 eggs
NUMBER OF BROODS	1 a year, occasionally 2
TYPICAL DIET	Insects
LIFE SPAN	Up to 4 years

The splendid Black Wheatear is able to fly almost vertically upwards to reach a favourite perch and then plunge in free fall back to roost.

WHERE IN THE WORLD?

Black Wheatears are found on sheer rockfaces and high mountainsides across Spain, eastern Portugal and northwestern Africa. Birds nest in rock crevices or any other convenient secluded hollow.

CREATURE COMPARISONS

Since the development of genetic testing, it has been possible to group birds much more accurately. Black Wheatears are one of the species whose scientific classification has changed because of this. They used to be classed as Thrushes (from the Family Turdidae), but are now classed as part of the Flycatcher Family.

Black Wheatear in flight

BILL
Most Wheatears have small bills. The bill of the Black Wheatear is longer and heavier, enabling it to tackle bigger prey, like beetles.

BODY
Males are all black except for their white rump and tail. Females are similar, but brown rather than black.

TAIL
The male Wheatear uses its tail during courtship displays to attract a mate.

HOW BIG IS IT?

SPECIAL ADAPTATION

Male Black Wheatears have been seen carrying stones up to one-quarter of their body weight into nest-caves. Such a display is thought to prove to potential mates that they are fit and healthy.

289

Wheatear (Northern)

• ORDER • Passeriformes • FAMILY • Muscicapidae *(debated)* • SPECIES • *Oenanthe oenanthe*

VITAL STATISTICS

WEIGHT	24g (0.85oz)
LENGTH	14–16.5cm (5.5–6.5in)
WINGSPAN	29cm (11.4in)
SEXUAL MATURITY	1 year
LAYS EGGS	May–July
INCUBATION PERIOD	10–16 days
NUMBER OF EGGS	4–7 eggs
NUMBER OF BROODS	2; occasionally 3 a year
TYPICAL DIET	Insects, invertebrates, seeds and berries
LIFE SPAN	Up to 7 years

CREATURE COMPARISONS

The plumage of the Northern Wheatear is designed to blend in with its surroundings, which are heathland and rocky scrub. Females are therefore browner than males, making it easier for them to stay hidden. Breeding males have bolder plumage but revert to a duller brown shade once winter arrives.

Male's winter plumage (left), female's winter plumage (right)

The perky Northern Wheatear is one of the easier moorland birds to spot, thanks to its habit of perching on a rock to announce its presence.

WHERE IN THE WORLD?

Wheatears breed in Europe, Asia, eastern Canada and Greenland but winter in Africa. This makes them one of the bird world's long-distance migrators, and they cross oceans without stopping.

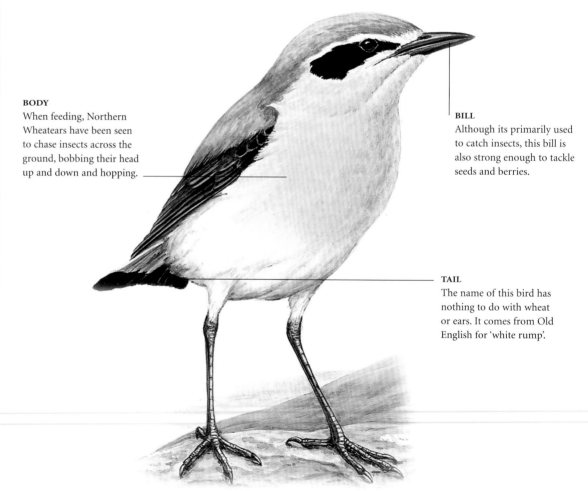

BODY
When feeding, Northern Wheatears have been seen to chase insects across the ground, bobbing their head up and down and hopping.

BILL
Although its primarily used to catch insects, this bill is also strong enough to tackle seeds and berries.

TAIL
The name of this bird has nothing to do with wheat or ears. It comes from Old English for 'white rump'.

HOW BIG IS IT?

SPECIAL ADAPTATION

The white patches on the rump of the Wheatear are not a form of camouflage or breeding display. They can be seen over considerable distances, so a quick flick of the tail warns others of danger.

Black Redstart

• **ORDER** • Passeriformes • **FAMILY** • Muscicapidae • **SPECIES** • *Phoenicurus ochruros*

VITAL STATISTICS

WEIGHT	16g (0.6oz)
LENGTH	14cm (5.5in)
WINGSPAN	24cm (9.4in)
SEXUAL MATURITY	1 year
INCUBATION PERIOD	12–16 days
FLEDGLING PERIOD	12–19 days
NUMBER OF EGGS	4–6 eggs
NUMBER OF BROODS	2–3 a year
TYPICAL DIET	Small invertebrates and fruit
LIFE SPAN	Up to 4 years

CREATURE COMPARISONS

Since the development of genetic testing, it has been possible to group birds much more accurately. Black Redstart used to be classed as members of the Thrush Family but have recently been reclassified as Old World Flycatchers, along with Black Wheatears, which were also classed as Thrushes.

Black Redstart

With their alert, upright stance and bold orange and black plumage, Black Redstarts are always an unexpected delight to spot.

WHERE IN THE WORLD?

The Black Redstart breeds across Europe, excluding the most northerly regions, and parts of Central Asia and northwest Africa. Populations tend to winter in southern Asia and North Africa.

PLUMAGE
The plumage of breeding males is a striking combination of grey-black upperparts, black breast and face and orangey-red rump and tail.

BODY
In shape, Black Redstarts have a typically thrush-like profile, with elongated bodies, a long neck and a round head.

FEET
Black Redstarts, which are passerine (perching) birds, have feet adapted for gripping a branch.

HOW BIG IS IT?

SPECIAL ADAPTATION

Black Redstarts originally nested on the sides of cliffs. But they have learnt that buildings, especially tall, inaccessible ones like churches and warehouses, make equally useful and safe nesting sites.

Redstart (Common)

• **ORDER** • Passeriformes • **FAMILY** • Muscicapidae • **SPECIES** • *Phoenicurus phoenicurus*

VITAL STATISTICS

WEIGHT	15g (0.5oz)
LENGTH	14cm (5.5in)
WINGSPAN	22cm (8.7in)
SEXUAL MATURITY	1 year
INCUBATION PERIOD	13–14 days
FLEDGLING PERIOD	16–17 days
NUMBER OF EGGS	6–7 eggs
NUMBER OF BROODS	1–2 a year
TYPICAL DIET	Insects and spiders
LIFE SPAN	Up to 6 years

The Redstart is a fine black and orange bird that can be immediately recognized thanks to its bright orange tail, which it often flicks nervously while perching.

WHERE IN THE WORLD?

The Redstart is a Flycatcher that breeds in Europe and in northern and Central Asia. In the winter, it migrates to the warmer climates of North Africa and Arabia. Its preferred habitat is woodland.

CREATURE COMPARISONS

Redstarts, especially the browner females and the juvenile birds, are easy to confuse with robins. It is not just their plumage that looks similar. They are also a comparable size, and have the same upright stance when perching. However, robins tend to be rounder in the body.

Common Redstart

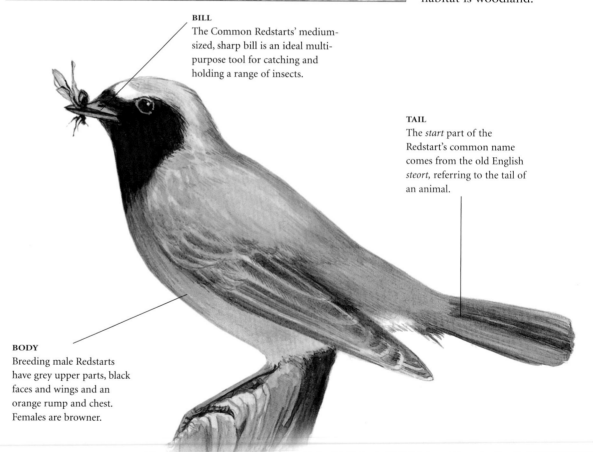

BILL
The Common Redstarts' medium-sized, sharp bill is an ideal multi-purpose tool for catching and holding a range of insects.

TAIL
The *start* part of the Redstart's common name comes from the old English *steort*, referring to the tail of an animal.

BODY
Breeding male Redstarts have grey upper parts, black faces and wings and an orange rump and chest. Females are browner.

HOW BIG IS IT?

SPECIAL ADAPTATION
Traditionally Redstarts make their homes in woodlands, nesting in holes in mature trees. However, as habitats vanish, many have adapted to an urban lifestyle, taking advantage of buildings and nest boxes.

Whinchat

Whinchats are most often seen perching on low-lying bushes or running and hopping across ground. Wherever they are seen, they are always a joy to watch.

VITAL STATISTICS

WEIGHT	17g (0.6oz)
LENGTH	12cm (4.7in)
WINGSPAN	22cm (8.7in)
SEXUAL MATURITY	1 year
INCUBATION PERIOD	13 days
FLEDGLING PERIOD	14–15 days
NUMBER OF EGGS	5–6 eggs
NUMBER OF BROODS	1 a year, but a second may be laid if the first clutch fails
TYPICAL DIET	Invertebrates; occasionally fruit and berries
LIFE SPAN	1 year

WHERE IN THE WORLD?

Whinchats breed in Europe and parts of northwestern Asia. In the winter, these little birds undertake huge migrations, flying south to enjoy the warmer climates found in tropical, sub-Saharan Africa.

CREATURE COMPARISONS

Whinchats feed mainly on insects and insect larvae. While the larvae are usually caught on the ground, insects are often captured, in flight. This common technique is used by many members of the wide-spread Flycatcher Family (Muscicapidae), to which the Whinchat belongs.

Whinchats in flight

WINGS
Male and female Whinchats can be differentiated by the white patches on their wings. The females usually lack these.

BODY
Male Whinchats have streaked brown upper parts and underparts, often described as apricot in colour. A white band highlights the eyes.

TAIL
Whinchats have a relatively short tail, which they can often be seen to flick in a nervous manner while perching.

HOW BIG IS IT?

SPECIAL ADAPTATION

Whinchats usually nest on the ground, among tall grasses. Ground-nesting allows them to take advantage of a range of environments, although predators, such as magpies, do steal their eggs.

European Stonechat

• **ORDER** • Passeriformes • **FAMILY** • Muscicapidae • **SPECIES** • *Saxicola rubicola*

VITAL STATISTICS

WEIGHT	14–15g (oz)
LENGTH	11.5–13cm (in)
WINGSPAN	24–27cm (in)
NUMBER OF EGGS	5–6 eggs
INCUBATION PERIOD	14–15 days
NUMBER OF BROODS	2 a year
TYPICAL DIET	Insects, worms, grubs, spiders
LIFE SPAN	Up to 7 years

The European Stonechat was once believed to be a species of thrush, but is now considered a relative of the Flycatchers.

WHERE IN THE WORLD?

The European Stonechat breeds in most of Europe and across Central Asia. In winter, the Asian birds migrate to southern Asia, and European birds migrate to Africa, south of the Sahara.

CREATURE COMPARISONS

In the breeding season, the male European Stonechat has a dark brown or black head, back and upper part of the wings, often with paler streaks. The wings have a distinct white band. The cheek is black, the throat and the breast are buff, and the belly is white. Females are drabber and lack white wing bars. During winter, the males also become drab, and appear brown.

Male European Stonechat

WINGS
The European Stonechat has distinctly shorter and rounder wings than its close relative, the Siberian Stonechat.

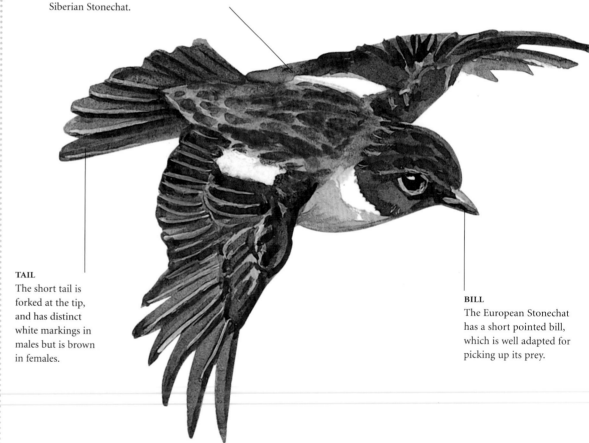

TAIL
The short tail is forked at the tip, and has distinct white markings in males but is brown in females.

BILL
The European Stonechat has a short pointed bill, which is well adapted for picking up its prey.

HOW BIG IS IT?

SPECIAL ADAPTATION

The male European Stonechat performs a mating dance to attract the female. She perches on a twig and he jumps over her up to 20 times while singing to her.

Golden Oriole (Eurasian)

• ORDER • Passeriformes **• FAMILY •** Oriolidae **• SPECIES •** *Oriolus oriolus*

VITAL STATISTICS

WEIGHT	68g (2.4oz)
LENGTH	24cm (9.4in)
WINGSPAN	46cm (18in)
SEXUAL MATURITY	2–3 years
INCUBATION PERIOD	16–17 days
FLEDGLING PERIOD	16–17 days
NUMBER OF EGGS	3–4 eggs
NUMBER OF BROODS	1 a year
TYPICAL DIET	Insects and spiders; occasionally fruit and berries
LIFE SPAN	Up to 10 years

Orioles get their name from the Latin word *aureolus,* which means 'made of gold' – a reference to the male bird's stunningly vivid yellow plumage.

WHERE IN THE WORLD?

The Golden Oriole lives in deciduous woodlands, where it nests in the tree canopy. Populations breed in Europe, Asia and northwestern Africa but winter in India and sub-Saharan Africa.

CREATURE COMPARISONS

The beauty of the fluting song of the Golden Oriole has been favourably compared to that of the tuneful Blackbird. It is easy to imagine that birds as bright and sunny as the Oriole come from tropical climates. Yet, Golden Orioles are the only members of this exotic Family who breed in the Northern hemisphere. There is even a tiny population in Britain's Lakenheath Fen Nature Reserve.

Female

PLUMAGE
The body is bright yellow and so colourful as to almost resemble a tropical bird.

BODY
In shape, Golden Orioles resemble birds of the Thrush Family, having elongated bodies, long necks and small, round heads.

WINGS
These agile fliers flit through the foliage with ease. Over longer distances they bob up and down in flight an undulating pattern.

HOW BIG IS IT?

SPECIAL ADAPTATION

The plumpage of the Golden Oriole provides good camouflage. In fact, it can be almost impossible to spot once nestled in the tree canopy hidden among dark shadows and sun-dappled foliage.

Raggiana Bird of Paradise

• ORDER • Passeriformes • FAMILY • Paradisaeidae • SPECIES • *Paradisaea raggiana*

VITAL STATISTICS

LENGTH	85–87cm (33.5–34.2in)
WINGSPAN	48–63cm (19–25in)
SEXUAL MATURITY	4–7 year
INCUBATION PERIOD	17–21 days
FLEDGLING PERIOD	25–30 days
NUMBER OF EGGS	1–2 eggs
NUMBER OF BROODS	2 a year are possible, but males may have multiple mates
HABITS	Diurnal, non-migratory
TYPICAL DIET	Fruit; occasionally insects and invertebrates
LIFE SPAN	Up to 25 years

CREATURE COMPARISONS

With their magnificent plumage and dramatic tail feathers, male Raggiana Birds of Paradise look like a picture-book tropical bird. Yet, underneath their colourful attire, their bodies, bills and claws are very similar in shape to the more familiar raven.

Male

Papua New Guinea is home to some of the world's most spectacular Birds of Paradise – of which the Raggiana is one of the most stunning.

WHERE IN THE WORLD?

The Raggiana Bird of Paradise is the National Bird of Papua New Guinea and can be found on the south and east of the island, from Milne Bay in to the border of Irian Jaya.

BILL
The bill varies from species to species, but bill of the Raggianas is powerful and slim, perfectly adapted for picking and eating fruit.

FEET
The feet are adapted for perching in the trees of the tropical rainforests of Papua New Guinea, their natural habitat.

TAIL
Only male Raggianas grow such extravagant tails, which can be up to up to 52cm (20in) long.

HOW BIG IS IT?

SPECIAL ADAPTATION

The male Raggiana Bird of Paradise is a riot of colour, an adaptation to help them compete for mates. Females are drab in comparison but thiskeeps them safely camouflaged on the nest.

Bearded Tit

• ORDER • Passeriformes **• FAMILY •** Paradoxornithidae **• SPECIES •** *Panurus biarmicus*

VITAL STATISTICS

WEIGHT	12–18g (0.4–0.6oz)
LENGTH	11–12cm (4.3–4.7in)
WINGSPAN	16–18cm (6.3–7.1in)
NUMBER OF EGGS	5–7 eggs
INCUBATION PERIOD	12–13 days
NUMBER OF BROODS	2–4 a year
TYPICAL DIET	Insects, seeds in winter
LIFE SPAN	Up to 5 years

The Bearded Tit does not migrate but is sensitive to hard freezing, so in cold winters many birds may die.

WHERE IN THE WORLD?

The Bearded Tit is found across much of Europe, except northern Scandinavia and into western Central Asia. It also lives in parts of North Africa.

CREATURE COMPARISONS

The back and wings are reddish-brown or cinnamon with darker marking on the wing feathers, and white along the wing edges. Males have a grey head and breast, with a distinct black marking along the neck (a beard). Females have a buff head. The breast is white, and the belly is buff or cinnamon.

Male

HEAD
Adult males raise the feathers forming the dark stripe across the cheek when they dance to attract females.

TAIL
The long tail of the Bearded Tit is used not only for flying but for display when males dance to attract females.

BILL
The very short stout bill enables the bird to eat tiny insects and small seeds.

HOW BIG IS IT?

SPECIAL ADAPTATION

The Bearded Tit is able to raise up to four broods every year. The chicks mature very quickly, and chicks from the first brood may breed themselves the same year they were born.

Blue Tit

• **ORDER** • Passeriformes • **FAMILY** • Paridae • **SPECIES** • *Cyanistes caeruleus*

VITAL STATISTICS

WEIGHT	11g (0.4oz)
LENGTH	10.5–12cm (4.1–4.7in)
WINGSPAN	18cm (7.1in)
SEXUAL MATURITY	1 year
INCUBATION PERIOD	13–15 days
FLEDGLING PERIOD	16–22 days
NUMBER OF EGGS	7–12 eggs
NUMBER OF BROODS	1 a year
TYPICAL DIET	Insects and seeds
LIFE SPAN	Typically 3 years

The Blue Tit is an intelligent and sociable bird. It is a natural woodland dweller, but will take advantage of a conveniently placed bird-box or well stocked feeder.

WHERE IN THE WORLD?

The Blue Tit is found throughout temperate Europe, western Asia and North Africa. Its preferred habitat is the forest, but will take up residence in gardens if suitable nesting holes are available.

CREATURE COMPARISONS

With their blue 'caps', vibrant yellow bellies and black and white face markings, adult Blue Tits are one of the most colourful members of the Tit Family. Generally, the females is slightly paler than the male while the juvenile (shown below) is paler still, with green-grey bodies and yellow cheeks.

Juvenile

HEAD
Blue Tits have small, rounded heads, which are set so close into the body that they seem to have no necks.

WINGS
Vivid blue wings and tail make these lively birds one of the easiest to spot and identify in the garden.

BILL
Although the bill is designed for cracking open seed cases, Blue Tits will eat a wide range of garden scraps.

HOW BIG IS IT?

SPECIAL ADAPTATION

Powerful feet are a fairly common trait for perching (passerine) birds, who spend much of their time sitting on branches. However, Blue Tits also use their feet to subdue and hold down their prey.

Crested Tit

• ORDER • Passeriformes **• FAMILY •** Paridae **• SPECIES •** *Lophophanes cristatus*

VITAL STATISTICS

WEIGHT	10–13g (0.4–0.5oz)
LENGTH	11–12cm (4.3–4.7in)
WINGSPAN	17–20cm (6.7–8in)
NUMBER OF EGGS	6–9 eggs
INCUBATION PERIOD	13–15 days
NUMBER OF BROODS	1 a year
TYPICAL DIET	Insects; caterpillars
LIFE SPAN	Up to 9 years

When frightened, the Crested Tit reveals its presence by letting off a loud, buzzing noise, before flying away.

WHERE IN THE WORLD?

The Crested Tit breeds in most of Europe (except parts of the British Isles and northern Scandinavia, and most of Italy) and is also found in western Asia.

CREATURE COMPARISONS

This tiny bird has a uniformly brown or greyish-brown upper part of the head, neck, back and wings. The cheek is white, often with a faint dark circle. Along the face are pale feathers edged in black, which form a small crest on top of the head. The throat is black and the breast and belly are white with buff along the flanks. Females look similar to males.

Crested Tit

HEAD
The crest of feathers on top of the head is used in display to other birds.

BEAK
The short, pointed beak is used for catching small creatures, and also to chisel into wood to build a nest.

LEGS
The legs are greyish-brown and the toes are long and strong for perching on twigs and fir needles.

HOW BIG IS IT?

SPECIAL ADAPTATION
The tiny, fragile-looking Crested Tit is able to chisel its own nest into an old log. Its beak is not enforced like that of a woodpecker, so the wood must be relatively old and soft.

Great Tit

• **ORDER** • Passeriformes • **FAMILY** • Paridae • **SPECIES** • *Parus major*

VITAL STATISTICS

WEIGHT	16–21g (0.6–0.7oz)
LENGTH	13–14cm (5.1–5.5in)
WINGSPAN	24–28cm (9.4–11in)
NUMBER OF EGGS	8–10 eggs
INCUBATION PERIOD	13–15 days
NUMBER OF BROODS	1–2 a year
TYPICAL DIET	Insects, caterpillars, oily seeds, nuts, berries
LIFE SPAN	Up to 12 years

The Great Tit is a colourful bird familiar to garden owners across Europe. It often bullies other smaller birds.

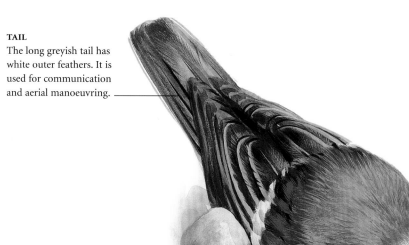

WHERE IN THE WORLD?

The Great Tit is found in most of Europe except the high north, and extends across central Russia and southeastern Asia. It is also found on the islands of Sumatra and Borneo.

CREATURE COMPARISONS

The male Great Tit has a shiny black head and throat, and a white chin. The breast is yellow with a wide central black tripe. The upper side of the wings are pale bluish, and the tail is greyish-blue. Females are similar to males, but are drabber with a much less distinct black stripe along the breast.

TAIL
The long greyish tail has white outer feathers. It is used for communication and aerial manoeuvring.

HEAD
An all-black head and a white chin are characteristics of this species of bird.

BILL
The short stout bill is well adapted for feeding on a wide-ranging diet.

Female

HOW BIG IS IT?

SPECIAL ADAPTATION

The Great Tit is a bully, and often harasses other small songbirds away from the best roosting places. Sometimes, it will even throw the residents out of their nest box.

Willow Tit

• ORDER • Passeriformes **• FAMILY •** Paridae **• SPECIES •** *Poecile montanus*

VITAL STATISTICS

WEIGHT	12g (0.4oz)
LENGTH	12cm (4.7in)
WINGSPAN	19cm (7.5in)
SEXUAL MATURITY	1 year
INCUBATION PERIOD	14 days
FLEDGLING PERIOD	17–20 days
NUMBER OF EGGS	6–8 eggs
NUMBER OF BROODS	1 a year
TYPICAL DIET	Invertebrates in the summer; seeds and berries in the winter
LIFE SPAN	Up to 10 years

These relatively unknown little birds were immortalized by Gilbert and Sullivan's famous comic opera *The Mikado* (1885), which featured the song 'Willow Titwillow Titwillow'.

WHERE IN THE WORLD?

Willow Tits are widespread throughout sub-Arctic Europe and northern Asia. Populations tend to be resident, and are found in mature woodlands, especially those with birch, willow and alder trees.

CREATURE COMPARISONS

Many species of bird, most famously woodpecker make their nests in cavities in tree trunks. Willow Tits, which do not have the woodpecker's pecking power, use soft or decaying tree stumps, which are much easier to excavate.

Willow Tits nesting

HEAD
Willow Tits can be distinguished from their relatives, Marsh Tits, by the fact that their head cap is slightly lighter and duller.

BODY
Willow Tits are smaller than Great Tits and larger than Blue Tits. Unlike other Tits, they have no yellow on their bodies.

FEET
The powerful feet are well adapted for perching.

HOW BIG IS IT?

SPECIAL ADAPTATION
We can tell a lot about bird's habits from their bills. All Tits have short bills, which are ideally adapted for pecking insects or seeds on the ground, but are equally useful at probing bark for insect larvae.

Yellow-rumped Warbler

• ORDER • Passeriformes • FAMILY • Parulidae • SPECIES • *Dendroica coronata*

With bright rumps and vivid patches of yellow on their wings, Yellow-rumped Warblers are one of the easiest species of American Warblers to identify.

VITAL STATISTICS

WEIGHT	11.5g (0.4oz)
LENGTH	14cm (5.5in)
SEXUAL MATURITY	1 year
INCUBATION PERIOD	12–13 days
FLEDGLING PERIOD	10–12 days
NUMBER OF EGGS	3–5 eggs
NUMBER OF BROODS	1–2 a year
HABITS	Diurnal, migratory
YPICAL DIET	Insects in the summer and berries and fruit in the winter
LIFE SPAN	Up to 10 years

WHERE IN THE WORLD?

Yellow-rumped Warblers are found in a wide variety of habitats, from coniferous forests to marsh lands. They make their homes throughout North America, migrating into Latin America for the winter.

CREATURE COMPARISONS

Warblers come in all sizes and colours. However, most are tree-dwellers and so, to avoid competition, birds of different species feed at different levels of the forest. Yellow-rumped Warblers, for instance, feed on the lower branches, while Blackburnian Warblers forage among the highest branches.

Blackburnian Warbler (top), Black-throated Green Warbler (middle), Yellow-rumped Warbler (bottom)

HEAD
During the breeding season, male and female Yellow-rumped Warblers have a yellow cap (and pure white patches on their tail).

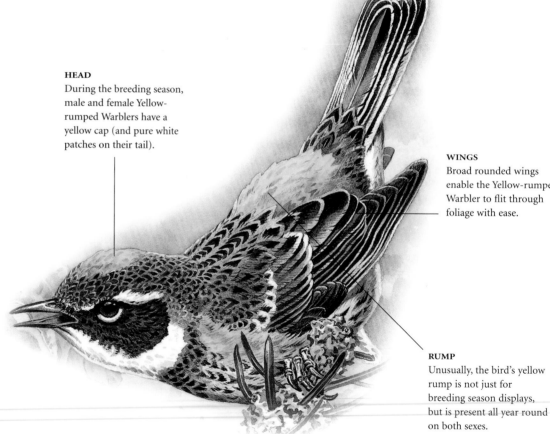

WINGS
Broad rounded wings enable the Yellow-rumped Warbler to flit through foliage with ease.

RUMP
Unusually, the bird's yellow rump is not just for breeding season displays, but is present all year round on both sexes.

HOW BIG IS IT?

SPECIAL ADAPTATION
Yellow-rumped Warblers have developed unique guts that allow them to digest the wax coating the skins of many berries and fruits. This offers the birds an additional food source in times of need.

Common Yellow Throat

• **ORDER** • Passeriformes • **FAMILY** •Parulidae • **SPECIES** • *Geothlypis trichas*

VITAL STATISTICS

WEIGHT	9–10g (0.3–0.3oz)
LENGTH	11–13cm (4.3–5in)
WINGSPAN	15–19cm (6–7.5in)
SEXUAL MATURITY	1 year
INCUBATION PERIOD	12 days
FLEDGLING PERIOD	8–10 days
NUMBER OF EGGS	3–5 eggs
NUMBER OF BROODS	2 a year
TYPICAL DIET	Insects, spiders; occasionally seeds
LIFE SPAN	Up to 7 years

With its bandit's mask and vibrant, yellow throat, the Common Yellow Throat is one of the most recognizable of all North American warblers. Only the male sings.

WHERE IN THE WORLD?

These wetland birds can be seen throughout North America, from the Yukon to southern Mexico. Southern birds tend to be resident, but northern races migrate to Central Latin America and the Caribbean.

CREATURE COMPARISONS

There are 13 known races of Common Yellow Throat, all of which vary in coloration across their range. As a general rule, the southern populations have brighter yellow underparts, and the northern birds have paler underparts. Females are usually duller and lack the males' black mask.

Female

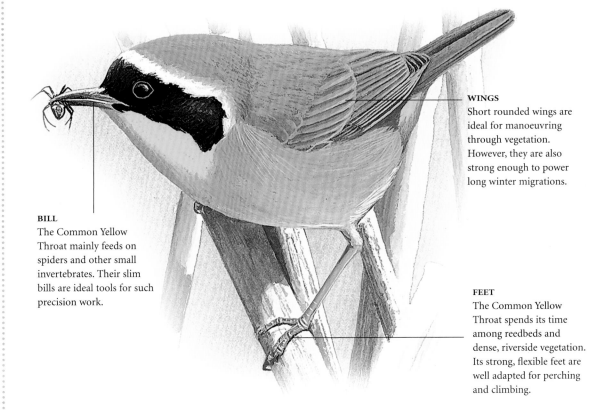

BILL
The Common Yellow Throat mainly feeds on spiders and other small invertebrates. Their slim bills are ideal tools for such precision work.

WINGS
Short rounded wings are ideal for manoeuvring through vegetation. However, they are also strong enough to power long winter migrations.

FEET
The Common Yellow Throat spends its time among reedbeds and dense, riverside vegetation. Its strong, flexible feet are well adapted for perching and climbing.

HOW BIG IS IT?

SPECIAL ADAPTATION
The Common Yellow Throats nests on the ground, but has learnt to build roofs to shields its eggs from predators.

White-winged Snow Finch

• **ORDER** • Passeriformes • **FAMILY** • Passeridae • **SPECIES** • *Montifringilla nivalis*

VITAL STATISTICS

WEIGHT	14–20g (0.5–0.7oz)
LENGTH	16.5–19cm (6.5–7.5in)
WINGSPAN	35–40cm (14–15.7in)
NUMBER OF EGGS	5–6 eggs
INCUBATION PERIOD	17–18 days
NUMBER OF BROODS	1–2 a year
TYPICAL DIET	Seeds, insects, grub, caterpillars, worms, spiders
LIFE SPAN	Up to 10 years

The White-winged Snow Finch was once regarded as a relative of the Finches, but is now considered to be a species of Sparrow.

WHERE IN THE WORLD?

The White-winged Snow Finch breeds high up in the mountains, often above the tree line. It is found in parts of southern Europe, across parts of Central Asia and east towards China.

CREATURE COMPARISONS

In summer, the male has a brown or greyish-brown back, and a grey head. The wings are brilliantly white with black wing tips. The throat has a black streak, and the flanks, breast and belly are pale grey. The tail is black with distinct white edges. The beak is blackish, but in winter it becomes yellowish. Females are similar to males.

White-winged Snow Finch

BODY
The White-winged Snow Finch has a stocky body. This is an adaptation for living in cold environments because a stocky body loses less heat.

WINGS
In flight, huge patches of white on the wings become visible.

FEET
The feet are stout with long toes and short, pointed claws, and are well adapted for hopping around on the ground.

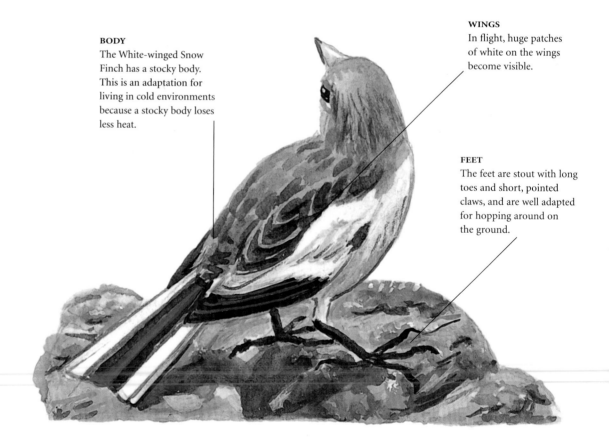

HOW BIG IS IT?

SPECIAL ADAPTATION

During the breeding season, the male performs a special spiralling flight, during which he sings loudly, to attract a female. He also displays his bright white feathers to her.

House Sparrow

The chirpy little House Sparrow is one of nature's great opportunists, enjoying everything that modern city living offers, from brick-built nest sites to ample food.

VITAL STATISTICS

WEIGHT	34g (1.2oz)
LENGTH	14–16cm (5.5–6.3in)
WINGSPAN	24cm (9.4in)
SEXUAL MATURITY	1 year
LAYS EGGS	April–August
INCUBATION PERIOD	12–15 days
NUMBER OF EGGS	3–5 eggs
NUMBER OF BROODS	2–3 a year, occasionally 4
TYPICAL DIET	Seeds, berries, small insects; food scraps
LIFE SPAN	Typically 3 years

WHERE IN THE WORLD?

House Sparrows have lived alongside humans for centuries. Resident populations can be found in Europe, North Africa, Asia, the Americas and Australia, where the species has been introduced.

CREATURE COMPARISONS

With its grey cap and black bib, male House Sparrows are a familiar sight and probably the one bird most people can identify with confidence. Spotting female House Sparrows is trickier, as they lack the bib and cap and thus look similar to many other little brown birds.

Female

BODY
A House Sparrow's body is stout and broad with a large head and prominent bill. Its plumage tends to look bushy and untidy.

BILL
The House Sparrow's multi-purpose bill is strong enough for cracking open seed cases, but delicate enough to catch insects.

WINGS
In flight, the House Sparrow can seem quite clumsy, with an up and down drilling flight pattern and whirring wing beats.

HOW BIG IS IT?

SPECIAL ADAPTATION

Although House Sparrows have the wedge-shaped bill of seed-eating species, they also hunt insects, eat cereal crops and have learnt how to use their feet to grip onto garden birdfeeders.

Golden Sparrow

• **ORDER** • Passeriformes • **FAMILY** • Passeridae • **SPECIES** • *Passer luteus*

The glamorous Golden Sparrow, like its cousin the House Sparrow, has an air of perky defiance that endears it to bird-watchers.

VITAL STATISTICS

LENGTH	10–13cm (4–5in)
SEXUAL MATURITY	2 years
INCUBATION PERIOD	1–12 days
FLEDGLING PERIOD	13–14 days
NUMBER OF EGGS	2–6 eggs
NUMBER OF BROODS	1; occasionally 2–3 a year
CALL	Chirrup
HABITS	Diurnal, non-migratory
TYPICAL DIET	Seeds, fruit; occasionally small insects
LIFE SPAN	Up to 14 years

WHERE IN THE WORLD?

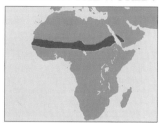

Golden Sparrows are found in parched, open savannah, semi-desert regions and dry scrublands. Populations swarm, in a broad band, across Africa and Arabia (bordering the Sahara Desert) in search of food.

CREATURE COMPARISONS

Golden Sparrows (or Golden Song Sparrows as they are sometimes called) vary in coloration across their range. African Males have a bright yellow head and underparts with a deep, chestnut-brown back. Arabian Golden Sparrows (right) are almost entirely yellow, with black wings and a black tip of the tail.

Male African Golden Sparrow (top), female (bottom).

BODY
Despite their exotic plumage, Golden Sparrows have a typical sparrow body shape: broad trunk, large head and prominent bill.

PLUMAGE
Male Golden Sparrows keep their bright plumage all year round, not just in the breeding season.

BILL
The multi-purpose bill is strong enough to crack open seed cases, but delicate enough to catch insects.

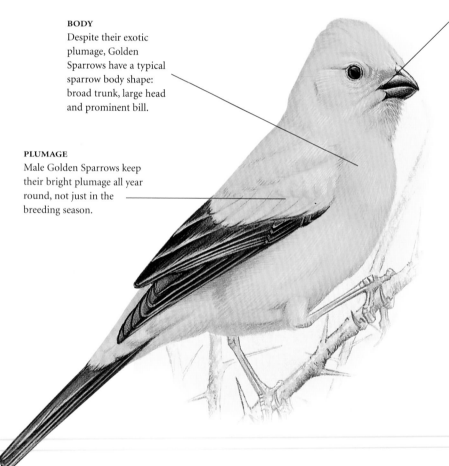

HOW BIG IS IT?

SPECIAL ADAPTATION

The Golden Sparrow takes several days to build its bulky nest and it is the quality of his building skills that helps him attract a potential mate. The birds have learnt to use stiff twigs to provide ventilation and drainage during the sudden flash floods that often occur in desert regions.

Tree Sparrow (Eurasian)

• ORDER • Passeriformes • FAMILY • Passeridae • SPECIES • *Passer montanus*

VITAL STATISTICS

WEIGHT	24g (0.8oz)
LENGTH	12.5–14cm (5–5.5in)
WINGSPAN	21cm (8.3in)
SEXUAL MATURITY	1 year
INCUBATION PERIOD	11–14 days
FLEDGLING PERIOD	15–20 days
NUMBER OF EGGS	5–7 eggs
NUMBER OF BROODS	1 a year
TYPICAL DIET	Seeds and cereals, insects in the breeding season
LIFE SPAN	Typically 2 years

Despite differences in their appearance, habits and habitats, the Eurasian Tree Sparrow is often mistaken for its more common cousin, the House Sparrow.

WHERE IN THE WORLD?

The Tree Sparrow is found naturally throughout Europe and Asia, and has also been introduced into Australia and North America. Its habitats are woods and farmland.

CREATURE COMPARISONS

Juvenile birds of both sexes usually resemble their mothers until they reach sexual maturity. However, male, female and juvenile Tree Sparrows look almost identical, although bird-watchers may be able to differentiate between the two, due to the juveniles' slightly duller coloration.

HEAD
Tree Sparrows can be distinguished from House Sparrows by their chestnut-brown crown and brighter plumage.

WINGS
The Tree Sparrow's white double wing bars are especially noticeable when the bird is in flight.

BODY
On average, Tree Sparrows are slightly smaller in size than House Sparrows, with a shorter neck and plumper body.

Juvenile

HOW BIG IS IT?

SPECIAL ADAPTATION

Being small can sometimes be an advantage, especially for a bird. Tree Sparrows nest in holes and crevices, and are small enough to find the tiniest spaces comfortable. This gives them an advantage over larger birds when it comes to choosing nesting sites.

Flame Robin

• **ORDER** • Passeriformes • **FAMILY** • Petroicidae *(under review)* • **SPECIES** • *Petroica phoenicea*

VITAL STATISTICS

WEIGHT	14g (0.5oz)
LENGTH	10–14cm (4–5.5in)
SEXUAL MATURITY	1 year
LAYS EGGS	Breeding from August–January
INCUBATION PERIOD	14 days
FLEDGLING PERIOD	14–16 days
NUMBER OF EGGS	3–4 eggs
NUMBER OF BROODS	1–2 a year
HABITS	Diurnal, non-migratory but may move locally in search of food
TYPICAL DIET	Insects

CREATURE COMPARISONS

Female Flame Robins look different from males. While the plumage of the male is flame red, the female has a drabber, olive-brown attire. Young Flame Robins of both sexes resemble their mothers, although they have more prominent streaks on the back and belly.

Female

With its bold, black and orange plumage and its equally vibrant personality, Australia's Flame Robin lives up to its colourful name.

WHERE IN THE WORLD?

The Flame Robin is found around the southeastern coast of Australia and on the Island of Tasmania. Its preferred habitat is woodland, although birds are often seen in gardens in the winter.

BODY
Male Flame Robins have a bright orange breast and throat. The plumage is white on the lower belly and under the tail.

WINGS
Short round wings enable the bird to fly among foliage. The short tail aids balance and manoeuvrability.

FEET
The feet have three long forwards-facing toes and one shorter backwards-facing toe, an arrangement well adapted for perching.

HOW BIG IS IT?

SPECIAL ADAPTATION

The bill of the Flame Robin is surrounded by short bristles, which protect its eyes from the flailing legs of their insect prey. This is an adaptation that has evolved separately in both the Flame Robin and in Flycatchers. Although unrelated, the birds share similar habits.

Common Chiffchaff

• **ORDER** • Passeriformes • **FAMILY** • Phylloscopidae • **SPECIES** • *Phylloscopus collybita*

The Common Chiffchaff looks similar to other warblers but its distinctive song differentiates it from the rest.

VITAL STATISTICS

WEIGHT	6–9g (0.2–0.3oz)
LENGTH	10–12cm (4–4.7in)
WINGSPAN	15–21cm (6–8.3in)
NUMBER OF EGGS	5–6 eggs
INCUBATION PERIOD	13–14 days
NUMBER OF BROODS	1–2 a year
TYPICAL DIE	Insects, spiders, caterpillars
LIFE SPAN	Up to 6 years

WHERE IN THE WORLD?

The Chiffchaff is widespread in large parts of Europe and across Central Asia. They migrate to the Mediterranean, Central Africa, and Southeast Asia for the winter.

CREATURE COMPARISONS

The Chiffchaff often has a dark streak across the eyes and a slightly darker cheek patch. The wings are olive-brown with darker steaks along the large feathers. The underside is off-white, becoming pale yellowish or buff along the flanks. Males and females look similar. In summer, the Chiffchaff sings from conifer trees a simple 'chiff-chaff' song that has given the bird its name.

Common Chiffchaff

BODY
The upper side of the head, neck and back are greyish-brown or dull olive-brown.

WINGS
The male flies in a peculiar, erect manner when he courts a female during the breeding season, fluttering his wings.

LEGS
The legs are brown and long with feet that are perfectly adapted for perching on small spruce and fir twigs.

HOW BIG IS IT?

SPECIAL ADAPTATION

The Common Chiffchaff is found across an enormous range, and is known to feed on over 50 different families of insects. It plays an important part in keeping certain pests under control.

Red-capped Manakin

• ORDER • Passeriformes **• FAMILY •** Pipridae **• SPECIES •** *Pipra mentalis*

VITAL STATISTICS

LENGTH	11cm (4.3in)
SEXUAL MATURITY	1 year
INCUBATION PERIOD	Unknown
FLEDGLING PERIOD	13–15 days
NUMBER OF EGGS	2 eggs
NUMBER OF BROODS	1 a year
CALL	Loud 'tik-tik' call
HABITS	Diurnal, non-migratory
TYPICAL DIET	Seeds and berries; occasionally insects
LIFE SPAN	Unknown

The male Red-capped Manakin is the supreme dancer of the bird world, performing elaborate acrobatics and shuffling rapidly backwards across a branch during mating displays.

WHERE IN THE WORLD?

The Red-capped Manakin is found in the lush, wet tropical and sub-tropical forests of Latin America. Populations can be found all along the Pacific coast, from Mexico to Equador.

CREATURE COMPARISONS

Male Red-capped Manakins may spend their lives trying to get noticed, but females (shown below) prefer to stay hidden safely in the undergrowth. It is their job to raise the young, which have cryptic coloration (so called because it blends in with the background). This helps them to avoid any unwanted attention.

Female

HEAD
Red-capped Manakins are named after their vivid head coloration. There are 51 other species of Manakin, with similarly descriptive names.

BODY
The round body is slightly plump with a stubby tail and short rounded wings.

WINGS
The loud cracking noise heard during mating is produced as the bird brings its wing tips together at incredible speed.

HOW BIG IS IT?

SPECIAL ADAPTATION
Red-capped Manakins have two of their toes fused together at the top, giving them a much better gripping ability on branches and creepers. This is especially useful when trying to reach out-of-the-way fruit, but may also help during the birds' elaborate courtship dances.

Hooded Pitta

The Hooded Pitta, a bold and brilliantly coloured bird, was once known by another equally appropriate name, the Jewel Thrush.

VITAL STATISTICS

WEIGHT	42–70g (1.5–2.5oz)
LENGTH	16–19cm (6.3–7.5in)
SEXUAL MATURITY	1 year
LAYS EGGS	February–August
INCUBATION PERIOD	15–16 days
FLEDGLING PERIOD	16 days
NUMBER OF EGGS	2–5 eggs
NUMBER OF BROODS	1 a year
HABITS	Diurnal, migratory
TYPICAL DIET	Insects

WHERE IN THE WORLD?

The Hooded Pitta is found throughout Southeast Asia, from the foothills of the Himalayan Mountains to New Guinea, and on several scattered islands groups in Indonesia and the Philippines.

CREATURE COMPARISONS

There are at least 12 known subspecies of Hooded Pitta. These stocky birds vary in coloration across their range, though they share many characteristics, typically a dark hood and a more colourful body. The Sulawesi subspecies has a completely black head. Females and juveniles have duller plumage than the male.

Sulawesi Hooded Pitta

EYES
The eyes of the Hooded Pitta are large in relation to the size of their body. This gives them excellent vision among the forest gloom.

BODY
The body is very colourful with dark feathers covering the head like a hood.

WINGS
When the Hooded Pitta is alarmed or annoyed, it will often bob its head, flick its tail or fan its wings.

HOW BIG IS IT?

SPECIAL ADAPTATION

Powerful legs and long, flexible feet indicate that the Hooded Pitta is a forest-dweller. Such adaptations are typical of a bird that spends its time scurrying over dense forest foliage and rooting for food among leaf litter. Long claws also help to scrape away soil in search of a meal.

Jackson's Widowbird

• **ORDER** • Passeriformes • **FAMILY** • Ploceidae • **SPECIES** • *Euplectes jacksoni*

VITAL STATISTICS

WEIGHT	Males: 40–49g (1.4–1.7oz). Females: 29–42g (1–1.5oz)
LENGTH	14cm (5.5in)
SEXUAL MATURITY	3 years
LAYS EGGS	Breeding can take place all year round, depending on local conditions
INCUBATION PERIOD	13 days
FLEDGLING PERIOD	15 days
NUMBER OF EGGS	2–3 eggs
NUMBER OF BROODS	1 a year
HABITS	Diurnal, non-migratory
TYPICAL DIET	Seeds and some insects

CREATURE COMPARISONS

Male Jackson's Widowbirds keep their bold, black breeding plumage for only a few weeks. After that, they revert to their usual dark brown plumage. Female and juvenile Widowbirds are brown all year round, although their bodies are generally paler than the males, with streaks of black.

Female

For most of the year, male Jackson's Widowbirds are just little brown birds. With the arrival of the breeding season, however, they transform into vibrant grassland exhibitionists.

WHERE IN THE WORLD?

Jackson's Widowbird is only found naturally in central Kenya and northern Tanzania, where it makes its home on mountain grasslands. Its existing habitats are now threatened by the spread of farming.

BILL
The short, wedge-shaped bill of Jackson's Widowbird is an excellent tool for crushing and de-husking seeds from grasses and cereal crops.

BODY
Jackson's Widowbird takes its name from the male's summer plumage, which resembles the black dress worn by Victorian widows.

TAIL
The sumptuously showy tail of the breeding male Jackson's Widowbird can grow up to 14cm (5.5in) in length.

HOW BIG IS IT?

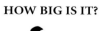

SPECIAL ADAPTATION

The male Jackson's Widowbird has found a dramatic solution to the problem of attracting a mate. It ditches its everyday plumage and becomes a magnificent show-off. In addition, it performs elaborate dances, swaying and jumping while holding its black tail plumes over its back.

Red Bishop (Southern)

• **ORDER** • Passeriformes • **FAMILY** • Ploceidae • **SPECIES** • *Euplectes orix*

VITAL STATISTICS

LENGTH	12–14cm (4.7–5.5in)
SEXUAL MATURITY	1 year
INCUBATION PERIOD	11–14 days
FLEDGLING PERIOD	13–16 days
NUMBER OF EGGS	3 eggs per nest
NUMBER OF BROODS	1–2 a year per breeding pair but more are possible, as males have up to 6 mates
CALL	Wheezing squeaks
HABITS	Diurnal, non-migratory
TYPICAL DIET	Seeds, cereals and insects
LIFE SPAN	Up to 15 years

CREATURE COMPARISONS

Sometimes male and female birds look so different from each other it is hard to believe they belong to the same species. This is certainly true of the Red Bishop. While breeding males are resplendent in black and red, females and juveniles are blandly brown.

Female

On Africa's grasslands, the startlingly vivid plumage of the male Red Bishop looks more like a wild poppy than a bishop's robe, from which it takes its name.

WHERE IN THE WORLD?

Red Bishops are common in wetlands and grasslands throughout much of sub-Saharan Africa. These are sociable birds, and are usually found nesting close to water, in large mixed-species groups.

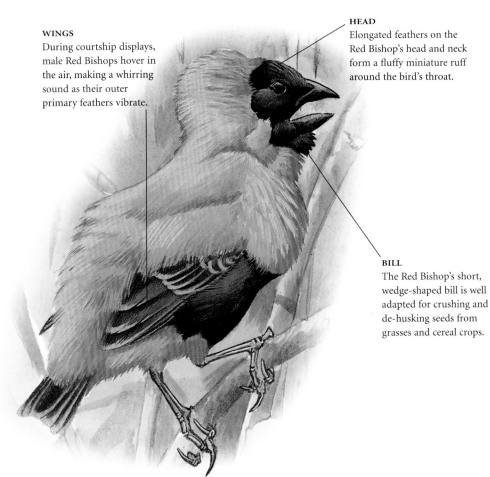

WINGS
During courtship displays, male Red Bishops hover in the air, making a whirring sound as their outer primary feathers vibrate.

HEAD
Elongated feathers on the Red Bishop's head and neck form a fluffy miniature ruff around the bird's throat.

BILL
The Red Bishop's short, wedge-shaped bill is well adapted for crushing and de-husking seeds from grasses and cereal crops.

HOW BIG IS IT?

SPECIAL ADAPTATION

Although many birds have long tails and elaborate head crests, simplicity is sometimes best. Red Bishops have short, rounded tails, which allows the birds to move rapidly through the undergrowth. More decorative plumage would simply get in their way.

313

Madagascar Red Fody

• **ORDER** • Passeriformes • **FAMILY** • Ploceidae • **SPECIES** • *Foudia madagascariensis*

VITAL STATISTICS

WEIGHT	14–19g (0.5–0.7oz)
LENGTH	12–14cm (4.7–5.5in)
WINGSPAN	27–30cm (10.6–12in)
NUMBER OF EGGS	3–5 eggs
INCUBATION PERIOD	11–14 days
NUMBER OF BROODS	1 a year
TYPICAL DIET	Mainly seeds, but also insects, nectar, fruit
LIFE SPAN	Unknown

The Madagascar Red Fody is one of the most common birds on the island of Madagascar, and is regarded as an agricultural pest.

WHERE IN THE WORLD?

This species of Fody lives on Madagascar, the Comoro Islands, the Mascarene Islands and the Seychelles. It has been introduced into the island of St Helena, and Bahrain.

CREATURE COMPARISONS

During the breeding season, males are most beautiful. The head, neck, body and underside of the tail are bright red, while the wings and tail are olive-brown, with yellow edges along the large feathers. Females are much drabber, and are greenish-brown with greyish-brown underparts. Non-breeding males look similar to females.

Female

HEAD
During the breeding season, the male Red Fody has a bright red head with a very handsome dark mask across the eye.

BILL
The Madagascar Red Fody has a short and very stout bill that is well adapted for collecting and crushing seeds.

WINGS
The wings are short and round. The bird usually makes only rather short bursts of flight from one tree to the next.

HOW BIG IS IT?

SPECIAL ADAPTATION

During the breeding season, males are often seen perching on telephone lines, while singing a loud hissing and spluttering song to attract females. Their brilliant red colour makes them visible from far away.

Sociable Weaver

• **ORDER** • Passeriformes • **FAMILY** • Ploceidae • **SPECIES** • *Philetairus socius*

Sociable Weavers are the architects of the bird world. Instead of constructing one nest for a single family, they build one for an entire community of up to 400 birds.

VITAL STATISTICS

LENGTH	14cm (5.5in)
SEXUAL MATURITY	1–2 years
INCUBATION PERIOD	13–14 days
FLEDGLING PERIOD	21–24 days
NUMBER OF EGGS	3–4 eggs
NUMBER OF BROODS	Up to 4 a year
CALL	Typically, a 'chi-chi-chi-chi'
TYPICAL DIET	Insects, seeds and grasses
HABITS	Diurnal, non-migratory
LIFE SPAN	Up to 4 years

WHERE IN THE WORLD?

Sociable Weavers are found throughout the Kalahari, Namibia, southern Botswana and central South Africa. Once they have established their nest, Weavers may spend their entire lives in it.

CREATURE COMPARISONS

Weavers are seed-eaters and are related to Finches. While Sociable Weavers are endemic to Africa, Finches, like the Green Finch, are found in Europe and Africa. In common with their cousins, Sociable Weavers have strong, rounded bills, relatively short tails and plump bodies.

Sociable Weaver in flight

BODY
Most Sociable Weavers never drink. Instead they get all of the moisture they need from their food.

EYES
Many species nest side by side with communities of Sociable Weavers. Some birds even move in. In return for lodgings, their visitors watch out for danger.

BILL
This strong bill is well adapted for cracking open seed cases, but delicate enough to catch insects.

HOW BIG IS IT?

SPECIAL ADAPTATION

There is safety in numbers, which is why Sociable Weavers construct such huge nests. They work together, using their bills to weave the straw together, then to maintain and extend the structure. The largest known nests can hold up to 100 separate, honeycomb-shaped chambers.

Wood Warbler

• **ORDER** • Passeriformes • **FAMILY** • Phylloscopidae • **SPECIES** • *Phylloscopus sibilatrix*

VITAL STATISTICS

WEIGHT	7–12g (0.2–0.4oz)
LENGTH	11.5–12cm (4.5–4.7in)
WINGSPAN	18–23cm (7–9in)
NUMBER OF EGGS	3–10 eggs (usually 6–7)
INCUBATION PERIOD	12–14 days
NUMBER OF BROODS	1 a year, sometimes 2
TYPICAL DIET	Tree-living insects and caterpillars
LIFE SPAN	Up to 6 years

The Wood Warbler sings two kinds of songs. One is short and soft, while the other is loud and trilling.

WHERE IN THE WORLD?

The Wood Warbler is widely distributed across northern and central Europe and into western Russia. It spends the winter in central and western Africa south of the Sahara desert.

CREATURE COMPARISONS

The Wood Warbler has a greenish upper side with faint yellow stripes, and it has more distinctive dark green and yellow stripes along the large wing feathers. It has a dark stripe across the face and eyes. The underside is whitish. In contrast to other Leaf Warblers, it has a lemon-yellow throat and breast. Females are similar to males.

Wood Warbler in flight

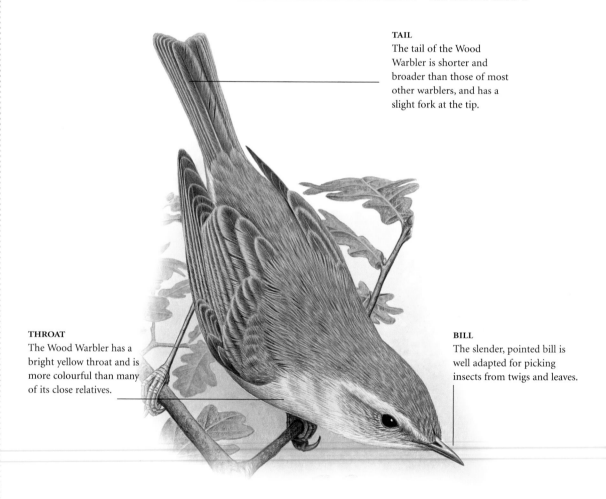

TAIL
The tail of the Wood Warbler is shorter and broader than those of most other warblers, and has a slight fork at the tip.

THROAT
The Wood Warbler has a bright yellow throat and is more colourful than many of its close relatives.

BILL
The slender, pointed bill is well adapted for picking insects from twigs and leaves.

HOW BIG IS IT?

SPECIAL ADAPTATION

This Wood Warbler lives in deciduous or mixed-type woodland, where its high-pitched metallic trill is often heard from the tops of trees. Singing loudly is strenuous, so the bird's heart beats a lot faster than when it is at rest.

Grey-crowned Babbler

• ORDER • Passeriformes • Pomatostomidae *(under review)* • SPECIES • *Pomatostomus temporalis*

Grey-crowned Babblers love a crowd. In fact, they spend their lives in huge extended families, sharing nest-building and feeding duties with the rest of the colony.

VITAL STATISTICS

WEIGHT	81g (3oz)
LENGTH	25–29cm (10–11.4in)
SEXUAL MATURITY	2–3years
LAYS EGGS	July–February
INCUBATION PERIOD	18–23 days
FLEDGLING PERIOD	20–22 days
NUMBER OF EGGS	2–6 eggs
NUMBER OF BROODS	1 a year
TYPICAL DIET	Insects, spiders and small reptiles
LIFE SPAN	Up to 12 years

WHERE IN THE WORLD?

Babblers are found across northern and eastern Australia, Indonesia and Papua New Guinea. They live in woodlands and sub-tropical forests, but are also seen near farms and golf courses.

CREATURE COMPARISONS

Grey-crowned Babblers are the largest of Australia's four species of Babbler, and they are highly sociable. Their most widely used colloquial name is Yahoo, after their distinctive call. Generally, it builds two types of nest to accommodate the extended family: roost-nests, which are used by the whole group, and brood-nests for breeding females.

Grey-crowned Babbler in flight

BODY
Grey-crowned Babblers are easily identified by their pale grey head stripe.

BILL
The long, pointed downwards-curving bill is a good tool for preying on a wide variety of insects and probing into crevices.

BREAST
There are two sub-species of Grey-crowned Babbler. These can be identified by comparing the breast colour of each bird.

HOW BIG IS IT?

SPECIAL ADAPTATION
The Grey-crowned Babbler feeds on a wide range of food, including insects, invertebrates and small reptiles. It has adapted a bill that can be used for a variety of tasks extending from probing in crevices for insect larvae, to rooting under leaf litter for spiders.

Alpine Accentor

• **ORDER** • Passeriformes • **FAMILY** • Prunellidae • **SPECIES** • *Prunella collaris*

VITAL STATISTICS

WEIGHT	18–24g (0.6–0.8oz)
LENGTH	15–17.5cm (6–7in)
WINGSPAN	32–37cm (12.6–14.6in)
NUMBER OF EGGS	3–5 eggs
INCUBATION PERIOD	14–15 days
NUMBER OF BROODS	1 a year
TYPICAL DIET	Insects, spiders, snails and slugs, seeds
LIFE SPAN	Up to 10 years

The Alpine Accentor is a mountainous bird, often living at altitudes more than 2000m (6562ft) above sea level.

WHERE IN THE WORLD?

The Alpine Accentor is found in high mountainous areas, often above the tree line, in southern Europe and across Central Asia. In winter, many move to lower altitudes.

CREATURE COMPARISONS

The back and upper part of the wings are brown with distinct dark stripes. The head and neck are grey, often with a pale and darkly spotted area around the throat. The breast and belly are light brown or greyish. The flanks are buff with reddish-brown streaks. The wings are darker brown with reddish-brown edges. Males and females are similar.

Alpine Accentor

BILL
The long pointed bill of the Alpine Accentor is well adapted for feeding on small-sized prey

TAIL
The brown and black tail is short and square, and is used during flight for manoeuvring and landing.

FEET
The legs are rather short, but the feet are long, and are adapted for walking on the ground and perching.

HOW BIG IS IT?

SPECIAL ADAPTATION

The Alpine Accentor often has a favourite stone on which it sits. These stones are often easy to locate because small plants and lichens on them are fertilized by the bird's droppings and so grow faster.

Dunnock

• ORDER • Passeriformes **• FAMILY •** Prunellidae **• SPECIES •** *Prunella modularis*

VITAL STATISTICS

WEIGHT	21g (0.7oz)
LENGTH	14cm (5.5in)
WINGSPAN	20cm (8in)
SEXUAL MATURITY	1 year
INCUBATION PERIOD	12–13 days
FLEDGLING PERIOD	12–15 days
NUMBER OF EGGS	4–5 eggs
NUMBER OF BROODS	2–3 a year
TYPICAL DIET	Insects; some seeds in winter
LIFE SPAN	Typically 2 years

CREATURE COMPARISONS

Dunnocks are often referred to as Hedge Sparrows, and for many years the two birds were thought to be the same species. However, Dunnocks actually belong to a group called accentors, which are shy insect-eaters with sharp pointed bills. Male and female Dunnocks look alike. Juveniles can often be identified by the lack of grey on the head and throat.

Dunnock in flight

Dunnocks have a complicated sex life. Birds form pairs of two males and one female, or two males and two females or, in fact, any combination of the above.

WHERE IN THE WORLD?

Dunnocks are a widespread species, found in Europe and the Near East. Birds are resident in the milder parts of their range, but those in cooler regions must migrate to feed.

HEAD
The Dunnock's call is most often heard as it sings from a perch. Otherwise it tends to stay well hidden.

BODY
With its short neck, plump body shape and brown plumage, the Dunnock strongly resembles the House Sparrow.

BILL
The bill of the Dunnock is thin and pointed but deeper at the base.

HOW BIG IS IT?

SPECIAL ADAPTATION

The Dunnock's unusual sex life was uncovered only after research to discover why male birds pecked the females' cloaca (reproductive orifice). The answer was that, because females mated so often, males had developed this technique to remove their rivals' sperm to ensure that only they fathered chicks.

Satin Bowerbird

• **ORDER** • Passeriformes • **FAMILY** • Ptilonorhynchidae • **SPECIES** • *Ptilonorhynchus violaceus*

VITAL STATISTICS

LENGTH	27–33cm (10.6–13in)
SEXUAL MATURITY	Males: 5–7 years Females: 2 years
INCUBATION PERIOD	21–22 days
FLEDGLING PERIOD	20–21 days
NUMBER OF EGGS	1–3 eggs
NUMBER OF BROODS	1 a year
CALL	Male makes a loud 'wee-oo' call
HABITS	Diurnal, non-migratory
TYPICAL DIET	Fruit and berries; some insects in the winter
LIFE SPAN	Up to 15 years

CREATURE COMPARISONS

Like females, juvenile male Satin Bowerbirds are grey-green with creamy speckled underparts. It takes around seven years for the males to take on the dark plumage of their adult counterparts. Females retain their protective coloration throughout their lives although, like males, they have striking lilac eyes.

Female

To attract a mate, the male Satin Bowerbird builds a bower and then collects items to decorate it.

WHERE IN THE WORLD?

For the Satin Bowerbird, home is the wet forests and tall sclerophyll areas of the eastern and southeastern coast of Australia. Isolated populations are also found north of Queensland.

EYES
The eyes of the Satin Bowerbird are one of its most striking features, varying from pale lilac to deep purple.

WINGS
Short, round-tipped wings allow the Satin Bowerbird to fly quickly and easily through thick foliage.

BODY
Male Bowerbirds appear to be black, but their feathers have an iridescent, dark blue sheen, which is visible on the wing tips in flight.

HOW BIG IS IT?

SPECIAL ADAPTATION

Bright plumage can help to attract a mate but it can also make a bird vulnerable to predators. The male Satin Bowerbird's solution is to build a bower, which he decorates with sticks and bright blue objects. Females choose the mate with the most skill and artistry.

Goldcrest

• **ORDER** • Passeriformes • **FAMILY** • Regulidae *(under review)* • **SPECIES** • *Regulus regulus*

The Goldcrest is Europe's smallest species of songbird. It is rarely seen but often heard twittering rhythmically among the forest foliage.

VITAL STATISTICS

WEIGHT	6g (0.2oz)
LENGTH	8.5–9.5cm (3.3–3.7in)
WINGSPAN	14cm (5.5in)
SEXUAL MATURITY	1 year
INCUBATION PERIOD	17–22 days
FLEDGLING PERIOD	18–20 days
NUMBER OF EGGS	6–13 eggs
NUMBER OF BROODS	2 a year
TYPICAL DIET	Insects and spiders
LIFE SPAN	Typically 2 years

WHERE IN THE WORLD?

The Goldcrest is found throughout Europe and temperate regions of Asia, from the United Kingdom in the west, to Japan in the east. Preferred habitats are forests and coniferous woodlands.

CREATURE COMPARISONS

Goldcrest are sometimes classed as members of the Sylviidae Family of Warblers. However, some ornithologists consider them part of the Regulidae Family of Kinglets, a name that comes from the Latin *regulus* for 'petty king', in reference to the crests worn by birds in this group.

HEAD
The Goldcrest's relatively large head and short neck makes this tiny bird look even more compact when viewed up close.

WINGS
Its wings are short and round, enabling the Goldcrest to fly among foliage. The short tail aids balance and manoeuvrability.

FEET
In common with other Warblers, the Goldcrest's feet are strong and flexible for gripping onto branches and other vegetation.

Juvenile

HOW BIG IS IT?

SPECIAL ADAPTATION
The Goldcrest takes its common name from the bold golden stripe that runs across its head. Unusually, both sexes have a crest, but only the male's features the orange colouring. This can be difficult to see ordinarily, but becomes obvious when the crest is raised during courtship displays to attract a partner.

Penduline Tit

• ORDER • Passeriformes • FAMILY • Remizidae • SPECIES • *Remiz pendulinus*

VITAL STATISTICS

WEIGHT	9–11g (0.3–0.4oz)
LENGTH	10–11.5cm (4–4.5in)
WINGSPAN	16–18cm (6.3–7.1in)
NUMBER OF EGGS	6–8 eggs
INCUBATION PERIOD	13–16 days
NUMBER OF BROODS	1–2 a year
TYPICAL DIET	Mainly small insects and spiders, but also fine seeds
LIFE SPAN	Up to 5 years

The Penduline Tit is not a true Tit, and unlike true Tits it makes a bag-like nest, which hangs down from a branch.

WHERE IN THE WORLD?

The Penduline Tit is found in parts of central and southern Europe, but mainly lives in eastern Europe, extending eastwards across central Asia and into parts of the Middle East.

CREATURE COMPARISONS

The tiny Penduline Tit has a pale off-white head and throat, with a distinctive black mask across the face. The upper part of the back is reddish brown, becoming dull brown towards the tail. The wings and the tail are dark brown. The underside is pale pinkish. In winter, the head becomes more brownish, and the face mask becomes indistinct. Males and females look similar.

Penduline Tit

BILL
The Penduline Tit has a distinctly finer and more pointed bill than the true Tits, and eats only small insects and fine seeds.

FEET
The Penduline Tit has strong gripping feet for perching, and sometimes hangs upside down when searching for food.

WINGS
The strong wide wings give this tiny bird a fast agile flight and enable it to migrate long distances.

HOW BIG IS IT?

SPECIAL ADAPTATION

The Penduline Tit weaves a bag-like nest from woolly parts of certain plants or animal fur. The nest has one entrance hole, and hangs down from a branch, where it is hard for predators to reach.

Willie Wagtail

• **ORDER** • Passeriformes • **FAMILY** • Rhipiduridae *(under review)* • **SPECIES** • *Rhipidura leucophrys*

Despite its comical name, the Willie Wagtail has a sinister reputation. In Aboriginal legends it is believed to be the bringer of bad news and stealer of secrets.

VITAL STATISTICS

Weight	20g (0.7oz)
Length	19–21cm (7.5–8.3in)
Sexual Maturity	1 year
Lays Eggs	August–February but can nest all year round
Incubation Period	12–14 days
Fledgling Period	13–14 days
Number of Eggs	3–4 eggs
Number of Broods	Up to 4 a year are possible
Habits	Diurnal, non-migratory
Typical Diet	Fish, some small mammals, amphibians and reptiles

CREATURE COMPARISONS

Although their names are similar, Australia's Willie Wagtail is not related to its European namesake. Arguably, Willies have more right to the name. While the Eurasian birds bob their tails up and down, Willie Wagtails actually do wag their tails from side to side.

Willie Wagtail in flight

WHERE IN THE WORLD?

The Willie Wagtail is found in Australia, New Guinea, the Solomon Islands, and the Moluccas. This adaptable bird has coped well with urbanization and is often seen in town parks and gardens.

HEAD
The Willie Wagtail can be distinguished from other, similarly-sized black and white birds by its black throat and the white stripe above each eye.

BILL
A layer of short bristles at the base of the bill protects the bird's eyes from damage when it catches prey.

BODY
Male and female Willie Wagtails are a similar size and coloration, with almost entirely black upper parts and white underparts.

HOW BIG IS IT?

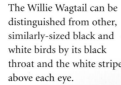

SPECIAL ADAPTATION

No one knows for certain why European Wagtails bob their tails up and down, but Willie Wagtails do it for a very practical reason. They use the fan-like motion of their tails to dislodge insects from leaves or to flush them from the foliage, making them easier to catch and eat.

Eurasian Nuthatch

• ORDER • Passeriformes **• FAMILY •** Sittidae **• SPECIES •** *Sitta europaea*

VITAL STATISTICS

WEIGHT	20–22g (0.7–0.8oz)
LENGTH	13–15cm (5–6in)
WINGSPAN	22–27cm (8.7–10.6in)
NUMBER OF EGGS	6–8 eggs
INCUBATION PERIOD	13–17 days
NUMBER OF BROODS	1 a year
TYPICAL DIET	Insects and grubs, nuts, oily seeds
LIFE SPAN	Up to 9 years

The Eurasian Nuthatch is a common sight in woodlands, where it is often mistaken for a small woodpecker.

WHERE IN THE WORLD?

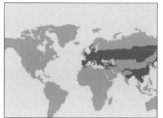

The Eurasian Nuthatch is widespread across most of Europe, even extending into northwestern Africa. It also extends eastwards across central Russia to the Sea of Okhotsk, and parts of southeast Asia.

CREATURE COMPARISONS

The upper side of the Eurasian Nuthatch is bluish-grey and the throat is white. There is a distinctive black stripe across the face. The chest and underside of the tail are pale orange, but birds from northern Europe and Asia tend to have a white chest and have only orange colouration below the tail. The tail feathers are also bluish-grey with white tips. Males and females are similar, although females are drabber.

Female

HEAD
The head is large, with a characteristic black stripe across the eye and cheek.

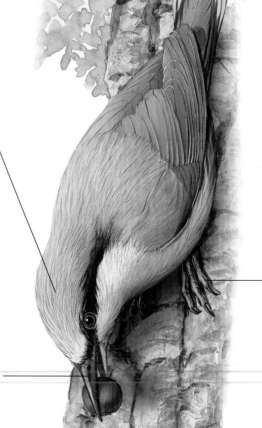

FEET
The bird has long legs with very long toes and short but very sharp claws. These are well adapted for gripping bark.

BILL
The large powerful bill is strong enough to crack open nuts and tough seeds.

HOW BIG IS IT?

SPECIAL ADAPTATION

The Eurasian Nuthatch is a fast and agile tree-climber, and unlike woodpeckers it can run both up and down a trunk. The name refers to its habit of wedging nuts in crevices and cracking them open with its strong bill.

Common Mynah

• **ORDER** • Passeriformes • **FAMILY** • Sturnidae • **SPECIES** • *Acridotheres tristis*

VITAL STATISTICS

LENGTH	22–25cm (8.7–10in)
SEXUAL MATURITY	1 year
INCUBATION PERIOD	16–18 days
FLEDGLING PERIOD	23–27 days
NUMBER OF EGGS	3–5 eggs
NUMBER OF BROODS	Up to 3 a year are possible
HABITS	Diurnal, non-migratory
TYPICAL DIET	Fruit, insects, especially grasshoppers; human food scraps
LIFE SPAN	Up to 12 years

Common Mynahs are also known as Talking Mynahs thanks to their ability to imitate human speech, which has made them popular as pets.

WHERE IN THE WORLD?

Common Mynahs thrive in urban and suburban areas throughout southern Asia (where it originates), the Middle East, South Africa, North America and Australasia, where it has been introduced.

CREATURE COMPARISONS

Like all starlings, Common Mynahs are raucous and quarrelsome birds, yet in their native India, they are famous symbols of love and fidelity because they mate for life. In fact, couples maintain two nests throughout the year, one for roosting and one for raising their young.

Common Mynah in flight

HOW BIG IS IT?

BODY
The body is stout with a large round head and short tail.

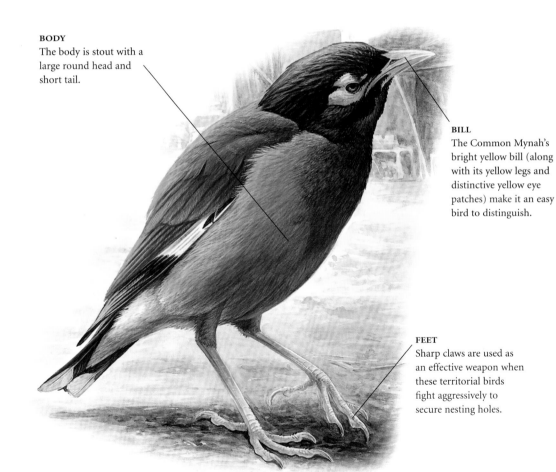

BILL
The Common Mynah's bright yellow bill (along with its yellow legs and distinctive yellow eye patches) make it an easy bird to distinguish.

FEET
Sharp claws are used as an effective weapon when these territorial birds fight aggressively to secure nesting holes.

SPECIAL ADAPTATION

Unusually for members of the Starling Family, Common Mynahs nest in hollows, either those occurring naturally in holes in trees, or man-made spaces, such as the eves of houses. Because of this, their eggs do not need to be camouflaged, so they lack the mottled pattern that is usual on Starling eggs.

Red-billed Oxpecker

• ORDER • Passeriformes • FAMILY • Sturnidae • SPECIES • *Buphagus erythrorhynchus*

VITAL STATISTICS

LENGTH	20–22cm (8–8.6in)
SEXUAL MATURITY	1 year
INCUBATION PERIOD	12–14 days
FLEDGLING PERIOD	26–30 days
NUMBER OF EGGS	1–5 eggs
NUMBER OF BROODS	1 a year
CALLS	Hissings and short twittering calls
HABITS	Diurnal, non-migratory
TYPICAL DIET	Ticks and the blood of its hosts
LIFE SPAN	Unknown

Red-billed Oxpeckers feast on the ticks and parasites that live on the skin of large African mammals.

WHERE IN THE WORLD?

Red-billed Oxpeckers make their home wherever there are grazing animals. Populations are found in eastern sub-Saharan Africa, from Eritrea in the north, to South Africa in the south of the continent.

CREATURE COMPARISONS

Male and female Red-Billed Oxpeckers look alike, with light brown plumage, red bills and red eyes. Juveniles look very different. As shown, their plumage is a sootier shade of brown, with an olive-coloured bill and brown eyes, in place of their parent's vivid coloration.

Juvenile

BODY
With its long, slender neck and streamlined body, the Red-billed Oxpecker is an elegantly proportioned bird, about the same size as a Starling.

TAIL
Long, stiff tail feathers help the Red-billed Oxpecker to keep its balance as it perches on its host's back to feed.

FEET
Short legs and long feet tipped with sharp claws enable the Red-billed Oxpecker to keep its grip on the back of a moving animal.

HOW BIG IS IT?

SPECIAL ADAPTATION

The Red-billed Oxpecker uses its specially adapted, scissor-shaped bill to dig ticks and parasites out of the hide of grazing animals. This does not always benefit the animal, though, because the bird deliberately keeps wounds open, feeding on the host's blood and leaving them susceptible to further parasitic infestation.

Hill Mynah

VITAL STATISTICS

LENGTH	27–33cm (10.6–13in)
SEXUAL MATURITY	1 year
INCUBATION PERIOD	17–18 days
FLEDGLING PERIOD	21–23 days
NUMBER OF EGGS	2–3 eggs
NUMBER OF BROODS	2–3 a year
CALL	Vast range of melodic calls
HABITS	Diurnal, non-migratory
TYPICAL DIET	Fruit, berries, nectar; occasionally insects and small reptiles
LIFE SPAN	Up to 20 years

CREATURE COMPARISONS

Captive Mynahs are famous for their ability as mimics. Wild birds may each have up to a dozen unique calls. Males and females are alike in both size and coloration, but juveniles have a brownish tint to their plumage and no wattle around the back of the head.

Juvenile

The Hill Mynah was a popular pet all over Asia. Now, this beautiful bird is protected by law and can live among the trees in the wild, safe from capture by humans.

WHERE IN THE WORLD?

The Hill Mynah lives in large groups in the forests and woodlands of Southeast Asia, ranging from India to southern China. It has also been introduced to the USA.

HEAD
A bright orange wattle extends all the way round the Hill Mynah's head

WINGS
The Hill Mynah's glossy iridescent black wings have large white patches. These make the birds highly visible in flight.

FEET
Long, strong and flexible feet are well adapted for gripping branches as the bird roosts and feeds.

HOW BIG IS IT?

SPECIAL ADAPTATION
The sides of the Hill Mynah's head are bare. In place of feathers are bright yellow or orange wattles, which extend all the way round the bird's head. It is thought that these wattles, which look so distinctive against the iridescent jet-black plumage, help the birds to identify one another.

Rose-coloured Starling

• **ORDER** • Passeriformes • **FAMILY** • Sturnidae • **SPECIES** • *Sturnus roseus*

VITAL STATISTICS

WEIGHT	78g (2.7oz)
LENGTH	19–22cm (7.5–8.7in)
WINGSPAN	38cm (15in)
SEXUAL MATURITY	1 year
INCUBATION PERIOD	11–12 days
FLEDGLING PERIOD	Around 24 days
NUMBER OF EGGS	3–6 eggs
NUMBER OF BROODS	1 a year, occasionally 2
HABITS	Diurnal, migratory
TYPICAL DIET	Insects in the breeding season; some fruit and berries in the winter

With their raucous calls and lilac plumage, Rose-coloured Starlings make a striking spectacle, whether on the ground or gathered in vast, squealing flocks.

WHERE IN THE WORLD?

Rose-coloured, or Rosy, Starlings breed in eastern Europe and the temperate regions of Southeast Asia. They may appear in northwest Europe, including the United Kingdom, in the summer.

CREATURE COMPARISONS

Starlings like to gather together in huge flocks, and Rose-Coloured Starlings are perhaps the most sociable members of the Family. These birds breed in large, noisy colonies and can often be seen swarming in swirling locust-like clouds over farmers' fields at dusk and dawn.

Rose-coloured Starling

HEAD
Male Rose-coloured Starlings have a longer head crest than females. This can be raised during courtship displays.

BODY
Although the body of some birds can be very pink, the amount of red tinting on the plumage varies from bird to bird.

FEET
The feet and long toes of Rose-coloured Starlings are typical of perching birds.

HOW BIG IS IT?

SPECIAL ADAPTATION

Rose-coloured Starlings rely on a ready supply of insects to feed their young. Insects are available at only certain times of the year, however, so Rose-coloured Starlings have adapted to have a much shorter incubation period than other starlings, so they do not have to compete for food.

Starling (Common)

VITAL STATISTICS

WEIGHT	78g (2.7oz)
LENGTH	19–22cm (7.5–8.7in)
WINGSPAN	40cm (15.7in).
SEXUAL MATURITY	2 years
LAYS EGGS	April–May
INCUBATION PERIOD	12 days
NUMBER OF EGGS	4–6 eggs
NUMBER OF BROODS	2 a year, are possible
TYPICAL DIET	Worms, insects, fruit and seeds
LIFE SPAN	Typically 5 years

The Starling has a reputation as a boisterous bully. In the summer, its shimmering metallic breeding plumage transforms the male into a suave sight.

WHERE IN THE WORLD?

Starlings are a familiar sight in parks and gardens. Found in Europe, Central Asia and North Africa, Common Starlings have also been introduced into South Africa, North America and Australasia.

CREATURE COMPARISONS

Starlings are skilled mimics and imitate other garden birds, as well as car alarms and mobile phone tones. Some bird species are sexually dimorphic, meaning the male and female look different. In the spring and summer, the female has a pink patch at the base of the bill while, appropriately, the male has a blue patch.

Male (top), female (bottom)

BODY
Male and female Starlings are similar in appearance except in spring and summer.

HEAD
An unusually narrow skull enables the Starling to look straight down its bill as it hunts for food.

LEGS
Long legs give the Starling a jerky, energetic gait as well as enabling it to perform surprisingly agile acrobatics on the garden bird-feeder.

HOW BIG IS IT?

SPECIAL ADAPTATION
With their dark bodies and yellow bills, juvenile Starlings are easily mistaken for Blackbirds. This is never true of adults. In the summer, an adult male's plumage takes on a dazzling multi-coloured sheen. This is especially obvious when he puffs out his neck feathers during a mating display.

Reed Warbler (European)

• **ORDER** • Passeriformes • **FAMILY** • Sylviidae • **SPECIES** • *Acrocephalus scirpaceus*

VITAL STATISTICS

WEIGHT	13g (0.4oz)
LENGTH	13cm (5in)
WINGSPAN	19cm (7.5in)
SEXUAL MATURITY	1 year
INCUBATION PERIOD	12 days
FLEDGLING PERIOD	12–13 days
NUMBER OF EGGS	4 eggs
NUMBER OF BROODS	1–2 a year
TYPICAL DIET	Insects, spiders and snails

Warblers can be tricky to spot but are easier to hear, especially the fast, uneven twitters of the lively, but well camouflaged, Reed Warbler.

WHERE IN THE WORLD?

European Reed Warblers are also known as Eurasian Reed Warblers, and are found across Europe and temperate regions of western Asia. Populations overwinter in sub-Saharan Africa.

CREATURE COMPARISONS

In common with many Warblers, these nimble birds weave small, cup-shaped nests, which they hide among vegetation. In the case of Reed Warblers, nests are built around the reed stems, usually positioned halfway down the reed. In this position they are safe from water- and airborne predators.

Reed Warbler

HEAD
The Reed Warbler's scientific name comes from Ancient Greek: *Acrocephalus* translates as 'pointed head', while *scirpaceus* means 'resembling reeds'.

TAILS
The Reed Warbler is usually well hidden among the reeds, but can sometimes be spotted flicking its tail nervously.

BODY
The Reed Warbler's body is camouflaged so it blends in perfectly with the reedbeds in which it nests.

HOW BIG IS IT?

SPECIAL ADAPTATION
Sparrowhawks prey on well over 120 different bird species. They specialize in hunting small birds such as the Reed Warbler, which is why this bird needs effective camouflage. Fortunately, the Reed Warbler's brown upper parts and buff underparts provide excellent cover.

Cetti's Warbler

• ORDER • Passeriformes **• FAMILY •** Sylviidae **• SPECIES •** *Cettia cetti*

VITAL STATISTICS

WEIGHT	10–14g (0.35–0.5oz)
LENGTH	13–14cm (5–5.5in)
WINGSPAN	30–32cm (12–12.6in)
NUMBER OF EGGS	3–6 eggs (usually 4–5)
INCUBATION PERIOD	14–16 days
NUMBER OF BROODS	2 a year
TYPICAL DIET	Insects, spiders, caterpillars, worms, spiders
LIFE SPAN	Up to 5 years

Cetti's Warbler is the only type of bush warbler to be found outside Asia and, although fairly common, it is rarely seen.

WHERE IN THE WORLD?

Cetti's Warbler is found in southern Europe and parts of central Europe, across the Middle East and into southern Asia. In hard winters, the northern populations migrate south.

CREATURE COMPARISONS

Cetti's Warbler has a dark or reddish-brown upper side. The tail and wings are usually darker than the body, and have more reddish stripes along the edges of the large feathers. The underside is pale buff or off-white. The cheek is darker than the rest of the underside. Females and males look very similar, but males are distinctly larger than females.

HEAD
Like many small songbirds, Cetti's Warbler has a dark line from the base of the beak to the eye, which it uses to gauge the distance to food objects.

BILL
The short pointed bill, is well adapted for snapping up insects and other small creatures.

TAIL
Cetti's Warbler has a large, fan-shaped tail consisting of 10 tail feathers, while all other European perching birds have 12 tail feathers.

Cetti's Warbler in flight

HOW BIG IS IT?

SPECIAL ADAPTATION

Cetti's Warbler takes its name from an Italian naturalist, Francesco Cetti (1726–78). The male has a loud beautiful song said to follow the rhythm of 'What's my name? Cetti, Cetti, Cetti! That's it.'

Spinifexbird

• ORDER • Passeriformes **• FAMILY •** Sylviidae **• SPECIES •** *Eremiornis carteri*

VITAL STATISTICS

LENGTH	15cm (6in)
SEXUAL MATURITY	Possibly 1 year
INCUBATION PERIOD	Uncertain
FLEDGLING PERIOD	Uncertain
NUMBER OF EGGS	2 eggs
NUMBER OF BROODS	Uncertain
CALL	Males make a short, melodic 'je-swee-a-voo' cry
HABITS	Diurnal, non-migratory
TYPICAL DIET	Insects and spiders; occasional seeds
LIFE SPAN	Unknown

CREATURE COMPARISONS

Spinifexbirds belong to a group of perching birds known as Warblers. Although their habits are different, all Warblers share certain characteristics with the Spinifexbirds, especially the European Reed Warbler which lives among tall grasses although usually in wet marshlands, not deserts.

Spinifex bird in flight

Mystery surrounds the Australian Spinifexbird. Hidden away in thickets of prickly, spinifex grass, this reticent little bird is rarely seen, and only sometimes heard.

WHERE IN THE WORLD?

Spinifexbirds are found only in Australia, throughout the northern interior. Their preferred habitat is spinifex, or porcupine grass, which grows well in dry and sandy desert regions.

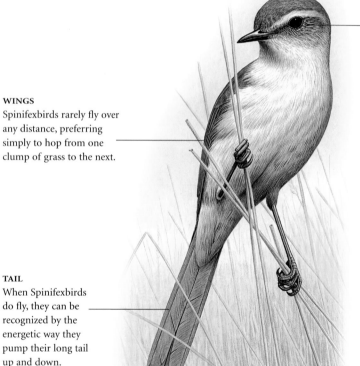

EYE
Eyes on the side of the head give a wide field of vision, which helps the Spinifexbird spot danger more easily.

WINGS
Spinifexbirds rarely fly over any distance, preferring simply to hop from one clump of grass to the next.

TAIL
When Spinifexbirds do fly, they can be recognized by the energetic way they pump their long tail up and down.

HOW BIG IS IT?

SPECIAL ADAPTATION

Long legs and strong dextrous feet allow the Spinifexbird to perch and walk with ease among swaying stems of spinifex grass. The long tail acts like a tightrope-walker's pole, and helps the bird maintain its balance as it leaps from stem to stem.

Icterine Warbler

• ORDER • Passeriformes **• FAMILY •** Sylviidae **• SPECIES •** *Hippolais icterina*

VITAL STATISTICS

WEIGHT	22g (0.8oz)
LENGTH	14cm (5.5in)
WINGSPAN	22cm (8.7in)
SEXUAL MATURITY	1 year
INCUBATION PERIOD	13–14 days
FLEDGLING PERIOD	13–14 days
NUMBER OF EGGS	4–5 eggs
NUMBER OF BROODS	1 a year
HABITS	Diurnal, migratory
TYPICAL DIET	Insects; occasionally fruit and berries

The Icterine Warbler takes its common name from the medical term *icterus*, which is used to describe jaundice, the illness that turns its sufferers yellow.

The Icterine Warbler, a sparrow-sized insect-eater, breeds across mainland Europe into Siberia, and migrates to southern Africa. It is replaced by the Melodious Warbler in southwest Europe.

CREATURE COMPARISONS

The Icterine Warbler is often confused with its relative the Melodious Warbler. Both are a similar size and shape and have the same brownish upper parts and yellowish underparts. Melodious Warblers have shorter wings with more rounded tips. All Warblers have a wide range of songs, but birds of the *Hippolais* genus sound more excitable.

Icterine Warbler in flight

BODY
The Icterine Warbler has olive-grey upper parts, yellowish underparts.

HEAD
A distinctive pale band runs across the bird's eyes.

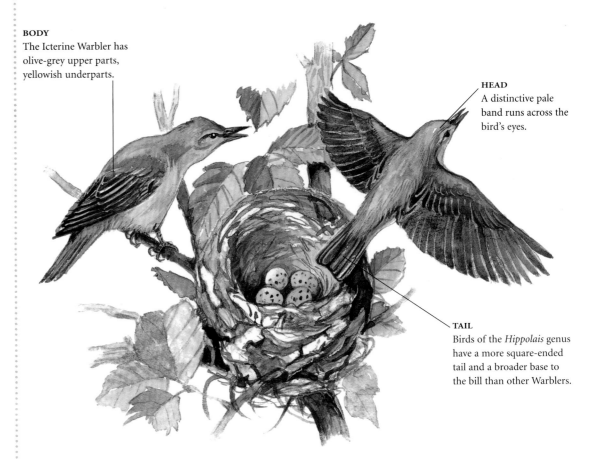

TAIL
Birds of the *Hippolais* genus have a more square-ended tail and a broader base to the bill than other Warblers.

HOW BIG IS IT?

SPECIAL ADAPTATION

Every year, the small Icterine Warbler flies from its breeding grounds in Eurasia to its winter feeding grounds in southern Africa. Its wings have therefore adapted to endure demanding journeys. They are more pointed, with longer primary feathers to aid soaring and manoeuvrability.

Melodious Warbler

• **ORDER** • Passeriformes • **FAMILY** • Sylviidae • **SPECIES** • *Hippolais polyglotta*

VITAL STATISTICS

WEIGHT	13g (0.4oz)
LENGTH	12–13cm (4.7–5in)
WINGSPAN	18cm (7in)
SEXUAL MATURITY	1 year
INCUBATION PERIOD	12–13 days
FLEDGLING PERIOD	11–13 days
NUMBER OF EGGS	3–4 eggs
NUMBER OF BROODS	1–2 a year
HABITS	Diurnal, migratory
TYPICAL DIET	Insects plus some fruit in autumn

Melodious Warblers are solitary birds that do not quite live up to their name, but they are still capable of producing fast and complex warbling songs.

The Melodious Warbler breeds in western and central Europe and northwest Africa, preferring forest clearings and woodland scrub. Populations winters in West Africa, south of the Sahara.

CREATURE COMPARISONS

All Warblers have a varied vocal repertoire, but Melodious Warblers are not especially musical. The *polyglotta* part of the species name offers a more accurate description of their abilities. Meaning 'many tongues', it refers to their habit of weaving other birds' songs into their own.

Melodious Warbler in flight

WINGS
The wings of the Melodious Warbler are short and round, enabling it to fly among the foliage. A short tail aids balance and manoeuvrability.

BODY
The adult's yellow-green breeding plumage blends perfectly with its surrounding habitat.

FEET
Half of all known bird species are perching birds with feet adapted for gripping branches. This includes Melodious Warblers.

HOW BIG IS IT?

SPECIAL ADAPTATION

Melodious Warblers undertake relatively short migrations to West Africa, while Icterine Warblers fly as far as southern Africa, so their wings have adapted to suit their different needs. The wings of Melodious Warblers are made for agility, while those of Icterine Warblers are designed for long-haul flights.

Eurasian River Warbler

• **ORDER** • Passeriformes • **FAMILY** • Sylviidae • **SPECIES** • *Locustella fluviatilis*

VITAL STATISTICS

WEIGHT	16–22g (0.6–0.8oz)
LENGTH	12.5–13cm (4.9–5.1in)
WINGSPAN	19–22cm (7.5–8.7in)
NUMBER OF EGGS	4–6 eggs
INCUBATION PERIOD	13 days
NUMBER OF BROODS	1 a year
TYPICAL DIET	Insects, caterpillars, spiders
LIFE SPAN	Unknown

The Eurasian River Warbler looks very similar to Savi's Warbler, but lives in moist, forested areas instead of lakes and swamps.

WHERE IN THE WORLD?

The Eurasian River Warbler is found in eastern Europe, and is widely distributed across central Russia eastwards towards the Ural Mountains. It usually winters in Africa.

CREATURE COMPARISONS

The Eurasian River Warbler has a uniformly olive-brown upper part of the head, neck and back. The upper side of the wing is also olive-brown with darker streaks along the large wing feathers. The underside is off-white or light buff, often with mottling of olive-green or brown. The tail is rather long and olive-brown, and speckled with small spots. Males and females are similar.

Eurasian River Warbler

HEAD
The Eurasian River Warbler often has a darker, greyish check patch and a white stripe running above the eyes.

BILL
The bill is long and slender with a needle-sharp tip, well adapted for catching small insects.

LEGS
The legs are quite long and very slender, and the feet are strong and well adapted for perching on a thin twig.

HOW BIG IS IT?

SPECIAL ADAPTATION

The Eurasian River Warbler often runs or hops along twigs. In order to get to another twig nearby, it will often simply make a long jump instead of flying – an adaptation that saves its energy.

Grasshopper Warbler

• **ORDER** • Passeriformes • **FAMILY** • Sylviidae • **SPECIES** • *Locustella naevia*

VITAL STATISTICS

Weight	11–15g (0.4–0.5oz)
Length	12–13cm (4.7–5.1in)
Wingspan	15–19cm (6–7.5in)
Number of Eggs	5–6 eggs
Incubation Period	13–15 days
Number of Broods	2 a year
Typical Diet	Insects, caterpillars, spiders, worms, snails
Life Span	Unknown

The Grasshopper Warbler has a peculiarly continuous song with a metallic timbre that can sound like that of a large grasshopper.

WHERE IN THE WORLD?

The Grasshopper Warbler is found across much of Europe except the southern part and most of Scandinavia, and eastwards across Russia and Central Asia.

CREATURE COMPARISONS

The upper part of the head, neck and back is olive-green or olive-brown with darker markings along the edges of the feathers. The wings are also olive-brown with darker streaks. The throat and parts of the breast are lightly buff with dark streaks, and the belly is white. Males and females look similar.

Grasshopper Warbler

TAIL
The tail is olive-brown above, but pale underneath. It is important in manoeuvring in shrubs and tall grasses.

BILL
The bill is long and very pointed, typical of small songbirds that feed on tiny insects.

FEET
The Grasshopper Warbler has a particularly long middle toe that allows it to cling to several blades of tall grass.

HOW BIG IS IT?

SPECIAL ADAPTATION

The Grasshopper Warbler often lives among tall grasses, and instead of flying around, it will often simply walk from one straw to the next. This uses far less energy than flying.

Long-tailed Tailorbird

• **ORDER** • Passeriformes • **FAMILY** • Sylviidae • **SPECIES** • *Orthotomus sutorius*

The Long-tailed Tailorbird, an Asian relative of the Warbler, has a very special way of making a home for itself: it belongs to a group of birds that sew their own nests.

VITAL STATISTICS

WEIGHT	8–12g (0.3–0.4oz)
LENGTH	13–17cm (5.1–6.7in)
WINGSPAN	20–30cm (8–12in)
NUMBER OF EGGS	2–6 eggs (usually 3)
INCUBATI`ON PERIOD	12–13 days
NUMBER OF BROODS	1 a year
TYPICAL DIET	Insects, caterpillars, spiders; also nectar and pollen
LIFE SPAN	Unknown

WHERE IN THE WORLD?

The Long-tailed Tailorbird is found across southern Asia from India to southeastern China, on the island of Sri Lanka, across Malaysia, and on the large islands of Sumatra and Java.

CREATURE COMPARISONS

The upper side of this species of Tailorbird is uniformly dark or olive-green, and gives good camouflage in the dense vegetation where it lives. The top of the head is reddish-brown, and the underside is white. The eyes are orange. The beak and the feet are usually reddish-brown or orange. Males and females are similar, but males are easily recognized by having distinctly longer tail feathers.

Long-tailed Tailorbird in flight

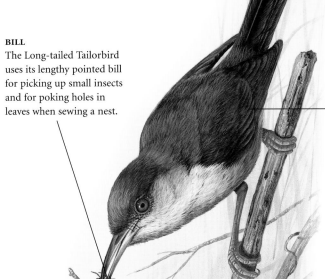

TAIL
The male uses its very long, slender tail for display. In both sexes the tail is used for manoeuvring in flight.

BILL
The Long-tailed Tailorbird uses its lengthy pointed bill for picking up small insects and for poking holes in leaves when sewing a nest.

WINGS
The short, round wings gives the Long-tailed Tailorbird a fast, manoeuvrable flight, which is important in its canopy habitat.

HOW BIG IS IT?

SPECIAL ADAPTATION
The Long-tailed Tailorbird uses its long pointed bill for poking holes through leaves and then uses wooden fibres to stitch the leaves together to form a round nest. The bill is also excellent for plucking insects from leaves and bark.

Blackcap

• ORDER • Passeriformes **• FAMILY •** Sylviidae **• SPECIES •** *Sylvia atricapilla*

VITAL STATISTICS

WEIGHT	21g (0.7oz)
LENGTH	13.5–15cm (5.3–6in)
WINGSPAN	22cm (8.7in)
SEXUAL MATURITY	1 year
INCUBATION PERIOD	13–14 days
FLEDGLING PERIOD	11–12 days
NUMBER OF EGGS	4–5 eggs
NUMBER OF BROODS	1–2 a year
TYPICAL DIET	Insects in the summer; some fruit, seeds and berries in winter
LIFE SPAN	Typically 2 years

It is easy to see why these Warblers are called Blackcaps. However, their delightful song has earned them another more appealing title, which is the Northern Nightingale.

WHERE IN THE WORLD?

The Blackcap breeds across Europe from Britain to central Russia, and into western Asia. Populations from the north and east of Europe tend to migrate, but are increasingly resident in Britain.

CREATURE COMPARISONS

Male and female Blackcaps have very different plumage. Males have dirty-grey upper parts and olive-grey underparts. Females and juveniles have a chocolate-brown cap, with browner upper parts and pale underparts. The Blackcap's call is a noticeable 'tek-tek-tek'. The Blackcap nests in low bushes, which makes it very hard to spot.

Female (left), male (right)

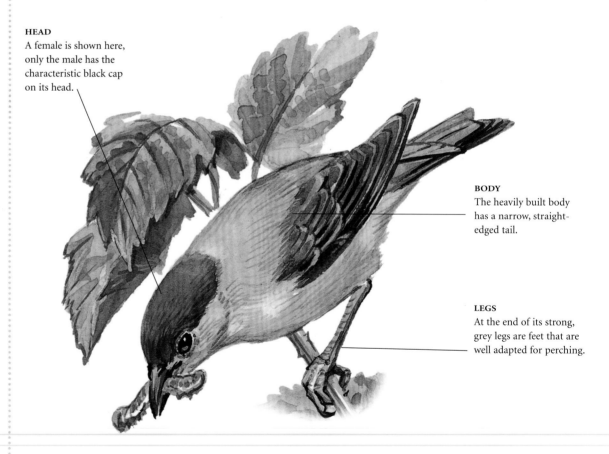

HEAD
A female is shown here, only the male has the characteristic black cap on its head.

BODY
The heavily built body has a narrow, straight-edged tail.

LEGS
At the end of its strong, grey legs are feet that are well adapted for perching.

HOW BIG IS IT?

SPECIAL ADAPTATION
Chicks call out to their parents to feed them. However, there isn't always enough food to go round. The louder and more aggressive a chick is, the more likely it is to gain parental attention, be fed and therefore survive.

Whitethroat (Common)

VITAL STATISTICS

WEIGHT	16g (0.6oz)
LENGTH	14cm (5.5in)
WINGSPAN	20cm (8in)
SEXUAL MATURITY	1 year
INCUBATION PERIOD	12–13 days
FLEDGLING PERIOD	12–14 days
NUMBER OF EGGS	4–5 eggs
NUMBER OF BROODS	1–2 a year
TYPICAL DIET	Insects, especially beetles; berries in winter
LIFE SPAN	Typically 2 years

The Whitethroat is easily confused with other species of Warblers. However, the pale throat patch that gives this bird its common name is a reliable way to identify it.

WHERE IN THE WORLD?

Common Whitethroats make their summer homes throughout Europe and across Central Asia and the Near East. These small perching birds typically winter in parts of southern Africa and Arabia.

CREATURE COMPARISONS

Cuckoos lay their eggs in the nest of the species that raised them. The most frequent unwitting hosts are Redstarts and White Wagtails. However, Whitethroats, which nest in hedges, also fall victim to these brood parasites. Some 30 per cent of Whitethroat nests have been found to contain Cuckoo eggs.

Whitethroat nest

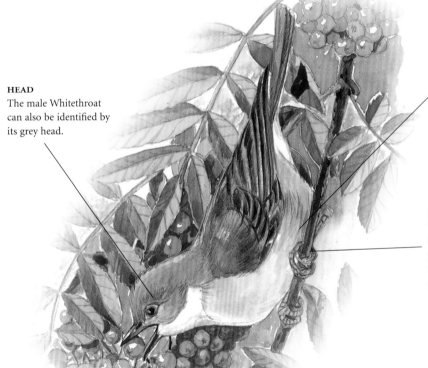

HEAD
The male Whitethroat can also be identified by its grey head.

BODY
Male and female Whitethroats have brownish upper parts, paler, buff underparts and the characteristic white throat after which they are named.

LEGS
These sturdily built birds have a pair of long, strong, yellowish-brown legs. Their feet are adapted for gripping perches.

HOW BIG IS IT?

SPECIAL ADAPTATION

Chicks have evolved a wide range of calls and physical traits, adapted to encourage their parents to feed them. For example, the inside of the chicks' mouth itself is often coloured or patterned to stimulate adults to regurgitate food.

339

Barred Warbler

• **ORDER** • Passeriformes • **FAMILY** • Sylviidae • **SPECIES** • *Sylvia nisoria*

VITAL STATISTICS

WEIGHT	25g (0.9oz)
LENGTH	15.5–17cm (6–6.7in)
WINGSPAN	25cm (10in)
INCUBATION PERIOD	12–13 days
FLEDGLING PERIOD	10–12 days
NUMBER OF EGGS	4–5 eggs
NUMBER OF BROODS	1 a year
CALL	Loud 'trrrr't't't't'
HABITS	Diurnal, migratory
TYPICAL DIET	Invertebrates and berries in winter

The Barred Warbler is a small dapper bird. Sadly, its numbers have fallen rapidly due to the loss of suitable habitats to urban developments.

WHERE IN THE WORLD?

The Barred Warbler breeds in eastern Europe, Central Asia and in the Near East. Its preferred habitats are open country or woodlands, where it nests. Winters are spent in east Africa and Arabia.

CREATURE COMPARISONS

Barred Warblers have some alarming neighbours. They share their range with Red-backed Shrikes, predators that eat mainly insects, but are also known to take small birds and chicks. Barred Warblers, however, tend to hide their nests deep in thick vegetation. The song of the Barred Warbler can be confused with that of the Whitethroat.

Barred Warbler nest

BODY
Barred Warblers are large and heavily built with a narrow straight-edged tail.

BILL
The long thin bill is well adapted for catching and eating insects, and plucking and eating small berries.

COLOURING
Adult Barred Warblers have grey upper parts and pale underparts, which are covered with a darker, worm-like pattern (called vermiculation).

HOW BIG IS IT?

SPECIAL ADAPTATION

The Barred Warbler relies almost entirely on insects and larvae to fuel itself. However when insects are scarce the Barred Warbler will eat berries and fruit. Its long, thin bill makes the ideal tool for the job.

Wallcreeper

• ORDER • Passeriformes • FAMILY • Tichodromadinae *(debated)* • SPECIES • *Tichodroma muraria*

VITAL STATISTICS

WEIGHT	17–19g (0.6–0.7oz)
LENGTH	15.5–17cm (6–6.7in)
WINGSPAN	30cm (12in)
SEXUAL MATURITY	1 year
INCUBATION PERIOD	19–20 days
FLEDGLING PERIOD	28–30 days
NUMBER OF EGGS	3–5 eggs
NUMBER OF BROODS	1 a year
HABITS	Diurnal, migratory
TYPICAL DIET	Small insects and spiders

Thanks to its spectacular carmine wing patches and slate-grey body, the Wallcreeper is known to the Chinese as the Rock Flower.

WHERE IN THE WORLD?

The Wallcreeper is found in central and southern Eurasia. It nests on inaccessible rock faces, but during harsh winters Wallcreepers have been known to make their nests inside of buildings.

CREATURE COMPARISONS

Adult birds of prey usually look alike, but in the rest of the bird world, males are generally more colourful, adopting bright breeding plumage to attract a mate. Typically, juvenile birds and non-breeding males look similar to females, as is the case with this female Wallcreeper.

Female

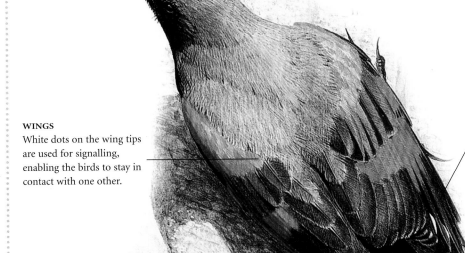

BILL
The Wallcreeper's slender, downwards-curved bill is a well adapted tool for probing into rock crevices in search of insects and spiders.

TAIL
Wallcreepers and nuthatches are often grouped together because they share similar physical characteristics, such as their short, straight-edged tails.

WINGS
White dots on the wing tips are used for signalling, enabling the birds to stay in contact with one other.

HOW BIG IS IT?

SPECIAL ADAPTATION

The Wallcreeper often makes its home at heights of 1000–3000m (3280–9842ft) above sea level. Its powerful legs and strong feet are therefore adapted for climbing up sheer cliff faces and clinging on to the most inaccessible of surfaces.

Rock Wren

• **ORDER** • Passeriformes • **FAMILY** • Troglodytidae • **SPECIES** • *Salpinctes obsoletus*

VITAL STATISTICS

WEIGHT	15–18g (0.5–0.6oz)
LENGTH	12–15cm (4.7–6in)
WINGSPAN	23cm (9in)
SEXUAL MATURITY	1 year
LAYS EGGS	June–July
INCUBATION PERIOD	12–18 days
NUMBER OF EGGS	3–5 eggs
NUMBER OF BROODS	2–3 a year
CALL	A loud, dry trill, or a clear 'tick-ear'
HABITS	Diurnal, migratory
TYPICAL DIET	Insects, spiders and worms

The Rock Wren, a popular little bird, is one of the few Wrens to live up to their Latin Family name *Troglodytidae,* which means 'cave-dweller'.

WHERE IN THE WORLD?

Rock Wrens live in semi-desert regions. Breeding populations can be found in southwestern Canada, and south into California, Mexico and Central America. Birds winter in the southern USA.

CREATURE COMPARISONS

Rock Wrens belong to the Troglodytidae Family. The name comes from the Greek for 'cave-dweller' which, in the case of the Rock Wren, is entirely appropriate. In Europe, however, species like the Winter Wren (also known as the Jenny Wren) prefer to make their homes in dark undergrowth.

Rock Wren in flight

BODY
The body is round and the tail is short. The rump is cinnamon coloured.

TAIL
The tail has bars and is tipped with pale feathers.

BILL
The Rock Wren's long, downwards-curved bill is well adapted for extracting insects from tiny crevices in rocks.

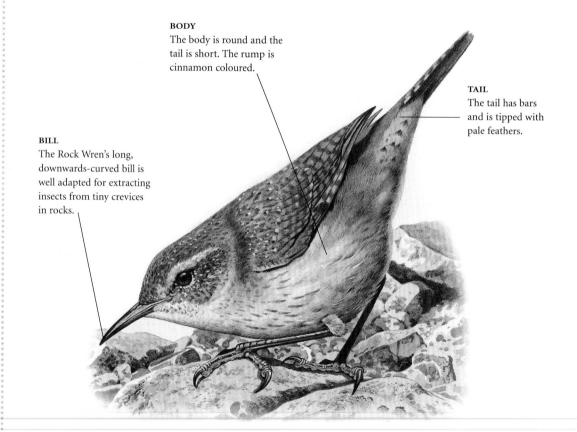

HOW BIG IS IT?

SPECIAL ADAPTATION
The body of the Rock Wren is designed so that it can squeeze into tight crevices in rocks. There, it takes shelter to escape the heat of the desert sun. At night, when temperatures fall, it fluffs out its feathers. This traps air and helps to insulate the bird.

Wren (Winter)

VITAL STATISTICS

WEIGHT	10g (0.35oz)
LENGTH	9–10.5cm (3.5–4in)
WINGSPAN	15cm (6in)
SEXUAL MATURITY	1 year
LAYS EGGS	From late April
INCUBATION PERIOD	16–18 days
NUMBER OF EGGS	5–8 eggs
NUMBER OF BROODS	2 are possible
TYPICAL DIET	Spiders and small insects
LIFE SPAN	Typically 2 years

Its tiny size, piercing song and jaunty upturned tail make the Winter Wren one of the easiest of the small brown garden birds to recognize. It also has the nickname Jenny Wren.

WHERE IN THE WORLD?

Winter Wrens can be found throughout Europe, Central Asia and northern North America. Most species are resident, but some northern European populations migrate south for the winter.

CREATURE COMPARISONS

Winter Wrens nest in dense undergrowth. They have a surprisingly loud 'zrrrr' alarm call. Worldwide there are around 80 species of Wrens, and several islands, such as the Fair Isles, off the northeastern coast of Scotland, have their own unique sub-species. The Fair Isle Wren is larger than its mainland counterpart and tends to have greyer underparts.

Fair Isle Wren

BILL
The slim downwards-curving bill is well adapted for catching and eating insects and spiders.

TAIL
The Winter Wren's upturned tail makes it easily identifiable.

BODY
From a distance Winter Wrens look uniformaly brown, but on closer examination their tiny, round bodies are actually reddish-brown above and brownish-white below.

HOW BIG IS IT?

SPECIAL ADAPTATION

The Winter Wren's slender downwards-curved bill is well adapted for catching the small spiders and insects that form the bulk of its diet. In the winter, when insects are scarce, it may also eat seeds, although its bill does not have the nut-cracking power of species like Finches.

343

Hermit Thrush

• ORDER • Passeriformes • FAMILY •Turdidae • SPECIES • *Catharus guttatus*

VITAL STATISTICS

WEIGHT	23–37g (0.8–1.3oz)
LENGTH	14–18cm (5.5–7in)
WINGSPAN	26–30cm (10.2–12in)
NUMBER OF EGGS	3–6 eggs (usually 4)
NUMBER OF BROODS	2 a year (sometimes 3)
TYPICAL DIET	Insects, worms, spiders, fruit, berries, seeds
LIFE SPAN	Typically 8 years

The Hermit Thrush is the smallest species of Thrush in North America, and is also considered to have the most beautiful song.

WHERE IN THE WORLD?

The Hermit Thrush is found across most of North America, from northern Alaska to California, except the midwestern states. Many birds winter in the southern USA, Mexico and Guatemala.

CREATURE COMPARISONS

The Hermit Thrush has brownish upper parts that become reddish-brown to orange towards the tail, which is also reddish-brown. The upper part of the wing is also brown, but the large feathers have a reddish edge. The underside is white with dark spots along the breast. Eastern birds have more olive-brown upper parts. Males and females are similar.

TAIL
The Hermit Thrush often cocks its long graceful tail up while searching for food on the ground.

BILL
The stout pointed bill is well adapted for eating a variety of food from soft fruits to hard seeds.

WINGS
Its wings are elongated and rounded, giving the Hermit Thrush a manoeuvrable flight, but also allowing it to migrate long distances.

Hermit Thrush in flight

HOW BIG IS IT?

SPECIAL ADAPTATION

Like many small songbirds, the Hermit Thrush is largely dependent on insects. However, in winter insects become scarce, and so the bird switches its diet to feed mainly on berries and seeds.

Robin (European)

With its striking red breast and melodic song, the Robin is one of Europe's most familiar birds, found in both woodlands and gardens.

VITAL STATISTICS

WEIGHT	16–22g (0.6–0.8oz)
LENGTH	12.5–14cm (5–5.5oz)
WINGSPAN	20–22cm (8–8.7in)
SEXUAL MATURITY	1 year
LAYS EGGS	March–June
INCUBATION PERIOD	14–18 days
NUMBER OF EGGS	4–6 eggs
NUMBER OF BROODS	Up to 3 a year
TYPICAL DIET	Worms, insects, fruit and seeds
LIFE SPAN	Typically 2 years

WHERE IN THE WORLD?

Robins enjoy a wide range of habitats, from urban parks to spruce forests. Typically populations can be found in northern Europe, as far as western Siberia and into North Africa.

CREATURE COMPARISONS

While young Robins have the same rounded body shape as adult birds, their plumage is much less dramatic in colour. In place of the familiar red breast and olive-brown body, juveniles have a spotted brown head and body. Their underparts are usually slightly paler.

Juvenile

BILL
The short sharp bill is an ideal tool for catching insects and taking advantage of seasonal foods like seeds and berries.

EYES
Like many woodland birds, Robins have large eyes. This enables them to see and hunt in the gloomy forest canopy.

BREAST
Male birds are often more colourful than females. In the case of the Robin, however, both sexes sport the familiar red vest.

HOW BIG IS IT?

SPECIAL ADAPTATION

Like all members of the Thrush Family, Robins are superb singers. However, while most birds sing just during the breeding season, the trembling warble of the Robin can be heard all year round. During evening reveille, listen for nervous Robins making their distinctive 'tik-ik-ik-ik' alarm call.

Blackbird (Common)

• **ORDER** • Passeriformes • **FAMILY** • Turdidae • **SPECIES** • *Turdus merula*

VITAL STATISTICS

WEIGHT	100g (3.5oz)
LENGTH	23.5–29cm (9.2–11.4in)
WINGSPAN	36cm (14.2in)
SEXUAL MATURITY	1 year
LAYS EGGS	March–July
INCUBATION PERIOD	13–14 days
NUMBER OF EGGS	3–5 eggs
NUMBER OF BROODS	2–3 a year; occasionally 4–5
TYPICAL DIET	Worms, insects and some fruit
LIFE SPAN	Typically 3 years

Justly renowned for its melodic song and gorgeous ebony plumage, the Blackbird is one of the most recognizable and welcome visitors to the garden.

WHERE IN THE WORLD?

Originally a woodland species, the Blackbird now makes its home on scrubland and in parks and towns throughout Europe and western Asia. It has also been introduced into Australia.

CREATURE COMPARISONS

Starlings have a similar size and body shape to Blackbirds and it is easy to confuse the two, especially females and juveniles, which are mottled brown, rather than black. However, the male Blackbird's brilliantly yellow bill is clearly unmistakable even from a distance.

Female (left), juvenile (right)

EYE
A year after they hatch, male Blackbirds develop a bold yellow ring around each eye.

WINGS
In flight, the wings give the Blackbird a more rounded silhouette than other members of the Thrush Family have.

TAIL
Blackbirds will often use a flick of their long tail to tell other birds when they are either nervous or annoyed.

HOW BIG IS IT?

SPECIAL ADAPTATION

Blackbirds eat a wide diet but are most often to be seen rooting in the soil for a worm, either in the early morning or after rainstorms. Because they are taller and have larger bills than other thrushes, they have greater leverage and so can pull up larger worms.

Song Thrush

• **ORDER** • Passeriformes • **FAMILY** • Turdidae • **SPECIES** • *Turdus philomelas*

VITAL STATISTICS

WEIGHT	65–90g (2.3–3.2oz)
LENGTH	22–23cm (8.7–9in)
WINGSPAN	33–36cm (13–14.2in)
NUMBER OF EGGS	4–6 eggs
INCUBATION PERIOD	12–13 days
NUMBER OF BROODS	2 a year
TYPICAL DIET	Insects, snails and slugs, worms, berries, fruit
LIFE SPAN	Up to 13 years

The Song Thrush migrates to southern Europe for the winter, but some birds from the high north migrate only as far as northern regions of central Europe.

WHERE IN THE WORLD?

The Song Thrush is found throughout most of Europe except the high north and the extreme south. It is also widely spread across Central Asia and parts of the Middle East.

CREATURE COMPARISONS

The Song Thrush has a light brown upper side, with pale spots on parts of the wings. The area around the large black eye is usually grey. The throat, breast and belly are off-white with numerous dark brown spots. The underside of the wing is pale with a large, pale-yellow area only visible in flight. Males and females appear to be similar.

Song Thrush

BILL
The bill is short, but stout and powerful, and is well adapted for grabbing hold of small prey.

BODY
The Song Thrush has a compact body and, when it gets cold, it will raise its body feathers to keep warm.

LEGS
The legs of the Song Thrush can be yellowish or pinkish. Its feet are adapted for walking on the ground and perching.

HOW BIG IS IT?

SPECIAL ADAPTATION

The Song Thrush eats snails. It breaks the shell by grabbing it, and then hitting it against a stone. Each thrush tends to have a favorite stone it will repeatedly return to in order to do this task.

Fieldfare

• ORDER • Passeriformes • FAMILY • Turdidae • SPECIES • *Turdus pilaris*

VITAL STATISTICS

WEIGHT	100g (3.5oz)
LENGTH	26cm (10.2in)
WINGSPAN	40cm (15.7in)
SEXUAL MATURITY	1 year
INCUBATION PERIOD	11–14 days
FLEDGLING PERIOD	12–16 days
NUMBER OF EGGS	5–6 eggs
NUMBER OF BROODS	1–2 a year
TYPICAL DIET	Invertebrates. Fruit in winter
LIFE SPAN	Up to 12 years

The Fieldfare's evocative name comes from the Anglo Saxon for 'a traveller through the fields', in reference to its wanderings in search of food.

WHERE IN THE WORLD?

The Fieldfare is found across northern and central Eurasia. It lives in forests, woods and scrublands. However, it will take advantage of urban parks and gardens if suitable food is available.

CREATURE COMPARISONS

Most birds aggressively defend their nest and territory from rival birds or predators. Fieldfares have developed their own unique technique for dealing with unwanted intruders: they bombard them with faeces. Such dirty tactics are so effective that many birds choose to roost beside the nests of Fieldfares.

Fieldfares

WINGS
Fieldfares fly with an even flight pattern, as opposed to the undulating pattern seen in other Thrushes in flight.

BODY
Fieldfares are large Thrushes, with slightly stockier bodies and a longer tail than other smaller members of the Thrush Family.

BELLY
In flight, the Fieldfare's pale grey underparts and the white colouring under their wings help to differentiate it from other Thrushes.

HOW BIG IS IT?

SPECIAL ADAPTATION
Fieldfares belong to the Thrush Family, which is a large and varied group. However, all members share certain characteristics, including slender bodies and long legs and bills. These adaptations have evolved because members of the Family are found in similar habitats and so have similar feeding habits.

Island Thrush

• ORDER • Passeriformes **• FAMILY •** Turdidae **• SPECIES •** *Turdus poliocephalus*

Identifying the elusive Island Thrush can present bird-watchers with a real challenge. Dozens of sub-species are known, and all of them look slightly different.

VITAL STATISTICS

LENGTH	22.5–25cm (9–10in)
SEXUAL MATURITY	1 year
LAYS EGGS	In 2–3 month seasons, but varies depending on location
INCUBATION PERIOD	Unknown
NUMBER OF EGGS	1–3 eggs
NUMBER OF BROODS	Probably 1 a year
CALL	Varies between sub-species, but many calls are reminiscent of blackbird alarm calls
HABITS	Diurnal, non-migratory
TYPICAL DIET	Invertebrates; berries and seeds
LIFE SPAN	Unknown

WHERE IN THE WORLD?

At least 49 sub-species of Island Thrush are scattered across the Pacific. This includes distinct sub-species in the Philippines, Indonesia, New Guinea and Taiwan, and as far east as Samoa.

CREATURE COMPARISONS

Ornithologists remain unsure of exactly how many sub-species of Island Thrush there are. At least 49 are known, and each varies in coloration, depending on where it is found. Many have black bodies, with a brighter head and neck plumage.

Island Thrush in flight

YELLOW RINGS
There are many different subspecies of Island Thrush, all with different markings, but they all have distinctive yellow rings around the eyes.

EYES
Relatively large eyes give the Island Thrush excellent vision for hunting in dense foliage.

BILL
The stubby bill is well adapted for rooting in the earth for insects, plucking berries from trees and shrubs and gathering moss.

HOW BIG IS IT?

SPECIAL ADAPTATION
The Island Thrush nests in trees. This keeps its chicks safe from ground predators, but not airborne attackers or other tree-dwellers, like snakes. To keep the nest well hidden, the Island Thrushes has learnt to cover it with moss, which its gathers in its bill.

Ring Ouzel

• ORDER • Passeriformes **• FAMILY •** Turdidae **• SPECIES •** *Turdus torquatus*

VITAL STATISTICS

WEIGHT	90–130g (3.2–4.6oz)
LENGTH	23–24cm (9.1–9.4in)
WINGSPAN	38-42cm (15–16.5in)
NUMBER OF EGGS	4–5 eggs
INCUBATION PERIOD	13–14 days
NUMBER OF BROODS	2 a year
TYPICAL DIET	Insects, snails, worms, spiders, fruit, berries
LIFE SPAN	Up to 8 years

The Ring Ouzel, a close relative of the Blackbird, lives mainly in mountainous areas. It has a lovely song.

WHERE IN THE WORLD?

The Ring Ouzel is found in Scandinavia, and also in central, eastern and southern Europe. It is also widely distributed in southwestern Asia east of the Black Sea.

CREATURE COMPARISONS

Males of the northern sub-species of Ring Ouzel are dark brown to black with slightly mottled plumage. Males of the southern sub-species are brownish with white edges along the breast and belly feathers. Both have a distinct, white crescent on the breast. Females are drabber. Their brown body feathers have pale edges. Females also have a pale crescent on the breast.

Female

HEAD
The male Ring Ouzel has an all-black head, and it lacks the orange ring around the eye present in its relative, the Blackbird.

BILL
The yellow bill is long and pointed, and is well adapted for catching insects and eating small fruits and berries.

FEET
The Ring Ouzel has pale greyish legs and long toes with sharp claws for both perching and hopping on the ground.

HOW BIG IS IT?

SPECIAL ADAPTATION

The Ring Ouzel is the same size as the closely related Blackbird, but it has more elongate, narrow wings than a blackbird, which it has adapted to cope with lengthy migrations.

Mistle Thrush

• ORDER • Passeriformes • FAMILY • Turdidae • SPECIES • *Turdus viscivorus*

The Mistle Thrush, a relative of the Blackbird, earned its name from its habit of eating berries from the mistletoe bush, among others.

VITAL STATISTICS

WEIGHT	120–180g (4.2–6.3oz)
LENGTH	26–28cm (10.2–11in)
WINGSPAN	40–45cm (15.7–17.7in)
NUMBER OF EGGS	4–5 eggs
INCUBATION PERIOD	13–15 days
NUMBER OF BROODS	2 a year
TYPICAL DIET	Insects, snails, worms, spiders, fruit, berries
LIFE SPAN	Up to 11 years

WHERE IN THE WORLD?

The Mistle Thrush is found in most of Europe except the high north, and is widely distributed across Central Asia. It migrates to southern Europe, North Africa or southern Asia for the winter.

CREATURE COMPARISONS

The Mistle Thrush has a greyish-brown upper side and a pale brown patch on the cheek. The large wing feathers are more olive-brown with a greyish hue. The underside is white with many large round or drop-shaped spots on the breast and belly. Males and females are similar. The Mistle Thrush can be confused with the closely related Song Thrush, which has smaller spots on the belly and is less grey.

Juvenile

WINGS
The wings of the Mistle Thrush are brown-grey above, but much paler below, making it more difficult to see the outline of a flying bird from the ground.

BODY
The Mistle Thrush has large round spots on the belly, distinguishing it from the closely related Song Thrush.

FEET
The legs are pale yellow and the toes are long and have sharp claws adapted for perching and hopping on the ground.

HOW BIG IS IT?

SPECIAL ADAPTATION

The Mistle Thrush has a long, elegant tail. During the breeding season, the male flicks and spreads his tail in amusing courtship displays to attract females.

351

Eastern Kingbird

• **ORDER** • Passeriformes • **FAMILY** • Tyrannidae • **SPECIES** • *Tyrannus tyrannus*

VITAL STATISTICS

WEIGHT	32–55g (1.1–2oz)
LENGTH	19–23cm (7.5–9in)
WINGSPAN	34–38cm (13.4–15in)
NUMBER OF EGGS	3–5 eggs
INCUBATION PERIOD	15–17 days
NUMBER OF BROODS	1 a year
TYPICAL DIET	In summer, mainly flying insects; in winter, mainly fruit and berries
LIFE SPAN	Unknown

The Eastern Kingbird is a Flycatcher, and despite the name is actually found across most of North America.

WHERE IN THE WORLD?

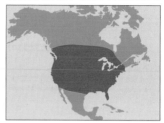

The Eastern Kingbird lives in pairs across much of North America except northern Canada. In winter, it migrates to South America, where it is found in flocks.

CREATURE COMPARISONS

The Eastern Kingbird has a greyish-black head and upper back, while the sides of the head are white. The wings and upper part of the tail are also greyish-black, and the tips of the large tail feathers are white. The throat, breast and belly are pale grey or off-white. The legs are also black. Females look similar to males.

Eastern Kingbird

HEAD
The male often has a slight crest on top of its head, which provides a way of distinguishing it from the female.

BILL
The bill, which is large for a Flycatcher, is also used to aggressively defend the nest and chicks from other birds.

TAIL
The long graceful tail is important for manoeuvring to catch flying insects in flight.

HOW BIG IS IT?

SPECIAL ADAPTATION
Eastern Kingbirds may nest in open or secluded areas. Studies have shown that birds nesting in the open are much more aggressive towards other birds encroaching on their territory.

Eastern Paradise Whydah

• **ORDER** • Passeriformes • **FAMILY** • Viduidae (*under review*) • **SPECIES** • *Vidua paradisaea*

VITAL STATISTICS

WEIGHT	21g (0.7oz)
LENGTH	Breeding males: 33–38cm (13–15in) Females: 15cm (6in)
SEXUAL MATURITY	2 years
FLEDGLING PERIOD	Around 20 days
NUMBER OF EGGS	Up to 22, 3–4 eggs per clutch
NUMBER OF BROODS	1 per mate, but males may mate with up to 12 females
CALL	Sparrow-like alarm calls
HABITS	Diurnal, non-migratory
TYPICAL DIET	Seeds and insects
LIFESPAN	Up to 6 years

The dramatic orange and black plumage of the male Eastern Paradise Whydah is unmistakable. Outside the breeding season, however, he is just another little brown bird.

WHERE IN THE WORLD?

This small bird makes its home in dry scrub and open woodlands in Central and eastern Africa. It is found in southern Sudan, western Somalia, Ethiopia, Kenya, western Tanzania and eastern Uganda.

CREATURE COMPARISONS

Except in the breeding season, male and female Eastern Paradise Whydahs can be difficult to tell apart. The Eastern Paradise Whydah, like the cuckoo is a breed parasite (raised by a different species), in this case the Pytilia. Females do not sing but choose as mates the males that imitate the Pytilia's song.

Female

BODY
During the breeding season males undergo a dramatic transformation, shedding their drab brown feathers for bright orange ones to impress females.

BILL
The bill of the Whydah is adapted for crushing seeds.

TAIL
The male's display tail can grow to a length of 36cm (14in), which is up to three times its body length.

HOW BIG IS IT?

SPECIAL ADAPTATION

Female Eastern Paradise Whydahs lay their eggs in the nests of other birds, usually green-winged Pytilias. This allows them to concentrate their energy on reproducing, while the Pytilias feed and raise their chicks. The Pytilias do this out of instinct, not because the chicks resemble their own.

353

American Darters (Anhinga)

• **ORDER** • Pelecaniformes • **FAMILY** • Anhingidae • **SPECIES** • *Anhinga anhinga*

VITAL STATISTICS

WEIGHT	1.3kg (3lb)
LENGTH	85cm (33.5in)
WINGSPAN	1.2m (4ft)
SEXUAL MATURITY	2 years
INCUBATION PERIOD	25–30 days
NUMBER OF EGGS	2–6 eggs
NUMBER OF BROODS	1 a year
CALLS	Usually silent but makes rattles and grunts when disturbed
TYPICAL DIET	Fish, aquatic invertebrates and insects
LIFE SPAN	Unknown

American Darters are also known as Snakebirds. This is because when they swim only their neck appears above the water, and looks like a snake preparing to strike.

WHERE IN THE WORLD?

Two sub-species of American Darter divide their range between them. One breeds east of the Andes, in Latin America, and in Trinidad and Tobago. The other is found as far north as Texas.

CREATURE COMPARISONS

American Darters are not closely related to cormorants, but both species lack the sebaceous gland that produces oil to waterproof their feathers. This makes it easier for them to swim and dive after prey but, after a dip, they must stretch out their wings in order for them to dry.

American Darter

BILL
The American Darter's spear-like bill has serrated edges, which enable the bird to grip wet, wriggling prey.

BODY
The male American Darter is greenish-black with bright silver patches on their wings. Females have a pale grey or light brown head.

TAIL
The American Darter's tail is long and is used for providing lift, steering, braking and balancing in flight.

HOW BIG IS IT?

SPECIAL ADAPTATION

The American Darter is an excellent hunter. Part of the reason for its success is due to it neck, which has adapted so that it has a hinge-like eighth and ninth vertebrae. This allows the bird's head to shoot forwards, with incredible speed, enabling it to catch prey unaware.

Shoebill

• **ORDER** • Pelicaniformes • **FAMILY** • Balaenicipitidae • **SPECIES** • *Balaeniceps rex*

The Shoebill, a huge weird-looking bird, is a relative of the heron, although lacks the heron's long bill and graceful appearance.

VITAL STATISTICS

WEIGHT	5–6.5kg (11–14.3lb)
HEIGHT	120–130cm (4–4.3ft)
WINGSPAN	220–245cm (7.2–8ft)
NUMBER OF EGGS	1–3 (usually 2)
INCUBATION PERIOD	28–32 days
FLEDGLING PERIOD	14–15 days
NUMBER OF BROODS	1 a year, occasionally 2
TYPICAL DIET	Fishes, amphibians, reptiles, birds eggs and chicks
LIFE SPAN	At least 30 years

CREATURE COMPARISONS

This large, stork-like bird can not be confused with any other. The plumage on the head, body, wings and tail is uniformly grey or bluish-grey. Along the throat and breast are dark stripes and the wing feathers often have pale edges. The belly is usually paler grey. The legs are black or greyish-black. Males and females are similar, but juveniles are brownish.

Shoebill in flight

WHERE IN THE WORLD?

The Shoebill has a wide, but often very local, distribution in swamps and marshy areas across eastern Africa, from Sudan in the north to Zambia in the south.

BILL
In Arabic, the bird is called *abu markub,* which means 'one with a shoe', in reference to the massive bill.

HEAD
Other than its huge bill, the Shoebill's head is characterized by the short crest of feathers, which it always holds erect.

LEGS
The Shoebill has very long, stilt-like legs and lengthy toes for walking on muddy and swampy ground.

HOW BIG IS IT?

SPECIAL ADAPTATION

The Shoebill nests in open areas in swamps. If the weather gets too hot, it may scoop up water with its huge bill, and drizzle it over the eggs to cool them down.

Magnificent Frigatebird

• ORDER • Pelecaniformes • FAMILY • Fregatidae • SPECIES • *Fregata magnificens*

The Magnificent Frigatebird is one of the bird world's most accomplished fliers. In fact, it is so skilled in the air that it can ride out a hurricane.

VITAL STATISTICS

WEIGHT	1–2kg (2.2–4.2lb)
LENGTH	89cm–1m (35 in–3.6ft)
WINGSPAN	2.2m (7.2ft)
SEXUAL MATURITY	5–7 years
INCUBATION PERIOD	50 days
FLEDGLING PERIOD	120–200 days
NUMBER OF EGGS	1 egg
NUMBER OF BROODS	Females produce 1 clutch every other year. Males mate every year
TYPICAL DIET	Fish
LIFE SPAN	Up to 30 years

WHERE IN THE WORLD?

This seabird is widespread across the tropical Atlantic and Pacific coastlines. It breeds from Florida to Ecuador and is especially common in southern Florida, along the Gulf Coast and the Caribbean.

CREATURE COMPARISONS

Frigatebirds feed mainly on fish, but do not always bother to catch it themselves. In common with Gulls and Skuas, Frigatebirds are kleptoparasites, meaning that they regularly steal food from others. They are such agile fliers that they attack birds in mid-air, forcing them to drop their catch.

Magnificent Frigatebird hunting

BODY
Frigatebirds have a very distinctive body shape. Their large heads, long, narrow wings and forked tails make them easy to identify.

THROAT
Only male Frigatebirds have this red, inflatable throat pouch, known as a gular sac.

LEGS
The legs of the Magnificent Frigatebird are not suited for walking. However, its webbed feet are strong enough to grip on to a perch.

HOW BIG IS IT?

SPECIAL ADAPTATION

During the breeding season, Magnificent Frigatebirds nest in coastal areas, but for the rest of the year, they spend their lives in flight. They can do this because their large wings enable them to glide on updraughts for hours at a time with a minimum of effort.

Great Frigatebird

• **ORDER** • Pelecaniformes • **FAMILY** • Fregatidae • **SPECIES** • *Fregata minor*

VITAL STATISTICS

WEIGHT	1–1.8kg (2.2–4lb)
LENGTH	85cm–1m (2.8–3.3ft)
WINGSPAN	2–2.3m (6.6–7.5ft)
SEXUAL MATURITY	8–10 years
INCUBATION PERIOD	45–55 days
FLEDGLING PERIOD	140–168 days
NUMBER OF EGGS	1 egg
NUMBER OF BROODS	1 every 2 years
TYPICAL DIET	Fish, squid, seabird eggs and chicks; occasionally carrion
LIFE SPAN	Up to 34 years

Flying together in massed squadrons, Great Frigatebirds are a common sight soaring over the warm, fish-rich waters of the Indian and Pacific Oceans.

WHERE IN THE WORLD?

The Great Frigatebird is a seabird found throughout the world's tropical and sub-tropical oceans. Birds can regularly travel up to 80km (50 miles) from their breeding colonies in search of food.

CREATURE COMPARISONS

Frigatebirds fly with their wings in an 'M' formation, known as a negative dihedral shape. This is commonly found on military aircraft and, although it reduces stability, it increases manoeuvrability. By contrast, Buzzards' wings have a positive dihedral shape, which gives them stability in the air.

Great Frigatebird in flight

BILL
The powerful hooked bill is used to pluck fish from below the water or, in the case of flying fish, the air.

THROAT
The male Frigatebird inflates its red gular sac to attract a mate.

BODY
The Great Frigatebird can be identified by its dark plumage, long, angled wings, forked tail and hooked bill.

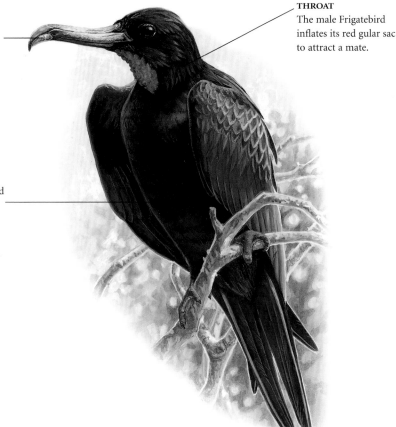

HOW BIG IS IT?

SPECIAL ADAPTATION

The Frigatebird is designed for a life spent almost entirely in the air. Its bones are incredibly light, making up just five per cent of its total body weight. Its long narrow wings enable it to glide with little effort for hours at a time.

357

Brown Pelican

• **ORDER** • Pelecaniformes • **FAMILY** • Pelecanidae • **SPECIES** • *Pelecanus occidentalis*

VITAL STATISTICS

WEIGHT	2.7–5.5kg (6–12lb)
LENGTH	1–1.5m (3.3–5ft)
WINGSPAN	1.8–2.5m (6–8.2ft)
SEXUAL MATURITY	2–5 year
INCUBATION PERIOD	28–30 days
FLEDGLING PERIOD	14–15 days
NUMBER OF EGGS	2–3 eggs
NUMBER OF BROODS	1 a year
TYPICAL DIET	Fish; occasionally carrion
LIFE SPAN	Typically 20 years

In the case of the Brown Pelican, the limerick boasting that 'his bill can hold more than his belly can' is really true.

WHERE IN THE WORLD?

The Brown Pelican is also known as the American Brown Pelican because it is found along the Atlantic, Pacific and Gulf coasts of North and South America. Populations are resident and do not migrate.

CREATURE COMPARISONS

Brown Pelicans are the smallest of the seven Pelican species found across the world. White Pelicans (shown) breed in Europe, Asia and Africa, and are the second-largest, weighing in at 10kg (22lb) and measuring up to 1.7m (5ft 6in) long.

Brown Pelican in flight

BILL
A flexible pouch suspended beneath the bill can hold up to three times more than the Brown Pelican's stomach.

EYES
The Brown Pelican has extremely good eyesight and can spot a shoal of fish from 18m (60ft) in the air.

FEET
Webbed feet give the Pelican speed in the water, making it an excellent swimmer.

HOW BIG IS IT?

SPECIAL ADAPTATION

The Pelican is clumsy on land and, for a bird of its size, getting airborne is tricky. However, its long broad wings help to power the bird's take-off. Once airborne, it is a strong flier, though a curious sight with its neck folded and its head resting on its back.

Great White Pelican

VITAL STATISTICS

WEIGHT	10kg (22lb)
LENGTH	1.4–1.7m (4.6–5.6ft)
WINGSPAN	2.3–3.6m (7.5–12ft)
SEXUAL MATURITY	3–4 years
INCUBATION PERIOD	35–36 days
FLEDGLING PERIOD	65–70 days
NUMBER OF EGGS	1–3 eggs
NUMBER OF BROODS	1 a year
TYPICAL DIET	Fish
LIFE SPAN	Up to 36 years in captivity

The Great White Pelican is a large bird famous for its distinctive bill-pouch, which it uses like an extendable fishing net to help catch its prey.

WHERE IN THE WORLD?

The Great White Pelican is a remarkable-looking bird found in southeastern Europe, Asia and Africa, where it builds huge, untidy nests out of heaps of vegetation, usually beside shallow lakes or in swamps.

CREATURE COMPARISONS

Juvenile Great White Pelicans are not white at all. In fact, their upper parts are a muddy grey-brown. Only their underparts are white, and this is a dirty, grey shade of white. It can take up to four years for juveniles to develop the brilliant snow-white plumage of the adult bird.

Juvenile

BODY
The Great White Pelican is the second-largest species of Pelican. Only Dalmatian Pelicans are bigger, weighing up to 15kg (33lb).

BILL
The pouch suspended from below the bill is used to scoop up fish.

WINGS
Long broad wings help to power the bird's take-off.

HOW BIG IS IT?

SPECIAL ADAPTATION
The Pelican uses its bill-pouch to scoop up fish. Excess water is drained away as the bird tilts its head upwards to swallow. It uses the hook at the end of its bill for snaring fish, which it tosses in the air, catches and then swallows whole.

White-tailed Tropicbird

• **ORDER** • Pelecaniformes • **FAMILY** • Phaethontidae • **SPECIES** • *Phaethon lepturus*

VITAL STATISTICS

LENGTH	70–82cm (27.5–32.3in)
SEXUAL MATURITY	unknown
INCUBATION PERIOD	40–42 days
FLEDGLING PERIOD	70–85 days
NUMBER OF EGGS	1 egg
NUMBER OF BROODS	1 a year
CALL	Shrill screams during courtship displays
HABITS	Diurnal, non-migratory
TYPICAL DIET	Fish, especially flying fish, some crustaceans and squid
LIFE SPAN	Up to 30 years

Soaring across the blue skies of the tropics, the graceful White-tailed Tropicbird spends much of its life at sea, coming inland only during the breeding season.

WHERE IN THE WORLD?

The White-tailed Tropicbird breeds primarily on tropical islands in the Atlantic, Western Pacific and Indian Oceans. Some birds also breed in the Caribbean, including Little Tobago. Some nest in Bermuda.

CREATURE COMPARISONS

Tropicbirds are also known as Bosun Birds because of their whistling call, which sounds like an old-fashioned bosun's pipe. There are five known sub-species, including the Golden Bosun (*Phaethon lepturus fulvus*), which is found only on Christmas Island and has an appealing gold tint to its plumage.

Adult

TAIL
The very long tail is used for stability in flight and in courtship displays.

BILL
The White-tailed Tropicbird has a stout, slightly downwards-curved bill with serrated edges. These are sharp enough to leave scars during territorial disputes.

FEET
Short legs end in a set of small, totipalmate feet (feet with all four toes joined by webbing).

HOW BIG IS IT?

SPECIAL ADAPTATION

The elegant tail streamers of the White-Tailed Tropicbird have a dual purpose. In flight, they act like stabilizers, to improve control and aid manoeuvrability. They are also used in courtship displays when males fly over their mate with such precision that their tail streamers touch.

Flightless Cormorant

• **ORDER** • Pelecaniformes • **FAMILY** • Phalacrocoracidae • **SPECIES** • *Phalacrocorax harrisi*

The Flightless Cormorant, the largest member of its family, is one of the rarest birds in the world.

VITAL STATISTICS

WEIGHT	2.5–5.5kg (5.5–12lb)
LENGTH	89–100cm (35–39.4in)
INCUBATION PERIOD	14–18 days
NUMBER OF EGGS	2–4 eggs (usually 3)
NUMBER OF BROODS	1 a year occasionally 2
TYPICAL DIET	Squid
LIFE SPAN	Unknown

WHERE IN THE WORLD?

The Flightless Cormorant is found only on some of the Galapagos Islands in the Pacific Ocean, off the coast of northern South America.

CREATURE COMPARISONS

The Flightless Cormorant does not have waterproof feathers but air bubbles trapped between the feathers prevent the bird becoming waterlogged. The bird has short legs set far back on the body, giving it an awkward gait. The feet are large and webbed. Males and females are similar, but females are smaller and have a shorter bill.

Flightless Cormorant

BILL
The bill is long and narrow, and has a large hook at the tip for holding on to slippery fish and squid.

WINGS
The Flightless Cormorant has stumpy wings with small weak flight feathers.

BODY
The Flightless Cormorant is a large heavy-set bird. Its upper parts are greenish-black and its underparts are more brownish or greyish.

HOW BIG IS IT?

SPECIAL ADAPTATION

The Flightless Cormorant evolved in an environment free of predators. It did not need to fly and therefore eventually lost the ability. It spends much of its time underwater and so is rarely seen.

361

Shag (European)

• **ORDER** • Pelecaniformes • **FAMILY** • Phalacrocoracidae• **SPECIES** • *Phalacrocorax aristotelis*

On land, the European Shag can seem clumsy and comical. In water, this bird's natural element, its skill and grace become apparent.

VITAL STATISTICS

WEIGHT	2kg (4.2lb)
LENGTH	68–78cm (26.8–30.7in)
WINGSPAN	95cm–1m (37.4 in–3.6ft)
SEXUAL MATURITY	3–4 years
LAYS EGGS	March–May
INCUBATION PERIOD	30–31 days
NUMBER OF EGGS	3–5 eggs
NUMBER OF BROODS	1 a year
TYPICAL DIET	Small fish such as herring and sand eels
LIFE SPAN	Up to 20 years

WHERE IN THE WORLD?

The European Shag's preferred habitat is on and around the rocky coastlines of western and southern Europe, and North Africa. It is a shy, nervous bird rarely seen inland.

CREATURE COMPARISONS

At first sight, it is easy to confuse the European Shag with its close relative the Cormorant. However, there is one obviously different characteristic. During the breeding season, only the Shag has an upturned black head crest.

European Shag at the end of the breeding season

HEAD
The Shag takes its name from the old Norse word *skegg,* which means beard, referring to the quiff worn by the birds during the breeding season.

BODY
European Shags have a distinctive metallic-green sheen on their feathers during the breeding season. The wing tips can look purple.

TAIL
The long, wedge-shaped tail of the European Shag has 12 feathers, unlike the tail of the larger cormorant, which has 14 feathers.

HOW BIG IS IT?

SPECIAL ADAPTATION

The European Shag is a benthic feeder, meaning that it catches its prey on the bottom of the sea. It is one of the most accomplished divers in the Cormorant Family. With powerful webbed feet to propel it through the water, its body is well adapted for swimming.

Cormorant (Great)

• **ORDER** • Pelecaniformes • **FAMILY** • Phalacrocoracidae • **SPECIES** • *Phalacrocorax carbo*

VITAL STATISTICS

WEIGHT	Males: 2.5kg (5.5lb) Females: 2.1kg (4.6lb)
LENGTH	77–94cm (30.3–37in) 1.2–1.5m (4–5ft)
SEXUAL MATURITY	3–5 years
INCUBATION PERIOD	27–30 days
FLEDGLING PERIOD	48–52 days
NUMBER OF EGGS	2–6 eggs
NUMBER OF BROODS	1 a year, occasionally 2
TYPICAL DIET	Fish
LIFE SPAN	Typically 11 years

CREATURE COMPARISONS

Looking like some ancient airborne reptile, the adult Cormorant has distinctive scaly black feathers. Juveniles look less reptilian, with dark brown upper parts and whiter underparts, especially in their first year, when they may have patchy areas of white on the breast and the belly.

Juvenile in flight

In Norse legend, those who die at sea spend eternity on the isle of Utrøst where they can visit loved ones disguised as the Cormorant.

WHERE IN THE WORLD?

The Cormorant is found on estuaries, lakes and rivers throughout Europe, Asia, North Africa, North America, Australasia and Greenland. Some populations migrate south, following fish supplies.

THROAT
A flexible throat pouch can be extended to enable the Cormorant to swallow especially large fish without choking.

BILL
The Cormorant's hook-tipped bill, which is similar to that of the Shag, can hold struggling prey in a vice-like grip.

LEGS
Like most diving birds, the Cormorant's legs are set well back on its body, making it an efficient swimmer but a poor walker.

HOW BIG IS IT?

SPECIAL ADAPTATION

Unlike other seabirds, the Cormorant lacks sebaceous glands, which produce an oil that waterproofs feathers. Its wings are also modified to let air out, and water in, an adaptation that makes swimming easier. After a dip, it is often seen with its wings outstretched, to allow them to dry.

Pygmy Cormorant

• ORDER • Pelecaniformes **• FAMILY •** Phalacrocoracidae **• SPECIES •** *Phalacrocorax pygmaeus*

VITAL STATISTICS

WEIGHT	750–1400g (26.5–49.4oz)
LENGTH	45–55cm (17.7–21.7in)
WINGSPAN	75–90cm (29.5–35.4in)
NUMBER OF EGGS	4–7 eggs
INCUBATION PERIOD	26–29 days
NUMBER OF BROODS	1 a year
TYPICAL DIET	Mainly fish; also amphibians, rodents, large shrimp
LIFE SPAN	Up to 15 years

The Pygmy Cormorant is easily distinguished from most other Cormorants because it is much smaller, has an unusually long tail for a Cormorant and is rarely found near the sea.

WHERE IN THE WORLD?

The Pygmy Cormorant is found in large colonies near large freshwater lakes and rivers in southeastern Europe and southwestern Asia. It is only rarely seen in western Europe.

CREATURE COMPARISONS

The Pygmy Cormorant does not grow to the same size as other cormorants. It has a greenish-black plumage with some mottling. The top of the head and parts of the upper side of the neck often have dull reddish-brown feathers. Males and females are similar, although males are larger. Adults have small white feathers on the head, neck and breast during the breeding season.

Juvenile

BILL
The bill is large, heavy and has a prominent hook for getting a secure hold on slippery fish.

FEET
The legs of the Pygmy Cormorant are short. Its feet are large and webbed, making efficient paddles when the bird is swimming on or under the water's surface.

TAIL
The long tail is used for steering while diving underwater for fish and other prey.

HOW BIG IS IT?

SPECIAL ADAPTATION

Unlike most birds, the feathers of Cormorants are not water-repellent, which helps them to dive. It does mean, though, that the bird gets wet when diving, and so has to allow its feathers to dry in the sun.

Gannet (Northern)

• **ORDER** • Pelecaniformes • **FAMILY** • Sulidae • **SPECIES** • *Morus bassanus*

VITAL STATISTICS

WEIGHT	3kg (6.6lb)
LENGTH	85–97cm (33.5–38.2in)
WINGSPAN	1.7–2m (5.6–6.2ft)
SEXUAL MATURITY	5 years
INCUBATION PERIOD	42–46 days
FLEDGLING PERIOD	84–97 days
NUMBER OF EGGS	1 egg
NUMBER OF BROODS	1 a year
TYPICAL DIET	Fish
LIFE SPAN	Typically 17 years

Seabirds are rarely eaten, but the inhabitants of the Isle of Lewis, United Kingdom, consider the Gannet a delicacy. The taste is described as fish-flavoured chewing gum.

WHERE IN THE WORLD?

The Gannet spends most of its life at sea, and nests along the North Atlantic. Though the largest colony is found at Bonaventure Island, Quebec, most Gannets breed around the United Kingdom.

CREATURE COMPARISONS

The Northern Gannet is one of the largest species of North Atlantic seabirds, and is comparable in size to the Canada Goose. Juveniles range in colour from almost completely dark brown to mostly white. It takes up to five years for young birds to attain their full adult plumage and, while in transition, they often have a speckled look.

Adult (left), juvenile (right)

HEAD
During the breeding season, the Northern Gannet's head and neck take on the distinctive pale yellow tint.

WINGS
Gannets use their powerful wings, as well as their webbed feet, to propel themselves through the water as they dive after prey.

BODY
The adult Northern Gannet has primarily white plumage.

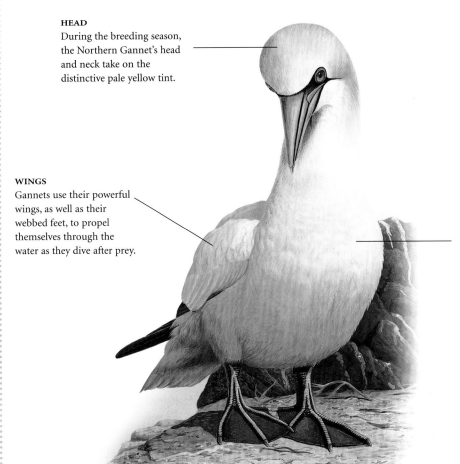

HOW BIG IS IT?

SPECIAL ADAPTATION

The Northern Gannets is an expert plunge diver. Diving from heights of up to 25m (82ft), they can reach speeds of 100km/h (62mph) as they hit the water. However, a specially adapted network of air sacs between its muscles and skin prevents impact damage.

Blue-footed Booby

• **ORDER** • Pelecaniformes • **FAMILY** • Sulidae • **SPECIES** • *Sula nebouxii*

VITAL STATISTICS

WEIGHT	1.5kg (3.3lb)
LENGTH	81cm (32in)
WINGSPAN	158cm (62.2in)
LAYS EGG	All year round
SEXUAL MATURITY	1 year
INCUBATION PERIOD	41–45 days
NUMBER OF EGGS	2–3 eggs
NUMBER OF BROODS	1 every 8–9 months, but varies with local conditions
TYPICAL DIET	Fish, squid and waste from fishing boats
LIFE SPAN	Typically 17 years

Thanks to its bright blue feet and clumsy waddle, this marine bird has earned itself the label Booby, from the Spanish *bobo,* which means 'stupid'.

WHERE IN THE WORLD?

The Blue-footed Booby breeds on islands off the Western Pacific coastline of the USA and Latin America, including the Galapagos Islands. For the rest of the year it can be found at sea.

CREATURE COMPARISONS

Male and female Blue-footed Boobies look alike, though females are slightly bigger. In the breeding season, many birds develop a brood patch (an area of bare skin that helps to transfer body heat from the parent to the egg). However, Blue-Footed Boobies do not have such a patch but instead use their oversized blue feet to help keep their eggs warm.

Blue-footed Booby

EYES
Female Boobies have large eyes that are sometimes described as star-shaped.

BILL
The Booby's spear-like bill has serrated edges that enable the bird to maintain a good grip on wet wriggling prey.

FEET
The male Booby shows off its large webbed feet during their elaborate courtship displays.

HOW BIG IS IT?

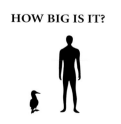

SPECIAL ADAPTATION

The Blue-footed Booby is clumsy on land, but it is an accomplished flier and swimmer, diving from height into water with barely a splash. Its long neck, long, pointed wings and narrow bill create a supremely streamlined shape, enabling it to slice through the water at speed.

Greater Flamingo

• **ORDER** • Phoenicopteriformes • **FAMILY** • Phoenicopteridae • **SPECIES** • *Phoenicopterus roseus*

VITAL STATISTICS

WEIGHT	Males: 3kg (6.2lb) Females: 2.2kg (5lb)
HEIGHT	1.1–1.5m (3.6–5ft)
WINGSPAN	1.4–1.6m (4.6–5.2ft)
SEXUAL MATURITY	3–6 years
INCUBATION PERIOD	27–31 days
FLEDGLING PERIOD	14–15 days
NUMBER OF EGGS	1 egg; occasionally 2 although this is rare
NUMBER OF BROODS	1 a year
TYPICAL DIET	Algae, molluscs and crustaceans
LIFE SPAN	Up to 40 years

CREATURE COMPARISONS

Pigeons, doves, penguins and Flamingoes are unusual because they feed their chicks a liquid that is similar to a mammal's milk. It takes over 11 weeks for chicks to begin developing their juvenile plumage and the hooked bill that enables them to feed themselves.

Juvenile

With its bright pink plumage, the Flamingo is a showy bird. Its origins can be traced back four million years.

WHERE IN THE WORLD?

It is generally agreed that there are six species of Flamingo. Two make their homes in Africa and Asia. A further four, including the American Flamingo, are found in Latin America and the Caribbean.

BODY
The Flaming's pink coloration comes from the high level of alpha and beta carotenes in its diet.

LEGS
Long bare legs allow the Flamingo to wade into deep water without getting waterlogged feathers, which would hamper its ability to fly.

FEET
Long webbed front toes help the Flamingo to swim, but also spread its body weight so it does not sink in mud.

HOW BIG IS IT?

SPECIAL ADAPTATION

The bill of the Flamingo is lined with keratinous plates called lamellae. These, in turn, are covered with tiny hairs that create a filtration system for capturing tiny shrimps and crustaceans. Although the scale is different, this is similar to the way that the baleen whale filters the water for plankton.

Black-throated Honeyguide

• **ORDER** • Piciformes • **FAMILY** • Indicatoridae • **SPECIES** • *Indicator indicator*

VITAL STATISTICS

WEIGHT	45–55g (1.6–2oz)
LENGTH	19–20cm (7.5–8in)
WINGSPAN	28–30cm (11–12in)
NUMBER OF EGGS	3–5 eggs
INCUBATION PERIOD	A brood parasite, it lays eggs in the nests of other birds; incubation time is 12–14 days
NUMBER OF BROODS	1 a year
TYPICAL DIET	Mainly bees eggs, larvae and pupae; also beeswax
LIFE SPAN	2–3 years

CREATURE COMPARISONS

Adult males have dark brownish-grey upper parts. The wing feathers are white along the edge. There are distinct yellow markings along the front edge of the wing. The bird's underside is white with a black throat. There is a white cheek patch and white patches along the tail. Females are similar to males, but lack a black throat. The bill is pinkish.

Juvenile male (left), female (right)

The Black-throated Honeyguide, a relative of the Woodpeckers, may guide people to a beehive full of honey, but scientists disagree whether it also acts as a guide for other animals.

WHERE IN THE WORLD?

The Black-throated Honeyguide is widely distributed in Africa south of the Sahara desert, in open country. It is not found in the rainforest belt in central Africa and in the deserts of the south.

HEAD
There is an obvious white patch on the cheek, often interrupted by a black band from the throat.

BILL
The short bill is yellow or pink in adult birds, but it is black in juvenile birds.

BODY
Adults may be recognized by having a white underside, but immature males have a yellow underside.

HOW BIG IS IT?

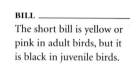

SPECIAL ADAPTATION
The Black-throated Honeyguide is known to guide people to a beehive. It will then wait while they take as much honey as they want before swooping in to claim the rest.

White-backed Woodpecker

• ORDER • *Piciformes* • FAMILY • Picidae • SPECIES • *Dendrocopus leucotos*

The White-backed Woodpecker is the largest of the Spotted Woodpeckers. It is often confused with the more common Great Spotted Woodpecker.

VITAL STATISTICS

WEIGHT	75–120g (2.6–4.2oz)
LENGTH	24–26cm (9.4–10.2in)
WINGSPAN	40–48cm (15.7–19in)
NUMBER OF EGGS	4–5 eggs
INCUBATION PERIOD	12–14 days
NUMBER OF BROODS	1 a year
TYPICAL DIET	Wood-boring beetles and grubs, ants, nuts, seeds, berries
LIFE SPAN	Up to 12 years

WHERE IN THE WORLD?

The White-backed Woodpecker is found in parts of Scandinavia, across eastern and parts of central Europe, and across central Russia and Central Asia.

CREATURE COMPARISONS

The upper part of the White-backed Woodpecker's back is black, while the lower part is white. The wings are black with distinctive white bars. The head, throat and breast are off-white with faint streaks, and the belly is pinkish-red. There is a distinctive black marking along the side of the face. Males and females are similar, except that males have a red cap, while it is black in females.

White-backed Woodpeckers

BILL
The long pointed bill is stout enough to enable the bird to chisel grubs from trunks and branches of dead trees.

FEET
The feet have two toes pointing forwards and two pointing backwards. The greyish legs are short.

TAIL
The short black tail has stiff feathers, which the bird often uses as a prop when it climbs around on tree trunks.

HOW BIG IS IT?

SPECIAL ADAPTATION

The White-backed Woodpecker chisels its nest chamber in an old rotting log. From the outside, only a 5cm (2in) round hole is visible, but the chamber itself may be 40cm (16in) deep.

Middle Spotted Woodpecker

• **ORDER** • Piciformes • **FAMILY** • Picidae • **SPECIES** • *Dendrocopus medius*

VITAL STATISTICS

WEIGHT	50–80g (2–3oz)
LENGTH	20–22cm (8–8.7in)
WINGSPAN	35–40cm (14–15.7in)
NUMBER OF EGGS	5–6 eggs
INCUBATION PERIOD	12–13 days
NUMBER OF BROODS	1 a year
TYPICAL DIET	Wood-boring beetles; grubs, ants, cone-seeds, fruit
LIFE SPAN	Up to 15 years

The Middle Spotted Woodpecker is sedentary and tends not to migrate great distances. It has yet to be recorded in the British Isles.

WHERE IN THE WORLD?

The Middle Spotted Woodpecker is found in much of Europe, except most of Scandinavia and the British Isles. It is also found across southwestern Asia.

CREATURE COMPARISONS

The back of the neck and back are predominately black with white markings. The wings are black with distinctive white bars and spots. The head, throat, breast and belly are white with dark streaks along the breast, and there is a pinkish hue along the belly. An elongated dark stripe runs along the sides of the neck, and the top of the head is red. Males and females are similar.

Middle Spotted Woodpeckers

HEAD
Unusually among spotted Woodpeckers, male and female Middle Spotted Woodpeckers both have a distinctive red cap.

BILL
The strong pointed bill is fairly short, which is a distinguishing feature from its close relative, the Syrian Woodpecker.

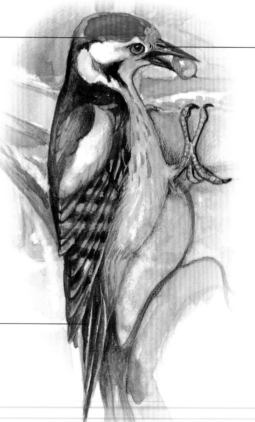

TAIL
The tail feathers are black above, but pale and spotted below, and are often used as a prop when climbing.

HOW BIG IS IT?

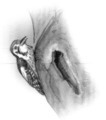

SPECIAL ADAPTATION

Many Woodpeckers peck their bill against dried-up old branches to make loud drumming sounds. The Middle Spotted Woodpecker rarely drums, but instead utters a hoarse croaky call.

Lesser Spotted Woodpecker

• ORDER • Piciformes • FAMILY • Picidae • SPECIES • *Dendrocopus minor*

VITAL STATISTICS

WEIGHT	18–22g (0.6–0.8oz)
LENGTH	14–15cm (5.5–6in)
WINGSPAN	25–27cm (10–10.6in)
NUMBER OF EGGS	4–6 eggs
INCUBATION PERIOD	12–14 days
NUMBER OF BROODS	1 a year
TYPICAL DIET	Wood-boring beetles, grubs, caterpillars, ants; cone-seeds, fruit
LIFE SPAN	Up to 6 years

Measuring only as large as a sparrow, the Lesser Spotted Woodpecker is the smallest true Woodpecker in Europe.

WHERE IN THE WORLD?

The Lesser Spotted Woodpecker is found through much of Europe, and across Central Asia to the Sea of Okhotsk. It is found in parts of North Africa and the Middle East.

CREATURE COMPARISONS

The upper sides of the wings, back and tail are black with distinctive white spots and bars. The underside is white with dark streaks along the flanks. The top of the head is red in adult males, but black in females. Otherwise the sexes are similar. The Lesser Spotted Woodpecker can be confused with the Great Spotted Woodpecker, but the Lesser is much smaller.

Juvenile female (left), juvenile male (right)

WINGS
The bold black and white patterns on the wings are visible in fluttering display flights.

TAIL
The tail feathers are stiff and stout, and are used as a prop when the bird is sitting on a vertical tree trunk.

FEET
On its feet are two toes that point forwards and two that point backwards, giving a good grip on bark. The legs are short and grey.

HOW BIG IS IT?

SPECIAL ADAPTATION

The bill of the Lesser Spotted Woodpecker (far left) is shorter than those of most other European Woodpeckers (left), and is used to pick off insects on the bark, and to chip away bark from rotting trees.

Black Woodpecker

• **ORDER** • *Piciformes* • **FAMILY** • Picidae • **SPECIES** • *Dryocopus martius*

The Black Woodpecker, an inquisitive bird, is Europe's largest species of Woodpecker and grows to almost twice the size of the impressively (but inaccurately) named Great Spotted Woodpecker.

VITAL STATISTICS

WEIGHT	330g (11.6oz)
LENGTH	40–60cm (15.7–23.6in)
WINGSPAN	67–73cm (26.4–28.7in)
SEXUAL MATURITY	1 year
LAYS EGGS	Courtship begins in January but nesting may not being until March–May
INCUBATION PERIOD	12–14 days
FLEDGLING PERIOD	27–28 days
NUMBER OF EGGS	3–5 eggs
NUMBER OF BROODS	1 a year
TYPICAL DIET	Insects, especially ants and their larvae, and wood-boring beetles

CREATURE COMPARISONS

All Woodpeckers are experts at drilling holes in trees, which they do both to construct nests and to find food. As they drill, they use their bills like chisels to chip away wood. Their skulls are shock absorbent to prevent the constant drilling from damaging their brains.

Black Woodpecker

WHERE IN THE WORLD?

The striking Black Woodpecker can be found in Eurasia as far north as the Arctic circle and as far east as Japan. Birds nest in tree trunks, so need mature woodland habitats to thrive.

HEAD
The male Black Woodpecker has a crown that is entirely red. In females, only the hind crown (back of the head) is red.

BODY
The crow-sized Black Woodpecker is very shy but bird-watchers can often lure it out of hiding by imitating its call.

FEET
The feet have sharp claws on the end of the toes, which help the bird climb and grip.

HOW BIG IS IT?

SPECIAL ADAPTATION

Sharp claws, in addition to two toes at the front of the foot and two at the back, give Woodpeckers excellent grip. Stiff tail feathers also help support the bird as it climbs. In fact, territorial displays (shown) can take place halfway up a tree.

Eurasian Wryneck

VITAL STATISTICS

WEIGHT	10–15g (0.35–0.53oz)
LENGTH	16–17cm (6.3–6.7in)
WINGSPAN	25–27cm (10–10.6in)
NUMBER OF EGGS	7–10 eggs
INCUBATION PERIOD	13–15 days
NUMBER OF BROODS	1 a year
TYPICAL DIET	Ants, worms, small insects, snails
LIFE SPAN	Up to 10 years

The Eurasian Wryneck takes its name from the unique snake-like way in which it twists its neck and hisses if threatened with capture.

WHERE IN THE WORLD?

The Eurasian Wryneck is widely distributed in temperate Europe except the high north, and across temperate Asia. It spends the winter in southern Asia and in tropical Africa south of the Sahara.

CREATURE COMPARISONS

The Eurasian Wryneck is rather bland in appearance compared to most other species of Woodpecker. The plumage is greyish-brown with brown and buff mottling. The top of the head and upper back are greyish with a wide dark stripe, and the underside is light brown and mottled. The wings are more buff with dark bars across the feathers. The tail feathers are stiff, and can be used as a prop.

Eurasia Wryneck

HEAD
The Eurasian Wryneck has a rather small head. Unlike its relatives, the Wryneck does not have a head specially constructed to absorb the forces from chiselling into wood.

BILL
If cornered, the Eurasian Wryneck will open its bill, raise the feathers on top of its head, and hiss loudly like an angry snake.

FEET
The Eurasian Wryneck has two toes pointing backwards and two toes pointing forwards, which give it good grip for climbing.

HOW BIG IS IT?

SPECIAL ADAPTATION

The Eurasian Wryneck has a shorter and weaker bill than most other woodpeckers, but like its relatives it makes a nest in a tree hollow. It cannot chisel its own, and so uses hollows abandoned by other woodpeckers.

Red-headed Woodpecker

• ORDER • Piciformes **• FAMILY •** Picidae **• SPECIES •** *Melanerpes erythrocephalus*

VITAL STATISTICS

WEIGHT	60–90g (2–3.2oz)
LENGTH	23–24cm (9–9.4in)
WINGSPAN	38–42cm (15–16.5in)
NUMBER OF EGGS	3–10 (usually 4–5)
INCUBATION PERIOD	12–14 days
NUMBER OF BROODS	1 a year (sometimes 2)
TYPICAL DIET	Insects, worms, spiders; fruit, berries, nuts, birds' eggs
LIFE SPAN	Up to 10 years

The popular children's cartoon character Woody Woodpecker was modelled on the Red-headed Woodpecker.

WHERE IN THE WORLD?

The Red-headed Woodpecker is distributed across eastern areas of North America, from southern Canada to Florida and the Gulf of Mexico. Northern populations migrate south for winter.

CREATURE COMPARISONS

The Red-headed Woodpecker is vividly coloured. Its head and neck are brick red, and the upper part of the back and the wings are jet black. The inner part of the wing is white. The underside and the upper and lower part of the tail are white, and the large tail feathers are black. Females are similar to males, but they are usually smaller and slightly drabber.

HEAD
The red head is a reliable way to distinguish this bird from the Red-bellied Woodpecker.

BILL
The large bill is strong enough for chiselling into trees, but is also slightly curved, making it useful for catching insects in the air.

WINGS
The wings are rounded at the tip, giving the Red-headed Woodpecker a fast and agile flight.

Red-headed Woodpecker in flight

HOW BIG IS IT?

SPECIAL ADAPTATION

The Red-headed Woodpecker has a wider-ranging diet than other Woodpeckers. It finds its food in trees by chipping away bark or on the ground, and even catches insects in the air.

Eurasian Three-toed Woodpecker

• **ORDER** • Piciformes • **FAMILY** • Picidae • **SPECIES** • *Picoides tridactylus*

VITAL STATISTICS

WEIGHT	50–80g (2–2.8oz)
LENGTH	21–23cm (8.3–9in)
WINGSPAN	34–39cm (13.4–15.4in)
NUMBER OF EGGS	3–4
INCUBATION PERIOD	11–13 days
NUMBER OF BROODS	1 a year
TYPICAL DIET	Beetles, grubs, butterflies, ants; fruit, berries, tree sap
LIFE SPAN	Up to 12 years

The Eurasian Three-toed Woodpecker tends to be resident, although birds from northern areas may fly south for the winter.

WHERE IN THE WORLD?

The Eurasian Three-toed Woodpecker is found in parts of central and eastern Europe, but is mainly found in northern Scandinavia, across northern and central Asia, and into North America.

CREATURE COMPARISONS

The Eurasian Three-toed Woodpecker has a pale or white back with some faint dark streaks. The wings are dark-brown or black with distinctive white bars. The sides of the face and neck are streaked with vividly contrasting black and white, and the throat and breast are white. The belly and flanks are off-white with dark streaks. Males and females are broadly similar.

Eurasian Three-toed Woodpecker

BILL
The Eurasian Three-toed Woodpecker has a large dark-grey or black bill, with which it chisels into bark and wood.

FEET
As the name implies, this woodpecker has only three toes, and not the four found on other woodpeckers.

HEAD
Adult males are easily recognized by their head-cap, which is yellow. Females have a grey and spotted cap.

HOW BIG IS IT?

SPECIAL ADAPTATION

Most Woodpeckers have four toes, but this one only has three. This Woodpecker likes to eat tree sap. It will often make long, deep trenches in the bark of conifer trees, from which the sap trickles out.

Grey-headed Woodpecker

• ORDER • Piciformes **• FAMILY •** Picidae **• SPECIES •** *Picus canus*

VITAL STATISTICS

WEIGHT	130–180g (4.6–6.3oz)
LENGTH	25–28cm (10–11in)
WINGSPAN	45–50cm (17.7–19.7in)
NUMBER OF EGGS	5–10 (usually 5–7)
INCUBATION PERIOD	15–17 days
NUMBER OF BROODS	1 a year
TYPICAL DIET	Ants, other insects, worms, grubs; seeds and berries in winter
LIFE SPAN	Up to 15 years

The large Grey-headed Woodpecker has a loud, laughing call that is very similar to that of the Green Woodpecker.

WHERE IN THE WORLD?

The Grey-headed Woodpecker is found across much of central and eastern Europe, in a wide belt across Central Asia, and in large parts of southeastern Asia.

CREATURE COMPARISONS

The back and upper part of the wings are olive-green, and the outer parts of the wings have distinctive dark olive-brown feathers with white bars. The upper part of the tail is yellowish. The face, throat, breast and belly are pale greenish-grey, and there are distinctive black streaks along the face. Males and females are of similar size, and also look much the same.

Grey-headed Woodpecker

HEAD
The top of the head has an obvious bright-red patch in adult males, while females have a grey head.

TAIL
The stout stiff tail feathers are often used as a prop when the bird is climbing tree trunks.

BILL
The tip of the long stout bill is bent slightly upwards for probing for grubs in rotting wood.

HOW BIG IS IT?

SPECIAL ADAPTATION

In early spring, which is the main breeding period, the Grey-headed Woodpecker is very vocal and highly conspicuous. The birds tend to be fairly quiet for the rest of the year.

Green Woodpecker

VITAL STATISTICS

WEIGHT	170–230g (6–8oz)
LENGTH	30–36cm (12–14.2in)
WINGSPAN	45–51cm (17.7–20in)
NUMBER OF EGGS	5–7 eggs
INCUBATION PERIOD	15–18 days
NUMBER OF BROODS	1 a year
TYPICAL DIET	Primarily ants and antgrubs; also other insects, worms and spiders
LIFE SPAN	Up to 13 years

The large Green Woodpecker is commonly seen in open woodlands which have large old trees. It often emits a loud laughing call.

WHERE IN THE WORLD?

The Green Woodpecker is found throughout much of Europe except Ireland and northern Scandinavia. It is also found throughout the central Caucasus, western Russia and eastern Turkey.

CREATURE COMPARISONS

The Green Woodpecker is the size of a pigeon. It has a predominantly green upper side, and darker wing feathers with white bars. The under side is pale yellowish green. The top of the head is bright red. Males and females are similar, but the male has a red spot on the cheek, while the female has only a black stripe.

Female

BILL
Its large, powerful bill is well adapted for chiselling into wood. The base of the bill acts as a shock-absorber to prevent brain damage.

TAIL
The short, stiff tail feathers are used as a prop when the bird is sitting on vertical tree trunks.

WINGS
Despite its large size and short, broad wings, the Green Woodpecker has a seemingly effortless bounding flight.

HOW BIG IS IT?

SPECIAL ADAPTATION
The Green Woodpecker lives in open forests, but it rarely uses branches for drumming in order to mark its territory. Instead it utters a loud, laughing call which, according to folklore, is a warning of rain.

Yellow-rumped Tinkerbird

• ORDER • Piciformes • FAMILY • Ramphastidae• SPECIES • *Pogoniulus bilineatus*

VITAL STATISTICS

LENGTH	10cm (4in)
SEXUAL MATURITY	1 year
INCUBATION PERIOD	13–15 days
FLEDGLING PERIOD	17–20 days
NUMBER OF EGGS	2–4 eggs
NUMBER OF BROODS	Up to 4 a year
CALL	Popping 'tonk-tonk-tonk' tones
TYPICAL DIET	Fruit, berries and insects
LIFE SPAN	Typically 8 years
HABITS	Diurnal, non-migratory

The boldly patterned Yellow-rumped Tinkerbird spends most of its life flitting around beneath the dense forest canopy of its African homeland in search of tasty titbits.

WHERE IN THE WORLD?

Tinkerbirds are distributed throughout tropical Africa. Their range covers a wide diagonal belt across the continent from Senegal in the far west to the island of Zanzibar in the east.

CREATURE COMPARISONS

There are 10 species of Barbets in the *Pogoniulus* Genus, a group of African arboreal birds. 'Barbet' refers to the bristles beneath the bird's bill. The variations in their common names reflect the wide range of plumage or body shape, for example, the Moustached Green-tinkerbird or the Red-fronted Tinkerbird.

Yellow-rumped Tinkerbird in flight

BILL
Bristles beneath the bill protect the Yellow-rumped Tinkerbird's face.

BODY
Tinkerbirds have a large head and a round stout body.

WINGS
The short rounded wings of the Tinkerbird are ideal for manoeuvring in undergrowth. The wings make a whirring sound when the bird is in flight.

HOW BIG IS IT?

SPECIAL ADAPTATION

The Tinkerbird has zygodactyl (yoke-toed) feet, similar in shape to the V-shaped collar fitted over the head of ploughing animals. Its feet have two toes facing forwards and two pointing backwards. This adaptation helps forest-dwelling birds to climb tree trunks and clamber through foliage.

Toco Toucan

• **ORDER** • Piciformes • **FAMILY** • Ramphastidae • **SPECIES** • *Ramphastos toco*

VITAL STATISTICS

WEIGHT	500–880g (17.6–31oz)
LENGTH	55–66cm (21.7–26in)
WINGSPAN	50–65cm (19.7–25.6in)
NUMBER OF EGGS	2–4
INCUBATION PERIOD	17–18 days
NUMBER OF BROODS	1 a year
TYPICAL DIET	Primarily fruits and seeds; also large insects, reptiles, amphibians; eggs and chicks of other birds
LIFE SPAN	Up to 26 years in captivity

The large unmistakable Toco Toucan is a common attraction in zoological gardens around the world.

WHERE IN THE WORLD?

The Toco Toucan is found in Guiana, Surinam and French Guiana, and in northeastern Bolivia, southeastern Peru, northern Argentina, eastern Paraguay, and eastern and central Brazil.

CREATURE COMPARISONS

This bird is famous because of its size and for its enormous yellow bill. Males are larger than females, but otherwise the sexes are similar. The plumage is uniformly black with a white throat and chest, and red patch under the tail. The eyes are dark and surrounded by a ring of bare blue skin, and another larger ring of yellow skin.

Toco Toucan in flight

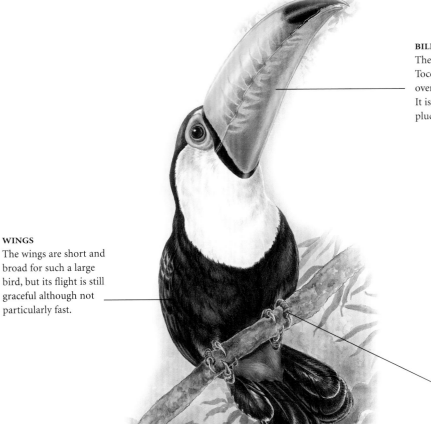

BILL
The enormous bill of the Toco Toucan can measure over 20cm (8in) in length. It is a precision-tool for plucking fruit and berries.

WINGS
The wings are short and broad for such a large bird, but its flight is still graceful although not particularly fast.

FEET
The greyish legs are short and the feet have long toes and curved claws for perching high in the canopy.

HOW BIG IS IT?

SPECIAL ADAPTATION
Although the enormous bill looks heavy, it is, in fact, extremely light. It is not solid inside but consists of a mesh of struts and hollows, which allows the Toco Toucan to use the huge bill with surprising dexterity during feeding.

Red-and-yellow Barbet

• ORDER • Piciformes • FAMILY • Ramphastidae • SPECIES • *Trachyphonus erythrocephalus*

VITAL STATISTICS

WEIGHT	40–55g (1.4–2oz)
LENGTH	22–24cm (8.7–9.4in)
WINGSPAN	37–40cm (14.6–15.7in)
NUMBER OF EGGS	4–5 eggs
INCUBATION PERIOD	12–15 days
NUMBER OF BROODS	1–2 a year
TYPICAL DIET	Fruit, berries, insects, caterpillars, worms, spiders, bird chicks
LIFE SPAN	Up to 15 years

The beautiful Red-and-yellow Barbet is a common sight in many villages in East Africa, often becoming quite tame.

WHERE IN THE WORLD?

The Red-and-yellow Barbet is found in East Africa from southeastern Sudan, eastern Ethiopia, across Uganda, Kenya and northern Tanzania.

CREATURE COMPARISONS

Males have black or blue-black wings and tail, adorned with bright white spots. The back is also black with white spots, but the throat, breast, belly and base of the tail are orange-yellow. There is a black and white spotted collar around the throat. The cheeks are brightly orange. Female Red-and-yellow Barbets are similar to males, but are drabber and lack the throat collar.

Red-and-yellow Barbet in flight

HEAD
The top of the head is black in males, but it is yellow or orange in females. The two sexes are otherwise similar.

WINGS
Its wings are short and round. The Red-and-yellow Barbet usually flies only short distances at a time.

FEET
Its feet are brown or greyish-brown, and have two toes that point forwards and two that point backwards, like those of a Woodpecker.

HOW BIG IS IT?

SPECIAL ADAPTATION

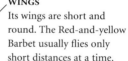

Most Barbets are either specialized insect- or fruit-eaters, and their bills are specially adapted for this. The Red-and-yellow Barbet eats both, and so has an all-purpose bill.

Great Crested Grebe

• **ORDER** • Podicipediformes • **FAMILY** • Podicipedidae • **SPECIES** • *Podiceps cristatus*

The graceful, synchronized courtship dance of the Great Crested Grebe is one of the most celebrated and eagerly awaited spectacles of the bird-watching year.

VITAL STATISTICS

WEIGHT	670g (23.6oz)
LENGTH	46–51cm (18–20in)
WINGSPAN	59–73cm (23.3–28.7in)
SEXUAL MATURITY	2 years
INCUBATION PERIOD	25–31 days
FLEDGLING PERIOD	71–79 days
NUMBER OF EGGS	3–5 eggs
NUMBER OF BROODS	1 a year, occasionally 2
TYPICAL DIET	Fish, crustaceans and insects
LIFE SPAN	At least 10 years
HABITS	Diurnal, migratory

WHERE IN THE WORLD?

The Great Crested Grebe is widespread across Europe, Central Asia, North Africa and Australasia. Birds nest on the edges of lakes and ponds, typically those edged with a border of reeds.

CREATURE COMPARISONS

With their remarkable breeding plumage, adult Great Crested grebes are unmistakable. Juveniles look even more dramatic than their parents, with a zebra-striped black and white head. In winter, however, adults lose their handsome crest and neck ruff, and are easy to mistake for other Grebes.

Juvenile

WINGS
In flight, Grebes have a long, skinny silhouette. White wing patches make their wings appear to flicker as they fly.

BODY
The Great Crested Grebe is the largest species of European Grebe. It has an elegant streamlined shape.

LEGS
The legs are set well back on the body, which helps the bird to dive.

HOW BIG IS IT?

SPECIAL ADAPTATION

The Great Crested Grebe has adapted a peculiar habit of its eating its own feathers. No one knows for certain why it does this, but ornithologists offer the theory that the feathers help to line the stomach and prevent it from being damaged by sharp fish bones.

Little Grebe

• **ORDER** • Podicipediformes • **FAMILY** • Podicipedidae • **SPECIES** • *Trachybaptus ruficollis*

The Little Grebe is the smallest European member of the Grebe Family and is commonly found on open bodies of water, rarely venturing on to dry land.

VITAL STATISTICS

WEIGHT	100–200g (3.5–7oz)
LENGTH	23–28cm (9–11in)
WINGSPAN	40–45cm (15.7–17.7in)
NUMBER OF EGGS	4–6 eggs
INCUBATION PERIOD	19–20 days
NUMBER OF BROODS	2 a year
TYPICAL DIET	Aquatic insects and insect larvae, crayfish, small fish, plants
LIFE SPAN	Up to 13 years

WHERE IN THE WORLD?

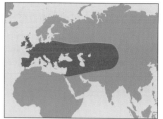

The Little Grebe is found throughout most of Europe, except northern Scandinavia, and across parts of the Middle East and southern Asia. Northern populations migrate south for winter.

BILL
The stout pointed bill is well adapted for hunting small water creatures, but also for nipping off plants.

CREATURE COMPARISONS

In summer, the Little Grebe has a fairly drab brown or greyish-brown, slightly mottled plumage, which is brighter along the breast and belly. It lacks the beautiful head plumes of many other grebes, but has a distinctive, reddish area along the neck. In winter, the plumage is lighter brown with pale or off-white underparts. Males and females are similar.

LEGS
The legs are short and set far back on the body and the feet are large and webbed.

TAIL
Like other Grebes, the Little Grebe has an extremely short tail. It often seems as if the tail is missing altogether.

Little Grebe

HOW BIG IS IT?

SPECIAL ADAPTATION

If the Little Grebe feels threatened, it will usually rapidly dive under the water while flapping its wings loudly on the water's surface to warn other birds in the vicinity.

Royal Albatross (Southern)

• ORDER • Procellariiformes • FAMILY • Diomedeidae • SPECIES • *Diomedea epomophora*

The world's largest seabird, the elegant Royal Albatross spends 80 per cent of its life on the ocean waves.

VITAL STATISTICS

WEIGHT	8.5kg (18.7oz)
LENGTH	1.2m (4ft)
WINGSPAN	3m (10ft)
SEXUAL MATURITY	9–11 years
LAYS EGGS	October–November
INCUBATION PERIOD	79 days
NUMBER OF EGGS	1 egg
NUMBER OF BROODS	1 every 2 years
TYPICAL DIET	Small fish, squid and crustaceans
LIFE SPAN	Up to 45 years

WHERE IN THE WORLD?

The Royal Albatross is pelagic (lives at sea, coming ashore only to breed). Most nest on the sub-Antarctic Campbell Island, with smaller populations around the Auckland Islands and New Zealand.

CREATURE COMPARISONS

Until recently, the Southern and the Northern Royal Albatross were considered the same species. There is still disagreement as to whether the species should have been divided, but Southern birds can recognized by the white areas on their upper wings. Northern birds have entirely black upper wings.

Southern Royal Albatross

BILL
Although silent at sea, the Albatross claps its bulky bill repeatedly to make a rattling alarm call when defending its nest.

WINGS
The Albatross is one of the easiest birds to identify in the air due to its long slender wings.

BODY
The Albatross does not hunt in the air. Instead it floats along on the water, seizing any passing prey in its bill.

HOW BIG IS IT?

SPECIAL ADAPTATION

Royal Albatross mate for life unless breeding fails repeatedly. Courtship plays a vital part in ensuring the suitability of a mate. Royal Albatross have elaborate displays, including bill-circling, sky-pointing, flank-touching with the bill, and full spreading of the wings.

Wandering Albatross

• **ORDER** • Procellariiformes • **FAMILY** • Diomedeidae • **SPECIES** • *Diomedea exulans*

VITAL STATISTICS

WEIGHT	8kg (18lb)
LENGTH	1.1–1.3m (3.6–4.4ft)
WINGSPAN	2.5–3.5m (8.2–11.5ft)
SEXUAL MATURITY	6–22 years
LAYS EGGS	December–March
NUMBER OF EGGS	1 egg
INCUBATION PERIOD	70–85 days
NUMBER OF BROODS	1 every 2 years; occasionally annually if previous year's clutch failed
TYPICAL DIET	Fish, squid and krill
LIFE SPAN	Typically 40 years

CREATURE COMPARISONS

There are few birds that can match the aerial grace of the Albatross. In fact, in the air, it has more in common with man-made gliders, as its exceptionally long, slender wings enable it to soar for long periods without active flapping. Albatross feed primarily by foraging from the ocean surface, but can dive to depths of 1m (3ft) in search of food.

Wandering Albatross

Albatross spend much of the year alone, soaring above the grey Antarctic. However, come the breeding season they return to their life-long partners.

WHERE IN THE WORLD?

In the breeding season, the Wandering Albatross inhabits small nesting territories across several sub-Antarctic islands. For the rest of the year, it earns its name by wandering over the southern oceans.

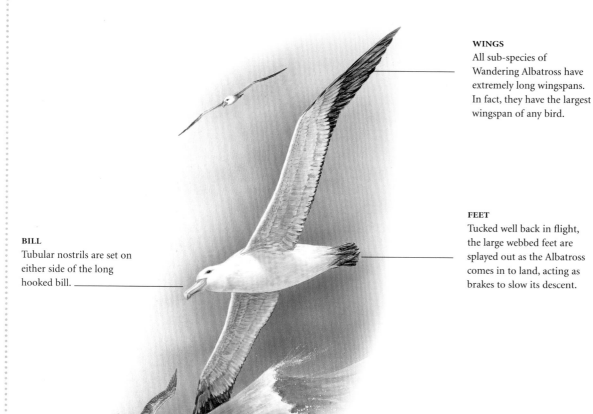

WINGS
All sub-species of Wandering Albatross have extremely long wingspans. In fact, they have the largest wingspan of any bird.

FEET
Tucked well back in flight, the large webbed feet are splayed out as the Albatross comes in to land, acting as brakes to slow its descent.

BILL
Tubular nostrils are set on either side of the long hooked bill.

HOW BIG IS IT?

SPECIAL ADAPTATION

A pair of tubular nostrils, set on either side of the Albatross's bill, give this bird an excellent sense of smell. This can be used both in the hunt for prey or to help a bird find its mate among the confusion of a crowded breeding colony.

Black-browed Albatross

• **ORDER** • Procellariiformes • **FAMILY** • Diomedeidae • **SPECIES** • *Thalassarche melanophry*

VITAL STATISTICS

WEIGHT	3.7kg (8.2lb)
LENGTH	80–95cm (31.5–37.4in)
WINGSPAN	2.1–2.5 (7–8.2ft)
SEXUAL MATURITY	7–9 years
INCUBATION PERIOD	Around 70 days
FLEDGLING PERIOD	122–141 days
NUMBER OF EGGS	1 egg
NUMBER OF BROODS	1 a year
TYPICAL DIET	Fish, krill, squid and carrion
LIFE SPAN	At least 34 years

Albatross are so admired for their expertise in flight that the British Royal Air Force officers' cap badge bears an image of this famous seabird.

WHERE IN THE WORLD?

Generally the Black-browed Albatross is found in southern waters, although juveniles tend to move north after they become independent. During the breeding season, adults nest on remote islands.

CREATURE COMPARISONS

Male and female Black-browed Albatross look the same, though the male may be slightly larger. Juveniles are similar to adults. However, in place of the all-white neck and head, young birds have a distinctive grey collar. Their bills and underparts are also darker.

Juvenile

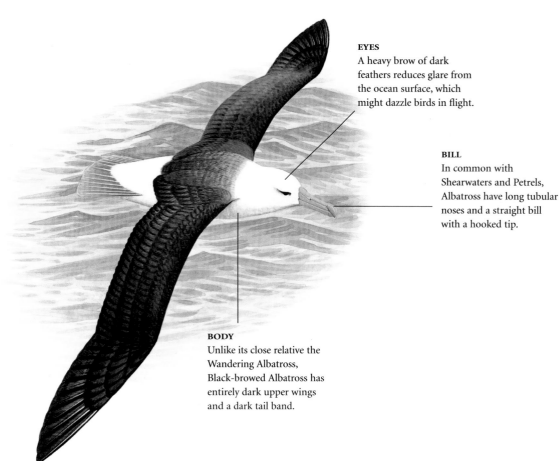

EYES
A heavy brow of dark feathers reduces glare from the ocean surface, which might dazzle birds in flight.

BILL
In common with Shearwaters and Petrels, Albatross have long tubular noses and a straight bill with a hooked tip.

BODY
Unlike its close relative the Wandering Albatross, Black-browed Albatross has entirely dark upper wings and a dark tail band.

HOW BIG IS IT?

SPECIAL ADAPTATION

Over-specialization has its drawbacks. Like many seabirds, the legs of the Albatross are legs set well back on its body. This adaptation produces a powerful and very efficient swimming stroke, which saves energy, but causes the bird to be unsteady walking on dry land.

Fulmar (Northern)

• **ORDER** • Procellariiformes • **FAMILY** • Procellariidae • **SPECIES** • *Fulmarus glacialis*

VITAL STATISTICS

WEIGHT	Males: 880g (31oz) Females: 730g (25.7oz)
LENGTH	43–52cm (17–20.5in)
WINGSPAN	1–1.2m (3.3–4ft)
SEXUAL MATURITY	6–9 years
LAYS EGGS	May
INCUBATION PERIOD	47–53 days
NUMBER OF EGGS	1 egg
NUMBER OF BROODS	1 a year
TYPICAL DIET	Fish, squid, crustaceans and carrion
LIFE SPAN	Typically 44 years

CREATURE COMPARISONS

Like many birds, Fulmars come in a number of morphs (colour variations). The commonest is Herring Gull-grey, but a wide variety of tones occur, from very pale to the darker, smoky grey of Blue Fulmar (shown below), which is found in the far north.

Blue Fulmar

The attractive Fulmar is best known for an ingenious unattractive habit. When danger strikes, it vomits oily gastric juices all over its attacker.

WHERE IN THE WORLD?

The Fulmar is a bird of the open sea, coming into land only during the breeding season. It is most widely spread over the North Atlantic and Pacific Oceans as far north as the Arctic.

BILL
Fulmars have a straight bill ending in a hooked tip and long, tubular nostrils.

EYES
Short bristly feathers just in front of the Fulmar's eyes are believed to help reduce glare from the ocean surface.

BODY
The Fulmar looks like a miniature Herring Gull, but it is stockier and has a shorter bill with prominent nasal tubes on either side of the bill.

HOW BIG IS IT?

SPECIAL ADAPTATION

The Fulmar is an expert glider, using strong ocean winds to help carry it back and forth across its breeding range. Once airborne, it rarely needs to flap its wings. Instead it holds them stiffly outstretched in order to catch the slightest breeze.

Great Shearwater

• ORDER • Procellariiformes • FAMILY • Procellariidae • SPECIES • *Puffinus gravis*

The Great Shearwater is a superb flier. It gets its name from its shearing motion it makes in the air as it moves sideways from air current to air current to save energy.

VITAL STATISTICS

WEIGHT	830g (29.3oz)
LENGTH	43–51cm (17–20in)
WINGSPAN	1–1.2m (3.3–4ft)
NUMBER OF EGGS	1 egg
INCUBATION PERIOD	Around 55 days
NUMBER OF BROODS	1 a year
HABITS	Diurnal, but nocturnal in the breeding season, migratory
FLEDGLING PERIOD	Around 105 days
TYPICAL DIET	Fish and squid
LIFE SPAN	At least 50 years

WHERE IN THE WORLD?

The Great Shearwater breeds on islands in the south Atlantic. It then travels up the eastern coastline of South and North America, before crossing to Europe for the European summer.

CREATURE COMPARISONS

Albatross and Shearwaters belong to different bird families, but they have similar lifestyles, spending much of their time at sea. This means they have the same long narrow wing profile, which enables them to glide for long periods without flapping their wings.

Great Shearwater in flight

WINGS
Long narrow wings are made for gliding. One Great Shearwater is known to have glided continuously for 2.4km (1.5 miles).

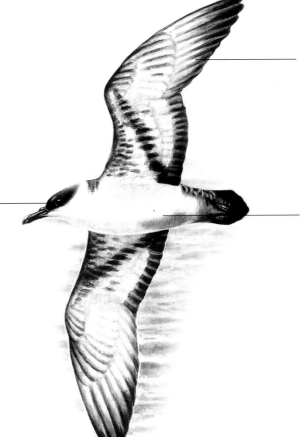

HEAD
The Great Shearwater can be identified by its distinctive chocolate-brown cap and its contrasting collar, which is almost white.

BODY
It may be called Great but it is not the largest Shearwater. That honour goes to Cory's Shearwater.

HOW BIG IS IT?

SPECIAL ADAPTATION

Thanks to large nostrils and a well developed olfactory bulb in the brain, the Shearwater has a superb sense of smell. It uses this while hunting, as well as to find its mate in crowded breeding colonies. In comparison other birds, like Flamingos (see left), have poor olfactory senses.

387

Manx Shearwater

• ORDER • Procellariiformes • FAMILY • Procellariidae • SPECIES • *Puffinus puffinus*

VITAL STATISTICS

WEIGHT	350–550g (12.3–19.4oz)
LENGTH	30–38cm (12–15in)
WINGSPAN	76–89cm (30–35in)
NUMBER OF EGGS	1 egg
INCUBATION PERIOD	47–55 days
NUMBER OF BROODS	1 a year
TYPICAL DIET	Mainly fish, such as sardines, also squid, shrimp
LIFE SPAN	At least 55 years

The Manx Shearwater is a graceful sea bird that spends most of the year fishing on the open oceans, returning each spring to breed on rocky islands.

WHERE IN THE WORLD?

Manx Shearwaters breed on islands throughout the North Atlantic. They fly all the way across the Atlantic and may be found as far south as the Cape of Good Hope and the Horn of South America.

CREATURE COMPARISONS

The Manx Shearwater is a medium-sized species of Shearwater, and looks similar to most of its relatives. The upper side is dark brown to black, the wings are elongated and slender and the tail is short. The underside is white with some dark stripes across the throat. The legs are short and the feet are large and webbed. Males and females are similar.

WINGS
The wings are long and narrow, and are well adapted for soaring above the waves of the open ocean.

BILL
The long slender bill has a distinct hook at the tip for holding on to slippery fish and squid.

LEGS
The legs of the Manx Shearwater are short and set far back on the body. The bird cannot walk properly on land, but shuffles along on its belly.

Manx Shearwater in flight

HOW BIG IS IT?

SPECIAL ADAPTATION
Male and female Manx Shearwaters form a strong pair-bond. The female lays just one very large egg in a shallow burrow, and then flies away to feed, while the male broods the egg.

Short-tailed Shearwater

• ORDER • Procellariiformes **• FAMILY •** Procellariidae **• SPECIES •** *Puffinus tenuirostris*

The Short-tailed Shearwater migrates to its breeding grounds in enormous flocks numbering tens of thousands of individuals.

VITAL STATISTICS

WEIGHT	600–900g (21.2–31.7oz)
LENGTH	40–45cm (15.7–7.7in)
WINGSPAN	95–120cm (37.4–47.2in)
NUMBER OF EGGS	1 egg
INCUBATION PERIOD	52–55 days
NUMBER OF BROODS	1 a year
TYPICAL DIET	Small fish, squid, krill and other crustaceans
LIFE SPAN	At least 30 years

WHERE IN THE WORLD?

The Short-tailed Shearwater breeds along the coasts of southern Australia and Tasmania, but later migrates through the eastern Pacific Ocean to winter in the North Pacific.

CREATURE COMPARISONS

The Short-tailed Shearwater has a uniformly dark brown plumage on the head, neck, body and wings. Often, the wings have some mottling of white. Females are similar to males, but are usually slightly smaller. This species may be confused with the slightly larger Sooty Shearwater, but it has a longer bill and more white on the underside of the wing.

Short-tailed Shearwater

WINGS
The Short-tailed Shearwater has very long narrow wings for efficient soaring and gliding across the ocean.

BILL
The bill is fairly short for a Shearwater, but it is powerful and has sharp edges for gripping slippery prey.

LEGS
The large webbed feet are set far back on the body, making the bird a graceful swimmer but a clumsy walker.

HOW BIG IS IT?

SPECIAL ADAPTATION
The Short-tailed Shearwater breeds in a burrow in the ground. It visits its nest at night, finding its own burrow by using its sense of smell, for which purpose it has two large, tube-shaped nostrils.

Sulphur-crested Cockatoo

• ORDER • Psittaciformes • FAMILY • Cacatuidae • SPECIES • *Cacatua galerita*

VITAL STATISTICS

WEIGHT	800–950g (28.2–33.5oz)
LENGTH	45–50cm (17.7–19.7in)
WINGSPAN	85–100cm (33.5–39.4in)
NUMBER OF EGGS	3–5
INCUBATION PERIOD	28–31 days
NUMBER OF BROODS	1 a year
TYPICAL DIET	Fruit, berries, seeds, nuts, leaves, roots
LIFE SPAN	Over 40 years

The Sulphur-crested Cockatoo is large and noisy and has become a favourite pet. As a result, several populations are threatened by the pet trade.

WHERE IN THE WORLD?

The Sulphur-crested Cockatoo is distributed along eastern Australia and Tasmania. It is also found on New Guinea and the Aru Islands, and has been introduced into New Zealand and Indonesia.

CREATURE COMPARISONS

The Sulphur-crested Cockatoo has a uniformly white head and neck. The upper side of the body, the wings and tail are also white. The underside of the wings and tail are pale yellow. Its most conspicuous feature is a large crest of bright yellow feathers on top of its head, which it uses for communication. It is similar to the Australian Corella, but the Corella is smaller and lacks the yellow crest.

Sulphur-crested Cockatoos

HEAD
Male Sulphur-crested Cockatoos can be distinguished from females by their black eyes. Females have reddish-brown eyes.

WINGS
The large wide wings are well adapted for flying through the forest environments in which they live, including tropical and sub-tropical rainforests.

BEAK
The large, dark grey bill is used to tear into food, such as fruit. The bird can be a pest in orchards or crops.

HOW BIG IS IT?

SPECIAL ADAPTATION
The Sulphur-crested Cockatoo eats plants, some of which contain toxins. To combat the poisons, the birds sometimes eat clay, which detoxifies the food.

Fischer's Love Bird

• ORDER • Psittaciformes • FAMILY • Psittacidae • SPECIES • *Agapornis fischeri*

Love Birds are extremely intelligent parrots. This makes them successful in the wild, but tricky to keep as pets because they are notoriously good at finding ways to escape.

VITAL STATISTICS

WEIGHT	1.5kg (3.3lb)
LENGTH	14cm (5.5in)
LAYS EGGS	January–April and June–July
SEXUAL MATURITY	4–6 months
INCUBATION PERIOD	23 days
FLEDGLING PERIOD	38–42 days
NUMBER OF EGGS	3–8 eggs
NUMBER OF BROODS	2–3 a year, but may breed all year round if conditions are right
TYPICAL DIET	Seeds, cereal and fruit
LIFE SPAN	Typically 10–15 years.

CREATURE COMPARISONS

Like the smaller African Love Birds, Eclectus Parrots are popular as pets. This has led them to be bred by enthusiasts, all over the world. However, they are naturally found in the forests of the Solomon Islands, New Guinea, the Maluku Islands and northeastern Australia.

Fischer's Lovebirds

WHERE IN THE WORLD?

Fischer's Love Birds are popular pets and are found worldwide. Their natural homes are in eastern and central Africa. During particularly dry years, populations may move west into lusher regions.

BILL
The bill is made up of a downwards-curving upper mandible, which fits over a smaller, upwards-curving lower mandible.

BODY
Many of the colour mutations have been produced by selective breeding of captive Love Birds.

BODY
Fischer's Love Bird, one of the smallest species of parrot, is easily identified by its stocky body and short, blunt-tipped tail.

HOW BIG IS IT?

SPECIAL ADAPTATION

Love Birds, like all parrots, are extremely dextrous. They may not have fingers and thumbs but their bills and feet have adapted to do a wide variety of jobs, and not just feed. Using their bill and feet together, they are able to manipulate a range of objects with ease.

Australian King Parrot

• **ORDER** • Psittaciformes • **FAMILY** • Psittacidae • **SPECIES** • *Alisterus scapularis*

VITAL STATISTICS

WEIGHT	400–600g (14.0–21.0oz)
LENGTH	38–44cm (15–17.3in)
WINGSPAN	48–65cm (19–25.6in)
INCUBATION PERIOD	20 days
FLEDGLING PERIOD	14–15 days
NUMBER OF EGGS	3–6 eggs (usually 4)
NUMBER OF BROODS	1 a year
TYPICAL DIET	Fruits, seeds; also small creatures such as insects
LIFE SPAN	Unknown in the wild. Captive specimens are reported to be able to live for up to 25 years

The Australian King Parrot lives in Australian forests, though its vivid colours make it a popular pet.

WHERE IN THE WORLD?

The King Parrot is found only in Australia where it is widely distributed in forest tracts along the eastern coast. It also lives in gardens and parks in Canberra and Sydney.

CREATURE COMPARISONS

Adult males of this beautiful parrot look different from females. The male has a striking red head and breast, a bluish lower back, green wings and a dark green tail, often with a bluish tint and tail. The beak is reddish-orange with a black tip and yellow eyes. Adult females have a green head and chest, but are otherwise similar to the males. Young birds look similar to females, but have brownish rather than yellow eyes.

Female

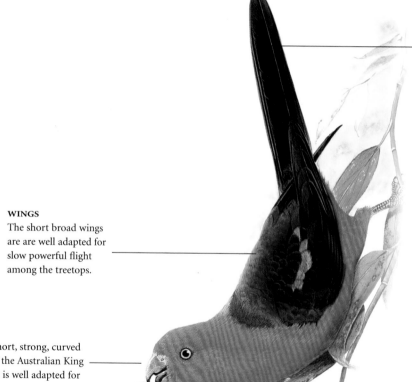

TAIL
The Australian King Parrot has a long wide tail, which may account for almost half of the bird's entire length.

WINGS
The short broad wings are are well adapted for slow powerful flight among the treetops.

BILL
The short, strong, curved bill of the Australian King Parrot is well adapted for tearing into fruit and seeds. It is red in males but brownish in females.

HOW BIG IS IT?

SPECIAL ADAPTATION

The Australian King Parrot is a slow flier, but it is able to weave from side to side and change direction suddenly when flying among the treetops. This means that it is not easily caught by predators.

St Vincent Amazon

• **ORDER** • Psittaciformes • **FAMILY** • Psittacidae • **SPECIES** • *Amazona guildingii*

VITAL STATISTICS

WEIGHT	400–700g (14–24.7oz)
LENGTH	40–46cm (15.7–18in)
WINGSPAN	65–75cm (25.6–29.5in)
NUMBER OF EGGS	2
INCUBATION PERIOD	23–26 days
NUMBER OF BROODS	1 a year
TYPICAL DIET	Fruit, mainly of the pennypiece plant, seeds, nuts, flowers
LIFE SPAN	Up to 30 years

The St Vincent Amazon is found on only one small island in the Caribbean, and is in danger of becoming extinct.

WHERE IN THE WORLD?

As its name suggests, this parrot is found only on the Caribbean island of St Vincent in the Lesser Antilles, which lies near the island of Barbados.

CREATURE COMPARISONS

The St Vincent Amazon is very colourful. The forehead is creamy or white, and the top of the head is yellow. The back of the head and around the throat is blue or bluish-green. The upper side is bronze-greenish or brownish, and the tail is yellow with a wide blue band. The feet are grey, and the eyes are reddish. Females are similar to males.

BILL
The bill is short and stout. The upper mandible has a long curved hook for tearing into fruit and seeds.

WINGS
The wings are wide and have a beautiful bronze upper side, but are more yellow on the underside.

TAIL
The short wide tail is yellow with a striking band of blue, and is important for manoeuvring during flight.

St Vincent Amazon in flight

HOW BIG IS IT?

SPECIAL ADAPTATION

Parrots use their feet extensively during feeding, some individuals favouring the left foot, others favouring the right. St Vincent Amazons are unusual in that they all seem to prefer using the left foot.

Yellow-crowned Amazon

• ORDER • Psittaciformes • FAMILY • Psittacidae • SPECIES • *Amazona ochrocephala*

VITAL STATISTICS

WEIGHT	250–400g (9–14oz)
LENGTH	33–38cm (13–15in)
WINGSPAN	58–65cm (23–25.6in)
NUMBER OF EGGS	2–3
INCUBATION PERIOD	25–26 days
NUMBER OF BROODS	1 a year
TYPICAL DIET	Fruits, berries, nuts, seeds, flowers
LIFE SPAN	Up to 50 years

The Yellow-crowned Amazon attracts a lot of attention in captivity because of its outstanding coloration and its ability to mimic the human voice.

WHERE IN THE WORLD?

The Yellow-crowned Amazon is widely distributed across much of Central America and northern South America. An isolated population lives on the island of Trinidad.

CREATURE COMPARISONS

As its name suggests, the Yellow-crowned Amazon has a strikingly yellow head, often with splashes of green at the base of the bill. The body and wings are bright green, and there is a red bar across the front of each wing. The large wing feathers often have bluish tips. The tail is green with yellow at the tip of the feathers. Females are similar to males.

Sub-species of Yellow-crowned Amazon have different colourings

HEAD
Some populations of Yellow-crowned Amazons have a less yellow head, while in others only the top of the head is yellow.

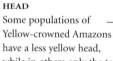

BILL
The large curved bill is powerful enough to crack hard-shelled seeds and nuts.

TAIL
The Yellow-crowned Amazon has a fairly short square tail, which is used for manoeuvring in flight through its canopy habitat.

HOW BIG IS IT?

SPECIAL ADAPTATION

Like many other parrots, the Yellow-crowned Amazon has adapted a specialized type of feather on the chest. This crumbles to produce a type of dust that helps to care for the plumage.

Hyacinth Macaw

• **ORDER** • Psittaciformes • **FAMILY** • Psittacidae • **SPECIES** • *Anodorhynchus hyacinthinus*

The Hyacinth Macaw is the world's largest flying parrot, but it is in danger of becoming extinct in the near future.

VITAL STATISTICS

WEIGHT	1.5–2kg (3.3–4.4lb)
LENGTH	95–100cm (37.4–39.4in)
WINGSPAN	120–140cm (47.2–55in)
NUMBER OF EGGS	1–3 (usually 2–3)
INCUBATION PERIOD	28–30 days
NUMBER OF BROODS	1 a year
TYPICAL DIET	Seeds, nuts, fruit, berries
LIFE SPAN	Unknown

WHERE IN THE WORLD?

Today the Hyacinth Macaw is confined to three populations, which live in the Pantanal region of Brazil, Bolivia and Paraguay; the Cerrado region of Brazil; and along several large Brazilian rivers.

CREATURE COMPARISONS

The Hyacinth Macaw is huge and makes an impressive sight in flight. The head, neck, body and upper side of the wings are strikingly blue. The underside of the wings and the tail are darker blue, and the tail may even be dark grey or even almost blackish on the underside. There is a bright yellow ring around the eye, and a yellow collar around the lower beak. Males and females are similar.

Juvenile

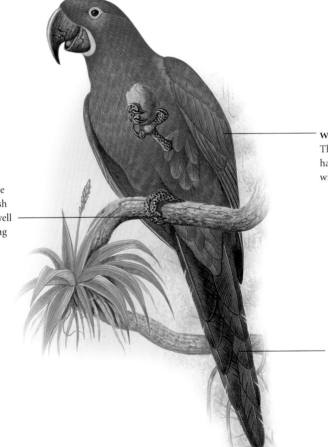

FEET
The legs and feet are powerful and greyish in colour, and are well adapted for grabbing onto a branch.

WINGS
The Hyacinth Macaw has huge, vivid blue wings.

TAIL
The long graceful tail is used for steering in the air, but not as much for fine manoeuvring because the Hyacinth Macaw is not a strong flier.

HOW BIG IS IT?

SPECIAL ADAPTATION

The Hyacinth Macaw has an enormous and extremely powerful bill. It is able to crack even the hardest nuts, such as macadamias, thought it prefers to eat palm nuts and pine nuts.

Blue-and-yellow Macaw

• **ORDER** • Psittaciformes • **FAMILY** • Psittacidae • **SPECIES** • *Ara ararauna*

VITAL STATISTICS

WEIGHT	0.9–1.3kg (2–3lb)
LENGTH	76–86cm (30–34in)
WINGSPAN	1.1m (3.6ft)
INCUBATION PERIOD	24–26 days
FLEDGLING PERIOD	91 days
NUMBER OF EGGS	1–3 eggs
NUMBER OF BROODS	1 a year
HABITS	Diurnal, non-migratory
TYPICAL DIET	Seeds, leaves and fruit

Of all the known members of the large and varied Psittacidae Family, the big, colourful Blue-and-yellow Macaw is perhaps the most recognizably parrot-like.

WHERE IN THE WORLD?

This parrot is distributed throughout Latin America's tropical forests and woodlands. Population sizes vary across the range from eastern Panama to Bolivia. The species is endangered in Trinidad.

CREATURE COMPARISONS

Scarlet Macaws live high in the evergreen forests of the tropics. Populations are found in Mexico, Peru and Brazil. However, deforestation has resulted in declining numbers through much of their habitat. Like the Blue-and-yellow Macaw, which are also forest dwellers, they are popular pets and illegal trapping has reduced wild populations.

Blue-and-yellow Macaw in flight

BILL
The hooked bill is powerful enough to crack through the tough outer shells of the rainforest seeds that form the bird's diet.

HEAD
Blue-and-yellow Macaws are extremely popular as pets, not just because of their stunning plumage but also because of their ability to mimic human speech.

FEET
Strong detrous feet enable the Blue-and-yellow Macaw to grasp a branch with ease.

HOW BIG IS IT?

SPECIAL ADAPTATION

A specially adapted throat pouch allows the Blue-and-yellow Macaw to carry caches of food. While the female remains on the nest, the male goes foraging. He eats until his belly is full, then tops up his throat pouch. He regurgitates the food once he returns to the nest.

Scarlet Macaw

• ORDER • Psittaciformes • FAMILY •Psittacidae • SPECIES • *Ara macao*

With its spectacular plumage and sociable nature, the Scarlet Macaw is one of the most famous ambassadors of the rapidly vanishing rainforests.

VITAL STATISTICS

WEIGHT	200g (7oz)
LENGTH	85–90cm (33.5–35.4in)
SEXUAL MATURITY	3–4 years
INCUBATION	24–28 days
FLEDGLING PERIOD	Around 100 days
NUMBER OF EGGS	2–4 eggs
NUMBER OF BROODS	Parents will not raise another brood until juveniles become fully independent
TYPICAL DIET	Fruit, nuts, nectar, flowers; occasionally clay to aid digestion
LIFE SPAN	Typically 40–50 years

CREATURE COMPARISONS

Parrots are well known for their ability to imitate a wide range of sounds from everyday noises, such as a car alarm to a human voice. Macaws are one of the most vocal members of the species and, like many parrots, can be trained to talk.

Scarlet Macaw in flight

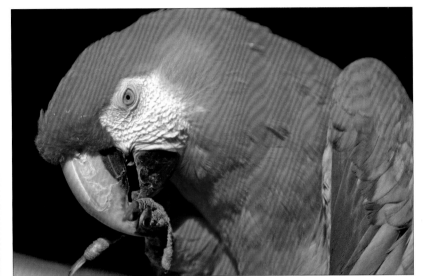

WHERE IN THE WORLD?

The Scarlet Macaw lives high in the evergreen forests of the tropics. It is found in Mexico, Peru and Brazil, but deforestation and illegal trapping has reduced numbers throughout its range.

EYES
Bare skin around the eyes and bill prevent feathers becoming soiled when the Scarlet Macaw feeds on ripe fruit.

BILL
The long thick bill is light in colour on the top and dark black beneath. Male bills may be slightly longer than those of females.

BODY
Scarlet Macaws owe their name to their bright red underwings and long red tail.

HOW BIG IS IT?

SPECIAL ADAPTATION
Macaws have zygodactyl (yoke-toed) feet, resembling the yoke (V-shaped collar) fitted over the head of a ploughing animals. Typically, Scarlet Macaw feet have two toes facing forwards and two pointing backwards. This adaptation helps forest-dwelling birds climb tree trunks and clamber through foliage.

Sun Conure

• **ORDER** • Psittaciformes • **FAMILY** • Psittacidae • **SPECIES** • *Aratinga solstitialis italic*

The Sun Conure is brilliantly coloured even for a member of the parrot family, and is therefore a popular species among breeders.

VITAL STATISTICS

WEIGHT	110–125g (4–4.4oz)
LENGTH	28–31cm (11–12.2in)
WINGSPAN	50–60cm (19.7–23.6in)
NUMBER OF EGGS	4–5
INCUBATION PERIOD	23–24 days
NUMBER OF BROODS	1 a year
TYPICAL DIET	Fruits, berries, flowers, nuts, seeds
LIFE SPAN	Up to 30 years

WHERE IN THE WORLD?

The Sun Conure is only found in a small area in South America: in the Roraima state in northern Brazil, southern Guyana, southern Surinam, and southern French Guiana.

CREATURE COMPARISONS

The Sun Conure is an extremely attractive parakeet. It has a yellow head with orange cheeks, a yellow throat and upper part of the neck and back, and yellow base of the tail. The breast and belly are a rich orange. The front part of the wing is also yellow, while the hind part of the wing and tail are green. The large wing feathers are tipped with blue. Females are similar to males.

Sun Conure in flight

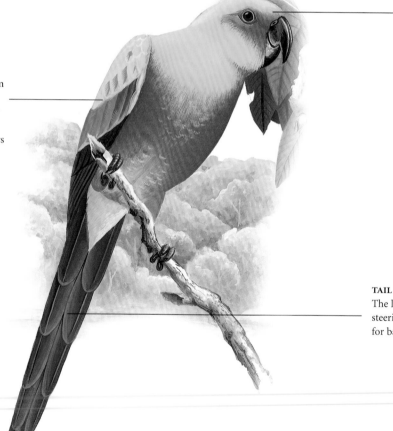

WINGS
The Sun Conure may be distinguished from the closely related Jenday Conure by its wings, which have green feathers tipped with blue.

HEAD
The yellow and orange head feathers can be raised and ruffled if the bird is angry or frightened.

TAIL
The long tail is used for steering during flight, and for balancing on a perch.

HOW BIG IS IT?

SPECIAL ADAPTATION
The Sun Conure has a bill that is well adapted for cracking nuts with hard shells. The top half of the beak fits over the bottom, acting like a vice for holding and splitting the shells of nuts and seeds.

Eclectus Parrot

• **ORDER** • Psittaciformes • **FAMILY** • Psittacidae • **SPECIES** • *Eclectus roratus*

The contrast between the green male and red female Eclectus Parrot is so extreme that they were once believed to belong to different species.

VITAL STATISTICS

WEIGHT	430g (15.2oz)
LENGTH	30.5–37cm (12–14.6in)
WINGSPAN	71cm (28in)
LAYS EGGS	No regular breeding season
FLEDGLING PERIOD	Around 85 days
INCUBATION PERIOD	26–28 days
NUMBER OF EGGS	3–5 eggs
NUMBER OF BROODS	1 a year
TYPICAL DIET	Fruit, nuts, seeds and flowers
LIFE SPAN	Up to 50 years in captivity

WHERE IN THE WORLD?

The Eclectus Parrot is a popular pet and can be found all over the world. However, it is native to the forests of the Solomon Islands, New Guinea, the Maluku Islands and North Eastern Australia.

BILL
The downwards-curving upper mandible fits over a smaller, upwards-curving lower mandible.

WINGS
These colourful birds are strong flyers and often travel long distances in search of food.

BODY
The female Eclectus Parrot (shown here) has a red head and bluish-purple breast. The male has predominantly green plumage.

CREATURE COMPARISONS

They may vary greatly in colour, but all Parrots share similar physical characteristics. The two most obvious are their hooked bill and dextrous feet. The toe arrangement of two pointing backwards and two pointing forwards enable the birds to grip and manipulate objects.

Male (left), female (right)

HOW BIG IS IT?

SPECIAL ADAPTATION

It is more usual for male birds to have the gaudiest plumage, but the Eclectus Parrot is an exception. Ornithologists have argued for decades about the reason for this, but it is believed to be a breeding adaptation that enables females to claim a nesting space.

Budgerigar

• **ORDER** • Psittaciformes • **FAMILY** • Psittacidae • **SPECIES** • *Melopsittacus undulatus*

The Budgerigar is probably the most popular of all pet birds. If cared for properly, it may thrive for many years.

VITAL STATISTICS

WEIGHT	20–35g (0.7–1.2oz)
LENGTH	17–19cm (6.7–7.5in)
WINGSPAN	30–35cm (12–14in)
NUMBER OF EGGS	4–6 eggs
INCUBATION PERIOD	18–21 days
NUMBER OF BROODS	2–3 a year
TYPICAL DIET	Seeds, nuts, fruits, berries
LIFE SPAN	Up to 10 years

WHERE IN THE WORLD?

Wild Budgerigars are found across the interior of the Australian continent in open areas such as scrubland. Introduced populations thrive in the southern USA.

CREATURE COMPARISONS

Captive Budgerigars may have all sorts of colours and patterns. The wild Budgerigar has a yellow forehead and face with a blue or purple cheek patch and three black spots across the throat. The neck, back and wings are yellow with black markings. The breast and belly are green. The tail is cobalt-blue. Males and females are similar.

Female (left), male (right)

HEAD
The wild Budgerigar has fewer puffy head feathers than the most common type of captive Budgerigar.

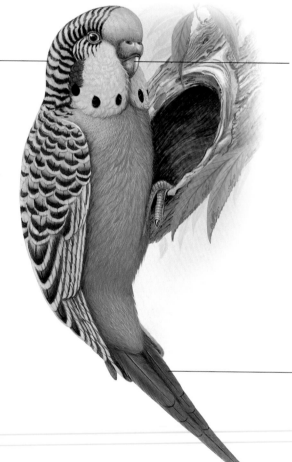

BILL
The upper hooked part of the bill is attached to the skull by a hinge that allows the bill to move up and down.

TAIL
The tail is used both for steering in the air and displaying to other Budgerigars.

HOW BIG IS IT?

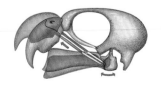

SPECIAL ADAPTATION

The Budgerigar is an intelligent and inquisitive bird, and will investigate and chew on all sorts of objects. It is also social, so captive birds should be kept in small flocks in large cages.

Kea

VITAL STATISTICS

WEIGHT	800–850g (28.2–30oz)
LENGTH	46–48cm (18–19in)
WINGSPAN	90–110cm (35.4–43.3in)
NUMBER OF EGGS	2–4 eggs
INCUBATION PERIOD	21–25 days
NUMBER OF BROODS	1 a year
TYPICAL DIET	Buds, shoots, leaves, fruit, berries; insects, worms, chicks, small mammals, carrion
LIFE SPAN	Up to 15 years

Like other Parrots, the large, noisy Kea eats both fruit and seeds. Unusually, though, it also eats carrion and refuse.

WHERE IN THE WORLD?

Today, the Kea is found only along the west coast of the South Island of New Zealand, where it lives on the mountain slopes in forests of southern beech.

CREATURE COMPARISONS

The Kea is a large powerful parrot. The head, neck, breast and belly are covered in large greenish feathers. The upper side of the wing is green and the large wing feathers have a bluish hue. The underside of the wing is brown or reddish-brown at the front, but grey at the rear. The tail is also grey. Females and males are similar.

Kea in flight

WINGS
With wings that are large and wide, the Kea is a powerful flyer and efficient glider.

BILL
The upper part of the bill is unusually long, and is often used for digging roots from the ground.

FEET
Two toes point forwards and two point backwards for efficient perching, but this makes walking on the ground awkward.

HOW BIG IS IT?

SPECIAL ADAPTATION

The New Zealand government used to pay a bounty for Kea bills, because the large, powerful birds were thought to prey on livestock, in particular lambs. The practice has now been stopped.

Crimson Rosella

• **ORDER** • Psittaciformes • **FAMILY** • Psittacidae • **SPECIES** • *Platycerus elegans*

VITAL STATISTICS

WEIGHT	120–135g (4.2–5oz)
LENGTH	32–36cm (12.6–14.2in)
WINGSPAN	25–30cm (10–12in)
NUMBER OF EGGS	4–8 (usually 5)
INCUBATION PERIOD	20–28 days
NUMBER OF BROODS	1 a year
TYPICAL DIET	Fruit, seeds, berries, nuts, nectar, insects
LIFE SPAN	Up to 20 years

There are five sub-species of Crimson Rosella, but only three are actually crimson.

WHERE IN THE WORLD?

The Crimson Rosella is found along the east and southeast coasts of Australia, Kangaroo Island and Tasmania. The appearance of the bird varies greatly depending on where it originates from.

CREATURE COMPARISONS

The Crimson Rosella is a medium-sized parrot that varies considerably in coloration. Often, the head and body are bright red, but the throat is blue. The wings have blue edges and are otherwise red with black markings. The long tail is blue above and pale blue underneath. Juveniles look very different, and are mostly olive-green. In some sub-species, the ground colour is yellow or yellowish-red instead of bright red.

Crimson Rosella

HEAD
A blue throat and cheeks are characteristic of all sub-species of Crimson Rosella.

WINGS
The wings of the Crimson Rosella are short and wide with long primary feathers, giving the bird a soft undulating flight pattern.

TAIL
The Crimson Rosella has a very long tail, often making up more than half the bird's entire length.

HOW BIG IS IT?

SPECIAL ADAPTATION

The Crimson Rosella has a powerful, curved beak and eats fruit and seeds. But, unlike many birds, this bird does not help spread seeds, because it crushes the seeds with its beak before eating them.

Rainbow Lorikeet

• **ORDER** • Psittaciformes • **FAMILY** • Psittacidae • **SPECIES** • *Trichoglossus haematodus*

Although the plumage of the Rainbow Lorikeet is dazzling, it does offer camouflage in the dense canopy. The plumage has also made this bird a popular pet.

VITAL STATISTICS

WEIGHT	140–160g (5–5.6oz)
LENGTH	26–32cm (10.2–12.6in)
WINGSPAN	40–55cm (15.7–21.7in)
NUMBER OF EGGS	2–3 eggs
INCUBATION PERIOD	24–27 days
NUMBER OF BROODS	1 a year
TYPICAL DIET	Mainly nectar and pollen; also fruits and insects
LIFE SPAN	Unknown but likely to be over 25 years

WHERE IN THE WORLD?

The Rainbow Lorikeet is found on Bali and the Molucca Islands, and on numerous other smaller islands; on Papua New Guinea; and eastern coastal areas of Australia.

CREATURE COMPARISONS

The medium-sized Rainbow Lorikeet is very colourful. The top of the head and back are bluish, while black and then yellow bands stretch across the neck. The breast is mottled brick-red and black, and the underside is greenish-black, except for the underside of the tail and upper part of the legs, which are mottled yellow and black. The tail is yellow. The male and female look similar.

New Guinea Sub-species (left) and Flores Island species (right)

BILL
The large bill is dark brown in juveniles, but becomes orange in adults. It is used to collect only soft foods.

FEET
The feet give a strong grip and are well adapted for perching on a branch high in the canopy.

TAIL
The lengthy tail is used both for display and for manoeuvring in the air.

HOW BIG IS IT?

SPECIAL ADAPTATION

The Rainbow Lorikeet feeds on nectar and pollen. It collects this with its tongue, which has a brush-like tip. The bird dips the tip of the tongue into a flower, where it sweeps up nectar like a broom.

Emperor Penguin

• ORDER • Sphenisciformes • FAMILY • Spheniscidae• SPECIES • *Aptenodytes forsteri*

VITAL STATISTICS

WEIGHT	22–37kg (48.5–81.6lb)
HEIGHT	122cm (48in)
SEXUAL MATURITY	3 years
LAYS EGGS	May–June
INCUBATION PERIOD	64 days
NUMBER OF EGGS	1 egg
NUMBER OF BROODS	1 a year
HABITS	Diurnal, non-migratory
TYPICAL DIET	Fish, crustaceans and cephalopods
LIFE SPAN	Typically 20 years

The tallest and the heaviest of all of the Penguins, this impressive Antarctic bird rightly deserves the title Emperor.

WHERE IN THE WORLD?

Emperor Penguins breed in the coldest environment tolerated by any bird: these remarkable birds make their home in the icy seas and oceans surrounding the South Pole.

CREATURE COMPARISONS

Newly hatched chicks are covered with only a thin layer of down. They rely entirely on their parents for food and warmth. For a young chick in the harsh Antarctic environment survival absolutely depends on keeping warm. This means they spend most of their time balanced on their parents' feet and sheltering in their brood patch.

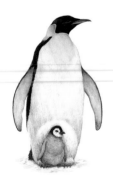

Emperor penguin with chick

BODY
Emperor Penguins have a layer of fat beneath the skin up to 3cm (1.2in) thick to help keep them warm.

FEATHERS
The Penguin's body is covered with lanceolate (spear-shaped) feathers. These are stiff and short and densely packed together, providing insulation against the cold.

FEET
The parents protect their chicks from the ice by balancing them on their feet, and shelter them from the cold in a brood pouch.

HOW BIG IS IT?

SPECIAL ADAPTATION

On land, Emperor Penguins may seem clumsy, even comical. However, they are perfectly adapted for swimming and hunting in the icy Antarctic waters. Their bodies are streamlined, like those of seals, and their stiff, paddle-shaped flippers are adapted to propel them though the water at speed.

King Penguin

• **ORDER** • Sphenisciformes • **FAMILY** • Spheniscidae • **SPECIES** • *Aptenodytes patagonicus*

VITAL STATISTICS

WEIGHT	11–16kg (24.2–35.2lb)
HEIGHT	90–95cm (35.4–37.4in)
NUMBER OF EGGS	1 egg
INCUBATION PERIOD	54–55 days
NUMBER OF BROODS	1 a year
TYPICAL DIET	Fish, squid, some krill and other crustaceans
LIFE SPAN	At least 15 years

The second-largest of all penguins, the King Penguin is perfectly adapted for life in the cold South Atlantic Ocean.

WHERE IN THE WORLD?

The King Penguin lives in the far south of the Atlantic, and breeds along the northern reaches of Antarctica, the Falkland Islands, South Georgia and several other islands within the Antarctic Circle.

CREATURE COMPARISONS

The King Penguin is one of the most impressive species of Penguin. Like many of its relatives, its back is bluish-black with a silvery hue, its breast and belly are uniformly white, and its wings are bluish-black above and pale underneath. The face is black, and the back of the head and the throat have bright yellow feathers. The males and female are similar, although the male is larger.

King Penguin chick

BODY
The streamlined body is adapted for fast swimming and manoeuvring underwater.

FEET
The legs are short and stout. The large webbed feet have strong claws that act as rudders when the bird swims.

BILL
The long pointed bill has a yellow streak along each side. Its shape is well adapted for catching fish.

WINGS
The wings have evolved into flippers, which are used for steering when swimming underwater.

HOW BIG IS IT?

SPECIAL ADAPTATION

Penguins use their wings in the water in the same way that other birds use their wings in the air. They gracefully slice through the water with extreme speed and suppleness. Their large webbed feet act as rudders in the water.

Adelie Penguin

• **ORDER** • Sphenisciformes • **FAMILY** • Spheniscidae • **SPECIES** • *Pygoscelis adeliae*

VITAL STATISTICS

WEIGHT	4–5.5kg (9–12lb)
LENGTH	50–70cm (19.7–27.6in)
HEIGHT	30–50cm (12–19.7in)
NUMBER OF EGGS	2
INCUBATION PERIOD	35–40 days
NUMBER OF BROODS	1 a year
TYPICAL DIET	Crustaceans, in particular krill; small fish
LIFE SPAN	Up to 20 years

The Adelie Penguin breeds on Antarctica and adjacent islands during the summer months, but spends the winter at sea.

WHERE IN THE WORLD?

The Adelie Penguin lives in the Ross Sea region in Antarctica. It is found on the Antarctic continent itself, and on many of the smaller islands in the Ross Sea.

CREATURE COMPARISONS

The Adelie Penguin is a medium-sized penguin, and like its relatives is coloured in a contrasting pattern of black and white. The head and the entire upper side are uniformly black or bluish-black, while the entire underside is uniformly white. The wings are black above but white underneath. The males and female are very similar.

Juvenile (left), adult (right)

HEAD
The jet-black head has a characteristic white ring around the eye, and often small white feathers at the base of the bill.

BILL
The Adelie penguin has a short stout bill that is well adapted for catching small fish and krill in the ice-cold Antarctic waters.

FEET
The Adelie Penguin has large webbed feet set far back on the body, which enable the bird to walk upright.

HOW BIG IS IT?

SPECIAL ADAPTATION

The Adelie Penguin is highly sociable. During the summer, it lives in large colonies, often numbering tens of thousands of birds. This offers each penguin protection from predators.

Gentoo Penguin

• ORDER • Sphenisciformes **• FAMILY •** Spheniscidae **• SPECIES •** *Pygoscelis papua*

VITAL STATISTICS

WEIGHT	5.5–8.5kg (12–18.7lb)
LENGTH	75–90cm (29.5–35.4in)
NUMBER OF EGGS	2
INCUBATION PERIOD	34–36 days
NUMBER OF BROODS	1 a year
TYPICAL DIET	Krill and other crustaceans; fish, squid
LIFE SPAN	Up to 20 years

The Gentoo Penguin builds its nest of stones, and males often obtain favours from females by offering them a choice stone.

WHERE IN THE WORLD?

The Gentoo Penguin breeds on Antarctica and many sub-Antarctic islands, including the Kerguelen Islands, South Georgia, the Heard Islands, South Shetland Islands, and on the Falkland Islands.

CREATURE COMPARISONS

The upper side of the body, wings and tail of the Gentoo Penguin are uniformly black, while the breast and belly are white. The underside of the wing is yellow. The Gentoo Penguin is easily distinguished from all other penguins by the bonnet of white feathers above the eyes. The female and male are similar, but the female is slightly smaller.

Gentoo Penguin swimming

HEAD
The jet-black head has a bonnet of bright white feathers above the eye.

BILL
The bill is black on top and yellow along the sides. It is well adapted for hunting fish and crutaceans.

FEET
The legs are short and set far back on the body. The webbed feet act as rudders during swimming.

HOW BIG IS IT?

SPECIAL ADAPTATION
A large penguin, the Gentoo Penguin is clumsy on land but in the water it is a powerful swimmer. It is the fastest of all penguins and can reach speeds of up to 36km/h (22 mph) underwater.

Galapagos Penguin

• ORDER • Sphenisciformes **• FAMILY •** Spheniscidae **• SPECIES •** *Spheniscus mendiculus*

VITAL STATISTICS

WEIGHT	2.5kg (5.5lb)
HEIGHT	48–53cm (19–21in)
SEXUAL MATURITY	Males: 4–6 years Females: 3–4 years
LAYS EGGS	Breeding season is year long, but most activity happens from May–January
INCUBATION PERIOD	38–42 days
FLEDGLING PERIOD	60–65 days
NUMBER OF EGGS	2 eggs
NUMBER OF BROODS	Up to 3 times a year is possible
TYPICAL DIET	Fish
LIFE SPAN	Typically 17 years

Other Penguins may spend their lives huddled together on freezing pack ice to stay warm, but Galapagos Penguins have to work hard to keep cool.

WHERE IN THE WORLD?

Penguins are usually found in the Southern Hemisphere, but Galapagos Penguins inhabit the Galapagos Islands, which lie across the equator. Most live on the larger islands of Fernandina and Isabella.

CREATURE COMPARISONS

Adult male and female Galapagos Penguins look so much alike that bird-watchers can distinguish them only by watching the body language. Fortunately, juveniles are much easier to identify because they have grey rather than black upper parts and lack the white face markings.

Juvenile

BILL
The long bill enables the bird to get a good grip on wet, slippery and fast-moving fish.

WINGS
Galapagos Penguins have stubby residual wings. These are useless for flying but have evolved to make superb paddles.

TAIL
Penguins stand upright and use their short tail and flippers to help them to maintain their balance on land.

HOW BIG IS IT?

SPECIAL ADAPTATION
To stay cool, Galapagos Penguins spread their flippers and lift up their feet in order to increase heat loss. When Charles Darwin (1809–82) visited the Galapagos, he noticed how other species had developed similar adaptations to survive the islands' unique environment, which inspired his theory of evolution.

Tengmalm's Owl

VITAL STATISTICS

WEIGHT	93–215g (3.3–7.6oz)
LENGTH	22–27cm (36.6–10.6in)
WINGSPAN	50–62cm (19.7–24.4in)
SEXUAL MATURITY	9 months
INCUBATION PERIOD	25–32 days
FLEDGLING PERIOD	28–36 days
NUMBER OF EGGS	3–7 eggs
NUMBER OF BROODS	1 a year; more are possible if food is plentiful
TYPICAL DIET	Small mammals, especially voles and mice
LIFE SPAN	Typically 11 years

CREATURE COMPARISONS

In the case of birds of prey, the female of the species is usually bigger than the male. This is certainly true of the female Tengmalm's Owl. Both sexes closely resemble each other, but the female is around one-and-a-half times the male's weight.

Tengmalm's Owl

Tengmalm's Owl, a medium-sized, chocolate-brown owl, takes its unusual name from Peter Gustaf Tengmalm (1754–1803), the Swedish naturalist who first identified the species.

WHERE IN THE WORLD?

Tengmalm's Owl is found in mountainous boreal forests, hence its other name, Boreal Owl. In North America, it ranges from Alaska to eastern Canada; in Europe, from Scandinavia to Siberia.

EYES
The eyes of this hunting bird point forwards, giving it binocular vision and enabling it to judge distances more accurately.

BODY
Tengmalm's Owls are larger than Pygmy Owls but the two are often confused because they share the same range and habits.

FEET
Tengmalm's Owl has large claws with which to grab on to prey.

HOW BIG IS IT?

SPECIAL ADAPTATION

Tengmalm's Owl has superb eyesight. However, because it hunts at night, and often under difficult conditions, it relies on its hearing to pinpoint the location of prey. This is possible because the Owl's ears are positioned to help them to judge distance more effectively.

Short-eared Owl

• **ORDER** • Strigiformes • **FAMILY** • Strigidae • **SPECIES** • *Asio flammeus*

VITAL STATISTICS

WEIGHT	260–350g (9.2–12.3oz)
LENGTH	26–40cm (10.2–15.7in)
WINGSPAN	90–105cm (35.4–41.3in)
NUMBER OF EGGS	4–8
INCUBATION PERIOD	24–29 days
NUMBER OF BROODS	1 a year
TYPICAL DIET	Rodents, in particular voles; frogs, lizards
LIFE SPAN	Up to 15 years

The Short-eared Owl often emits a series of deep 'po-po-po' sounds while flying, but hunts in complete silence.

WHERE IN THE WORLD?

The Short-eared Owl is found in northern Europe, and across most of eastern and Central Asia and into northern regions of North America. It is also found in parts of South America.

CREATURE COMPARISONS

The Short-eared Owl is a fairly small and elongate species of owl. The neck, back and upper part of the wings are mottled off-white or beige and buff or reddish-brown. The throat and upper breast are buff with faint dark streaks, while the rest of the breast and belly are paler, with fewer dark streaks. The face is wide and flat. The eyes are a distinctive shade of yellow.

HEAD
The pattern of the head feathers above the eyes give the bird an angry expression. The two ear tufts are raised when the owl is attentive.

WINGS
The wings are very long and narrow for an owl, and have special soft plumes, giving the Short-eared Owl an almost silent flight.

LEGS
The legs are short, but the feet are large and powerful, and armed with sharp talons for killing prey.

Short-eared Owl in flight

HOW BIG IS IT?

SPECIAL ADAPTATION
Although the Short-eared Owl usually lays about six eggs, it can lay more than a dozen if prey is plentiful, enabling it to raise many chicks when conditions are favourable.

Long-eared Owl

Unlike many other Owls, the sizable, arresting-looking Long-eared Owl often hunts in complete darkness.

VITAL STATISTICS

WEIGHT	200–500g (7–17.6oz)
LENGTH	31–37cm (12.2–14.6in)
WINGSPAN	86–98cm (34–38.6in)
NUMBER OF EGGS	1–6 eggs (usually 3–5)
INCUBATION PERIOD	20–30 days
NUMBER OF BROODS	1 a year but occasionally 2
TYPICAL DIET	Small rodents, especially voles and lemmings.
LIFE SPAN	Up to 28 years

WHERE IN THE WORLD?

The Long-eared Owl is widely distributed across southern Canada and the northern regions of the USA; large parts of Europe, except the high north; and across Central Asia to the Sea of Okhotsk.

CREATURE COMPARISONS

The Long-eared Owl is tall and slender and has orange-yellow eyes. The back is mottled brownish, and the underside is lighter brownish-grey, and looks like the bark of a large tree. The wings are rather slender for a large Owl, and lack a white stripe along the trailing edge. It is sometimes confused with the Short-eared Owl, which is similar in size but has smaller ear tufts.

Long-eared Owl in flight

HEAD
The Long-eared Owl has two large tufts of feathers above its ears. These are raised when it is attentive, but are otherwise kept hidden.

WINGS
The back edges of the large primary feathers are softened to give the Long-eared Owl a silent flight.

FEET
The large powerful feet are equipped with big sharp talons for stabbing small prey to death instantly.

HOW BIG IS IT?

SPECIAL ADAPTATION

If disturbed near the nest, the owl tries to blend in with the tree trunk by sitting erect and very still. It has a deep, soft, booming voice, which is most often heard at the beginning of the breeding season in March–April.

Burrowing Owl

• **ORDER** • Strigiformes • **FAMILY** • Strigidae • **SPECIES** • *Athene cunicularia*

VITAL STATISTICS

WEIGHT	1.5kg (3.3lb)
LENGTH	52–60cm (20.5–23.6in)
WINGSPAN	1.5–1.7m (5–5.6ft)
SEXUAL MATURITY	1 year
LAYS EGGS	April
INCUBATION PERIOD	21–28 days
FLEDGLING PERIOD	About 28 days
NUMBER OF EGGS	3–5 eggs
NUMBER OF BROODS	1 a year
TYPICAL DIET	Small mammals, birds and insects, especially beetles
LIFE SPAN	Up to 9 years

CREATURE COMPARISONS

Male and female Burrowing Owls are similar in size and coloration, although some males may be slightly paler. However, juveniles (see illustration below) have quite different plumage. They lack both the characteristic white mottling on their upper parts and the brown bars on their underparts.

Juvenile

Strange as it may seem, the small Burrowing Owl spends most of its life underground in specially excavated burrows.

WHERE IN THE WORLD?

The Burrowing Owl is found in southwestern Canada, western USA and the drier regions of Central and South America. It roosts in the burrows of grassland and desert animals, such as prairie dogs.

EYES
The eyes of the Burrowing Owl point forwards, giving the bird binocular vision. This allows it to judge distances more accurately.

HEAD
Forwards-facing eyes offer a limited field of vision. To compensate for this Burrowing Owls can rotate their head in a wide arc.

FEET
The Burrowing Owl uses its talons to capture prey and excavate burrows.

HOW BIG IS IT?

SPECIAL ADAPTATION

Most Owls have short legs and talons designed to grasp prey. However, Burrowing Owls have long legs and long-toed feet. These are perfectly designed for excavating burrows. A short, fur-like down covers the legs instead of feathers, which would easily get clogged with dirt.

Little Owl

• ORDER • Strigiformes • **FAMILY** •Strigidae • **SPECIES** • *Athene noctua*

The Little Owl is quite common in many places, and unlike most owls, is often active during the day.

VITAL STATISTICS

WEIGHT	200–300g (7–10.6oz)
LENGTH	23–28cm (9–11in)
WINGSPAN	50–57cm (19.7–22.4in)
NUMBER OF EGGS	3–5
INCUBATION PERIOD	26–29 days
NUMBER OF BROODS	1 a year
TYPICAL DIET	Large insects, worms, spiders, amphibians, rodents and small birds
LIFE SPAN	Up to 15 years

WHERE IN THE WORLD?

The Little Owl is widely distributed throughout much of Europe, but is absent in most of Scandinavia. It is found throughout Central Asia, the Middle East and into northern Africa.

CREATURE COMPARISONS

The upper side is light brown with white spots and bars along the wings. The underside is pale whitish with brown stripes. The eyes are handsomely bright yellow and the broad flat face has wide whitish eyebrows, giving it a characteristically angry appearance. Birds from open country tend to be paler than forest-dwelling birds. Males and females are similar.

Paler Little Owl from a desert habitat.

BILL
The short hooked bill is equipped with long touch-sensitive bristles around the base.

TAIL
The short stumpy tail is very wide and is often fanned out during aerial manoeuvring and landing.

FEET
The feet are big and powerful with large sharp talons for killing prey. The legs are short and stout.

HOW BIG IS IT?

SPECIAL ADAPTATION

The Little Owl often rests in trees in full view. If disturbed, it will bob its head up and down to assess its precise distance away from the intruder, and will flee if the intruder comes too close.

Eurasian Eagle Owl

• ORDER • Strigiformes **• FAMILY •** Strigidae **• SPECIES •** *Bubo bubo*

VITAL STATISTICS

WEIGHT	1600–4200g (56.4–148oz)
LENGTH	58–71cm (22.8–28in)
WINGSPAN	150–190cm (59–75in)
NUMBER OF EGGS	1–4 (usually 2–3)
INCUBATION PERIOD	31–36 days
NUMBER OF BROODS	1 a year
TYPICAL DIET	Rodents, hares, foxes, fawns, birds, snakes, lizards, frogs, fish
LIFE SPAN	Up to 60 years

The Eurasian Eagle Owl is one of the most massive and robust of all owls, and even been known to prey on fawns.

WHERE IN THE WORLD?

The Eurasian Eagle Owl is found across a large area in eastern and southern Europe, across Central Asia, and into parts of North Africa and the Middle East.

CREATURE COMPARISONS

The upper back, neck and upper part of the wings are tawny or brown with a pattern of dark brown spots and bars. The head and upper part of the neck are tawny or buff with darker stripes. The breast and belly are also buff or brown, with distinctive bark stripes. Females look similar to males but are larger and considerably heavier.

Eurasian Eagle Owl

HEAD
The Eurasian Eagle Owl has two large tufts on top of the head, which are raised when the owl is inquisitive or frightened.

WINGS
The Eurasian Eagle Owl has huge wide wings, which give it a powerful yet silent flight when hunting.

FEET
The large feet are extremely strong, enabling the Eurasian Eagle Owl to kill foxes and even deer fawns with its large, black talons.

HOW BIG IS IT?

SPECIAL ADAPTATION

The Eurasian Eagle Owl usually builds its nest on cliff ledges or in rock crevices, which are hard for predators to reach. If these are not available, it may nest between rocks and boulders on the ground.

Snowy Owl

• **ORDER** • Strigiformes • **FAMILY** • Strigidae • **SPECIES** • *Bubo scandiacus*

The voluminous and angelic Snowy Owl is also known as the Arctic Owl or Great White Owl, and is well adapted for life in the high north.

VITAL STATISTICS

WEIGHT	1.7–3kg (3.7–7lb)
LENGTH	53–65cm (21–25.6in)
WINGSPAN	125–150cm (49.2–59in)
NUMBER OF EGGS	5–14 eggs (usually 7–9)
INCUBATION PERIOD	32–34 days
NUMBER OF BROODS	1 a year
TYPICAL DIET	Rodents, especially lemmings, voles, ptarmigans
LIFE SPAN	Up to 30 years

WHERE IN THE WORLD?

The Snowy Owl is found in northern Scandinavia, across northern Russia and northern Canada. Many fly south for the winter, and have even been recorded as far south as the Caribbean.

CREATURE COMPARISONS

The male is truly snowy, having plumage that is almost entirely white, with only faint mottling of off-white or greyish-white. Females are also white, but have more distinctive darker spots and bars along the wings, back, breast and belly. The tail is quite large for an owl, and is wide and fan-shaped. Juvenile birds are more greyish with distinctive back bars.

Male Snowy Owl (left) and female (right)

HEAD
The Snowy Owl has a wide flat face, and two prominently yellow staring eyes capable of detecting prey in the dark.

BILL
The bill is short and powerful. The strongly hooked upper bill is adapted for tearing into flesh.

FEET
The Snowy Owl has large powerful feet armed with sharp talons. The feet are covered in white feathers as protection from cold.

HOW BIG IS IT?

SPECIAL ADAPTATION

The Snowy Owl is often found in barren areas, where it builds its nest on the ground. It often constructs its nest on top of a mound or boulder to gain good visibility of its surroundings.

Great Horned Owl

• **ORDER** • Strigiformes • **FAMILY** • Strigidae • **SPECIES** • *Bubo virginianus*

VITAL STATISTICS

WEIGHT	900–2500g (31.7–91.7oz)
LENGTH	46–68cm (18–27in)
WINGSPAN	100–155cm (39.4–61in)
NUMBER OF EGGS	1–5 (usually 2)
INCUBATION PERIOD	30–37days
NUMBER OF BROODS	1 a year
TYPICAL DIET	Rats, voles, squirrels, marmots, weasels, skunks; a variety of birds, including other birds of prey
LIFE SPAN	20–30 years

The huge and commanding Great Horned Owl will even kill and consume other birds of prey.

WHERE IN THE WORLD?

The Great Horned Owl is widely distributed throughout North and South America. It lives in a wide range of habitats, from tundras to rainforests, and may also be found in urban areas.

CREATURE COMPARISONS

The Great Horned Owl has a mottled brown upper side, and mottled, lighter grey-brown underside. The head is large and round, and usually reddish-brown with large yellow eyes. The legs and feet are almost completely covered in grey-brown feathers. The females is usually larger than the male. The largest Great Horned Owls are usually found in the northern parts of the range.

Great Horned Owl in flight

EYES
The large eyes face forwards, giving the bird excellent night vision and depth perception.

HEAD
The Great Horned Owl has two large tufts of feathers above its ears. These are used as display signals to other owls and have no role in hearing.

FEET
The enormously powerful feet are equipped with large talons for killing prey. Each foot has a crushing power of several hundred pounds.

HOW BIG IS IT?

SPECIAL ADAPTATION

Like its relatives, the Great Horned Owl has a smooth, disc-like area surrounding each eye. This is made up of specialized feathers that form a smooth surface for transmitting faint noises to the owl's ears, enabling it to pinpoint the direction the sound is coming from.

Eastern Screech Owl

• **ORDER** • Strigiformes • **FAMILY** • Strigidae • **SPECIES** • *Megascops asio*

The tiny Eastern Screech Owl has piercing yellow eyes and prominent ear tufts. It is the most strictly nocturnal of all North American owls.

VITAL STATISTICS

WEIGHT	130–180 g (4.6–6.3oz)
LENGTH	16–25cm (6.3–10in)
WINGSPAN	30–38cm (12–15in)
NUMBER OF EGGS	2–7 (usually 3–4)
INCUBATION PERIOD	26–34 days
NUMBER OF BROODS	1 a year
TYPICAL DIET	Large insects, crayfish, worms, small reptiles, amphibians, rodents
LIFE SPAN	Unknown

WHERE IN THE WORLD?

The Eastern Screech Owl is widely distributed in large parts of eastern North America, and is found from Florida to southern Canada. Birds vary in colour depending on where they come from.

CREATURE COMPARISONS

The Eastern Screech Owl has a camouflaged plumage with many bars, stripes and patterns, but the background colour of the plumage varies. It may be dark greyish to mouse-grey, but some populations are rusty. The underside has distinctive dark stripes. The wings are also mottled greyish or brownish. A pale grey form lives in western Canada.

Eastern Screech Owls

HEAD
The large head has a very square flat face. There are two distinctive tufts above its ears.

WINGS
The Eastern Screech Owl has large wide wings for its size, and special soft feathers that give it a silent flight.

TAIL
The Eastern Screech Owl has a short wide tail, which is important for manoeuvring in flight through wooded areas.

HOW BIG IS IT?

SPECIAL ADAPTATION

The Eastern Screech Owl relies on its camouflage plumage as a defence against predators. It often perches in trees, and if disturbed will sit motionless to blend into the background.

417

Elf Owl

• **ORDER** • Strigiformes • **FAMILY** • Strigidae • **SPECIES** •*Micrathene whitneyi*

VITAL STATISTICS

WEIGHT	35–55g (1.2–2oz)
LENGTH	12.4–14.2cm (5–5.6in)
SEXUAL MATURITY	1 year
INCUBATION PERIOD	24 days
FLEDGLING PERIOD	28–33 days
NUMBER OF EGGS	1–5 eggs
NUMBER OF BROODS	1 a year, but will replace a lost brood
CALL	Male makes repeated yelps
HABITS	Nocturnal, non-migratory, but may move north in summer
TYPICAL DIET	Fish; some small mammals, amphibians and reptiles
LIFE SPAN	Typically 5 years

The Elf Owl may be no bigger than a sparrow, but from its rounded head to its hooked claws it is every inch an owl.

WHERE IN THE WORLD?

The Elf Owl often makes its home in the stem of a giant desert cactus. Populations are also found in woodlands, and even urban areas of the southwestern USA and into northern Mexico.

`CREATURE COMPARISONS

Elf Owls are the second-smallest species of owl. As the name suggests, the smallest are Pygmy Owls, which belong to the same Order and Family as Elf Owls, but a different genus, called *Glaucidium*. No one knows exactly how many species of Pygmy Owl exist.

Elf Owls

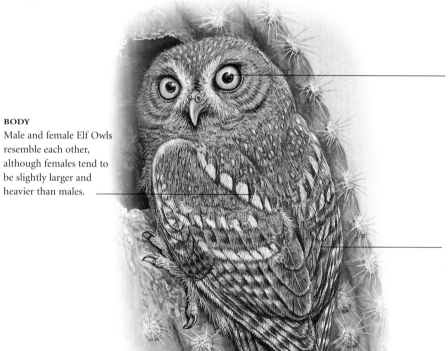

BODY
Male and female Elf Owls resemble each other, although females tend to be slightly larger and heavier than males.

EYES
Like all nocturnal hunters, the Elf Owl relies on its superb eyesight to track down and catch prey.

BODY
Elf Owls have mottled greyish-brown plumage, a greenish bill and feet that are tan to yellow in colour.

HOW BIG IS IT?

SPECIAL ADAPTATION

Because it hunts other birds and small mammals, the Pygmy Owl (top left) has adapted stronger feet and sharper bills than its American cousin. The Elf Owl (bottom left) has no need for strong talons or a flesh-tearing bill because it hunts only insects.

Boobook Owl

• ORDER • Strigiformes **• FAMILY •** Strigidae **• SPECIES •** *Ninox boobook*

VITAL STATISTICS

WEIGHT	194–360g (7–12.7oz)
LENGTH	23–36cm (9–14.2in)
WINGSPAN	70–85cm (27.6–33.5in)
NUMBER OF EGGS	2–5 (usually 2–3)
INCUBATION PERIOD	30–35 days
NUMBER OF BROODS	1 a year
TYPICAL DIET	Rodents, especially mice; small birds, large flying insects
LIFE SPAN	Unknown

It was once believed that there was only one species of Boobook Owl, but ornithologists now recognize that there are two.

WHERE IN THE WORLD?

The Boobook Owl is found across virtually all of the Australian continent, and also Tasmania, New Zealand, the Lesser Sunda Islands, Timor Island and parts of New Guinea.

CREATURE COMPARISONS

The upper part of the head, neck and back are light to dark brown, depending on where the animal originates from. There are many small white spots across the back and wings. The throat, breast and belly are buff or cream-coloured with dark brown streaks and mottling. Males and females are similar, but females are larger and more richly coloured.

HEAD
The Boobook Owl has a dark face mask and large yellow eyes for seeing in the dark.

WINGS
The large broad wings have specialized soft plumes, giving the owl a powerful but almost silent flight.

FEET
The yellow legs end in powerful toes equipped with large black talons for stabbing and crushing prey.

Boobook Owl in flight

HOW BIG IS IT?

SPECIAL ADAPTATION

The Boobook Owl has a variety of calls. One is a hoot, repeated every few seconds. Another is a soft 'pot-pot' between mated pairs. The male also has a loud, tremulous breeding call.

419

White-faced Scops Owl

• **ORDER** • Strigiformes • **FAMILY** • Strigidae • **SPECIES** • *Otus leucotis*

VITAL STATISTICS

WEIGHT	80–170g (3–6oz)
LENGTH	18–24cm (10.2–12.6in)
WINGSPAN	35–45cm (15.7–21.7in)
NUMBER OF EGGS	1–2 eggs (usually 2–3)
INCUBATION PERIOD	26–30 days
NUMBER OF BROODS	1–3 a year
TYPICAL DIET	Rodents, small birds, lizards, amphibians; large insects, scorpions, and spiders
LIFE SPAN	Unknown

This White-Faced Owl belongs to a group of over 60 species of owls collectively known as Scops Owls.

WHERE IN THE WORLD?

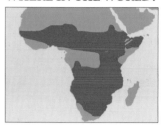

The White-faced Scops Owl is found in large parts of Africa south of the Sahara desert. It lives in a wide range of habitats, but it is usually absent from dense rainforests.

CREATURE COMPARISONS

The small White-faced Scops Owl has an attractive plumage of mottled greyish and reddish-brown colour. The face is wide and white, and is edged in black or dark brown. The large eyes are an intense shade of orange. The legs are covered in short greyish or light brown feathers all the way to the feet. On top of the head are two large feather tufts. Males and females are similar.

White-faced Scops Owl in flight

HEAD
The large head has two large tufts of feathers, which are used to convey the owl's mood.

WINGS
Large wide wings with soft feathers allow the White-faced Scops Owl to fly swiftly and silently.

LEGS
The feet are rather small for an owl of this size, but they are powerful and there are piercing talons on the toes.

HOW BIG IS IT?

SPECIAL ADAPTATION
The White-faced Scops Owl often hides from predators in trees by raising its body into an elongated shape and closing the eyes, relying on its mottled plumage to provide camouflage against the bark.

Pel's Fishing Owl

• **ORDER** • Strigiformes • **FAMILY** • Strigidae • **SPECIES** • *Scotopelia peli*

VITAL STATISTICS

WEIGHT	2–2.5kg (4.4–5.5lb)
LENGTH	55–63cm (21.7–25in)
WINGSPAN	120–145cm (47.2–57in)
NUMBER OF EGGS	2
INCUBATION PERIOD	30–35 days
NUMBER OF BROODS	1 a year
TYPICAL DIET	Fish, amphibians, snakes
LIFE SPAN	Up to 25 years

Ample and energetic, Pel's Fishing Owl specializes in hunting fish, which it snatches from the surface of the water.

WHERE IN THE WORLD?

Pel's Fishing Owl is distributed in many countries throughout Central Africa and parts of eastern Africa, extending all the way to northeastern South Africa.

CREATURE COMPARISONS

Pel's Fishing Owl is a large species of owl. The plumage is brownish-grey or brownish, and many of the large body feathers have distinctive dark markings and dark tips. The upper side is more reddish-brown with distinctive dark markings, and the wings are reddish or yellowish-brown, also with dark markings. The tail is dark brown.

Pel's Fishing Owl

BILL
The large heavily curved bill is adapted for tearing into large fish.

WINGS
The lengthy wide wings have soft flight feathers that enable the owl to fly in silence.

FEET
The legs are fairly long for an owl. The lower part are naked, so the bird does not become waterlogged while fishing.

HOW BIG IS IT?

SPECIAL ADAPTATION

Because of its unusual diet, Pel's Fishing Owl rarely lives far from the water. It prefers to nest in a tree with large branches hanging out over the water, from which it swoops down to catch fish.

Tawny Owl

• **ORDER** • Strigiformes • **FAMILY** • Strigidae • **SPECIES** • *Strix aluco*

VITAL STATISTICS

WEIGHT	450–550g (16–19.4oz)
LENGTH	37–43cm (14.6–17in)
WINGSPAN	81–96cm (32–38in)
NUMBER OF EGGS	1–8 (usually 2–4)
INCUBATION PERIOD	28–30 days
NUMBER OF BROODS	1 a year
TYPICAL DIET	Mainly field voles and mice; also rats, shrews, amphibians, small birds, earthworms, and large insects
LIFE SPAN	Up to 20 years

The hefty, handsome Tawny Owl is common in many European countries, although it is rarely seen.

WHERE IN THE WORLD?

The Tawny Owl is the most common European owl, although it is absent from Ireland and the high north. It is also found in northern Africa, across central Russia, in China and parts of the Middle East.

CREATURE COMPARISONS

The upper side and wings are greyish or reddish brown with dark and white bars on the wings, and a mottled pattern on many of the feathers. The tail is of a similar colour, and has pale and dark bands. The underside is paler, and has numerous longitudinal dark interrupted stripes. The sexes are similar. In flight, it can be mistaken for the Long-Eared owl, which is larger.

Tawny Owl in flight

HEAD
The head of the Tawny Owl is characteristically large and round. Saucer-like dark eyes give it a friendly-looking face.

WINGS
Large, broad wings and wing feathers with softer plumage allow for a swift and silent approach from the air.

LEGS
Long legs and strong feet armed with sharp talons enable the Tawny Owl to kill smaller prey animals with ease.

HOW BIG IS IT?

SPECIAL ADAPTATION

The Tawny Owl is normally a secretive nocturnal hunter, but it is notorious for being aggressive during the breeding season. It is not uncommon for a Tawny Owl to attack humans who venture too near its nest.

Spotted Owl

• ORDER • Strigiformes **• FAMILY •** Strigidae **• SPECIES •** *Strix occidentalis*

VITAL STATISTICS

WEIGHT	600–800g (21.2–28.2oz)
LENGTH	41–46cm (16–18in)
WINGSPAN	112–120cm (44–47.2in)
NUMBER OF EGGS	1–4 (usually 2)
INCUBATION PERIOD	27–30 days
NUMBER OF BROODS	1 a year
TYPICAL DIET	Rodents, also reptiles, amphibians, birds, large insects
LIFE SPAN	Up to 15 years

The Spotted Owl nests impressively high up in trees, sometimes in places as much as 60m (197ft) above the ground.

WHERE IN THE WORLD?

The Spotted Owl is found along western North America, from southern British Columbia through Washington, Oregon, California and into northern Mexico.

CREATURE COMPARISONS

The upper side of the head, neck and body are buff or pale brown, with a variety of pale or white spots, bars and other markings. There are distinctive brown bars across the wings. The breast and belly are pale or almost white with a mesh of pale to dark brown patterns. The female is similar to the male, but is usually slightly larger.

Spotted Owl in flight

HEAD
The head of the Spotted Owl is large and round, and has a buff or pale face-mask and dark brown eyes.

TAIL
The short wide tail is used for steering and manoeuvring. Soft plumage enables it to fly silently.

LEGS
The legs are fairly long, and the feet are powerful and armed with sharp talons for killing prey.

HOW BIG IS IT?

SPECIAL ADAPTATION
Like most owls, the Spotted Owl has feathers that allow it to fly almost silently. This enables the owl to listen out for prey without being disturbed by the sound of its own beating wings.

Ural Owl

• ORDER • Strigiformes **• FAMILY •** Strigidae **SPECIES •** *Strix uralensis*

VITAL STATISTICS

WEIGHT	550–1200g (19.4–42.3oz)
LENGTH	50–60cm (19.7–23.6in)
WINGSPAN	110–130cm (43.3–51.2in)
NUMBER OF EGGS	2–4
INCUBATION PERIOD	27–34 days
NUMBER OF BROODS	1 a year
TYPICAL DIET	Rodents, especially mice; rabbits, birds, frogs
LIFE SPAN	Up to 15 years

Biologists have estimated that a single pair of Ural Owls may consume over 4000 mice each year.

WHERE IN THE WORLD?

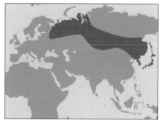

The Ural Owl is present in parts of northern and eastern Europe, but is mainly found across northern and Central Asia, extending eastwards and southwards to Japan and North and South Korea.

CREATURE COMPARISONS

The Ural Owl superficially resembles a Tawny Owl but is much bigger. The plumage is mottled brown and off-white or white, with dark streaks along the back. The wings are also mottled brown and white, but are pale below. The underside is whitish with dark streaks. Males and females are similar, but females are slightly larger.

Ural owl

HEAD
The wide flat face-mask and the intensely yellow eyes give this owl a characteristic stare.

BEAK
The beak is short and stout. The upper beak is markedly hooked and is well adapted for tearing into the flesh of prey.

TAIL
The lengthy wide tail is important for manoeuvring when flying at night in the forest.

HOW BIG IS IT?

SPECIAL ADAPTATION
If disturbed the Ural Owl sits completely still. If this tactic fails, it often tries to scare off its enemies by spreading its wings to look large and threatening.

Barn Owl

VITAL STATISTICS

WEIGHT	300g (10.6oz)
LENGTH	33–39cm (13–15.3in)
WINGSPAN	80–95cm (31.5–37.4in)
SEXUAL MATURITY	1 year
NUMBER OF EGGS	3–5 eggs
INCUBATION PERIOD	14–18 days
NUMBER OF BROODS	Often 2 a year
TYPICAL DIET	Small mammals, especially voles; occasionally birds
LIFE SPAN	Typically 3 years

With its pale face, dark eyes and unearthly shrieks, the Barn Owl is responsible for its share of countryside ghost stories.

WHERE IN THE WORLD?

The Barn Owl is found in Europe, southern Asia, Africa, Australia and the Americas. It makes its home wherever there are suitable buildings, for example, in country church yards, ruins or farms.

CREATURE COMPARISONS

The plumage of the Tawny Owl varies across its range. In western and southern Europe, North Africa and the Middle East, it tends to have grey or ochre upper parts and almost pure white underparts. In the rest of Europe, the underparts are often orange-brown.

Species with brown underparts

EARS
One of the Barn Owl's ears is higher than the other, which enables the bird to locate its prey more accurately.

BODY
The Barn Owl is a nocturnal hunter. In the darkness, it is the Barn Owl's white face and underparts that are most likely to be visible.

FEET
The Barn Owl captures its prey with its large talons.

HOW BIG IS IT?

SPECIAL ADAPTATION

Many birds have eyes on the side of their head, offering a wide field of vision and enabling them to spot danger more easily. The eyes of hunters, however, point forwards. This binocular vision allows them to compare images from both eyes and so judge distances better.

425

Southern Cassowary

• **ORDER** • Struthioniformes • **FAMILY** • Casuariidae • **SPECIES** • *Casuarius casuariusitalic*

VITAL STATISTICS

WEIGHT	Males: 40kg (88.2lb) Females: 85kg (187lb)
HEIGHT	2m (6.6ft)
LAYS EGGS	June–October
SEXUAL MATURITY	Around 2 years
INCUBATION PERIOD	49–61 days
NUMBER OF EGGS	3–5 eggs per mate
NUMBER OF BROODS	1 per mate, but females have several partners
HABITS	Diurnal, non-migratory
TYPICAL DIET	Fish; some small mammals, amphibians and reptiles
LIFE SPAN	Up to 40 years in captivity

CREATURE COMPARISONS

Flightless birds are not unusual. In fact, Australasia is home to several famous examples of such birds, including the Emu and the Kiwi. Like their flightless relatives, Cassowaries have replaced wing power with leg power and can run up to 50km/h (31mph).

Southern Cassowary

The female Southern Cassowary has solved the problem of how to raise a family by getting the male to do the job.

WHERE IN THE WORLD?

The Southern Cassowary lives in tropical rainforests on the islands of Indonesia and Papua New Guinea, and in northeastern regions of Australia, from Mount Halifax to Cooktown, and the Cape York Peninsula.

HEAD
Cassowaries have a tall, brown helmet-like casque on top of their head and a pair of vivid red, fleshy wattles on the neck.

BODY
The Southern Cassowary is the second-heaviest bird on Earth. Females are almost twice as heavy as the males.

WINGS
These huge birds are flightless, so they do not need flight feathers. Their long black plumage is more like fur.

HOW BIG IS IT?

SPECIAL ADAPTATION

Birds that cannot fly develop powerful legs. In fact, the Cassowary is one of the few birds that is dangerous to people. Its can deliver bone-breaking kicks with its legs, while the elongated claws can rip flesh open with ease.

Emu

The continent of Australia has its fair share of curious-looking birds, but the Emu is perhaps the most bizarre of them all.

VITAL STATISTICS

WEIGHT	30–60kg (66–132.3ft)
LENGTH	2m (3.3ft)
HEIGHT	1.8m (6ft)
SEXUAL MATURITY	2–3 year
LAYS EGGS	May–June
NUMBER OF EGGS	5–15 eggs
INCUBATION PERIOD	52–60 days
NUMBER OF BROODS	Usually 1 but more if the female mates with more than one male
TYPICAL DIET	Plants, fruit, seeds, insects
LIFE SPAN	Between 10–20 years

WHERE IN THE WORLD?

Emus are found in most parts of Australia, although fewer numbers live in drier regions. These birds are solitary by nature, but occasionally large flocks form to follow known sources of food.

CREATURE COMPARISONS

It is the male Emu that has the mothering instinct. Although newly hatched Emus are independent within a few days of being born, the males stay with them for almost 18 months, teaching them how to forage for food and look after themselves.

Juvenile

LOWER BODY
The pelvic muscles of the Emu weigh as much, in terms of total body mass, as the flight muscles of flying birds.

WINGS
The Emu cannot fly and has only tiny residual wings. However, it is so swift on its feet that it can normally outrun predators.

FEET
The Emu has only three toes. This is a common adaptation for birds who spend their time walking and running.

HOW BIG IS IT?

SPECIAL ADAPTATION
To stay cool in the baking Australian summer, the Emu has loose, hair-like feathers that allow heat to escape more quickly than conventionally shaped feathers. By lifting its wings, it exposes a network of veins close to the skin, and this also helps it to cool down.

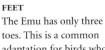

Greater Rhea

• **ORDER** • Struthioniformes • **FAMILY** • Rheidae • **SPECIES** • *Rhea americana*

VITAL STATISTICS

WEIGHT	20kg (50.6lb)
HEIGHT	1.4m (4.6ft)
SEXUAL MATURITY	2 years
LAYS EGGS	August–January, depending on location
INCUBATION PERIOD	35–40 days
NUMBER OF EGGS	Up to 60 eggs
NUMBER OF BROODS	Males court up to 12 females, who all lay eggs in his nest. He incubates up to 60 eggs at a time.
HABITS	Diurnal, non-migratory
TYPICAL DIET	Plants; small insects and reptiles
LIFE SPAN	Up to 40 years

The Greater Rhea is Latin America's version of the Ostrich. It may not be as big as its African counterpart, but it is just as feisty.

WHERE IN THE WORLD?

The Greater Rhea prefers habitat with tall vegetation, such as pampas grass, close to sources of water. It is native to Latin America, but a small population escaped from a farm to establish itself in Germany.

CREATURE COMPARISONS

It is the male Greater Rhea that builds the nest, incubates the eggs and raises the young. The female (shown) moves from male to male during the breeding season, leaving the slightly larger male to defend the brood, which it does with vigour.

Female

NECK
The Greater Rhea sweeps the ground with its long flexible neck in search of both plants and animals to eat.

BODY
Populations of the wild Greater Rhea are declining. However, the bird is now farmed commercially because of the value of its meat, feathers and eggs.

FEET
With three sturdy toes, the feet of a Greater Rhea are more like those of a grazing animal than a bird.

HOW BIG IS IT?

SPECIAL ADAPTATION

It may not be able to fly but the Greater Rhea can run at incredible speeds, and with great precision. In fact, its seemingly useless wings are invaluable. They help the bird to keep its balance and steer by lifting one and then the other to change direction while running.

Ostrich

VITAL STATISTICS

WEIGHT	100–160kg (220–353lb)
HEIGHT	Males: 1.8–2.7m (5.9–8.8ft) Females: 1.7–2m (5.6–6.6ft)
WINGSPAN	2m (6.6ft)
SEXUAL MATURITY	2–4 years
LAYS EGGS	April–September
INCUBATION PERIOD	35–45 days
FLEDGLING PERIOD	14–15 days
NUMBER OF EGGS	12–15 eggs laid in a communal nest
NUMBER OF BROODS	If eggs are taken from the nest, hens will continue to lay until they have a successful brood
TYPICAL DIET	Plants, roots, seeds; occasional insects and small reptiles
LIFE SPAN	Typically 50 years

CREATURE COMPARISONS

There are four living sub-species of Ostrich: the Southern Ostrich, North African Ostrich, Masai Ostrich and Somali Ostrich. All vary in size and coloration. For example, the neck and thighs of the male Somali Ostrich (shown) are grey-blue. Those of the Masai Ostrich are pink-orange.

Somali Ostrich

The Ostrich is the world's largest living species of bird, and it lays the largest eggs.

WHERE IN THE WORLD?

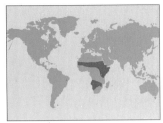

The Ostrich makes its home in the African savannah. Over the last few decades, it has become popular with farmers in Australia and the Americas, who raise large herds for eggs and meat.

NECK
The species name for this bird comes from the Greek words for 'camel sparrow', a reference to its long neck.

WINGS
Despite having ample wings, the Ostrich cannot fly. Instead, it uses the wings in mating displays and to shade its chicks.

FEET
The powerful legs of the Ostrich can cover 3–5m (10–16ft) in a single stride. They also make formidable weapons.

HOW BIG IS IT?

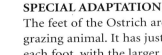

SPECIAL ADAPTATION

The feet of the Ostrich are like those of a grazing animal. It has just two toes on each foot, with the larger inner toe resembling a hoof. This adaptation is designed to help it run, which it does at speeds of up to 70km/h (43.5mph).

429

Broad-billed Hummingbird

• **ORDER** • Trochiliformes • **FAMILY** • Trochilidae • **SPECIES** • *Cynanthus latirostris*

VITAL STATISTICS

WEIGHT	3–4g (0.11–0.14 oz)
LENGTH	9–10cm (3.5–4in)
WINGSPAN	12cm (4.7in)
LAYS EGGS	January–May in Mexico. April–August in the USA
INCUBATION PERIOD	14–23 days
NUMBER OF EGGS	2–3 eggs
NUMBER OF BROODS	1 a year per mate, but males may have several mates
HABITS	Diurnal. American birds are migratory
TYPICAL DIET	Nectar; occasionally insects
LIFE SPAN	Up to 12 years

The Broad-Billed Hummingbird is a particularly small hummingbird that looks like an iridescent jewel in flight as it flits from flower to flower in search of nectar.

WHERE IN THE WORLD?

Populations of Broad-Billed Hummingbirds breed from southeastern Arizona to southwestern New Mexico. Their preferred habitats are scrubland, forests and any dry open habitats with a plentiful supply of food.

CREATURE COMPARISONS

The wings of all Hummingbirds are attached at the shoulder. This allows the birds to adjust their wing direction to hover, to fly vertically upwards or even to fly backwards. The Broad-billed Hummingbird uses this skill to perform elaborate courtship displays, hovering in front of the female and flying backwards and forwards in arcs.

Broad-billed Hummingbird

BILL
Although its bill looks like a straw, the Broad-billed Hummingbird does not suck up nectar. Instead it lap its up with a long extendable tongue.

BODY
Male Broad-Billed Hummingbirds (shown here) have a blue throat and green breast. Females have a white throat and grey breast.

WINGS
Most of the surface of the Broad-Billed Hummingbird's wing is taken up by finger-like primary feathers, which give the bird thrust.

HOW BIG IS IT?

SPECIAL ADAPTATION

Hummingbirds have a metabolism that works at a very high rate, so they need vast amounts of food (around three times their body weight) to survive. When food is short, however, they can enter a sleep-like torpor, reducing their metabolism to one-fiftieth of its usual rate.

Resplendent Quetzal

• **ORDER** • Trogoniformes • **FAMILY** • Trogonidae • **SPECIES** • *Pharomachrus mocinno*

Never was a species so well named as the Resplendent Quetzal, a bird that was sacred to the Aztecs and Maya of South America, who worshipped it as a symbol of goodness.

VITAL STATISTICS

WEIGHT	210g (7.4oz)
LENGTH	35–38cm (14–15in)
LAYS EGGS	March–June
INCUBATION PERIOD	18–19 days
FLEDGLING PERIOD	17–18 days
NUMBER OF EGGS	2 eggs
NUMBER OF BROODS	1 a year
CALL	Male's song is 'keow-kowee-keow-k'loo-keow-keloo'
HABITS	Diurnal, non-migratory
TYPICAL DIET	Fruit; occasionally insects, small frogs and lizards

WHERE IN THE WORLD?

The Resplendent Quetzal is often all but invisible in the canopy of the cool high cloud forests of Central America where it makes its home. Decaying trees and tree stumps are favourite haunts.

CREATURE COMPARISONS

The female Resplendent Quetzal is less vibrantly coloured than the male, but their plumage is still remarkably vivid, with an iridescent body and a black and white barred tail. This is because there are fewer predators in the rainforest treetops, and so camouflage is less important.

Female

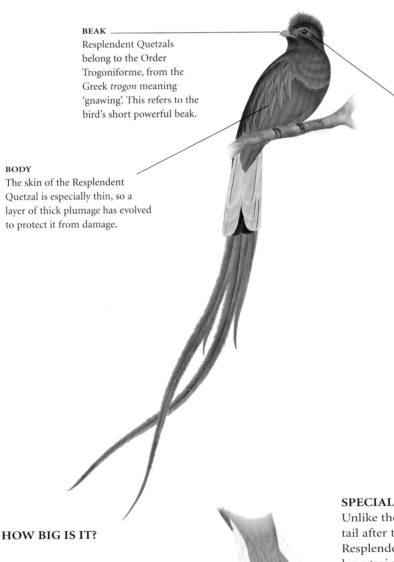

BEAK
Resplendent Quetzals belong to the Order Trogoniforme, from the Greek *trogon* meaning 'gnawing'. This refers to the bird's short powerful beak.

BODY
The skin of the Resplendent Quetzal is especially thin, so a layer of thick plumage has evolved to protect it from damage.

EYES
Like many forest-dwellers, the Resplendent Quetzal has large eyes, which help it to see in the gloom of the forest canopy.

HOW BIG IS IT?

SPECIAL ADAPTATION

Unlike the male peafowl, which sheds its tail after the breeding season, the male Resplendent Quetzals wears a 1m (3.3ft) long train all year round. This is not as impractical as it seems because the tail streamers are adapted to coil up during displays or when nesting.

Small Buttonquail

• ORDER • Turniciformes • FAMILY • Turnicidae • SPECIES • *Turnix sylvatica*

When danger threatens, the timid Small Buttonquail does not fly away but remains motionless on the ground, relying on its camouflaged plumage to keep it safe.

VITAL STATISTICS

WEIGHT	39–54g (1.4–2oz)
LENGTH	14–16cm (5.5–6.3in)
SEXUAL MATURITY	As early as 4 months
NUMBER OF EGGS	2–7 eggs per nest
INCUBATION PERIOD	11–13 days
FLEDGLING PERIOD	18–20 days
NUMBER OF EGGS	2–7 eggs per nest
NUMBER OF BROODS	Females mate with different males through the breeding season, leaving them to incubate each clutch of eggs
TYPICAL DIET	Insects and seeds
LIFE SPAN	Up to 9 years

WHERE IN THE WORLD?

The Small Buttonquail makes its home in fields, grassy plains and on open scrubland. It is found in Spain, North Africa and southeastern Asia. Large numbers are also found in sub-Saharan Africa.

CREATURE COMPARISONS

The mating call of the Small Buttonquail is often heard, but spotting this elusive bird is much trickier. Its plumage is designed to mimic the brown and yellow tones found on dry grasslands, allowing it to blend with the surroundings. True quails have equally effective cryptic camouflage.

Small Buttonquail in flight

BODY
Although this round-bodied bird resembles the true quail, it belongs to a separate and ancient bird group known as the Hemipodes.

WINGS
In the air, the Small Buttonquail is a very strong flier, powering through the sky with a succession of rapid noisy wing beats.

FEET
The Small Buttonquail can fly but prefers to walk. It has three forwards-pointing toes that give it stability on the ground.

HOW BIG IS IT?

SPECIAL ADAPTATION

It is the female Small Buttonquail, rather than the male, that initiates breeding. Once a nest is built, it calls to potential mates with a deep, 'hoom-hoom-hoom' cry. This is possible thanks to an elongated windpipe, which produces a deep tone that resonates over long distances.

Bird resources

Birds of Britain
http://www.birdsofbritain.co.uk

Birds of North America
http://bna.birds.cornell.edu/bna

American Bird Conservancy
http://www.abcbirds.org/

Bird news from Australia and around the World
http://featherz.proboards33.com/

Discovering the history of birds
http://www.historyoftheuniverse.com/birds.html

The Royal Society for the Protection of Birds
http://www.rspb.org.uk/

The National Geographic
http://animals.nationalgeographic.com/animals/birds.html

Presented by the Ornithological Council
http://www.nmnh.si.edu/BIRDNET/

Bird Watching In the USA and Around the World
http://www.birding.com/

Website for birdlovers
http://www.birdchannel.com/default.aspx

The British Trust for Ornithology
http://www.bto.org/

World Bird Guide
http://www.mangoverde.com/birdsound/

The Peregrine fund
http://www.peregrinefund.org/world_center.asp

Bird Life International
http://www.birdlife.org/

IOC World Bird List
http://www.worldbirdnames.org/index.html

Finding rare birds
http://www.worldtwitch.com/

Endangered Species International
http://www.endangeredspeciesinternational.org/birds.html?gclid=CNXq2eT0jZgCFQvilAod_VRBBw

Bird watching
http://www.birdwatching.com/

Bird watching breaks
http://www.birdwatchingbreaks.com/index.htm

Data resource for birders
http://www.zestforbirds.co.za/

American Birding Association
http://www.aba.org/

HawkWatch International
http://www.hawkwatch.org/home/

The Owl pages
http://www.owlpages.com/

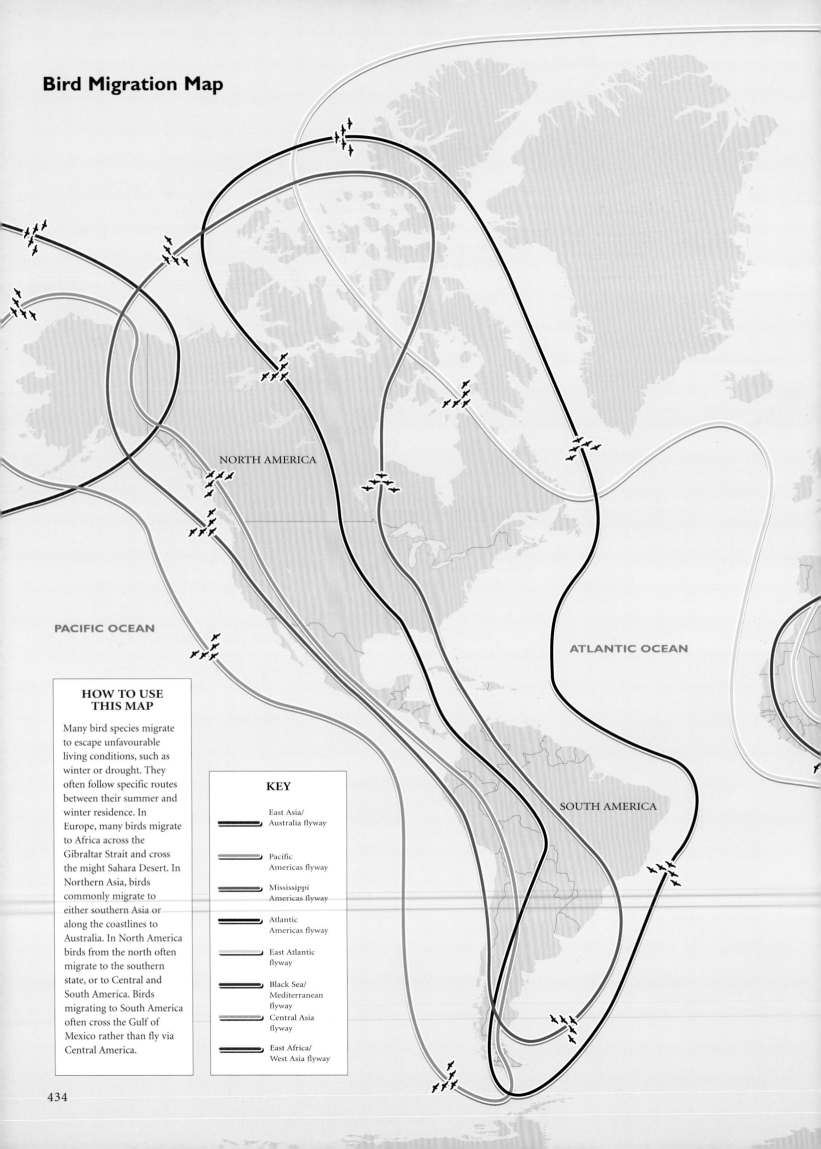

Bird Migration Map

NORTH AMERICA

PACIFIC OCEAN

ATLANTIC OCEAN

SOUTH AMERICA

KEY

— East Asia/ Australia flyway

— Pacific Americas flyway

— Mississippi Americas flyway

— Atlantic Americas flyway

— East Atlantic flyway

— Black Sea/ Mediterranean flyway

— Central Asia flyway

— East Africa/ West Asia flyway

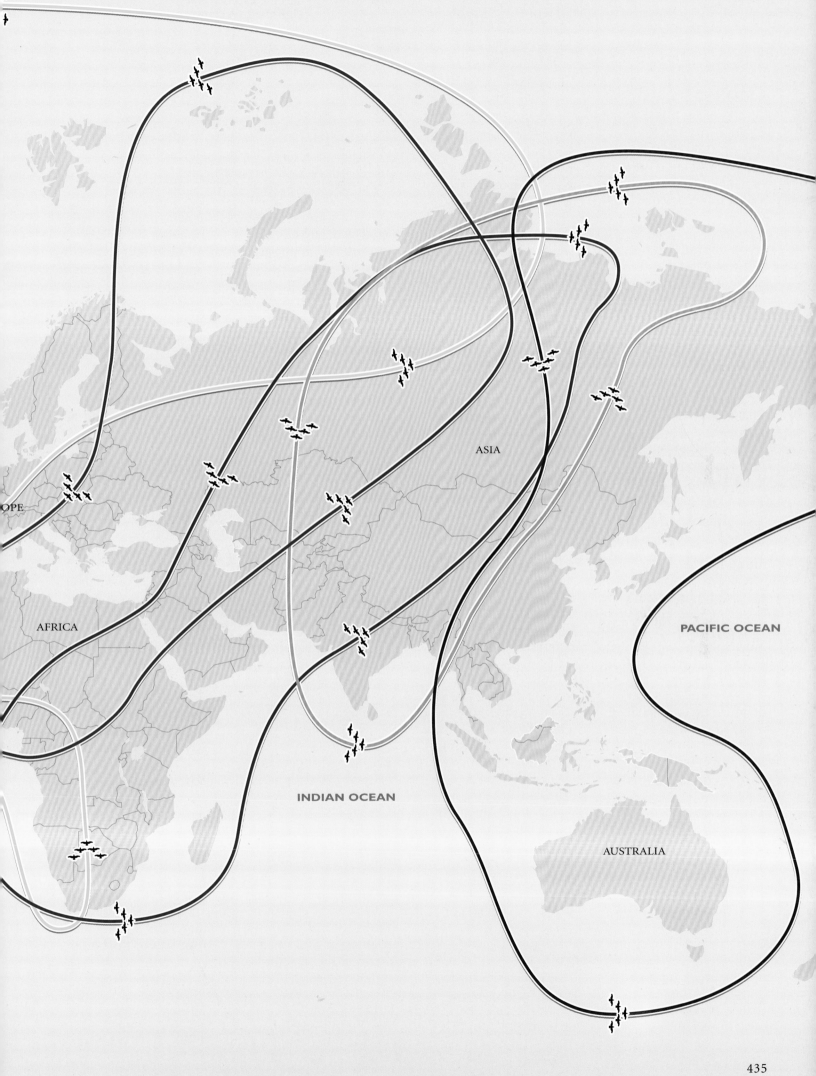

ASIA

PACIFIC OCEAN

AFRICA

OPE

INDIAN OCEAN

AUSTRALIA

ANTARCTICA

435

Glossary

ADAPTATION
A special physical or behavioural ability that has allowed a species to adjust to a particular way of life.

ASYNCHRONOUS HATCHING
Hatching that does not occur at the same time but that may take place over two to three calendar days.

BILL
Beak.

BILL-SWEEPING
The display in which a pair of birds sweep their bills back and forth over the bark near their nest hole. Often the birds have crushed insects in their bills.

BREEDING CYCLE
The time period beginning at nest building through egg laying and raising young to the point of independence.

BROOD
(as a noun): The young of a bird that are hatched or cared for at one time: (as a verb): To sit on and keep warm (chicks).

CACHING
The storage of berries, seeds and other food items in the crevices of bark and under leaves. The retrieval of the food is not accidental, unlike scatterhoarding.

CARNIVOROUS
Flesh-eating birds (usually fresh or live as opposed to carrion). Raptors (hawks and owls) are carnivorous birds.

CAVITY-NESTING BIRD
A bird that nests inside a hole in a tree trunk or limb or in a nest box.

CLOACA
The posterior-most chamber of the digestive tract in birds.

CLUTCH
The total number of eggs laid by a female bird in one nest attempt.

CONIFEROUS
Type of trees consisting of evergreens such as pines and firs.

CONTOUR FEATHER
The predominate feather type found on the body, wings, and tail of the bird (as opposed to other feather types: down, bristles, semiplumes, etc.)

CREPUSCULAR
Active at twilight, dawn, and dusk.

DECIDUOUS
Trees that have leaves that fall off or shed either seasonally or at a certain stage of development in the life cycle.

DIHEDRAL
Wings of a flying bird held at an angle appearing to form a "V."

DIMORPHISM
Existing in two forms, such as two colours or two sexes.

DIURNAL
Used to describe birds that are active during the day. Most birds are diurnal.

DUMMY NEST
A decoy nest that is built in order to attract females, reduce the loss of egg or birds to predators or reduce the risk of the nest being used by other birds. If eggs are disturbed in the primary nest, they can be moved to the alternate nest.

ECTOPARASITE
A parasite that lives on the exterior of its host.

EGG DUMPING
This occurs when a female lays her egg(s) in the nest of another bird, sometimes creating very large clutches.

FACIAL DISCS
Rounded, earlike areas on the face.

FECAL SAC
A tough mucous membrane containing the excrement of nestling birds.

FLEDGE
The act of leaving the nest or nest cavity after reaching a certain stage of maturity.

FLEDGING
The development in young birds of the feathers necessary for flight. More generally, developing enough independence to leave the nest.

FLEDGLING
A young bird that has left the nest but is not yet completely independent of parental care.

FLOCK
A group of birds made up of either the same or different species.

FRUGIVOROUS
Birds that feed primarily on fruit. Cedar Waxwings are frugivorous birds.

GIZZARD
Muscular organ that is part of the digestive system. Food in the gizzard is ground up by the combination action of muscular contraction and the hard stones (grit) retained in the gizzard.

GUANO
Large deposits of bird faeces that accumulate in sites that birds regularly use, such as breeding colonies.

HABITAT
The place or environment where a plant or animal naturally or normally lives and grows.

HATCH
To emerge from an egg, pupa or chrysalis.

HATCHING
The moment an organism emerges from an egg, pupa or chrysalis.

HERBIVOROUS
Birds that mainly eat plants, such as the Canada Goose.

HIBERNATION
A state of dormancy or reduced activity typically entered at the onset of winter. Hibernating saves energy when food is scarce.

INCUBATION
The act of rearing and hatching eggs by the warmth of the body.

INSECTIVOROUS
Birds that eat mainly insects. Swallows are a good example.

INVERTEBRATE
An animal that does not have a spinal column.

JUVENILE
A young bird that is no longer dependent on its parents but has not gained its adult plumage.

KLEPTOPARASITISM
The strategy of stealing items, such as food or nest materials, from other individauls. Frigatebirds employ this strategy.

LARVAE
The immature, wingless and often wormlike stage of a metamorphic insect that hatches from the egg, alters chiefly in size while passing through several molts, and is finally transformed into a pupa or chrysalis from which the adult emerges.

LATITUDE
South to north measurement of location.

LONGITUDE
East to west measurement of location.

LOWER MANDIBLE
Lower part of the bill.

MAMMAL
Warm-blooded, higher vertebrates that nourish their young with milk secreted by mammary glands and have the skin usually more or less covered with hair.

MIGRATION
Regular, extensive, seasonal movements of birds between their breeding regions and their wintering regions.

MOBBING
A form of behaviour in some birds where a group of birds harrass a predator or other intruding animal in order to force that animal to leave the area.

MOLT
The process by which a bird renews part or all of its plumage by shedding old, worn feathers and growing new ones.

MONOGAMY
The mating of an animal with only one member of the opposite sex at a time.

MONOMORPHIC
Having a single form.

NEST BOX
A box, usually made of wood, in which cavity-nesting birds can nest; sometimes called a birdhouse.

NESTLING
A young bird that has not yet left, or abandoned, the nest

NEST PARASITISM
Reproduction by laying eggs in the nests of other birds, leaving the nest owners to provide parantal care. This may be birds of the same species (intraspecific) or birds of other species (interspecific).

NOCTURNAL
Birds that are more active at night than during the day.

OMNIVOROUS
Birds that eat anything that is considered digestible/edible. American Crows are a common example.

PAIR BOND
The association between two birds who have come together for reproduction; can be short-term (lasting only through egg-laying or the rearing of young) or lifelong.

PARASITE
An organism that lives in or on an organism of another species (known as the host). Usually a parasite causes some degree of damage to the host.

PLUMAGE
The feathers that cover a bird's body.

PREENING
The process by which a bird cleans, arranges, and cares for its feathers, usually by using its bill to adjust and smooth feathers.

PRIMARIES
The main flight feathers along the outer part of the edge of the wing.

PUPA
An intermediate stage of a metamorphic insect (such as a bee, moth, or beetle), usually enclosed in a cocoon or protective covering.

REPLACEMENT CLUTCH
The eggs laid to replace a clutch in which none of the eggs hatched.

RETRICES
The long flight feathers of the tail.

ROOST
To settle down for rest, sleep, or to perch.

RUFFS
Fringe of feathers growing on the neck.

SCATTERHOARDING
Where birds hide food items in bark crevices and under leaves, moss, or lichen. Retrieval of food items is accidental, not memory-based, unlike caching.

SEXUAL DIMORPHISM
When male and female birds differ in plumage.

SNAG
A standing dead tree.

SPECIES
Related organisms or populations having common attributes and potentially capable of interbreeding.

SUPERCILIUM
Line of feathers above the eye. Synonym(s): eyebrow, superciliary line.

SYNCHRONOUS HATCHING
Hatching that occurs at the same time or nearly the same time, usually within one calendar day.

SYNCHRONOUS NESTING
Nesting by a local population in which breeding pairs initiate egg laying within a relatively short period of time (a few days to a few weeks)

TAXONOMY
Scientific naming of organisms and their classification with reference to their precise position in the animal or plant kingdom.

TERRESTRIAL
Living or growing on land.

THERMOREGULATION
The act of maintaining a constant body temperature.

UPPER MANDIBLE
Upper part of the bill.

BLACKHEADED GULL

Name Index

Scientific bird names are italicised.

Eurasian Eagle Owl

Kestrel

RED CRESTED POCHARD

General Index

King Penguin

Grey Heron

445

BALD EAGLE

WHITE STORK

447

Picture Credits

Illustrations
All illustrations © Art-Tech

Photographs:
Alamy: 122 (A. Bramwell), 125 (Blickwinkel), 185 (J. Lens), 310 (D. Tipling), 369 (O. Martinsen), 375 (Arco Images GmbH) **Ames:** 400 **Ardea:** 332 (D. Hadden) **Richard Bartz:** 145, 156, 210 **Peter Békési:** 391 **Tobias Biehl:** 157 **Mathias Bigge:** 243 **Buiten-Beeld:** 12t (D. Occhiato), 72 (L. Hoogenstein), 75 (H. Van Diek), 90 (A. Ouwerkerk), 105 (H. Gebuis), 109 & 139 (A. Sprang), 146 & 148 (D. Occhiato), 162 (L. Hoogenstein), 187 (W. De Groot), 195 (D. Occhiato), 203 (J. Folkers), 209 (N. Paklina), 211 (J. Folkers), 213 (H. Van Diek), 214 (C. Van Rijswijk), 225 (R. Nagtegaal), 237 (P. Cools), 244 (D. Occhiato), 251 (R. Messemaker), 261 & 268 (H. Van Diek), 273 (D. Occhiato), 283 (H. Van Diek), 288 (D. Occhiato), 289 (H. Van Diek), 290 (C. Van Rijswijk), 302 (J. Luit), 331 (C. Van Rijswijk), 333 & 334 (R. Schols), 335 (R. Schols), 340 (N. Paklina), 350 (H. Van Diek), 370 (H. Bouwmeester), 372 (C. Van Rijswijk), 373 (P. Van Rij), 377 (J. Van Der Greef), 383 (J. Folkers), 409 (D.J. Van Unen) **Rhett A. Butler:** 280 (mongabay.com) **Roger Butterfield:** 197 **Calibas:** 28 **Copetersen:** 232 **Corbis:** 101 (W. Jacobi), 158 & 416 (A. Carey), 432 (H. Reinhard/Zefa) **Jason Corriveau:** 357 **Steve Deger:** 52 **Dezidor:** 164 **Dorling Kindersley:** 194 (F. Greenaway), 349 (C. Laubscher) **Myk Dowling:** 223 **Dreamstime:** 14 (M. Hackmann), 19 (C. Arranz), 29 (J. Gough), 33 (S. Byland), 49 (Susinder), 53 (Davthy), 57 (S. Ekernas), 62 (J. Maree), 65 (S. Foerster), 69 (M. Smith), 74 (Edurivero), 76 (C. Moncrieff), 87 (Alain), 89 (N. Smit), 93 (Dohnal), 98 (S. Tor Peng Hock), 116 (W. Cattaneo), 118 (R. Thornton), 121, 127 (L. Ferreira), 130, 131 (J.G. Swanepoel), 135 (A.M. Abrao), 144 (J. Gottwald), 150 (M. Vasicek), 151 (P. Rydzkowski), 152 (J. Joseph), 163, 165 (D. Han), 169 (K. Canning), 171 (ODM), 173 (Y. Polosina), 183 (B. Macqueen), 191 (K. Broz), 198 (R. Caucino), 199 (Z. Camernik), 200 (T. Jesenicnik), 208 (A. Huszti), 218 (R. Kukasch), 220 (T. Morozova), 221 (S. Byland), 230 (J. Anderson), 235 (K. Broz), 239, 254 (X. Marchant), 256 (A. Duasbaew), 262 (M. Perkowski), 263 (F. Christophe), 267 (M. Perkowski), 274 (J. Joseph), 275, 282 (C. Arranz), 286 (I. Konoval), 287 (A. Yurchenko), 291, 294 (I. Konoval), 295, 298 (A. Schulte), 299 & 301 (M. Perkowski), 314 (P.Cowan), 316 (R. Hansson), 325, 327 (S. Zhang), 329 (I. Timofeev), 330 (I. Konoval), 342 (M. Woodruff), 352 (S. Ekernas), 360 (C. Franck), 362 (J. Whittingham), 363, 371 (A. Duasbaew), 381 (U. Ohse), 382 (K. Broz), 384, 398 (K. Bain), 420 (A. Keruzore), 424 (J. Gottwald), 426 (M. Thomas), 428, 442 (J. Gottwald), 445 (M. Blajenov) **Glen Fergus:** 54 **FLPA:** 12b (T. Whittaker), 21 & 22 (R. Wilmshurst), 41 (R. Tidman), 44 (M. Jones/Minden Pictures), 46 (H.D. Brandl), 47 (T. Whittaker), 48 (R. Brooks), 50 (K. Wothe/Minden Pictures), 51 (R. Van Muers/Foto Natura), 58 (G. De Hoog/Foto Natura), 61 (M. Schuyl), 67 (N. Bowman), 84 (C. Schenk/Foto Natura), 91 (N. Bowman), 110 &123 (D. Hosking), 126 (R. Chittenden), 132 (N. Bowman), 174 (R. Brooks), 178 (M. Lane), 181 (L.L. Rue), 182 (E. Woods), 215 (F.W. Lane), 217 (G. Moon), 222 (D. Middleton), 226 (D. Hosking), 228, 236 (J.&C. Sohns), 246 (N. Bowman), 248 (S. Maslowski), 253 (D. Hosking), 255 (F. Lanting), 260 (H. Jegen/Imagebroker), 276 (B. Zoller/Imagebroker), 278 (N. Bowman), 279 & 296 (J.&C. Sohns), 304 (N. Bowman), 306 (F. Merlet), 308 (T.&P. Gardner), 311, 312 (D. Hosking), 317 (N. Bowman), 318 (S. Huwiler), 320 (H. Lansdown), 341 (R. Tidman), 353 (D. Hosking), 364 (R. Tidman), 368 (W. Dennis), 376 (D. Hopf/Imagebroker), 378 (J. Karmali), 388 (S. Jonasson), 389 (T.&P. Gardner), 393 (K. Szulecka), 394 (Foto Natura Stock), 423 (G. Ellis/Minden Pictures), 431 (M.&P. Fogden/Minden Pictures) **Fotolia:** 8t (L. Lucide), 8b, 9t (Wild Geese), 9b (R. Ainsworth), 10t, 11 (L. Macpherson), 24 (A. Middleton), 45 (L. Lucide), 59 &60 (Mdalla), 63 (Butorétoilé), 77, 81, 85 & 95 (Mdalla), 137 (F. Leviez), 141 (P. Betts), 143 (P. Spychala), 149 (M. Gallasch), 153 (Fotohans), 160 (D. Ho), 176 (K. Wendorf), 207 (A. Lindert-Rottke), 229 & 249 (J. Barber), 250, 258 (Kaphoto), 269, 270 (A. Bolbot), 285 (J. Barber), 321, 322 (J. Barber), 326 (D. Garry), 328 (L. Lachmann), 337 (Z. Camernik), 338, 351 (J. Barber), 354, 380, 392 (S. Lovegrove), 399 (A. Lindert-Rottke), 410 (P. Rydzkowski), 413 (S. Mutch), 419 (S. Flashman) **Tom Friedel:** 412 **Getty Images:** 13t & 40 (Stockbyte), 68 & 99 (Stockbyte), 112 &136 (Stockbyte), 138 (Stockbyte), 154 (Digital Vision), 155 & 159 (Stockbyte), 167 & 180 (Stockbyte), 184 & 421 (Stockbyte) **K.M. Hansche:** 422 **Yoshikazu Hara:** 307 **John Haslam:** 233 **Manfred Heyde:** 447 **David Iliff:** 70, 438 **iStockphoto:** 15 (E. Snow), 20 (F. Leung), 37 (J. Swanepoel), 43 (B. Balestri), 82 (P. Tessier), 86 (R. Hirsch), 92 (A. Howe), 96 (M. Martin), 129 (P. Mills), 134 (A. Tobey), 161 (G. Shimmin), 231 (J. Weston), 245 (R. Szajkowski), 257 (A. Howe), 277 (S. Flashman), 292 (I. Konoval), 309 (A. Howe), 313 (P. Pazzi), 315 (A. Maritz), 336 & 339 (A. Howe), 343 (A. Howe), 387 (J. Doucette), 402 (S. Graafmans), 418 & 430 (F. Leung) **Nigel Jacques:** 247 **Kevin Law:** 284 **Alan Liefting:** 212 **Mdf:** 78, 79, 168, 238, 264 **Artur Mikolajewski:** 293 **Malgorzata Milaszewska:** 440 **Chris Morgan:** 271 **Morguefile:** 23 (Juditu), 30 (K.W. Kiser), 106 (M. Hull), 128 (J.W. Blonk), 186 (M. Hull), 305 (L.C. Tejo), 324 (K. Bishop), 345, 444 (N. Moon) **NASA:** 179 **Martin Olsson:** 25, 348 **Dave Pape:** 34 **Pavlen:** 411 **Photos.com:** 13b, 17, 26, 35, 42, 64, 100, 102, 103, 108, 113, 115, 166, 170, 190, 192, 196, 201, 224, 241, 344, 356, 365, 366, 367, 385, 386, 390, 396, 405-407, 415, 425, 429, 443, 446 **Photoshot:** 193 (D.N. Dalton) **Adrian Pingstone:** 10b, 32, 36, 39, 119, 441 **Public Domain:** 16, 54, 55 56, 66, 71, 73, 80, 94, 104, 107, 111, 120, 133, 172, 175, 177, 188, 240, 281, 323, 346, 358, 359, 361, 374, 379, 401, 408, 414, 427 **Randy Read:** 395 **Paul Sapiano:** 397 **Sebastian Ritter:** 114 **Johan Spaedtke:** 439 **Stock.xchng:** 140, 403 **Stockxpert:** 319 (Joe Gough) **L.B. Tettenborn:** 234 **Thermos:** 142, 252, 259, 265, 297, 300 **Andreas Trepte:** 27, 38, 55, 83 **Matthias Trischler:** 147 **Geiser Trivelato:** 227 **Mindaugas Urbonas:** 124 **U.S. Fish & Wildlife Service:** 18 (J.&K. Hollingsworth), 31 (G. Smart), 88 (Arctic National Wildlife Refuge), 189 (L. Karney), 202, 206 (L. Goldman), 219 (L. Karney), 242 (J.C. Leupold), 272 & 303 (D. Menke) **Linda De Volder:** 216 **Wolfgang Wander:** 417 **Tony Wills:** 347 **Alan D. Wilson:** 117 **Elaine R. Wilson:** 266 **Frank Wouters:** 355 **Duncan Wright:** 97 **Jon Zander:** 204 **Giuseppe Zibordi:** 404 **L. Zinkova:** 205

Dome Tiepolo

SOTHEBY'S
ART AT AUCTION

The Art Market Review 1992–93

SOTHEBY'S

ART AT AUCTION

The Art Market Review 1992–93

CONRAN OCTOPUS

First published in 1993 by
Conran Octopus Limited
37 Shelton Street,
London WC2H 9HN

Copyright © Conran Octopus Limited 1993
Sotheby's illustrations (see p. 312) © Sotheby's
Sotheby's is a registered trade mark.

Trade distribution in the United States of America by
Rizzoli International Publications, Inc.
300 Park Avenue South, New York, NY 10010
ISBN 0-8478-5755-7

British Library Cataloguing in Publication Data
A catalogue record for this book is available from
the British Library

ISBN 1-85029-538-7

Printed in Great Britain by
Jolly & Barber Ltd, Rugby, Warwickshire

ENDPAPERS: GIOVANNI DOMENICO TIEPOLO
Putti flying among clouds
SIGNED, PEN AND BROWN INK AND WASH,
18.9 x 25.6cm (7½ x 10⅛in)
London £4,620 ($7,250). 14.XII.92

PAGE 1: **An Attic lekythos fragment**
NEAR THE THANATOS PAINTER, c. 440BC, 18.1cm (7⅛in)
London £20,900 ($32,600). 10.XII.92

PAGE 2: HENRI MATISSE
L'Asie
SIGNED AND DATED 46, OIL ON CANVAS,
116.2 x 81.3cm (45¾ x 32in)
New York $11,000,000 (£7,284,700). 10.XI.92

PAGES 4-5: **A selection from The Uruguayan
Treasure of the River Plate**
New York 24-25.III.93

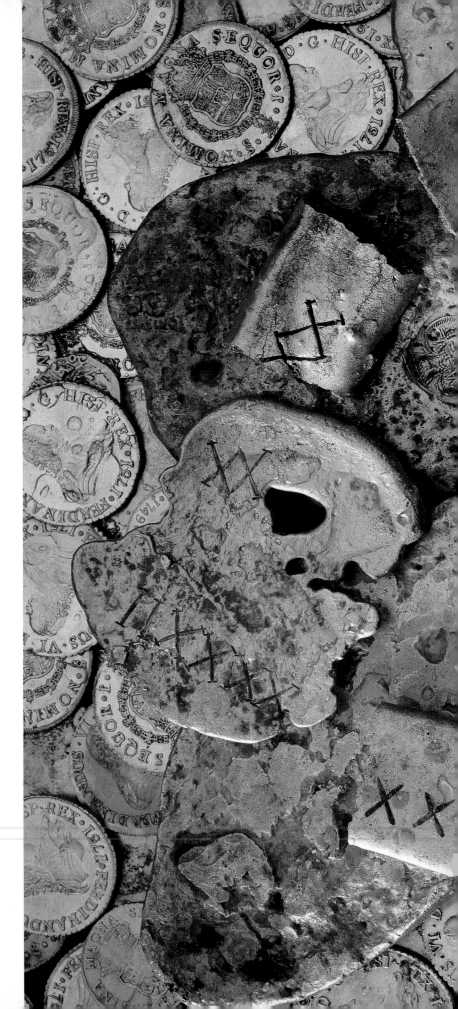

CONTENTS

CONTRIBUTORS

JOHN D. BLOCK is a Senior Vice President and member of the Board of Directors of Sotheby's North and South America. He is currently in charge of the Jewellery and Precious Objects Division in New York and has played a formative role in establishing the company's international pre-eminence in both these markets.

MELVYN BRAGG first started to work in television in 1961. In 1964 he helped launch BBC2, for which he edited several arts programmes. In 1978 he set up *The South Bank Show* for London Weekend Television, and he continues to edit and present that series. He is also currently Controller of Arts at London Weekend Television and Director of LWT Productions. He is the author of several books, screenplays and libretti, including that for the award-winning *The Hired Man*. He has also won the TRIC Award for Radio Programme of the Year (*Start the Week,* 1990) and a record three Prix Italia.

MABEL H. BRANDON has worked at Harvard University and the Metropolitan Museum of Art, and served on the John F. and Robert Kennedy presidential campaigns. In 1976 she founded Washington Corporate Arts Inc., which functioned as a liaison between the cultural and corporate communities in all aspects of corporate sponsorship. In 1980 she was asked by President Reagan to act as Social Secretary to the White House, during which time she also served as Special Liaison for the President's Committee on the Arts and Humanities. In 1989 she joined the Ford Motor Company where she is now Director of Corporate Planning.

DIANA D. BROOKS is President and Chief Executive Officer of Sotheby's Worldwide Auction Operations, a position that was created for her in 1993. She joined the company in 1979 and in 1990 was appointed President and Chief Executive Officer of Sotheby's North and South America. In both capacities she is closely involved with all major sales held by the company and has made a vital contribution to the co-ordination and integration of Sotheby's operations throughout the world.

EDWARD BULMER has been working in the conservation and restoration of historic buildings since 1986. Latterly with Alec Cobbe and now in independent practice, his work has included picture hanging and decorative work in privately-owned houses such as Harewood House in Yorkshire, and also in National Trust properties, including Petworth House, Sussex. In addition, he is a council member of the Ancient Monuments Society and a trustee of the Mappa Mundi Trust, Hereford.

MICHAEL CONFORTI is the Chief Curator and Curator of Decorative Arts and Sculpture at the Minneapolis Institute of Arts. He worked for Sotheby's in both London and New York between 1968 and 1971, before entering Harvard University's PhD programme in art history. Since the beginning of his museum career at the Fine Arts Museum in San Francisco he has written numerous articles and exhibition catalogues on nineteenth- and twentieth-century decorative arts, as well as on American institutional and private collecting practices over the past 150 years.

RICHARD CORK is the Art Critic of *The Times* and the Henry Moore Senior Research Fellow at the Courtauld Institute of Art. He has organized major exhibitions at the Hayward Gallery, the Royal Academy and the Tate. His books include *Vorticism* (1976) and *Art Beyond the Gallery* (1985), both prize-winning studies, and *David Bomberg* (1987), a monograph. From 1989-90 he was Slade Professor of Fine Art at Cambridge University. His latest book, *A Bitter Truth: Avant-Garde Art and the Great War*, will be published early in 1994.

PHILIPPE GARNER joined Sotheby's in 1970 and rapidly achieved a specialization in Photography and Twentieth-century Decorative Arts. He has remained one of the leading experts in both these fields and has published numerous books, including *The Contemporary Decorative Arts* (1980), *Eileen Gray: Architect and Designer* (1993) and a study of the work of Emile Gallé (1976).

THE RT HON. THE EARL OF GOWRIE is Chairman of Sotheby's Europe and a Director of Sotheby's Holdings Inc. He was Minister for the Arts from 1983 to 1985 as well as being responsible for the management of the Civil Service and a spokesman for HM Treasury in the House of Lords. His many books include *The Genius of British Painting: The Twentieth Century* (1975).

HILARY KAY joined Sotheby's in 1977. In 1978, aged 21, she became head of the Collectors' Department and one of Britain's first female auctioneers. In 1981 she set up the first-ever sale of Rock and Roll memorabilia, and in 1985 was made a Director of Sotheby's. She regularly appears on BBC Television's *Antiques Roadshow,* and is the author of *Rock 'n' Roll Collectables: An Illustrated History of Rock Memorabilia* (1992).

JOHN MARTIN ROBINSON is a partner in Historic Buildings Consultants, librarian to the Duke of Norfolk and Maltravers Herald of Arms. His books include *Country Houses of the North West* (1991), *Georgian Model Farms* (1984), and *Royal Residences* (1982). He is a Fellow of the Society of Antiquaries and a member of the Executive Committee of the Georgian Group.

PHILIP MOULD is a picture dealer specializing in paintings of the English face. He is well-known for his discoveries, including the lost half of Gainsborough's first portrait and major works by van Dyck, Dobson and Kneller. In 1987 he wrote and presented *Changing Faces,* a six-part history of British portraiture for Channel 4. He is Works of Art Advisor to the House of Commons and the House of Lords.

PAUL NEEDHAM is Director of the Books and Manuscripts Department for Sotheby's New York and a Senior Vice President. Before joining Sotheby's he served for eighteen years as the Astor Curator of Printed Books and Bindings at the Pierpont Morgan Library. A widely respected scholar, Dr Needham has published extensively on the histories of printing, binding and paper.

LYNN STOWELL PEARSON was an editor at the International Foundation for Art Research before joining Sotheby's New York in 1987, where she is an Assistant Vice President in the Publications Department and also editor of *Sotheby's Newsletter.* Other publications include a paper developed from her doctoral dissertation research, *Ancient Stones: Quarrying, Trade and Provenance,* published in 1992.

SIMON DE PURY is Deputy Chairman of Sotheby's Europe, Chairman of Sotheby's Switzerland and head of the European Fine Arts Division. He is based in Geneva and London but devotes a large amount of his time to travelling. He is an auctioneer, conducting major sales in London, Geneva, Monte Carlo, St Moritz and Zürich, and from 1979 to 1986, prior to joining Sotheby's, he was curator of the Thyssen-Bornemisza Collection, Lugano.

JOHN L. TANCOCK is Director of the Impressionist and Modern Paintings Department of Sotheby's New York and a Senior Vice President of the company. His publications include *The Sculpture of Auguste Rodin* (1976) and *Multiples: The First Decade* (1971).

RONALD VARNEY is a Vice President of the Marketing Department, Sotheby's New York. He has written extensively on the arts for *Esquire, Smithsonian* and *Connoisseur* magazines as well as for *The New York Times* and *The Wall Street Journal.*

GILES WATERFIELD trained at the Courtauld Institute of Art, London and subsequently worked at the Royal Pavilion, Brighton. Since 1979 he has been Director of the Dulwich Picture Gallery, London and from 1994 he will also serve as joint Director of the Attingham Summer School. During his time at Dulwich he has organized a number of exhibitions around the theme of architecture and collecting, including *Palaces of Art: Art Galleries in Britain 1790-1990.* He is currently working on a history of art museums in Britain.

INTRODUCTION *by Diana D. Brooks*

In this edition of Sotheby's Art at Auction: The Art Market Review, we continue to focus our editorial attention, as we did in last year's edition, on important developments and issues in the world art market. At the same time we again provide a comprehensive record of the past auction season at Sotheby's, a story vividly told in the many colour photographs we have presented here of the paintings, furniture, antiquities, jewellery and other works which highlighted the 1992-93 season.

For our cover image we have chosen a work which perhaps best represents the successes of the 1992-93 season at Sotheby's – Paul Cézanne's monumental still life, Nature Morte: Les Grosses Pommes. By way of historical footnote, Sotheby's offered this same painting in the famous Jakob Goldschmidt Collection sale in 1958 in London, where it achieved the then remarkable price of £90,000. On the evening of 11 May 1993 in New York, Sotheby's again offered this extraordinary work. With six active bidders it sold for $28,602,500, far outstripping the previous record for the artist. This was the first time since 1990 that any painting had broken the $20 million barrier.

The overall success of this sale – which saw nine paintings in all sell for more than $1 million – was followed in June by a strong Impressionist sale at Sotheby's London featuring the distinguished Durand-Ruel Collection. Judging from comments by journalists, dealers and private collectors, all seemed to agree that the Impressionist and Modern art market had gained a healthy amount of confidence and momentum from the success of these sales, and they brought the 1992-93 season at Sotheby's to a most encouraging conclusion.

The international art market is complex and highly sophisticated, blending together very different cultural, aesthetic and professional viewpoints. As a company with a global presence, Sotheby's must understand these very different cultures and be responsive to the changes within them. On the following pages we provide our readers with timely, informative articles examining a range of issues to do with the international art market. Mabel H. Brandon

SIR LAWRENCE
ALMA-TADEMA
The Baths of
Caracalla (Thermae
Antoniniane)
(detail)
SIGNED, OIL ON CANVAS,
152.4 x 95.3cm (60 x 37½in)
New York $2,532,500
(£1,633,800). 26.V.93 (LEFT)

Jewelled gold
and hardstone
snuff box made for
Frederick II of
Prussia
AFTER A DESIGN BY JEAN
GUILLAUME GEORGE KRÜGER,
BERLIN, c.1770,
width 10cm (4in)
Geneva SF2,530,000
(£1,150,000:$1,805,500).
17.XI.92
From the Thurn und Taxis
Collection (BELOW)

discusses the growth of art collecting by commercial companies around the world, Melvyn Bragg reviews the history of television programmes on the visual arts, and Lord Gowrie examines different attitudes towards national heritage and the ownership of works of art.

The markets of Asia are the subject of John Tancock's article, and in it he discusses the implications of the growing economic strength of the nations of Asia. The process of 'discovering' works of art is a subject of abiding fascination, and Philip Mould delves into some recent notable stories. On another front Edward Bulmer reviews different philosophies in architectural restoration and conservation.

Complementing these articles are ones on American museum acquisitions, the popular collecting areas of Victorian paintings and photographs, and the major international exhibitions of the season. On a related theme, Giles Waterfield looks at the history of various styles of picture hanging and the reasons behind their use. And, in anticipation of our 250th anniversary next year, John Martin Robinson describes the various buildings Sotheby's has occupied since 1744.

Sotheby's performance in the saleroom in the 1992-93 season is vividly chronicled in these pages. Sotheby's conducts nearly 500 auctions a year in over 70 collecting areas, and the past season witnessed the sale of many exceptional works in such disparate fields as postage stamps and French furniture, medieval manuscripts and Chinese porcelain, Old Master paintings and Hollywood posters. Once again we have asked our senior specialists to provide summaries of the sale highlights and trends of individual specialist departments in Sotheby's worldwide offices during the past season. Each of these essays prefaces an extensive photographic selection of highlights that provides a rich, tapestry-like view of Sotheby's saleroom activity.

This view is further refined by Ronald Varney's article on many of the fine collections offered this season, which included those of Mrs Harry Winston (jewellery), Madame Hélène Beaumont (French furniture), Earl Mountbatten of Burma (paintings and works of art), Pierre Jourdan-Barry (silver), Norbert Schimmel (antiquities), Rudolf von Gutmann (books, drawings and prints), Otto Kallir (music manuscripts), Joseph M. Meraux (clocks) and Mollie Parnis Livingston (Impressionist and Modern paintings). The most glittering and publicized event of the auction

FRANÇOIS BOUCHER
L'Heureuse Fécondité
SIGNED AND DATED *1764*,
OIL ON CANVAS,
64.8 x 54cm (25½ x 21¼in)
New York $800,000
(£512,800). 20.V.93. (ABOVE)

Wucai Wine Jar and Cover
JIAJING MARK AND PERIOD,
overall height 45.4cm (17⅞in)
New York $2,860,000
(£1,845,100). 1.XII.92
(BELOW)

season was our sale in November in Geneva of exquisite silver, jewellery and objects of vertu from the princely collections of Thurn und Taxis.

The story of the season is only partly told in the saleroom activity. There are also lectures, exhibitions, receptions, client dinners, symposiums, concerts, gallery walks, classes, free appraisals, wine tastings, benefit auctions and many other events involving our staff around the world. Sotheby's in London hosted an exhibition of mosaics from Jordan loaned by the Jordanian Government, as well as an exhibition of tapestries by London's leading tapestry studios. Sotheby's also sponsored a major exhibition in Prague of the work of the renowned Greek artist, Jannis Kounellis. In another vein Sotheby's sponsored the first ever 'stately home car boot sale' at Nostell Priory, West Yorkshire, with the proceeds benefiting the National Asthma Campaign. In New York, we hosted an array of benefit events, exhibitions and receptions, including a benefit auction and reception for the AIDS organization God's Love We Deliver. We also contributed to such causes as Art Against AIDS, the International Foundation for Art Research, the Neighorhood Coalition for Shelter and the New York City Partnership, as well as to many museums. These non-auction related activities are an integral part of the calendar at Sotheby's, and we are pleased to lend our support to these and other worthy causes.

As we prepare to celebrate our 250th anniversary in 1994, we are mindful of the great events in our long history that have helped shape and define Sotheby's. We are also mindful of the many individuals who have played leading roles throughout the firm's history. During this past year two such individuals – the Earl of Westmorland in London and Eunice (Sandy) Carroll in New York – passed on. David Westmorland, the former Chairman of Sotheby's, was associated with the firm for more than two decades and participated in the company's growth in the United States and Canada. He also served in Elizabeth II's household for more than 25 years. He was a wonderfully warm and generous person. Sandy Carroll served Sotheby's for over 40 years, and as the longtime director of Special Client Services was a legendary figure, and dear friend, to hundreds of her clients throughout the world. We honour the memory and contributions of both these colleagues.

Lord Gowrie, HRH Princess Sumaya El Hassan and Her Majesty Queen Noor Al Hussein of Jordan at the opening of the Mosaics of Jordan exhibition at Sotheby's London in January 1993. (LEFT)

I
ART
AT
ISSUE

GAMEKEEPERS V. POACHERS *by The Rt Hon. The Earl of Gowrie*

A VIEW OF THE NATIONAL HERITAGE

Gamekeepers who decide to become poachers are viewed with understandable suspicion, their opinions taken with a pinch of salt. For nearly three years, in the early 1980s, I was concerned with the measures taken by one country, Britain, to prevent the indiscriminate export of works of art considered important enough to be part of our national patrimony or heritage. For nearly seven years since, I have found myself arguing the case from another part of the wood and defending the interests of a free and open market in works of art, as in other goods. I have at least been consistent in my belief that protectionism is, after war, the worst threat to civilization and to our cultural as well as economic well-being. 'Grub first, then ethics', said Brecht. Protectionism is the enemy of both.

The tension between people's right to own property and the interest of the state or community in the products of its past is a very old one. Any right to own property should include the right to dispose of it freely; anything less is only partial or qualified ownership. There is also an extreme view which holds that cultural goods are unlike all other goods: they are products of the human spirit and in some undefined way should be held in common.

When Sotheby's held an auction of works by contemporary painters in Moscow in 1988, I tried to persuade officials and museum curators there how important it was to allow the works of young artists to be sold and exported if they were ever to become known in the West. 'But they are ours,' I was told, 'and you can of course borrow them for exhibitions.' This attitude conveniently overlooked the need for young artists to live, and ignored the fact that taste, in a culture, is built up in layers of individual activity. Museum shows and exhibitions reflect only what specific artists and their dealers or patrons have been getting up to: they are bulletins from the artistic front. Ideal-

istic supporters of a commonwealth of artistic goods are usually sentimental about other kinds of ownership, sentimentally opposed that is. You can argue that the 'modern' era that we inhabit is still only a product of that revolution in sensibility we call the Renaissance. At that time, the Church was losing its intellectual and cultural monopoly. The Empire or super-state was already fragmented. Conflict and competition raged: between states, classes, individuals and organizations. The modern world is a child of such circumstances, and does not make for a quiet life. It does, however, allow for great adventures in science and art. Like many merchant princes today, the Medici were neither model citizens nor model human beings. But more than committees they offered what artists want and need.

Our modern social democracies are seldom, of course, philosophically consistent. They listen to voters and voters often want contradictory things. In Britain, private property rights have eroded steadily throughout this century; this started long before the advent of Socialist governments. Indeed when Socialist governments have been in power they have often proved rather conservative in practice. In the same paradoxical way, highly conservative individuals fight for the right of owners of historic houses, for example, not to be allowed to alter them in any way. Most of the stately houses of England are (from one point of view) modest neo-classical phoenixes rising from the ashes of late-medieval, Tudor or Jacobean buildings. Some were destroyed by accident; some, in what today we would consider acts of vandalism, by design. Part of the fascination of Boughton House, for instance, the principal residence of the Dukes of Buccleuch, is that in the 1680s the family built a French-influenced château without altogether destroying the Tudor Boughton, so the house looks like a small village from the air. I see no reason why a contemporary

PABLO PICASSO
Weeping Woman
SIGNED AND DATED *37,*
OIL ON CANVAS,
60 x 49cm (23 x 19¼in)
Acquired by private treaty
through Sotheby's in October
1987. Now in the collection of
the Tate Gallery, London.
(LEFT)

Duke of Buccleuch should not be allowed to add a comfortable twentieth-century house, if he wished. I cannot see even a Conservative council or government giving him permission to do so.

Perhaps because the erosion of freedom has been slow, Britain at the end of our century does seem to have useful lessons to offer to other states worried by the balance between freedom to own or dispose of property and a nation's sense of its heritage. We should also add the interests of trade

in cultural artifacts to the equation. The art trade earns money and pays taxes and employs people. It is also an essential part of the culture itself, a disseminator. It is surely no coincidence that the decision of the French authorities, after the War, to maintain domestic restrictive practices in the art trade (the *commisseur priseur* system) saw the gradual erosion, against all environmental and historical odds, of Paris as the artistic capital of Europe. The action turned to London and New

ANTONIO CANOVA
The Three Graces
This version of this famous subject (which is similar to another version formerly at Woburn Abbey) is in the collection of the Duke of Rutland at Belvoir Castle. The Belvoir Estate does not have, nor has had, any plans to sell the Belvoir Castle Canova.
(ABOVE)

York, and later to German cities like Cologne. These centres were more open and international in respect of markets. The art market is not an evil imposed on a culture, or even a necessary evil for a culture to endure. It is part of that culture and tradition, part of the heritage; next year, for instance, Sotheby's will celebrate its two-hundred-and-fiftieth birthday. There are signs that Paris may be changing its view. If that is so, London must look to its laurels. The collecting hinterland of Britain is rather small for Britain to remain at the centre of the international trade for ever.

Since before the First World War, Britain has nevertheless balanced three important interests: the nation's concern for its heritage; the ownership of private property; the needs of legitimate commerce. The system gives a committee of expert advisors the chance to recommend to the Government that a work be denied an export licence for a sufficient period of time to allow a national institution (the system does not distort trade between individuals) to raise the funds needed to acquire it. There are also financial incentives for individuals to settle tax demands, usually estate duty, by deeding works of art to the nation. In exceptional circumstances these may be allowed to remain in the collections from which they came. Most of the works here illustrated entered national collections by the last method; it is the business of auction houses and dealers to negotiate the monetary values of any settlements made. Few people criticize the system; many are anxious whether sufficient funds are earmarked by governments to allow it to work effectively. My own view is that no great work of art of the unarguable first rank has left the country since Velasquez's *Portrait of Juan de Perrea* was sold to the Metropolitan Museum in New York in 1972. Canova's *The Three Graces* is to my mind a candidate but that is not a view shared by everyone in the art world.

Today, fifty years after the Second World War, Britain is trying, so far without much success, to edge its European partners towards a comparable balance of interests. Although trade in cultural goods is an immeasurably small part of the total European Community economy, it is also immeasurably sensitive. Issues such as value added tax on works of art, or the free movement of works of art, have created a log-jam of proposed directives. Most have failed to secure agreement and much polite blood has been spilled on official carpets.

Within the Community, there is something of a north-south divide. Italy has threatened to list thirty million works of art as being of national importance. Under this definition you can own such works, in the sense of keeping them on your walls; you may in some cases be able to sell them within the country; you will never be allowed to export them. As any fine art auctioneer knows, Italians are by nationality the most vigorous group of collectors in the world. Italian suspicion of the Italian fiscal system, however, and hostility to the immoderate restrictiveness of Italian heritage laws, have led to substantial holdings of works of art off-shore. A more liberal regime would ensure an influx of works of art for Italy, particularly if the system were guaranteed constitutionally. To a lesser extent, the same is true of Spain. The Spanish do not consider the export of works of art by Velasquez or Goya to Germany, say, as the free movement of goods envisaged by the Treaty of Rome. Nor, to be fair, did the Treaty of Rome. Article 36 of the Treaty allows members to protect their national patrimony. The difficulties arise when you try to define a national patrimony (can it possibly consist of thirty million works of art?) or suggest how member states can come to some kind of working agreement about it.

The northern states, as befits their protestant and nonconformist tradition, are more liberal. If Britain, or Germany, wish to prevent you from exporting a work of art they can do so. The instrument is delay only: they must in the end purchase the work at a fair market price. Before we get too sentimental about the northern states, it must be said that their fiscal arrangements, notably capital taxation, result in shooting themselves (or rather their taxpayers) in the foot. If conserving works of art is your aim, taxing capital is crazy. You want more capital, not less of it. Even held passively, in the form of works of art, capital generates interest, activity and employment. Most of the private treaty sales Sotheby's conducts between individuals and national institutions are dictated by the need to settle estate or capital taxes. The state ends up having to pay for something it had no need to acquire in the first place. A great majority of British private collections are open to the public on a regular basis; all but very few may be visited by appointment. Open market countries like Switzerland – at the heart of Europe though not of the Community – are much more sensible. Nor is there any evidence that the Swiss suffer cultural deprivation where works of art are concerned.

In some ways the pivot of the European Community, France may in the end determine how things turn out. It is understandably pro- tective of an earlier part of its heritage, having lost so much as a consequence of the French Revolution, not least to Britain and thence, over time, to the United States and the wider world. Yet France has been generous to the point of profligacy in recent times, its astonishing dominance in the visual arts in the century to 1950 notwithstanding. Perhaps a self-confident culture is always outward looking. A lively artistic scene is to a

SIR ANTHONY VAN DYCK
Portrait of Lord John and Lord Bernard Stuart
OIL ON CANVAS,
237 x 121cm (93½ x 47½in)
Acquired by private treaty through Sotheby's in April 1988. Now in the collection of the National Gallery, London.
(ABOVE)

The Gospels of Henry the Lion
LOWER SAXONY, C.1175-80
London £8,140,000
($11,314,600). 6.XII.83
Now in the Herzog-August-Bibliothek, Wolfenbüttel, Lower Saxony (ABOVE RIGHT)

A three-quarter suit of armour made for Henry of Valois,
DECORATED BY GIOVANNI PAOLO NEGROLI, C.1540-45, London £1,925,000 ($3,080,000). 5.V.83 (ABOVE)

very great degree eclectic. It borrows. It exchanges ideas and objects and styles. It values the immigrant and approves of exile. You do a lot of harm by trying to restrict it. Henry Moore is the most famous modern British sculptor. He was for years better known, and more widely seen, in the United States than in Britain. With the inevitable shift in reputation following his death, he is perhaps most appreciated now in Italy and Japan. The only queues I have seen for the work of another modern British master, Francis Bacon, were in Paris and Moscow. Ebb and flow of reputation is a requisite of artistic freedom. The hope today must be for Paris to resume its place as one of the most outward-looking, cosmopolitan and culturally dynamic cities of the world.

It is odd that the European Community, in aggregate the richest group of nations in the world, is still so conditioned by the psychology of poverty. An obsession with heritage or export controls – with the feeling that your culture is up for grabs: raped by rich foreigners, ripped off by unscrupulous dealers – such is the embodiment of defeat: a folk-memory, almost, of tanks riding over your fields and trains carting off your paintings. Fifty years after the War, it is time we Europeans rid ourselves of such memories.

Britannia, as so often, is in some respects the odd woman out. Most other European countries consider their patrimony to be works of art owned by national collections or created by national artists. This applies very broadly and of course there are circumstances in which it would be extremely difficult to obtain an export licence for a Dutch painting from Italy, say, or an Italian painting from France. But in the case of Britain, about 80 per cent of our patrimony (including, in this instance, works in public collections), was once the patrimony of other people. That is the legacy of long periods of wealth and stability while others were less wealthy and less stable. It is also the legacy of imperialism. One nation's idea of heritage may be another nation's idea of loot. There are times, therefore, when the re-export of works of art is thoroughly desirable; how proud we were at Sotheby's to 're-patriate' the Gospels of Henry the Lion to Germany in 1983, or the Irish Bronze Age gold to Ireland in 1989. There are also times when it may be desirable to export a work by a national artist. When we sold John Constable's *The Lock* in 1990, an export licence was not issued for a considerable length of time as the Tate Gallery hoped to raise funds to acquire it. The Tate had every right to do so under our system, which does not confiscate but gives national institutions time to match the open market price. Nevertheless I myself believed we should have won the Queen's Award for Exports. Constable is not sufficiently seen in Europe, in spite of his substantial influence on the development of French painting. *The Lock's* arrival in a great European collection, the Thyssen-Bornemisza Collection in Madrid, should have been an occasion for rejoicing, and not only at Sotheby's. Were I a benevolent dictator, I would even consider selling one or two Turners or Constables from our national collections in order to purchase a great Goya, say, or a Georges de la Tour. The call is unlikely to come.

Of course death and taxes, money and trade are not the only threats to a nation's heritage. There is accident – this year in Britain we recall with great sympathy the dreadful fire at Windsor Castle – and theft. One of the greatest paintings in the long distinction of British portraiture is Lucian Freud's 1952 painting of Francis Bacon. It is at once a Memling-like masterpiece of the northern Renaissance and a thoroughly modern work; the critic Robert Hughes memorably described Bacon's face as looking like a hand-grenade about to go off. It is very small and painted on copper and belongs to the Tate Gallery. It was stolen off the wall at a loan exhibition in Berlin in 1988.

I suspect it was stolen by someone who liked it, not a commercially minded thief. It is a portrait of one great painter by another. It would be easy to return anonymously. Whoever you are, please give it back. It belongs to a national gallery. It is incontrovertibly ours.

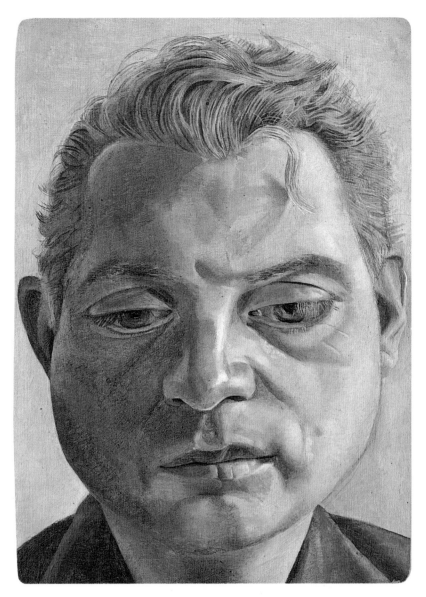

LUCIAN FREUD
Portrait of Francis Bacon
OIL ON COPPER,
17.8 x 12.7cm (7 x 5in)
From the collection of the Tate
Gallery (ABOVE)

THE NEW MEDICI *by Mabel H. Brandon*

The famous prices paid by Japanese organizations for Impressionist paintings during the late 1980s make it impossible to ignore the importance of corporate collectors in the art world. In the United States in recent years corporate buying has at times been responsible for over 30 per cent of all new art bought in the country, and while in Britain and other Western countries the figures are not quite as startling, the corporate collecting of works of art is both widespread and lively. The buying power of corporate collectors now exerts phenomenal muscle in many of the major art market centres in the world, and corporate collections of art now amount to an extraordinary resource, rivalling, in some cities, collections made by public institutions. Corporate support for the arts in the form of sponsorship also plays a mighty role in the international art world, and few great exhibitions of recent years have not relied upon such support to some degree or other.

Although the enormous influence of corporate patronage is largely a phenomenon of the last twenty years, corporate patronage is not a new invention, nor indeed solely a twentieth-century one. It could be argued that many of the great dynastic collectors of past centuries, such as the Medici, the Hapsburgs and the Bourbons, collected for reasons that were not entirely private, nor entirely altruistic. More direct ancestors of today's corporate collectors might be claimed amongst the guilds of late medieval Europe, who are renowned for having commissioned many precious and splendid works of art, chiefly as ceremonial objects.

The advent of the corporate collector in a wholly modern sense can be traced to the early eighteenth century, when a number of British merchant houses and banks commissioned prominent artists to paint portraits of leading members of staff. The Bank of England, Lloyds Bank and the Midland Bank still display collections of such portraits in their boardrooms and offices, and continue to add to them intermittently with new examples.

The level of commitment to the arts by these 'new Medici' was enhanced dramatically by the growing importance of advertising in corporate affairs. In the nineteenth century shops, hotels and other organizations employed graphic artists and illustrators to help promote business, but it was not until the first few decades of the new century that fine art came to be used regularly in advertising. One of the most famous examples in Britain of such a union is that originated by the oil company Shell. One of Shell's London employees in the 1920s, Jack Beddington, was offered responsibility for the company's advertising after having complained that existing efforts were too mundane. He it was who started a tradition of commissioning contemporary artists to design posters depicting places

PAUL NASH
The Rye Marshes
POSTER
One of a series of works commissioned by Shell for its 1930s' campaign 'Everywhere you go you can be sure of Shell'.
(BELOW)

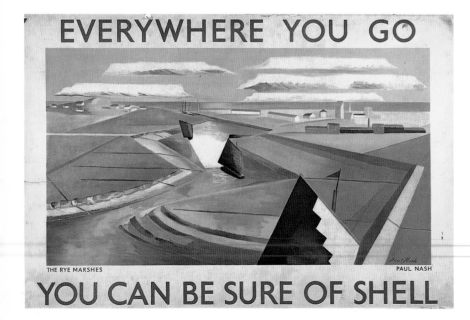

Find Michelangelo at the V&A
Nearest station South Kensington

Find Michelangelo at the V&A by R B Kitaj RA
A new work of art commissioned by London Underground

R. B. KITAJ
**Find Michelangelo
at the V&A**
POSTER
One of a series of works
commissioned by London
Underground for its current
campaign 'Art on the
Underground'. (RIGHT)

to visit in the British Isles using Shell petrol. Although many of the artists who were asked to take part in the campaign were little known at the time, they are now considered as having been some of the greatest of those years: Ben Nicholson, Graham Sutherland, Rex Whistler, Vanessa Bell, Edward Bawden, Paul Nash, Edward Ardizzone and Tristram Hillier.

Beddington was not alone at that time in using such ideas. Stephen Tallents at the Post Office and Frank Pick at London Transport were also commissioning works from 'serious' artists to convey simple messages to the public. The early posters Pick commissioned were designed by commercial artists employed by the printers, but he soon moved beyond this limited source and made direct contact with established artists like Frank Brangwyn, also experimenting with new and untried names. His greatest 'discovery' was the American-born Edward McKnight Kauffer, who produced his first poster for the Underground in 1915 and went on to design over a

hundred more during the next twenty-five years. In the 1920s and 30s Pick commissioned posters from a huge variety of known and unknown artists, offering them the kind of massive exposure they could not hope to find through the usual gallery system. As well as having an unquestionably modern approach to the commercial application of art, Pick passionately believed that his posters should fulfil a loftier purpose: to enrich the quality of urban life in London, and it is certainly true that it was through the London Underground posters of the 1920s and 30s that many members of the public were first introduced to such concepts as Cubism, Futurism and Vorticism. London Transport has produced advertising campaigns using posters by contemporary artists ever since. There have been lean years, particularly in the 1950s and 60s, but the current campaign – 'Art on the Underground' – seems to have revived much of the success of those early years, using works by such established British artists as John Bellany, Ruskin Spear, Anthony Green, Frederick Gore and R. B. Kitaj.

In the United States, similar developments were underway in the 1920s and 30s. There, the first company to commission paintings specifically for advertising purposes was Steinway and Sons, which asked artists such as Harvey Dunn, N. C. Wyeth, Ernest L. Blumenschein and Rockwell Kent to create images in keeping with Steinway's musical interests. Other corporations soon began to appreciate the potential usefulness of such art, notably Hallmark Cards, which purchased works by Norman Rockwell, Charles Sheeler and Grandma Moses for use on its products. Before Steinway's involvement, the Atchison, Topeka and Santa Fe Railway Company had started to buy paintings representing the history of the American West by artists such as Walter Ufer, E. I. Course, Oscar Berninghaus and William Robinson Leigh. Many of the images were used for advertisements and dining-car menus, but it is particularly noteworthy that this was one of the first instances of an American corporation making a collection of art.

The idea of building a major 'museum-quality' corporate art collection was first taken seriously in the United States by International Business

Machines (IBM) which set out in 1939 to create two distinct collections. One was to be composed of international contemporary art, representing countries where IBM did business; the other was to gather together works by contemporary American artists. The IBM collections now include important paintings by Frederick Church, Alfred Bierstadt, Edward Hopper and Andrew Wyeth.

The post-War period popularized many different ways of involving art and artists in corporate affairs. Art was thought of as a good business investment, and a growing number of companies began to believe that it could add to their overall image of sophistication and prestige, while also helping to create a stimulating environment for employees and clients. Other facets of corporate patronage emerged in the United States, including the sponsorship of art competitions. Hallmark Cards, Pepsi-Cola, Metro-Goldwyn Mayer and Abbott Laboratories all initiated competitive events, and then purchased the winning entries to add to their permanent collections.

The 1960s saw a sharp increase in the numbers of American companies becoming involved in corporate collecting. The Chase Manhattan Bank started its extraordinary collection, which now comprises over 2,000 works including pieces by Francis Bacon, Francesco Clemente and Naim June Paik. Also in the 1960s, Time Inc. began its collection of commissioned works for use on the magazine's front cover. Among the artists commissioned for this task were such leading contemporary figures as George Segal, Alex Katz, Alice Neel, Irving Penn and Richard Avedon. Other American corporate collectors of this period included the Atlantic Richfield Company and Coca-Cola, which focused on major contemporary artists like Frank Stella, Andy Warhol and Picasso. At the same time Pepsico was creating an extraordinary sculpture garden designed by Russell Page in Purchase, New York, to show its outstanding collection of twentieth-century sculpture. During the last thirty years other companies in the United States have built indoor gallery spaces to display their collections. AT&T, IBM, the Prudential Insurance Company, General Mills, Paine-Webber, Bristol-Myers Squibb, the Equitable Life Assurance Company,

Security Pacific National Bank (now part of BankAmerica), and the Bank of Boston have all created their own galleries housed in large modern buildings. Two corporations have even built their own separate museums to house their collections: in Dearborn, Michigan, the Ford Motor Company built the Henry Ford Museum and Greenfield Village, and in Corning, New York, the Owens-Corning Fiberglass Corporation has set up the Corning Museum of Glass.

In Britain, the corporate collecting scene had been active since the 1930s. Baring Brothers, one of the oldest and most distinguished of London's private banks, had started its collection in the late 1920s when the late Lord Ashburton gathered together extraneous portraits and other pictures from Baring family collections. In this way Barings obtained, mostly on a loan basis, a fine collection of eighteenth- and nineteenth-century pictures including works by Lawrence, Reynolds, Gainsborough and Linnell. Further collecting at Barings was quiet until the 1970s, when a new generation of partners took over and the bank moved to new buildings. The nature of merchant banking was changing fast, creating the need for large numbers of rooms for meeting and entertaining clients, all of which had to be furnished to a high standard. Barings' response, like IBM's before it, was to build two distinct collections. One comprised eighteenth- and nineteenth-century British watercolours, complementing the existing collection of Baring family pictures; the other concentrated on works by modern British artists. These two collections, now firmly established, provide reflections of two sides of the essential character of the company: one modern and one traditional.

A number of different individuals had been involved in building the Barings collections, but in other cases in Britain the clear tastes of one person can easily be discerned. Robert Hiscox at Hiscox Holdings, Sir Nicholas Goodison at the Trustees Savings Bank and Alex Bernstein at Granada Television have all had strong influences on their companies' collections. All, significantly, in the area of modern British paintings.

There is no doubt that the 1980s provided the liveliest decade for corporate collecting, and it is

not difficult to see why. Equally unsurprising is the more circumspect attitude that seems to be common in the 1990s. By 1988, some 80 per cent of the business support for the arts worldwide came from profits and revenues, compared to only 61 per cent in 1991. The recent economic recession, international mergers and acquisitions, and the decrease in corporate building construction have all contributed to a general climate of retrenchment. At BankAmerica the acquisition of Security Pacific Bank and Valley Bank doubled the size of the parent corporate art collection, requiring a completely new inventory and evaluation of the enlarged collection. Additional budget cuts have reduced the purchasing funds which are now restricted to acquisitions of art for new buildings. Similar budget reductions indicate profound changes in corporate patronage budgets around the world.

Corporate support for the arts in general, however, remains surprisingly healthy. A new relationship between business and the arts has developed that is now an integral part of corporate affairs, just as it is a vital part of the art world. In many Western nations government initiatives have encouraged such a union. In the United States encouragement for corporate support of the arts was generated in 1935 when the United States Internal Revenue Services permitted corporations to deduct up to 50 per cent of pre-tax income for gifts to qualified charities. Museums were amongst the early beneficiaries, but at the conclusion of the Second World War businesses were still contributing only a relatively small percentage. It was not until the mid-1960s, with the establishment of the National Endowment for the Arts, that corporations and the arts in the United States forged a partnership that was to have strong repercussions in museums and art markets around the world.

The first such organizations to be formed in Europe were the Association for Business Sponsorship of the Arts in Britain (founded in 1976) and ADMICAL in France (formed in 1979). These initiatives encouraged other countries to follow suit, producing the Stichting Sponsors voor Kunstin in the Netherlands, and similar organizations in Belgium, Greece, Ireland and

MICHAEL AYRTON
Night-Fall
SIGNED AND DATED 49,
OIL ON BOARD,
69 x 51cm (27 x 20in)
London £8,250 ($17,100).
7.XI.90
Now in the collection of Baring Brothers & Co. Ltd. (LEFT)

JOHN DICKSON INNES
Cactus
SIGNED, OIL ON PANEL,
23 x 33cm (9 x 13in)
London £9,600 ($20,100).
7.XI.90
Now in the collection of Baring Brothers & Co. Ltd. (BELOW LEFT)

Outside the Toledo Museum of Art, during the 1989 touring exhibition *Impressionism; Selections from Five American Museums,* sponsored by the Ford Motor Company. (RIGHT)

PAUL SIGNAC
Place des Lices, Saint-Tropez
OIL ON CANVAS,
65.8 x 82cm (25¾ x 32⅛in)
This work from the Carnegie Museum of Art was included in the 1989 touring exhibition *Impressionism; Selections from Five American Museums.*
(ABOVE)

The main entrance of the Henry Ford Museum in Dearborn, Michigan, built by the Ford Motor Company.
(ABOVE RIGHT)

Austria. In Britain, business sponsorship of the arts increased significantly through the 1980s. 1984 saw the creation of the Business Sponsorship Incentive Scheme managed by the Association for Business Sponsorship of the Arts. The British Government offered to match funds, pledging one pound for every three pounds donated by new business sponsors. This brought a great number of new corporate patrons and sponsors into the arena, and increased financial support for the arts by some £27 million.

American corporations, despite the recent economic recession, continue to be the world leaders in arts support. According to a recent Business Committee for the Arts survey, 38 per cent of the businesses in the United States gave $518 million to the arts in 1991. This was a decrease from the $634 million given in 1988, but at that time only 35 per cent of businesses were involved. In comparison with such sums, Japanese businesses donated approximately $195 million in 1991-2, while British businesses gave the equivalent of around $129 million during the same year.

It is universally recognized by museum directors throughout the world that the era of the 'blockbuster' exhibition of the 1980s is drawing to a close. It is more than likely that such major American exhibitions as *Gauguin* and *The Age of Sultan Suleiman the Magnificent,* both sponsored by Phillip Morris, the *Post-Impressionism* show, sponsored by GTE, and *The New Impressionism,* sponsored by AT & T, will become less frequent in the future. The prohibitive costs of insurance have driven sponsorship requests too high for most major companies. A recent innovative experiment by a consortium of five American museums may, however, indicate a pattern for the future. Combining their permanent French Impressionist collections in 1989, museums in Kansas City, St Louis, Minneapolis, Toledo and Pittsburgh created a major travelling exhibition entitled *Impressionism: Selections from Five American Museums.* The event was sponsored by the

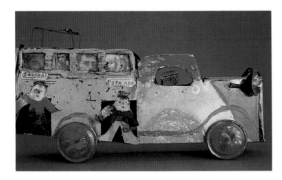

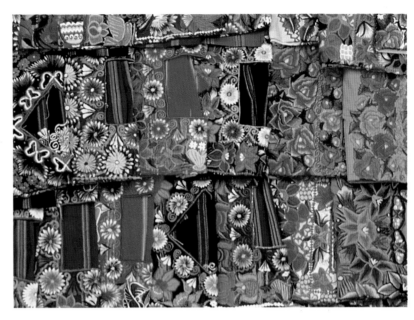

Ford Motor Company. An additional grant from the sponsor enabled the creation of strong educational and community outreach programmes, as well as strategic marketing and advertising campaigns. Each of the five cities became the beneficiary of these combined programmes, heightening the visibility of the corporate sponsor, as well as furnishing needed educational materials to teachers and pupils in local schools. By sharing their splendid collections and pooling staff resources, the museums were able to reduce greatly the cost of hosting such an exhibition.

Aware of current debates, the corporate community is increasingly turning its attention to critical social problems, which demand a more sophisticated involvement in the arts. In fragmented and diverse urban societies the corporate support of arts is now seen as being able to provide real benefits for common cultural education, as well as creating a possible bridge of understanding in ethnically polarized communities. In this new mode, the Ford Motor Company is sponsoring an innovative travelling exhibition of Latin American folk art, *Visiones del Pueblo: the Folk Art of Latin America*. Exhibition materials are bilingual and distributed widely throughout the educational system. Teacher-training workshops have been supported at each host museum to integrate the exhibition material into the arts and history curricula of local schools.

The roles that companies interested in the arts can play are many. The use of fine art in advertising can greatly help to give known and unknown artists a level of exposure unavailable elsewhere, while also introducing large sections of the public to works of art they might otherwise not see. The

building of art collections by corporations can also offer support to the artistic community, especially since the majority of corporate collectors seem to favour the work of contemporary artists. There has been a great deal of research compiled on the reasons why companies involve themselves in the arts. A survey taken in the United States in 1991 by the Business Committee for the Arts revealed that 91 per cent of companies involved in sponsorship were motivated by the desire to create an image of good corporate citizenship within the community. Some of the other motivations unearthed by the survey include the strengthening of employee relations, and the drive for higher visibility in the marketplace through the use of corporate advertising highlighting the arts.

The effect of corporate patronage on the art world is now substantial. Business sponsorship of museums, travelling exhibitions and other events is now a vital element in arts programming in many countries. Art markets, too, have come to rely heavily on corporate buyers. Clearly, the levels of cultural influence and responsibility gained by the 'new Medici', if not quite yet on a par with the achievements of the most glorious Renaissance princes, have earned the corporate sector a significant place in art historical study.

Exhibits from the 1993 travelling exhibition *Visiones del Pueblo: the Folk Art of Latin America*, sponsored by the Ford Motor Company. (ABOVE AND ABOVE LEFT)

ART ON TELEVISION *by Melvyn Bragg*

There are those who believe that the arts and television are mutually incompatible. There are others who claim that television itself is the arts centre of the second half of this century, a period impossible to understand or evaluate without giving television the fullest recognition. The former think that in the future television will be seen to have been a wart on the true values and civilization of the late twentieth century. The latter believe that, in a hundred years' time, those wishing to know about this extraordinary century will watch endless loops of videos. Somewhat aside from the larger debates which could be generated by the clash of such polarities, there are arts programmes.

Arts programmes flourish in British television. In one way this is surprising: they are not widely watched, they are often quite specialised, they

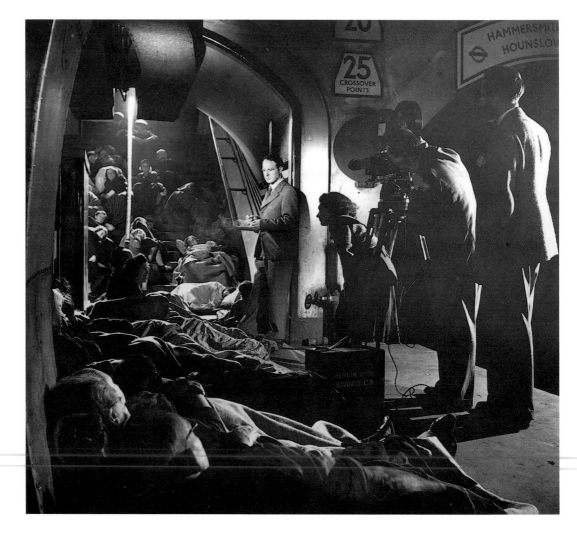

Henry Moore sketching in the Underground in 1943, filmed by Jill Craigie for *Out of Chaos*, a film organized and presented by Kenneth Clark. (RIGHT)

cater for one of the smaller segments of a richly segmented society, and they serve an audience which can have wider access to their core material elsewhere. Why watch the television programme, you might ask, when you could read the book, see the play, go to the gallery, go to the opera, watch the movie or hum the tune? But people do, in numbers that may be low by television's soap opera standards, but which are vast by, say, Covent Garden's opera attendance standards. A programme like *The South Bank Show* or *Omnibus*, provided it is transmitted at around 10.30 in the evening, can claim an average audience of two and a half to three million, and this sometimes for subjects which could be considered as way out of the mainstream, and not given much attention even by the sterner broadsheets.

It was a very much smaller audience that began watching television when the BBC first mounted regular transmissions in 1936. These were suspended in 1939, to restart in 1946. The pattern of arts programmes was set early, and owed much to the developments made by BBC Radio in the 1930s and 40s. Early in the field was John Read, son of Sir Herbert Read, who educated two generations in the Isms of twentieth-century art. His finely crafted documentary profiles on artists of the day encouraged the artist to reflect on his own work, and showed that work sympathetically to a public assumed to be interested but not especially learned. The first of Read's film profiles – on Henry Moore – was made for the BBC in 1951 and lasted twenty-six minutes.

The piece introduces Moore's art with views of his sculpture and film of him at work, accompanied by music composed for the film by William Alwyn. After a narration noting early career details, we are shown Primitive sculpture in the British Museum, with Moore speaking into camera on the immediacy of Primitive art. The artist then enthuses about the qualities of natural forms – stones, shells and bones – before we move to shots of Moore's life drawings, war drawings and maquettes, followed by four large stone and bronze works of the 1940s shown *in situ*. We cut to Moore drawing in his notebook, with voice-over quotations on

the creative process. The film finishes with our following a large-scale work from drawing and maquette through plaster and casting process to finished work and installation.

As a film study of the work of one artist it is a classic format, and one that Read was to explore and expand throughout the decade with films on Graham Sutherland, Stanley Spencer, John Piper, L.S. Lowry and others.

Read's films were a response to the age, and would not have been possible without an accompanying rise in the British public's interest in art. The post-War optimism of the 1950s generated an atmosphere that was as exciting for the arts as it was for television. The Festival of Britain awoke an enormous audience to new cultural adventures; John Osborne and Harold Pinter were electrifying the theatre; Pop Art was waiting in the art-school wings; a new age had begun and television was to play a leading role.

In 1958, all of Read's profiles were re-run as part of the opening of a new arts magazine programme that, for many years, was to set the pace – *Monitor*. *Monitor* was edited by Huw Wheldon, who had an infectious enthusiasm for the arts, and whose background had been in children's programmes. He was a fierce

Henry Moore helps to arrange his sculpture for the camera during the filming of John Read's BBC documentary *A Sculptor's Landscape* in 1958. (ABOVE)

editor, holding to clarity, teasing the best out of directors and gravely tackling artists about their work. It was the combination of good film-making, accessibility and the un-concealed view of art as a celebration which caught a mood. Although much of Wheldon's work has been mocked and knocked since that time, both the mood and the approach were true enough to give the programme lasting fame. Marcel Duchamp, Ezra Pound, Paul Tortelier, Ben Shan, Orson Welles – *Monitor's* roll call of those who were per-suaded to give insights into their own work is very impressive indeed.

Not all of *Monitor's* investigations into art were in the manner of a John Read profile. Apart from head-to-head interviews, there was also a number of dramatized biographies by Ken Russell, providing an extra dimension to the programme and a new format for the exploration of art on television. Russell's openly poetic films, notably those on the lives of Elgar, Debussy and Delius, have some claim to being works of art themselves, and were to set off a confidence in film for film's sake which was to ignite talent throughout 1960s' television.

Although *Monitor* set many of the standards for arts magazine programmes for years to come, it was by no means the only television pro-gramme covering the arts at that time that was to have a lasting influence. *Panorama* and *Tonight* – both current affairs programmes – included inter-views with authors in the 1950s, and established the idea of dealing in a topical way with living artists, something which continues today, most abundantly on *The Late Show*. Kenneth Tynan's ITV programme *Tempo*, which first came on the air in 1961, attempted to cast a cooler eye on the arts world – an approach now finely honed in the *Without Walls* series.

In the 1960s, although ITV produced arts programmes (some, as today, regional magazines which outclassed the BBC) it was the BBC which began the build-up to the present heavy representation of the arts on the screen. BBC2 came along a little like an afterthought, and the younger end in television were given precious air time, small budgets and *carte blanche*. Many new programme ideas reached the screen, including such pieces as *New Release*, a topical arts pro-gramme which aimed to do what *Monitor* did but for a younger or different audience. *New Release* included films on Salvador Dali in New York, David Jones in his bedsit in Harrow, and Jean Renoir in his house in Paris. On BBC1, *Omnibus* took over from *Monitor*, which, in an exhilarating roller-coaster run with Jonathan Miller as editor, had introduced a shocked British public to the seriously questing world of Susan Sontag, Robert Lowell and others of the New York Intelligentsia.

The 1960s also saw the rise of a new phen-omenon in arts programming, a format that was to gain enormous popularity and command huge budgets: the blockbuster series. The first of these, broadcast in 1968, was *Civilisation – A Personal View*. The 'person' was the art critic and former Director of the National Gallery, Kenneth Clark. His chosen task, to summarize the artistic achievements of man. Clark had already had some involvement in television and film, and as early as 1937 had chaired a quiz programme that he later claimed to have been the first arts programme on British television. In 1943 he organized and presented *Out of Chaos*, a docu-mentary on artists in wartime involving Moore, Sutherland, Paul Nash and Spencer. The format of *Civilisation*, with the presenter as lecturer, was an idea born in the academic world, but one which transferred to television with remarkable success. Clark's superbly confident manner was the key to that success. Twenty-five years on, his manner seems almost ludicrously grandiose. As Isaiah Berlin is said to have commented, 'It was all very well, but Clark did rather give the impression that civilisation wouldn't have happened without him.'

A small sample will serve to remind us of the style of the programme. Clark, dressed in a tweed suit with head held high, is walking towards the camera past an Adam fireplace in an ordered eighteenth-century drawing room. He is talking. 'An enclosed world becomes a prison of the spirit, one longs to get out, one longs to move, one realises that uniformity and consistency, whatever their merits, are

Kenneth Clark on the Isle of
Iona in western Scotland during
the filming of his BBC series
Civilisation – A Personal View in
1968. (LEFT)

enemies of movement.' A chord is struck on
the soundtrack. 'And what is that I hear? That
note of urgency, of indignation, of spiritual
hunger. Yes, it's Beethoven, it's the sound
of European man, once more reaching for
something beyond his grasp. We must leave
this trim, finite room and go to confront the
infinite.' At which point Clark flings open a
pair of doors at the end of the drawing room to
reveal the sea crashing on some rocks below.
'We've a long, rough voyage ahead of us.'
Whether this was good history or not, it was
certainly a wonderful piece of television.

This kind of 'personal view' lecture series
became a frequently used format in the 1970s
and on into the 80s. Some of the more memorable include Professor Bronowski's *The Ascent of
Man*, John Berger's *Ways of Seeing*, Ronald Har-
wood's *All the World's a Stage*, Margot Fonteyn's
The Magic of Dance, Jonathan Miller's *The Body
in Question* and Robert Hughes' *The Shock of the
New*. All of these offered us a personal view,
although in the majority of cases, it was easy to
mistake that personal view for some concept of
established truth. Berger's *Ways of Seeing* stands
out as one of the few of such programmes to

Leon Golub in his studio from Sandy Nairne's 1987 Channel 4 series *State of the Art.* (ABOVE)

question seriously the validity of having only one point of view about a subject. This was something that was tackled head on in Sandy Nairne's series *State of the Art*, which looked at contemporary art in the 1980s. Instead of having a single, visible presenter on screen to take us through the subject, Nairne provided a collage of disembodied voices reading, commenting and reminiscing.

State of the Art was made for Channel 4, which was introduced in 1982 as the fourth British television broadcast service, with an obligation to service minority audiences, and to 'encourage innovation and experiment in the form and content of programmes'. With its arrival, the stream of arts programmes became a flood. Channel 4 was, and remains, frequently bolder than the other channels, and the current vigour of its arts programme is exemplary.

ITV now puts out about thirty hours a month of arts programming nationally, and many more in its regions. The BBC has recently beefed up its commitment to *Omnibus* on BBC1, where the number of hours had fallen sadly, although surprisingly the numbers still fall short of its mirror image on ITV. Channel 4 darts around the territory and also keeps a regular presence. BBC2 relays opera – as does Channel 4 – and sets itself big targets, especially in its current preoccupation with film, while *The*

Late Show fulfils an arts news and review role too long neglected by television.

We have come a long way since John Read first filmed Henry Moore. The arts are now a wider brief. The choice is not, for example, Dylan or Keats, but both, with a current leaning towards the former. It is taken for granted by editors of all the television programmes that Rembrandt can be included in the same season as John Lee Hooker; that a series by John Berger can be commissioned by the same editor who wants to bring in the Blues. Television dramatists, film directors and screen writers are as much on the agenda as poets and painters. The 'low' art of television has gobbled up its inheritance and redelivered it in a variety of forms, including cannibalizing and redelivering its own self.

One of the main pulses is still the educative – even evangelical – notion that art can be discussed, be explained, to some extent be taught, and that this will do the viewer good. This is now challenged far more than it used to be, but the tendency is still very strong. The observation that television programmes lack a critical edge is justified, both in the general failure to challenge the strong current thinking that art is good for you, and in a particular failure to take on artists with the sort of oppositional vigour found in so many newspapers and magazines. What is not argued so much is that there are other ways of doing, other ways of meeting and embracing artists, different places to stand.

Unpredictability must be allowed to play its part. It could not have been planned, for example, that Francis Bacon would join in his own *South Bank Show* self-portrait in 1985 with such a vengeance, and with such compelling results. It must surely always be exciting and enlightening to attempt, with an artist as collaborator, the journey towards uncovering what that artist had in mind. If the producer and the researcher have genuine respect and admiration for the artist, it is a quest which, though it can never fully succeed, can, on the road to failure, bring some valuable revelations.

One thing that is not in doubt is the calibre of those involved. That Kenneth Clark took the necessary time and trouble, not merely to top and

Carlo Maria Mariani in his studio from the 1987 Channel 4 series *State of the Art*. (ABOVE)

tail a series or do a short voice-over, but to write and help construct what was, for so many, a defining arts experience, is testimony to the attractions that British television has held and still holds for all those connected with the arts. Building on the Reithian experience of BBC Radio in the 1930s and 40s, with its determined alliances with the best creative talents of the day, British television was from very early on considered a place where composers, authors and artists of all kinds saw that they could do good work, have it produced with care, and reach an audience of millions. They were willing to come into the arena with television and join forces with a medium which in other countries artists despised. Thanks to the basic trust that grew up in radio days, British television in the second half of the twentieth century now has an archive of artists creating, performing, discussing and dissecting their own and others' work which will be of unparalleled value in the future.

Nor is there any doubt, as Clark said towards the end of his series, that 'the informed audience for art is much bigger and more thoroughly informed than ever before'. Television has played some part in this. Its failures have often occurred when it has tried to ape the newspapers and the magazines, and simply deliver review columns in hardback chairs. Its successes have been when it has gone back to its own medium, to documentary, the eclectic collage which may indeed make television itself an art form. It is a mongrel beast, but it seems that in the area of the arts, it is also a commendably energetic and frisky beast.

THE GROWING MARKETS OF ASIA *by John L. Tancock*

During the period since the Gulf War, when recessions of varying degrees of severity have affected the fortunes of developed countries around the world, the ability of the economies of the Asian nations to weather international trends and local traumas has been remarkable. At a time when the annual economic growth rate of the developed member countries of the Organization of Economic Cooperation and Development amounts to only 1½ per cent, the nations of Asia (the newly industrialized economies, the members of the Association of Southeast Asian Nations and China) have been achieving rates of 7 per cent and more. The 'New World Order' has yet to materialize, but in Asia far-reaching political changes, together with industrial might,

have led to a situation in which the Asian nations are much more likely to show strong economic growth in the next decade than the countries of Europe or America.

On the political front, events such as the lifting of martial law in Taiwan in 1987 and the removal of restrictions on travel to China have had major repercussions. In August 1992 China established diplomatic relations with South Korea and, at the fourteenth Congress of the Communist Party of China, reaffirmed the country's market-oriented 'reform and opening' policy. Against this background of major political change the Asian nations have been able to create a multilateral trade structure. As a result of rising labour costs in their own countries, Japan and the newly industrialized economies have vastly increased their investments in Indonesia, Malaysia and Thailand. It is a fluid situation, but without doubt Asia is the area of the world where most wealth is currently being created. With such a shift in the balance of economic power taking place, the implications for the international art market are clear: henceforth, the nations of Asia will assume an increasingly important role.

Of all the Asian nations, Japan has the most developed and diversified art market, and the longest history of collecting Western art. The Japanese enthusiasm for Western art, particularly French Impressionism and the École de Paris, was certainly one of the main factors contributing to the extraordinary rise in prices during the second half of the 1980s. Equally, the abrupt withdrawal of these newly affluent buyers was one of the main causes of the steep decline of this market in 1990-1. Long before this episode, however, there was a tradition of collecting that was the opposite in all respects to this very public display of wealth. Discreet and intensely private, Japanese collectors demanded similar characteristics of the dealers who handled their affairs.

ZHANG DAQIAN
Grand View of the Blue Mountains (detail)
SIGNED AND DATED *REN YIN* [1962], SET OF FOUR HANGING SCROLLS, INK AND COLOUR ON PAPER, 195 x 555.4cm (76¾ x 218¾in)
Hong Kong HK$7,480,000 (£613,100:$971,400). 29.X.92
(RIGHT)

Long-established relationships based on trust characterized an art market that was essentially closed. Goods changed hands at private auctions organized with great frequency by the *bijutsu-kai* (association of dealers), but this was never headline news. As a result of an increasing knowledge of the generally more open practices of the West, a much more competitive and ultimately public approach was grafted onto this traditional way of doing business. Today, in the pages of *Nikkei Art*, graphs chart the rise and fall of the fortunes of Renoir and Utrillo, as well as the masters of *yoga* (Japanese Western-style oil painting) and *nihonga* (traditional Japanese-style painting), formerly traded only with the utmost discretion. Now, as the result of a severe recession, the art market in Japan is in a state of shock as it adjusts to the dramatic changes of the last three years. There is still a large amount of collecting, however, albeit at a lower level and in diverse fields, and this is surely an encouraging sign for the future.

In Hong Kong, Taiwan and South Korea the emergence of a developed art market is of more recent origin. There were, of course, sophisticated collectors of Chinese art in Hong Kong when Sotheby's held its first auction there twenty years ago, but it could not have been predicted that this small British colony, until then not known for its cultural sophistication, would shortly become one of the world's leading markets for Chinese art, rivalling London and New York. Many factors account for this startling transformation, not least the colony's economic prowess and its proximity to the other major centres for collecting Chinese art: Japan and Taiwan. Hong Kong did not have the long history of fascination with European culture that characterizes Japan and as a result, when newly affluent businessmen reached a stage when they could begin collecting, pride in the achievements of their own culture prevailed. The Min-Chiu Society, founded in 1960, gathered together a group of fifteen collectors and connoisseurs who would hold fortnightly meetings to discuss new acquisitions of Chinese art. In recent years, essentially private activities of this nature have become the basis for private museums. In 1981 Dr K. S. Lo made his initial donation of Yixing ware, which is now housed in Hong Kong's Flagstaff House Museum of Teaware. More recently, in September 1992, the new facilities of the T. T. Tsui Museum opened in the Old Bank of China building in Central District. The taste of today's Hong Kong collectors is not limited to the traditional areas of Chinese collecting or to the scholarly pursuits of the Min-Chiu Society. Jewellery and Modern Chinese painting are both important areas of collecting activity, with a younger generation responding as much to Western-influenced oil painting as to work in more traditional media. Zhang Daquian's 1962 *Grand View of the Blue Mountains* sold for HK$7,480,000 on 21 October 1992 to a Taipei gallery. On 29 April 1993 a cabochon jadeite ring sold for $684,783 to an Asian collector, giving some idea of the potential of the jewellery market in this part of the world.

The development of the jewellery market by Sotheby's over the last twenty years is paradigmatic of the way other areas of the art market may be expected to develop in the next decade. Through travelling exhibitions, local interest is cultivated and collectors are eventually brought into the international market. At first, a wide range of jewellery was sold in Hong Kong, but recently the emphasis has been on jadeite,

PARK SOO-KEUN
Two Seated Men
OIL ON BOARD,
21.5 x 27.5cm (8½ x 10¾in)
Sold privately through
Sotheby's New York. (BELOW)

PAUL CÉZANNE
Esquisse de
Baigneurs
OIL ON CANVAS,
20.3 x 33cm (8 x 13in)
New York $1,102,500
(£715,900). 11.V.93 (ABOVE)

the stone for which there has been most local enthusiasm, and for which record prices have been achieved. Such exhibitions have led to an increase in the activities of Asian buyers in New York and Geneva, and at the Thurn und Taxis sale on 17 November 1992, 11 per cent of the buyers were Asian. A mutually beneficial dialogue between East and West has been established.

In Taiwan and South Korea the development of active markets is of even more recent origin. In Taipei and Seoul the handful of well-established galleries has been joined by many newcomers representing a broad range of specialities. Although there is a growing familiarity with the art of the West, it is the taste of the older generation that characterizes the first forays of new collectors who can afford to start buying art. The National Palace Museum in Taipei and the National Museum in Seoul are symbols of national pride, setting standards to which private collectors cannot hope to aspire, but the

repatriation of national treasures and the support of more contemporary artists is more possible. Recent Sotheby's auctions in Taipei and auctions of Korean art in New York give clear examples of these trends. Since Taiwanese law forbids the export of works of art more than 100 years' old, Sotheby's devoted its first auction in Taipei (27 March 1992) to Modern and Contemporary Chinese Paintings. Taiwanese collectors had already been an important factor in the success of the Chinese painting sales in Hong Kong and at the first auction *Turtle Mountain Island* by Lia Chi-Chun was bought for $290,820, a world record for a Chinese oil. Taiwanese collectors favour the works of the first generation of modern Taiwanese artists (born just before 1900), and in buying their works feel they are buying part of the history of their newly powerful country.

In South Korea, too, there is an extremely active market for Korean art. In its troubled history of invasions and domination by foreign powers, much has been destroyed or is now in the hands of foreign collectors. Korean celadons, early Buddhist paintings, eighteenth- and nineteenth-century blue and white wares, and works by twentieth-century Korean masters are all eagerly sought after by Korean collectors. On 22 October 1991 a rare silk hanging scroll of the late fourteenth-century Koryo dynasty, the *Water-Moon Avalokitesvara*, was sold at Sotheby's for $1.76 million. Very few scrolls of this type remained in Korea itself, and the possibility of returning this historic work to that country was the cause of enormous pride and excitement.

The art market in such growing economies tends initially to focus on the achievements of indigenous culture, both ancient and modern. Although Japan, with its long engagement with the West, has seen the establishment of an art market in which Western art forms a significant component, elsewhere in Asia this is not yet the case. There are, however, numerous signs that the internationalization of the local art markets will occur with surprising speed. Perhaps the most important factor is the establishment of museums which can provide standards of comparison and criteria for new collectors. In Japan, the building of numerous local and prefectural museums has not always had the desired effect since the building itself often seems to have had priority over the forming of a collection, but the most important of the new museums, including the recently opened Aichi Prefectural Museum in Nagoya, the Tokyo Metropolitan Art Museum and the Osaka Municipal Museum of Art (the last two scheduled to open in 1995 and 1997 respectively), should do much to remedy the currently rather deficient presentation of Modern and Contemporary art in Japan. Other privately founded museums, such as the Idemitsu Museum in Tokyo, and the Kawamura Memorial Museum of Art in Sakura (the collection of the Dai Nippon Ink Company), are models of their kind. Mention has already been made of the new private museums in Hong Kong, but the newly reopened and expanded Hong Kong Museum of Art has provided a much needed forum for the display of its permanent collections and special exhibitions. In South Korea, in addition to the

Imperial *Famille-Rose* 'Nine Peach' vase
QIANLONG SEAL MARK AND PERIOD, height 51.4cm (20¼in)
New York $374,000
(£241,200). 1.XII.92 (LEFT)

massive National Museum of Contemporary Art and the privately funded Seoul Arts Centre, there are numerous corporate museums, including the distinguished Hoam Museum set up by Lee Byung-Chull, the founder of the Samsung Electronics Corporation, and the Sonje Museum of Contemporary Art in Kyongju. In Singapore in 1992 plans were announced to create a museum precinct, to include a Singapore Art Museum scheduled to open by the end of 1994, and an Asian Civilizations Museum. In order to facilitate the rapid building of collections, favourable tax incentives have been announced.

During the past decade the number of international art fairs has increased tremendously in the West, but only recently has the viability of this method of displaying and selling works of art been tested in Asia. The Nihon International Contemporary Art Fair (NICAF) in Yokohama in March 1992 and the first Art Asia Hong Kong held in October 1992 both benefited from extensive international participation as well as generating considerable local interest. The introduction of public auctions in Asia has also begun to change the internal dynamics of the localized art markets, since the public nature of the process and the provision of verifiable information regarding prices is having a strong regulatory

effect. There is no doubt that the introduction of regular, properly catalogued auctions in Hong Kong twenty years ago has done much to stabilize and strengthen the market for Chinese art worldwide. In Japan, the process has been less straightforward, since a highly stratified network of dealers and private auctions already existed. The example provided by Sotheby's with its first auction in Tokyo in October 1989 was shortly followed not only by a newly established auction company Shinwa, but also by the Tokyo Bijutsu Club itself. Unfortunately the timing was bad; the sudden proliferation of auctions coincided with the downturn in the economy.

In China, recent developments have provided a clear indication of the role that that vast country will almost inevitably play in the next century. For the first time since 1949, the authorities in Beijing permitted an auction to take place in which foreigners were officially allowed to purchase works dating back to the earliest periods of Chinese civilization. The Beijing International Auction, held in October 1992, suffered from organizational problems and appears not to have been a success. As a clear signal of the Chinese government's intention to suppress smuggling and establish a regulated art market, however, it was an encouraging step. At a more recent event, the first auction of Duo Yua Xuan Chinese paintings held in Shanghai in June 1993, there was a much higher rate of success, with collectors from Hong Kong, Taiwan and South Korea buying many of the top lots.

In spite of a number of unresolved political problems, the general outline of the art market in Asia seems to be reasonably clear. Not only

will there be a growth in buying power, but ultimately a vast increase in the geographic spread of potential collectors. For classic Chinese, Japanese and Korean art there is both a local and worldwide demand that is destined only to grow. As China becomes increasingly integrated into the capitalist world, more works of art may come into circulation and the Chinese diaspora will compete to own them. For the Modern and Contemporary art of these nations the international demand is more limited, although local markets will remain strong. As knowledge of Western art increases through exhibitions, art fairs, magazines and auctions, collectors may start to diversify and look more seriously at European or American art although, for historical reasons, this enthusiasm is unlikely to rival the Japanese passion for the culture of the West.

In August and September 1993, part of the controversial, politically and sexually oriented Whitney Biennial was transferred from New York to be exhibited at the National Museum of Contemporary Art in Seoul: an event that is more likely to have influenced the work of young artists than the taste of collectors. Earlier this year, however, a major exhibition of sculptures by Auguste Rodin, including the monumental *Thinker*, travelled from Paris to Beijing, Shanghai and Taipei. This was followed shortly after by an exhibition of recent pieces by the London artists Gilbert and George at the National Gallery in Beijing and the Arts Museum in Shanghai. If the Chinese can move from Rodin to Gilbert and George in a matter of a few months, the prospects for the future development of the art market in Asia look favourable indeed.

LI MEISHU
Scenery of Sanxia
SIGNED, OIL ON CANVAS,
61 x 73cm (24 x 28¾in)
Taipei NT$5,000,000
(£124,100:$196,700). 18.IV.93
(ABOVE LEFT)

HANGING AND REHANGING *by Giles Waterfield*

'Enjoyment of the beauty of works of art is exquisite and sensitive, easily marred, easily dissipated. A picture, like a scented flower, has a charm and an essence peculiarly its own. Every effort should be made to preserve its individuality unspoiled and undisturbed.' This comment by an Aesthetic critic in *The Studio* in 1893 reflects a very particular attitude to the display of paintings, typical of its period. Ways of showing paintings have always reflected evolving attitudes to the social and historical role of works of art, and it is enlightening to explore some of the approaches to what superficially might appear a simple matter.

Some of the earliest picture collections, made in the sixteenth century, were intended to present dynastic statements of the importance of individuals and their social groupings. This was usually done through sets of portraits, hung in straight lines or in massed formations in galleries or cabinets. On the evidence of contemporary depictions of galleries in the Netherlands, it appears to have been the practice of leading collectors such as the Archduke Leopold William to hang their fine pictures as densely as possible, often leaving no space at all between the frames.

During the eighteenth century princely and noble owners began to organize their collections differently. One of the prime examples of this new style was the Electoral Gallery at Düsseldorf, where the collection of the Elector Palatine with its outstanding Rubenses (now in Munich) was arranged in a special picture gallery. Although this was an assertively private collection, with a statue of the Elector in front of the building, the paintings were more than personal possessions. As is made clear in the impressive catalogue of 1778, *La Galerie Electorale de Düsseldorf*, the collection played a particular political role in reinforcing the status of the prince. The placing of the paintings in the rooms of the Gallery combined symmetry with systematic grouping. They were shown in three galleries and two cabinets, with the Northern and the Italian works (these being regarded as the two major schools) segregated. The hang is recorded in the catalogue in prints delineating each wall's arrangement. A large important painting was placed in the centre of each principal wall. On each side hung paintings of similar, preferably identical, size, arranged in symmetrical patterns. These might be double or even triple hung. Underneath this set piece, a continuous row of small cabinet paintings was often placed in a line, about a yard from the floor.

This style of symmetrical courtly hang shaped the character of princely galleries in many European countries during the eighteenth century. In Italy, surviving examples can be seen in such ensembles as the Pitti Palace. In England, largely intact schemes of symmetrically hung saloons survive in such houses as Kedleston Hall in Derbyshire and Holkham Hall in Norfolk. In such arrangements of paintings, much thought was given to a pleasing overall visual appearance. In fact it was common practice to cut down, or add to, paintings in order to accommodate them within a decorative scheme – a practice which poses an interesting ethical problem for the modern restorer. In some cases, frames were adapted to suit the character of the collection: thus the Elector of Saxony decreed in the 1760s that all his paintings should be displayed in identical frames. Early catalogues generally identified the size of figures within a painting, whether life size, half size, or smaller, even though very little other information might be given about the work. It was important for such schemes that the proportions of figures within the whole arrangement should be properly related, and that the figures in the paintings on the upper tiers should not be on a smaller scale to those below.

The principle of the symmetrical hang depended on a generally accepted canon of major artists. The supremacy of artists was much discussed in the eighteenth century, with Raphael, Michelangelo and the Carracci variously hailed as the predominant masters. Conventional taste regarded Italian art of the sixteenth and seventeenth centuries as of particular importance, with Flemish and Dutch artists playing an important but subsidiary role.

In the later eighteenth century enlightened monarchs increasingly made their collections available to a limited public, often organizing their pictures and classical sculpture to be shown at stated times in special galleries. These galleries were generally adapted stables or palaces rather than purpose-built structures. The experts who arranged the works investigated the possibilities of placing them in chronological order, with the schools separated. One of the most important examples of this approach was the Imperial Gallery at Vienna, shown in the Upper Belvedere Palace from 1781. The Gallery was organized by the scholar Christian von Mechel. In the introduction to his catalogue of 1781, von Mechel commented that the collection was important not only for its intrinsic quality but for the light it shed on the development of art from the earliest days, and claimed that, as a work of reference and instruction, it was comparable to a library.

WILLIAM KENT
One of two designs for the elevations of the north and south walls of the Saloon, Houghton Hall, Norfolk
SIGNED AND DATED *1725*,
PEN AND BLACK INK WITH GREY
AND BROWN WASHES,
25.7 x 25.7cm (10⅛ x 10⅛in)
London £57,200 ($87,500).
19.XI.92 (LEFT)

The visitor to this temple of art, as it was described, would find the Italian paintings subdivided by region, and all the schools shown in chronological order.

The ideas of von Mechel and a small number of contemporary experts dominated the development of museums of art in the nineteenth century. However, they did not represent the only approach. Academies of art, when in control of collections, tended to arrange pictures in a much more visually dominated way, with comparisons between the composition of works of art underlying their position on the walls. A good example of this from the later eighteenth century was the hang at the Luxembourg Palace in Paris, which showed selected works from the royal collection in a way which specified the visual connections between the works.

In the best organized museums, notably those of Germany, which led the world in art historical studies, a chronological display was applied throughout the nineteenth century, though there was much discussion over the relative values of chronology and geography as guiding principles. Such debates were inspired by a new attitude to the display of paintings: instead of the accepted range of sixteenth-, seventeenth- and some eighteenth-century works, museums were expected to show pictures of all periods, notably of the early Italian and Northern schools. Though these were often regarded as barbarous and of no intrinsic merit, they demonstrated the development of art, and indeed the progress made by mankind. In the Altes Museum in Berlin, which opened in Schinkel's building in 1830, and in the Alte Pinakothek in Munich of the same period, early paintings acquired for their archaeological interest were shown by school and period. In the National Gallery in London, which opened in its new building in Trafalgar Square in 1838, the efforts of the staff to organize a display on historical principles were frustrated by the hopeless inadequacies of space. It was a problem not solved until the 1880s.

The problems experienced at the National Gallery were reflected by numerous museums in the nineteenth century. In France, regional museums were afflicted by the *envoi* system, by which

large numbers of paintings were despatched by central government to local museums, the latter having no say in what they received. The result tended to be ill-organized and incongruous collections on a massive scale. In Britain, the municipal museums which flourished from the 1860s often showed their paintings in highly crowded settings, while in the United States some museums which were ostensibly public centred on commemorative displays of the possessions of wealthy families. Views of mid- and late nineteenth-century galleries frequently show rooms hung much like a chaotic academy exhibition, with pictures piled up the walls with little thought for clarity of presentation or the total effect.

The arrangement of paintings, both in public galleries and in private houses, was closely related to changing ideas about interior decoration. As taste moved in the last quarter of the nineteenth century away from richly decorated rooms towards more spare and discriminating interiors, so the style of showing works of art altered. Under the influence of such figures as the painter J. M. Whistler and the writer Edith Wharton, artists and their friends began to decorate their

Interior of one of the exhibition rooms at the Altes Museum, Berlin, in 1910. (ABOVE)

houses in a new manner, with paintings and other works of art carefully related to one another and to the whole room. Olana, the house of Frederick Church on the Hudson River, is a notable surviving example of this approach. The change in attitude was partly encouraged by a new style of painting practised by many artists. Instead of painting on the traditional dark ground and applying forcefully coloured layers of paint, painters such as the Pre-Raphaelites used paler grounds and lighter colours. They found that the dark wall colours of nineteenth-century rooms provided an unsympathetic background to their works, and preferred less intense shades, in particular maroon, sage green or in some cases grey. White was generally considered suitable only for showing prints. At the same time, they wanted their paintings to be hung with a greater degree of independence from their surroundings. Double hanging was to be avoided, and a reasonable space was to be provided between each work. The new approach to hanging (though not to wall colours) was pioneered in Britain at the Grosvenor Gallery, which opened in Bond Street in 1876 for temporary exhibitions by living artists. At much the same time, Whistler organized a number of influential exhibitions, beginning with his one-man show at the Flemish Gallery in 1874. Influenced by the Japanese cult of light-coloured pure interiors which encouraged the contemplation of a small number of exquisitely chosen objects, Whistler showed his own works in a way that carried the ideas of his contemporaries much further. In particular, his presentation of prints and watercolours, in broad mounts with narrow dark frames, overturned the traditional attempt to make works on paper resemble oil paintings.

The idea of showing paintings in pale settings, and of allowing space around them so that they do not fight with the surrounding images, has become so unfashionable in some circles in recent years that it is helpful to recall the origins of this approach. By the end of the nineteenth century it was usual for museums and for advanced private collectors to show their works of art in this new sparse manner. Throughout Europe, it became customary to seek qualities of harmony and

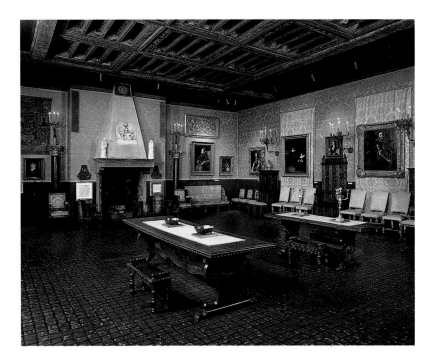

repose while arranging galleries, qualities in sympathy with the interiors created by the proponents of Art Nouveau and Jugendstil. Much attention was devoted to the introduction of carefully selected pieces of furniture and ceramics, as well as to suitable wall hangings.

At the end of the nineteenth century an alternative style was explored in Berlin. This was the period room, developed by the great director of the Berlin museums, Wilhelm von Bode. In a typical Bode installation, paintings in contemporary frames, sculpture and furniture, all of the same period, were shown together in an architecturally sympathetic setting, underlining the importance of the historical context of a work of art, as well as the relevance of the contemporary decorative arts. The paintings were not usually densely arranged in such a scheme, playing only one part in the total performance. Bode's ideas were extremely influential, shaping the character of many interiors, especially those belonging to great American collectors around the turn of the century. The Isabella Stewart Gardner Museum in Boston and the Pierpont Morgan Library in New York remain fine examples of the style. It was symptomatic of the importance

The Dutch Room at the Isabella Stewart Gardner Museum, Boston. (ABOVE)

Interior view through five galleries at the Dulwich Picture Gallery, London. (ABOVE)

Interior view of one of the newly refurbished rooms at the National Gallery of Scotland, Edinburgh. (ABOVE RIGHT)

attached to the effect of historic interiors that Isabella Stewart Gardner stipulated that none of the interior arrangements in her museum should be altered.

This period should be distinguished from the 1930s and later, when the impact of Modernism inspired a quite different approach. 'Meaningless' decoration came under increasing criticism, and a belief in the neutral interior became established under the impact of such innovatory institutions as the Museum of Modern Art in New York, which opened its first exhibition in 1929. Under the influence of the Bauhaus, the Museum of Modern Art presented paintings and sculpture in small, unintimidating, quasi-domestic white rooms, in which paintings were placed in a single line with considerable spaces between them, often with a deliberately irregular aesthetic in their hang. While such museums benefited from purpose-built rooms, older institutions were faced with apparently out-of-date interiors. From the 1930s until at least the 1970s, efforts were made in museums throughout the world to introduce false partitions and walls, and to conceal roof lights and dadoes in pursuit of the neutral setting. For contemporary art such an approach was doubtless appropriate; the problem was that

this bare style was applied to paintings of every period. Curators neglected the Victorian principle that paintings should be shown on a background darker than the light tones in a painting, but lighter than the dark tones. Instead, they tended to use light backgrounds which turned traditional oils, painted on a dark ground and possibly covered with old discoloured varnish, into looming masses of blackness.

By the late 1970s the white wall and the single hang were under fire, especially in Britain, where the work of the National Trust and the Victoria and Albert Museum was of pioneering importance in the restoration of historic interiors. In the early 1980s the Manchester City Art Gallery, London's Dulwich Picture Gallery and the National Galleries of Scotland all underwent major restorations, intended to emphasize the architectural character of the building and to return, not to nineteenth-century museum practice, but to the symmetrical, aristocratic aesthetic of an earlier period. In Britain, at least, the restoration of country house interiors has often shown a similar tendency: at Holkham the principal rooms have recently been reinstalled, with paintings which had been removed to the attics being returned to the positions they occupied in the eighteenth century. Petworth House, rehung after the Second World War by Anthony Blunt according to school and period, has recently been restored, allowing the extraordinary collection of early nineteenth-century British paintings to throng the rooms.

The hanging of paintings has recently been much discussed. The 'historic' style has not met with universal approval. Though generally considered suitable for historic houses, it has often been thought inappropriate for major Old Masters. At the Walters Art Gallery in Baltimore, for example, the upstairs picture galleries have recently been sumptuously refurbished with strongly coloured brocades, but this approach has not been supported by the hang: the paintings continue to be hung in a single line, creating for some spectators the uncomfortable effect of great areas of empty red and green fabric above the pictures. The present Director of the London National Gallery has made it clear that his galleries will not be double hung. The paintings are too important to be sacrificed for decorative effect. The Gallery has, on the other hand, cautiously questioned the traditional rigid division of paintings by school, by introducing Northern works into the new galleries of the Sainsbury Wing.

In very recent years, experiments have continued. One positive development has been the display of drawings along with paintings, a practice explored at the Art Institute of Chicago and in the French galleries at the Louvre in Paris. In other museums the recent interest in examining paintings as the products of social and political developments has produced a radically new approach. In one installation at the Laing Art Gallery in Newcastle, the paintings are primarily used to illustrate the history of the city, and in the Kelvingrove Museum and Art Gallery in Glasgow, many of the paintings are arranged by theme, rather than by school or period. The only point generally accepted among all this experimentation is that the arrangement of a painting within a space radically affects the impact it makes on the spectator. For better or worse, the creation of a neutral setting for paintings is a virtually impossible target.

The North Gallery at Petworth House, Sussex, showing a recent programme of rehanging nearing completion. (ABOVE)

Rooms in the Sainsbury Wing of the National Gallery, London, opened in 1991. (TOP)

EXHIBITIONS OF THE SEASON *by Richard Cork*

ERIC GILL
Mother and Child
BATH STONE,
height 58.8cm (23in),
London £61,600 ($96,000).
4.XI.92
This work was featured in the
exhibition of the artist's work
held at the Barbican Art
Gallery, London, from
November 1992 to February
1993. (RIGHT)

HENRI MATISSE
La Plage Rouge
SIGNED, OIL ON CANVAS,
33 x 40.6cm (13 x 16in)
From the collection of
Wright S. Ludington
This work was included in the
exhibition *Matisse: A
Retrospective*, held at the
Museum of Modern Art, New
York, from September 1992
to January 1993, as well as in
the exhibition *Henri Matisse
1904-1917*, held at the Musée
National d'Art Moderne,
Paris, from February to June
1993. (BELOW)

In a year when the most outstanding exhibition failed to reach Britain at all, questions were inevitably raised about London's continuing ability to mount the shows which everyone wants to see. The great Matisse survey, commencing with enormous success at New York's Museum of Modern Art before travelling in a much-altered form to the Pompidou Centre in Paris, carried everything before it. In New York, two entire floors of the Museum of Modern Art building were devoted to John Elderfield's immense, magisterial round-up of Matisse's long and prolific career. Despite the waning intensity noticeable in his inter-war years, the event as a whole was a triumph. Even visitors who are normally averse to exhausting blockbusters found themselves energized by Matisse's exuberance and inventiveness.

The Paris version, concentrating on the heroic years between 1904 and 1917, filled only a single floor of the Pompidou Centre. But it was just as enthralling. Matisse was at his finest in the decade after he gained widespread notoriety as a Fauve, and virtually all his most impressive works of the period were assembled in a superb, all-white installation. Even though the grand *Music* canvas was too frail to travel from St Petersburg, its companion *Dance* provided the exhibition with a joyful climax. A profusion of other Russian loans, combined with key pictures from Europe and the United States, made for an exhilarating experience. The powerful *Interior with Aubergines*, unavailable for the New York show, made the journey to Paris from Grenoble to prove that Matisse in 1911 was already on the brink of exploring the pictorial possibilities which would give his final phase of painted paper cut-outs their audacity and zest after the Second World War.

Patrick Heron, who had tried so hard to procure the Russian Matisses for a London show during his time as a Tate Gallery trustee, was not alone in deploring Britain's inability to stage this

sumptuous survey. Many commentators shared his dismay, and asked whether London was now in danger of missing the most impressive shows touring the international circuit. The answer, in Matisse's case, was that Paris and New York held the trump cards in their ability to negotiate. Between them, the Museum of Modern Art and the Pompidou own many of his masterpieces, and so were far more likely to achieve deals with their Russian counterparts. The Tate, by contrast, has meagre Matisse holdings.

But what of the Royal Academy, equipped with the gallery space and resources needed to mount surveys on the grand scale? Its principal achievements this year have centred on home-grown artists. *The Great Age of British Water-colours* achieved great popularity, but included only a sparing sample of the visionary images of Blake and Palmer, whose formidably original contributions revolutionized the British water-colour tradition in the early nineteenth century. Cotman was one of the show's heroes, exploring the advent of blast furnaces in the English

landscape with the same passion for order and lucidity that he bestowed on pastoral subjects. Girtin's work was displayed with equal gener-osity. His capacity to invest *The White House at Chelsea* with a beacon-like luminosity was one of the high points of the exhibition – notwith-standing the presence of well-selected Turners representing many phases of his protean career. If Girtin had lived longer, he might have equalled Turner's achievement as a watercolourist. But his untimely death at the age of twenty-seven meant that Turner went on without him, tirelessly opening up new expressive directions for a medium where he often seems more at home than in his surprisingly uneven oil paintings.

Sickert, whose work was summarized in a well-balanced Royal Academy retrospective, likewise benefited from longevity. A slow starter, who spent some time as a professional actor before committing himself to art, he was over-shadowed as a young painter by older mentors. The shades of Whistler, and more particularly Degas, dominated the first room of the show.

THOMAS GIRTIN
The White House at Chelsea
DATED *1800*, WATERCOLOUR, 29.8 x 51.4cm (11⅜ x 20in)
From the collection of the Tate Gallery, London
This work was included in *The Great Age of British Watercolours* exhibition held at the Royal Academy, London, from January to April 1993. (ABOVE)

WALTER SICKERT
Baccarat
SIGNED AND DATED *1920*,
OIL ON CANVAS,
61 x 44.5cm (24 x 18in)
London £95,000 ($143,400).
30.VI.93
This work was included in the
Walter Sickert exhibition held at
the Royal Academy, London,
from November 1992 to
February 1993. (ABOVE)

Sickert shared Degas' love of popular urban entertainment, but his early music-hall paintings reveal signs of an independent vision. Fascinated by the encrusted architecture of the Old Bedford Theatre's interior, Sickert showed as much interest in the audience as he did in performers like Little Dot Hetherington, spotlit on the stage.

If he had died in mid-career, Sickert would be remembered best today as an artist who applied the lessons of Impressionism to exploring the dingy streets of north London. His paintings of dilapidated, claustrophobic interiors in Mornington Crescent are often as sombre as the murderous subjects he favoured. Having fathered

a whole school of young painters, who shared his devotion to Camden Town, Sickert might easily have rested content with such an achievement. After the First World War, though, he underwent an extraordinary transformation. The latter-day Impressionist cast aside his former reliance on empirical observation. Photographs, often of the most blurred and ephemeral kind, became his starting-point. Many of his earlier admirers were affronted, and Sickert's late work suffered from widespread critical disfavour long after his death. Now, however, the paintings of the 1930s can be seen as an unpredictable final flowering. The octogenarian artist took the whole of society as his subject, from monarchs to miners. His handling of paint became astonishingly broad and summary, adept at disclosing the vulnerability of the newly-crowned Edward VIII as well as the self-confident vigour of Lord Beaverbrook. For the first time, the Royal Academy disclosed the full scope and underlying unity of Sickert's work in exhibition terms. It was well received, and the market duly responded to the enhanced reputation of this hitherto under-valued artist. His *Baccarat*, a work of 1920 which had been included in the exhibition, fetched a surprising £95,000 at Sotheby's in June.

Munch, whose multi-part *Frieze of Life* was brought together in a powerful survey at the National Gallery in London, is in no need of a boost to his reputation. His paintings, though, are scarcely visible in British public collections, and the loan of his finest early canvases from Norwegian museums added up to an unnerving experience. Although some of the paintings from the *Frieze of Life* were dispersed during his lifetime, he always regarded them as an ensemble. The National Gallery's exhibition, therefore, did Munch a particular service by reuniting all these haunted testaments to the artist's obsessive reactions to life, love and death.

Basing most of the paintings on the water's edge enabled Munch to confront his figures with a sense of immensity. Apart from reinforcing the work's dreamlike character, these deserted settings accentuate the pervasive sense of isolation. Even when seen in groups, talking or dancing, Munch's people always appear marooned within their own introspection. At its quietest, this alienation results in the melancholy of the young man seated on a rock, brooding over his unrequited infatuation with the woman glimpsed in the distance. At its most disturbing, the outcome centres on trauma. The celebrated image of *The Scream*, accompanied here by a fascinating wall of preliminary studies and related versions, reduces the protagonist to a shuddering, bald-headed victim of indeterminate gender stranded on a bridge. While the sunset fills the sky with an almost blood-red vehemence, the sufferer's mouth parts in a cry loud and primal enough to echo round the world.

If we knew more about the mysterious rituals of ancient Mexico, its sculpture might well take on a similarly ominous character. The carvings assembled at the Hayward Gallery, London, in October 1992 were frequently associated with ceremonial purposes, servicing religions which insisted on the need for sacrificial victims. Seen in this light, the monumental deities standing on tall plinths throughout the dramatically sloping first room assume an implacable identity. They seem ready to preside over the most merciless proceedings imaginable, and their fixed, staring expressions add to their air of stony detachment. It is a wonder that Henry Moore, who made no secret of his indebtedness to the Chac Mool carvings, transformed them into embodiments of beneficence. While retaining the monumentality of Chac Mool prototypes, Moore's recumbent women enjoy a reassuring identity. They are as fertile as the earth itself, whereas the Chac Mool figures have a more sentinel-like character, vigilant and even defensive as they twist their heads to scan the surrounding space.

Although the Hayward show was splendidly installed, it did raise the question of cultural misrepresentation. By uprooting these artifacts from their original context, and displaying them in the spotless, sanitized environment of a modern gallery, the exhibition was bound to show its contents in a distorting light. Credit, then, to the organizers for concluding the survey with a spectacular audio-visual presentation of the principal surviving sites. Ruined and awesome, they provided a salutary reminder of how

these carvings often originated in a close alliance with architecture of monumental proportions.

Of all the twentieth-century artists who owe a debt to Mexican culture, Georgia O'Keeffe acknowledged it most freely. She spent the last decades of her long career living in Abiquiu, sustained by the isolation and serenity of a location at the furthest possible remove from the Manhattan gallery world where her reputation was made. Legendary in her own country, and in recent years revered as an icon by feminist art historians with whom she had little in common, O'Keeffe has been neglected in Britain. The retrospective at the Hayward Gallery offered London an opportunity to become acquainted with her paintings, watercolours and drawings.

EDVARD MUNCH
The Scream
TEMPERA AND PASTEL
ON BOARD,
91 x 73.5cm (35¾ x 29in)
From the collection of
The National Gallery, Oslo
This work was included in the
*Edvard Munch: The Frieze of
Life* exhibition held at the
National Gallery, London, from
November 1992 to February
1993. (ABOVE)

The first room of *The Art of Mexico* exhibition, held at the Hayward Gallery, London, from September to December 1992. (ABOVE)

Were enough of them on display, however? O'Keeffe, a prolific artist, can be properly assessed only if a substantial cross-section of her output is available. The selection here bordered on the frugal. New York, where she spent some of her most energetic years alongside Alfred Stieglitz, inspired a group of memorable paintings. They were barely represented here, in an exhibition bent on establishing O'Keeffe as a ruralist at the expense of her urban scenes. To that end, it offered a whole roomful of her flower paintings, where sexual symbolism is overplayed to a cloying, repetitive extent. Her prowess as a landscape painter seemed strangely limited, too. The Mexican subjects often bordered on the merely picturesque, so it was a relief to go upstairs where James Turrell had prepared a rigorous series of installations.

This visionary Californian transformed his allotted rooms into a sequence of breathtaking spaces. Turrell is a master-manipulator of light, but to approach *Wedgework IV* visitors groped their way through corridors as dark as midnight. Then blackness gave way to a vast and airy chamber, filled with misty red light. In the distance, beyond public access, a large rectangular opening led to a distant room. Partially visible and veiled with a softer radiance than before, its effect was intensified by an aura of unattainability. Spare yet overwhelmingly sensuous, *Wedgework IV* seduced at once. The neighbouring exhibit, though, worked far more stealthily. A dark corridor led, this time, into a far cooler chamber. The main illumination was provided by pools of light on the left and right walls, flanking an opening as wide as a cinema screen. As you approached, the opening gave out onto an infinitely mysterious emptiness beyond. It seemed to be swimming with fog; under Turrell's deft manipulation light almost becomes palpable.

His wizardry was at its most captivating in the final installation, a room specially built on the gallery forecourt. Seen from Waterloo Bridge, this bunker-like structure looked as unprepossessing as the Hayward's own architecture. Inside, though, it was a thing of wonder. A tunnel-like entrance guided us through to a startlingly bright space, lined on all four walls with plain wooden benches. Their high backs sloped away, inviting you to lean against them and look upwards without neck-strain. They terminated in a hidden strip of light, running round the room and brilliantly illuminating the walls extending about twenty feet in the air to a plain ceiling. Here, a square aperture had been cut out, giving directly onto the sky. Heavy clouds, combined with the encroaching dusk, should have ensured a dull spectacle beyond the roof. But by contrasting it with the brightness of the room below, Turrell intensified the sky's colours with extraordinary potency. By the time darkness settled in, the square opening had been turned into an irresistible expanse of deep, rich blue. It was as if a swathe of velvet had been attached to the ceiling, and the effect was mesmeric.

During the 1960s, when Turrell was only beginning to define his singular vision, London witnessed the burgeoning of far more frenetic art forms. Many of them were reassessed in a large, crowded and multi-faceted survey at London's Barbican Art Gallery in 1993. Its organizer, David Mellor, tried to challenge the stereotyped notion that Pop Art dominated everything else in the city. He resurrected the forgotten William Green, a young action painter who enjoyed brief notoriety for attacking his canvases and setting fire to them. Such activities culminated in the Auto-Destructive art devised by Gustav Metzger, who systematically assailed his work in public demonstrations on the South Bank.

The Barbican show made clear that a widespread interest in abstraction also characterized avant-garde painting in the early 1960s. Stimulated by recent developments in American art, young painters experimented with a remarkably simplified, hard-edged language. They could hardly have been more divorced from the concerns of Pop-orientated artists like the

young David Hockney, whose precocious early work was underplayed to a falsifying extent in this show. Mellor called attention to the short-lived Pauline Boty, a proto-feminist artist preoccupied with gender and sexuality. He also celebrated the single-minded optical attack of another woman artist still active today: Bridget Riley, whose eye-battering images looked at home in the same room as a sprightly aluminium sculpture by Anthony Caro.

Although some of the work on show turned out to have fared badly, bearing the hallmark of the 60s at their most superficial, the leanest and most energetic of these abstractionists forged a language which served them long after the decade had ended. They, rather than the much-hyped practitioners of Pop, emerged with credit from an event which, like all worthwhile exhibitions, changed our perception of the subject it set out to explore.

One of the exhibition spaces at *The Sixties Art Scene in London* show, held at the Barbican Art Gallery, London, from March to June 1993, showing works by Bridget Riley and Anthony Caro.(ABOVE)

II
ART
AT
AUCTION

THE FINE ARTS

The past season saw the gradual reappearance on the market of top quality paintings in the Impressionist and Modern field. The boom period in the late 1980s attracted an unprecedented number of major paintings that were being consigned by discretionary vendors. The severe readjustment to that market which followed was not so much due to the withdrawal of Japanese buyers, but to a dramatic drop in the volume of paintings coming onto the market, an absence of first quality works and a near standstill in discretionary selling. Before the beginning of this season, observers were questioning if there was 'any life' above the $10 million mark.

The appearance of two major Matisses in the November series of sales answered the question impressively. The sales coincided with the milestone exhibition dedicated to the artist held at the Museum of Modern Art in New York. On 10 November Matisse's L'Asie, a seminal late work of 1946 from the collection of the late Mollie Parnis Livingston, sold for $11 million. The next day the artist's Harmonie Jaune of 1927-28 sold for $14,520,000.

While the market above $10 million is quite different from that below this watershed, and even more different from the market below $1 million, what happens at the top end sets the tone for the overall market. This was evident during the sales that followed, starting with Sketch 1 for Composition VII painted in 1913 by Wassily Kandinsky, which was consigned by the Klee family to our December auction in London where it sold for £5,500,000.

What happened in the autumn gave sufficient confidence to discretionary vendors for them to consign outstanding works to the May sales in New York. Cézanne's Nature Morte: Les Grosses Pommes had been in the same hands since 1958 when it was sold at Sotheby's as part of the collection of Jakob Goldschmidt for £90,000. This time its estimate was $12-15 million. Its superb quality, freshness to the market and realistic estimate caused fierce competition amongst bidders, and the price rose rapidly to $28,602,500 – a figure that even at the height of the market would have been hard to match.

MARY CASSATT
Young Lady in a Loge, gazing to the right
SIGNED, PASTEL AND GOUACHE ON PAPER,
64.8 x 54.6cm (25½ x 21½in)
New York $2,530,000
(£1,675,400). (LEFT)

SIR EDWARD COLEY BURNE-JONES
The Godhead Fires, from the Pygmalion series
SIGNED AND DATED 1870,
66 x 51cm (26 x 20in)
London £661,500 ($992,200)
for the series of four. 8.VI.93.
(ABOVE)

The scarcity of great works on the market means that when something of major quality and rarity does turn up, it causes greater competition amongst potential purchasers. In the same sale as the Cézanne, we offered a rare Matisse entitled La Mulâtresse Fatma. Painted in 1912, it was bought around 1916 by one of the great collectors of this century, Josef Müller. Again, brisk bidding by several contenders drove the price to $14,302,500, nearly matching the record for Matisse set six months before.

These results further strengthened the confidence of collectors. The June sales in London not only achieved the highest total for a sale of Impressionist and Modern art held there since 1989, but also had the lowest percentage of unsold works since then. Several records were achieved, notably for Le Fardeau (La Blanchisseuse) by Honoré Daumier (£1,651,500) and La Joie de Vivre by Paul Delvaux (£1,013,500).

Unlike last season, when works by Rembrandt and Bellotto were sold in London, this season saw fewer works of the finest quality appear on the Old Master paintings market. This fact, coupled with the somewhat more discreet participation of the Italian buyers (who traditionally are key players in this area), produced a season that was a little subdued. There were, however, notable exceptions such as Goya's Bullfight. Suerte de Varas, the last late bullfighting scene by Goya left in private hands, which sold in London in December for £4,950,000. Other highlights were a School of Bruges Portrait of Jacob Obrecht which sold for $2,422,500 in New York in January and a group of seven paintings by various Italian artists depicting the history of the Medici family, from the collection of Lord Elgin, that brought £1,651,000 in London in April.

The Latin American art market continued to be highly active this season, with fourteen new records established. The November sale in New York saw strong competition for nineteen works by Joaquín Torres-García from the Estate of Royal S. Mark which made $1,856,250. During the same sale artists' records were set for Fernando Botero (La Casa de las Gemelas Arias, $1,540,000) and Rufino Tamayo (Mujer en éxtasis, $1,485,000).

Sotheby's American paintings sale in New York in May was exceptionally strong, achieving the highest result in this category since 1989. An important Childe Hassam, The Room of Flowers, was sold for $5,502,500 (a record for an American Impressionist painting) and a William Merritt Chase, entitled Peonies, fetched $3,962,500 (a record price for the artist).

ROBERT RAUSCHENBERG
Press
SIGNED AND DATED 1964,
OIL AND SILKSCREEN INK
ON CANVAS,
213.4 x 152.4cm (84 x 60in)
New York $1,100,000
(£728,400). 17.XI.92. (ABOVE)

HONORÉ DAUMIER
**Le Fardeau
(La Blanchisseuse)**
SIGNED, OIL ON CANVAS,
116.3 x 89.2cm (44¾ x 35⅛in)
London £1,651,500
($2,510,200). 22.VI.93
(ABOVE)

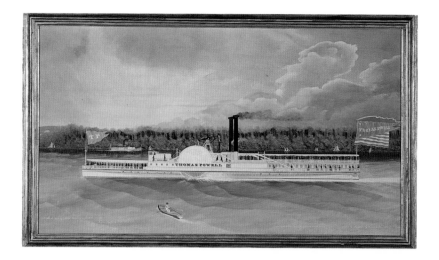

This season has been the best ever in the Victorian paintings area. Strong prices were fetched in both London and New York, including two major works by Sir Lawrence Alma-Tadema. The first, The Baths of Caracalla, was sold in New York for a record price of $2,532,500, and the second, Caracalla and Geta, was sold in London for £1,431,500. Academic French ninteenth-century painters also fared well, with good prices being achieved for works by Jean-Léon Gérôme and William Adolphe Bouguereau.

The renewed confidence that has brought back works of great quality to the Impressionist and Modern paintings department has been less evident in the Contemporary art market. Nevertheless, there were some fine results such as Andy Warhol's Marilyn x 100 which sold for $3,740,000 in New York in November and Bruce Nauman's One Hundred Live and Die which achieved a record $1,925,000. The total for the Contemporary art sale in London in June, £4,979,963, was the highest since June 1991. The sale included two portraits by Francis Bacon. The first, Study for a Portrait, made £562,500, the second, a Portrait of Lucian Freud, £221,500. Strong prices were also obtained for works by Gerhard Richter, Anselm Kiefer and Eduardo Chillida. These results suggest that with the return of top quality works the market for Contemporary art might show a similar resilience to that for Impressionist and Modern paintings.

Lastly, Prints and Photographs are both areas which continue to win more collectors. Solid sales for the Print department this season included the Dr Otto Schäfer collection of etchings by Rembrandt, which made $3,871,925 in May in New York, while the Photography department established a new world record for a single photograph at auction when Glass Tears by Man Ray sold for £122,500 in London in May.

JAMES AND JOHN BARD
The Steam Engine
Paddle Wheeler
Thomas Powell:
A Ship's Portrait
SIGNED AND DATED 1846,
OIL ON CANVAS,
78.7 x 139.7cm (31 x 55in)
New York $96,000 (£65,300).
24.VI.93. (ABOVE)

OLD MASTER PAINTINGS

SCHOOL OF BRUGES
Portrait of Jacob Obrecht
OIL ON PANEL, 43.8 x 27.9cm (17¼ x 11in)
New York $2,422,500 (£1,583,333). 15.I.93

The sitter for this late fifteenth-century portrait
has been identified as Jacob Obrecht, a renowned
Flemish composer who died in 1505. At the time
it was painted Obrecht was living in Antwerp, and
the picture may be by an artist from that city.
However, no Antwerp painter is known who
would have been capable of producing a work of
this quality, and Dirk de Vos of the Bruges
Stedelijke Museum has suggested that it is by the
Bruges artist Hans Memling. Obrecht had strong
enough links with Bruges for this to be possible,
and a very similar treatment of the facial features
can be found in major works by Memling.

It is difficult, though, to substantiate such a
hypothesis given the absence of any comparable
portraits by Memling from this late period in his
career. The panel is probably the left-hand wing
of a diptych or triptych, as there are hinge marks
on the frame. (LEFT)

JACOB CORNELISZ. VAN
OOSTSANEN
The Crucifixion
DATED 1507, OIL ON PANEL,
99.1 x 78.7cm (39 x 31in)
New York $607,500 (£397,059).
15.I.93

The Crucifixion is an
important, previously
unpublished addition to
the corpus of Jacob van
Oostsanen, sometimes
called Jacob van Amsterdam
(Oostsanen lies a few miles
north of Amsterdam), and is
obviously the central panel
of a triptych. Only a dozen
dated pictures by van
Oostsanen are extant, and
the discovery of this work
adds considerably to our
understanding of the artist's
style at the beginning of his
known career. By 1507 van
Oostsanen was about 37
years old and must already
have established an artistic
reputation: in addition to
paintings, he is also known
to have illustrated books,
painted choir vaults and
made designs for stained
glass, embroidery and
prints. Amsterdam was,
until the time of his arrival,
almost utterly devoid of an
artistic tradition. It may
well be that he was the
earliest artist of note to
work in the city. (LEFT)

NICOLAS POUSSIN
Rest on the Flight into Egypt
OIL ON OAK PANEL, 46 x 31cm (18¼ x 12¼in)
Monaco FF3,663,000 (£449,400:$672,100).
2.VII.93

Until the recent reappearance of this
work (for which previously only
photographs were available) its
attribution to Poussin was disputed. The
evidence provided by the painting itself,
however, leaves no doubt that this is an
important early work by the master
dating from around 1627, the same time
as the celebrated painting, the *Death of
Germanicus*. Undoubtedly painted in
Rome, the style of the work is vigorous,
direct and yet romantic, for the painter
was clearly still preoccupied with the
breadth and warmth of the art of
Renaissance Venice. (RIGHT)

LAURENT DE LA HYRE
Landscape with Two Women at a Fountain
SIGNED AND DATED *1653*, OIL ON CANVAS,
63.5 x 88.3cm (25 x 34⅝in)
New York $415,000 (£266,026). 20.V.93
From the Estate of Paul Henreid

Laurent de la Hyre has been considered
a quintessential Parisian artist of the first
half of the seventeenth century despite
the fact that he did not study with
Vouet, the leading painter of the day.
He received sacred commissions from
the Capucins and the Jacobins and, by
the mid 1630s, Cardinal Richelieu had
become his fervent protector. This work
is a major addition to his late œuvre – a
time when his attention was turning
increasingly to landscape. It reveals the
artist gently eliminating traces of the
'literary' and concentrating instead on
the 'natural', absorbing the lessons of
the Parisian community in Rome
(especially Claude), but allying them
with a direct feeling for nature. (BELOW)

ANASTASIO FONTEBUONI
Troilo Orsini, who brings Aid from Cosimo I de' Medici for King Charles IX
OIL ON CANVAS, 179 x 245.5cm (70½ x 96⅝in). London £1,651,500 ($2,493,700) for seven paintings. 21.IV.93

This is one of a series of paintings commissioned by Marie de' Medici in 1623 for the *Cabinet Doré* of the Luxembourg Palace in Paris. Following Henri IV's death in 1610, Marie had acted as Regent for their eldest son until he was able to assume the throne in 1617 as Louis XIII. By 1623, following a period of exile, Marie was anxious to re-establish her position. Her plans for the decoration of the Palace were intended to help achieve this and to serve as a reminder of France's debts to the Medici. The series was to be a history of the Medici family, seen in terms of the marriages that had allied it to various European royal families. The pictures, by several Florentine artists, were delivered to Paris by the end of 1627. In 1803 seven of them were bought by the Earl of Elgin and removed to Fife, where they stayed until this sale. (ABOVE)

JUAN DE ARELLANO
Still Life of Flowers in a Basket
SIGNED, OIL ON CANVAS,
81.9 x 102.9cm (32¼ x 40½in)
New York $1,102,500 (£706,731).
20.V.93

Juan de Arellano was the most important painter of floral still lifes in Spain in the seventeenth century. His fame was considerable during his own lifetime, most of which he spent in Madrid.

The present work, dating from 1670-6, is undoubtedly among the finest of its kind.

It is possible that it was conceived as one of a series of floral still lifes. (RIGHT)

JAN DAVIDSZ. DE HEEM
Still Life with Grapes, Peaches, Oysters and a Glass of Wine
SIGNED, OIL ON PANEL,
39.7 x 47cm (15⅝ x 18½in) New York
$1,542,500 (£1,008,170). 15.I.93

Although there is a dearth of dated works by de Heem after 1655, it is likely that this painting was executed in the early 1670s. The artist was born in Utrecht, where he studied under Balthasar van der Ast. He is renowned for sumptuous flower pieces and large compositions of richly laid tables which exude the full opulence of Flemish Baroque painting. (BELOW)

JACOB VAN HULSDONCK
Still Life of Oranges, Lemons and Pomegranates in a Blue and White Bowl
SIGNED, OIL ON PANEL, 32 x 42.5cm (12½ x 16¾in) Amsterdam Dfl759,000 (£279,000:$421,600). 11.XI.92
This work had been in the possession of the family who consigned it to Sotheby's for sale since at least the beginning of the century. Its directness and immediacy are beautifully complemented by the intimacy of its small scale. (RIGHT)

PHILIPS DE KONINCK
A Panoramic River Landscape
SIGNED AND DATED *164...*, OIL ON CANVAS, 86 x 121cm (33 x 47½in) London £990,000 ($1,554,300). 9.XII.92
From the Collection of the Rt Hon. the Earl Mountbatten of Burma.
It is possible that Philips de Koninck was a pupil of Rembrandt in Amsterdam. His panoramas convey a unique vision of his native land, in which towns, villages, rivers and signs of human activity are encompassed in a broad sweep. (BELOW)

FRANÇOIS BOUCHER
The Marriage of Cupid and Psyche
OIL ON PAPER LAID ON CANVAS, 44.8 x 56.8cm (17½ x 22¼in)
London £221,500 ($332,200). 7.VII.93

The story of Cupid and Psyche was very popular among Italian Renaissance artists, and its high drama contributed to a vogue for the theme in eighteenth-century France. In 1744, Boucher executed a painting of *The Marriage of Cupid and Psyche* (recently acquired for the Louvre) for which this picture would appear to be a preparatory oil sketch. (RIGHT)

GIOVANNI ANTONIO CANALE, CALLED CANALETTO
A View of Riva degli Schiavoni, Venice, Looking East
OIL ON CANVAS, 57.2 x 92.7cm (22½ x 36½in)
New York $2,642,500 (£1,693,910). 20.V.93

This panoramic work by Canaletto is one of only two known depictions of this view in which both the column of the Lion of Saint Mark and that of Saint Theodore appear. Only in this canvas, however, did Canaletto depict work in progress on the *fondamenta* in the foreground. It has been suggested that the painting dates from the late 1730s. (BELOW)

FRANCISCO DE GOYA
Bullfight. Suerte de Varas
OIL ON CANVAS, 50 x 60cm (19¾ x 23½in) London £4,950,000 ($7,771,500). 9.XII.92
From the Collection of Marquesa de la Gándara.

With the restoration of King Ferdinand VII of Spain in November 1823, Goya felt politically insecure and, in June 1824 at the age of 78, moved to Paris, where he executed this important work. The composition echoes that of one of the prints in his *Tauromaquia* series, issued in 1816. The bull has gored two horses and now stands impassively in the arena, eyeing the picador whose own horse has a gaping wound. X-rays have revealed that originally the horse was blindfolded, as in the *Tauromaquia* print; Goya's decision to paint out the bandage has heightened the poignancy of the physical encounter between these two animals. The freedom of Goya's technique in this work, using a palette knife as well as a brush (and maybe even his fingers and a rag), reveals an extraordinarily modern sensibility. The work is a formidable demonstration of the artist's creativity at the end of a long and courageous career. (ABOVE)

OLD MASTER DRAWINGS

JEAN-BAPTISTE GREUZE
The Departure for the Wet-Nurse
BLACK AND GREY INK AND WASH
OVER BLACK CHALK,
38.4 x 50.7cm (15⅛ x 20in)
New York $151,000 (£97,419).
13.I.93
This impressive work is characteristic of Greuze's genre and moralizing subjects. The topic of wet-nurses and the raising of children was hotly discussed in eighteenth-century France. This drawing is a study for one of a series of paintings the artist intended to execute, but never completed.
(RIGHT)

JEAN-HONORÉ FRAGONARD
The Garden of an Italian Villa with a Gardener and Two Children Playing
BROWN WASH OVER BLACK CHALK,
33.8 x 45.1cm (13½ x 18in)
New York $343,500 (£221,600).
13.I.93
This drawing is likely to have been made during or soon after Fragonard's second Italian journey of 1773-4, a period considered to be a watershed in the artist's career. In this work Fragonard reveals himself to be preoccupied with atmospheric effects, built up through tones of wash.
(BELOW)

BENOZZO GOZZOLI
Study of a male nude
PEN AND BROWN INK
ON PAPER WASHED PINK,
diameter 9.3cm (3⅝in)
London £28,750 ($43,400). 5.VII.93
Drawings by Gozzoli appear
very rarely on the market
and it has not been possible
to connect this drawing with
a surviving work or even be
sure for what purpose it
might have been intended.
The naturalism of the figure
suggests that it was drawn
from life, while the refined
facial type is one that can
be seen in a number of the
artist's works. (ABOVE)

PAOLO CALIARI, CALLED
IL VERONESE
The Rest on the Flight
into Egypt
BROWN WASH HEIGHTENED WITH
WHITE ON PAPER WASHED BLUE-GREY,
40.8 x 41.8cm (16 x 16⅜in)
London £177,500 ($268,000).
5.VII.93
Veronese made a large
number of *chiaroscuro*
drawings that are generally
complete compositions and
are thought to have been
executed as independent
works rather than as
preparatory studies for
paintings. Many may have
been kept in the artist's studio
for the use of his pupils and
so their dating is problematic;
they are, nevertheless, highly
prized by collectors. (LEFT)

BRITISH PICTURES 1500 – 1850

POMPEO BATONI
Portrait of Sir Charles Watson, Bt
SIGNED AND DATED *1775*,
OIL ON CANVAS,
97 x 73.5cm (38¼ x 29in)
London £463,500
($690,600).14.VII.93

Batoni was one of the most successful (and ostentatious) painters of the eighteenth-century Roman School. He executed a large number of religious and mythological pieces, but achieved greatest renown for his portraits of British nobility making the Grand Tour. The sitter in this work, who is wearing van Dyck dress, was the son of Vice-Admiral Charles Watson, former Commander-in-Chief of the Fleet in the East Indies. (LEFT)

WILLEM WISSING
Portrait of Queen Anne, when Princess of Denmark
SIGNED AND DATED *1687*, OIL ON CANVAS, 124.5 x 101cm (49 x 39¾in)
London £54,300 ($80,900). 14.VII.93

Having studied and worked in Holland, Wissing came to London to work in Lely's studio in 1676. On Lely's death in 1680 he took over much of his master's thriving and fashionable practice. The sitter in this work, the future Queen Anne, was the second daughter of James II. In 1683 she married Prince George of Denmark, and bore him seventeen children, only one of which – William, Duke of Gloucester – survived infancy. She succeeded the throne on the death of William III in 1702. (ABOVE)

SIR PETER LELY
Portrait of Mary II, when Princess of Orange
OIL ON CANVAS, 214.5 x 99cm (49 x 39in)
London £54,300 ($80,900). 14.VII.93

Lely came to London from the Low Countries in around 1643 and by 1650 he had built up a considerable practice as a portrait painter. At the Restoration in 1660 he became Principal Painter to Charles II. He was knighted in 1679 and died a year later. The sitter of this work, the future Mary II, was the eldest daughter of James II. In 1677 she married William of Orange and moved to Holland. In 1689 James II fled the kingdom, leaving no male heir, and William and Mary were invited to rule jointly in his place. (ABOVE)

WILLIAM ASHFORD
Carton, the seat of the Duke of Leinster – a horse-drawn carriage crossing the bridge
SIGNED AND DATED *1779*, OIL ON CANVAS, 110 x 150cm (43 x 59in)
London £84,000 ($125,100). 14.VII.93

Although commissioned by the 2nd Duke of Leinster, this painting testifies to the extraordinary creation at Carton of his father James, 20th Earl of Kildare and 1st Duke of Leinster (1722-73), and his wife Emily. It was they who, in the 1750s and 60s, transformed the formal gardens into a vast picturesque landscape. Amongst other improvements, a series of dams was built to create a lake and serpentine river. Other features included a shell house, an ornamental bridge and an ornamental dairy. (ABOVE)

THOMAS GAINSBOROUGH
Portrait of Peter Darnal Muilman, Charles Crockatt and William Keeble
OIL ON CANVAS, 75 x 62cm (29½ x 24½in) London £1,079,500 ($1,608,400). 14.VII.93

This fine conversation piece, dating from around 1753-55 when the artist was still in his early twenties, represents an ideal fusion of portraiture and landscape. It is one of a very small group of portraits of local friends and landowners which Gainsborough painted in his native Suffolk shortly after his return from London in 1748; portraits in which his natural gifts are shown unclouded by the requirements of fashion. While in London the artist had studied the works of the great Dutch seventeenth-century naturalistic painters, whose influence can be detected in parts of this work. (RIGHT)

JOHN FERNELEY, SNR
Lord Robert Manners, Lord Charles and the 5th Duke of Rutland hunting at Belvoir Castle
SIGNED AND DATED *1838*, OIL ON CANVAS, 89 x 142.4cm (35 x 55¼in)
London £132,400 ($198,600). 6.IV.93

In 1814, John Ferneley set up a succesful practice at
Elgin Lodge in Melton Mowbray, painting society figures
who hunted with the Quorn and the Belvoir. (RIGHT)

SIR EDWIN HENRY LANDSEER
Alpine Mastiffs Reanimating a Distressed Traveller
OIL ON CANVAS, 188 x 236cm (74 x 93in)
New York $525,000 (£347,600). 4.VI.93
Property of the Warner Collection of Gulf States Paper Corporation

This work of 1820, when Landseer was 18, was his most
ambitious picture to date, and was rapturously received at
its exhibition at the British Institution. (BELOW)

BRITISH WATERCOLOURS

SAMUEL PALMER
Oxen Ploughing at Sunset
SIGNED, WATERCOLOUR OVER PENCIL AND RED CHALK,
39.5 x 27cm (15½ x 10½in)
London £60,500 ($90,150). 15.VII.93

The distant mountains in this watercolour of 1863 are reminiscent of the Apennines, through which Palmer and his wife travelled on their honeymoon in Italy in 1837-9. The classically composed figure of the woman with an earthenware vase on her head on the right of the work is probably based on the antique gem carvings in which Palmer was interested.

The composition of the piece is one that Palmer returned to many times in later work, and close comparisons can be made with etchings such as *The Morning Spread upon the Mountains* and *The Early Ploughman.* (RIGHT)

JOSEPH MALLORD WILLIAM TURNER
Lichfield, Staffordshire
WATERCOLOUR, 28.6 x 43.8cm (11 x 17in)
London £187,000 ($286,000). 19.XI 92

The first of Turner's works to be exhibited at the Royal Academy, in 1790, was a watercolour, and it was for his work in this medium that the artist first achieved public acclaim. *Lichfield, Staffordshire* dates from between 1830 and 1835, when Turner's popularity was at its zenith, and shows Lichfield Cathedral from the south-west. This work was intended to form part of the *Picturesque Views in England and Wales,* the most important series of engravings with which Turner was involved. The series was commissioned from the artist by Charles Heath in 1825, though was not completed until 1837. (ABOVE)

JOHN ROBERT COZENS
Vesuvius from Sir William Hamilton's Villa at Portici
WATERCOLOUR OVER PENCIL, 36 x 52.5cm (14¼ x 20½in)
London £140,600 ($209,000). 15.VII.93

The majority of John Robert Cozens' watercolours are connected with the journeys
he made to Switzerland and Italy between 1776 and 1783. He did not confine
himself to topographical exactitude and often transposed landscape features in the
interests of a more lyrical composition. Some of his Italian travels were made in the
company of William Beckford, whom Alexander Cozens, John's father, had once
instructed. It was Beckford who introduced John Cozens to Sir William Hamilton.
This work is based on a drawing made in August 1783. (ABOVE)

THOMAS GAINSBOROUGH
Wooded Landscape with Drover and Packhorses

SIGNED, WATERCOLOUR AND
BODYCOLOUR OVER PENCIL,
28.3 x 34.2 cm (11¼ x 13½in)
London £88,000 ($134,500). 19.XI.92

It was between 1760 and 1774, during his sojourn in Bath, that Gainsborough used watercolour most extensively, turning to the local countryside for inspiration. This drawing, which dates from around 1765 and comes from a group of presentation drawings probably intended for sale, was first owned by the Hon. Mrs Graham, a famous beauty whose portrait Gainsborough painted many times. It is a fine example of the artist's increasing interest in *chiaroscuro* and the effects of light on his subject.
(LEFT)

JOHN CONSTABLE
Helmingham Dell, Suffolk

PENCIL AND GREY WASHES,
53.3 x 66.4cm (21 x 26⅛ in)
London £98,000 ($147,000). 1.IV.93

In 1800, the year in which this drawing was executed, Helmingham Hall in Suffolk was the seat of Wilbraham Tollemache, 6th Earl of Dysart. Constable was not introduced to the Earl until 1807 and it therefore seems that this work was not linked to any commission. The dell is still identifiable, although the wooden footbridge was replaced by a stone bridge in 1815. Constable executed a number of drawings at Helmingham Park, this work being on a far more ambitious scale than the others. It was to form the basis for four oil versions of the subject, one of which is now in the Louvre.
(RIGHT)

BRITISH PICTURES FROM 1850

SIR FRANK DICKSEE
The Mirror
SIGNED AND DATED *1896,*
OIL ON CANVAS,
95.3 x 118.1cm (37½ x 46½in)
New York $725,000
(£467,700). 17.II.93

This work was exhibited to considerable critical acclaim at the Royal Academy in 1896, and shows Dicksee's passion for the contemporary taste amongst London artists for exotic subjects. It also displays his virtuoso handling of texture, not least in the depiction of the mother-of-pearl inlay that embellishes the sitter's silver throne. (RIGHT)

SIR FRANK DICKSEE
Leila
SIGNED AND DATED *1892,*
OIL ON CANVAS,
101.5 x 127cm (40 x 50in)
London £793,500 ($1,190,200).
8.VI.93

In 1905 Dicksee's biographer Dibdin wrote of his subject's 'lovingly elaborated decoration of surfaces' and his 'delight in rich colour combinations'. No work demonstrates this more eloquently than *Leila.* The subject of the work is the heroine of the Arabian love story *Layla and Majnun,* which dates from the seventh century AD. (LEFT)

SIR EDWARD COLEY BURNE-JONES
Portrait of Amy Gaskell
SIGNED AND DATED *1893*, OIL ON CANVAS, 96.5 x 52cm (38 x 20½in)
London £496,500 ($744,700). 8.VI.93

Amy Gaskell was the daughter of Helen Mary Gaskell, with whom in 1892 Burne-Jones entered into a close friendship. This sombre portrait was first exhibited at the New Gallery, London, in 1894, and was seized upon by the critic of *The Art Journal* as 'one of the most masterly works produced by this artist'. The picture was sold with letters from Burne-Jones to Amy Gaskell containing his plans for the portrait. (BELOW)

DANTE GABRIEL ROSSETTI
La Ghirlandata
SIGNED AND DATED *1873*, COLOURED CHALKS, 90.5 x 76cm (35½ x 30in)
London £463,500 ($695,200). 8.VI.93

La Ghirlandata is literally 'she who is adorned with garlands of flowers'. The drawing was executed at Kelmscott Manor in the summer of 1873 as the cartoon for Rossetti's oil painting of the same title, now in the Guildhall Art Gallery, London. The sitter was Alexa Wilding, and William Morris's daughter May appears twice in the picture (as both angels). Rossetti seems to have worked further on the drawing after the painting was completed. (ABOVE)

EDWARD LEAR
The Pyramids Road, Giza
SIGNED AND DATED *1873*, OIL ON CANVAS, 53 x 104cm (21 x 41in)
London £232,500 ($348,700). 8.VI.93

In his diary entry for 14 October 1872 Lear described the scene depicted in this painting: 'Nothing in all life is so amazingly interesting as this new road & avenue – literally all the way to the Pyramids.... The effect of this causeway in the middle of wide waters is singular... & were one sure of quiet, there is much of poetry in the scene, but it wants thought and arrangement.' The avenue of trees that lined the Pyramids Road had been planted three years earlier to celebrate Empress Eugenie's visit for the opening of the Suez Canal. (ABOVE)

DAVID ROBERTS
The Island of Philae, Nubia
SIGNED AND DATED *1843*, OIL ON CANVAS, 77 x 153.5cm (30¼ x 60in) London £177,500 ($266,250). 8.VI.93

David Roberts was the first British oil painter of any standing to travel up the Nile. He landed at Alexandria on 24 September 1833, and a fortnight later was on his way up the river, writing in his journal 'I am the first artist at least from England who has been here and there is much in this.' He returned home in July 1839, having traversed Egypt, the Holy Land, Syria and the Lebanon. By that time he had 272 sketches and three full sketchbooks, one of the single greatest bodies of work from any artist's journey. (LEFT)

ARCHIBALD THORBURN
Voices of the Forest – Red Deer
SIGNED AND DATED *1912*, WATERCOLOUR, 53.5 x 74cm (21 x 29¼in)
London £69,500 ($102,500). 31.III.93
From the collection of the Thorburn Museum

Like many painters of his time, Thorburn was the son
of an artist. His father Robert, a successful miniaturist
patronized by Queen Victoria, was his first teacher
and a stern critic. (RIGHT)

ARCHIBALD THORBURN
Woodcock and Chicks
SIGNED AND DATED *1932*, WATERCOLOUR, 19 x 28cm (7½ x 11in)
London £30,000 ($44,500). 31.III.93
From the collection of the Thorburn Museum

In 1930 Thorburn underwent an operation for cancer
and his final years were accompanied by almost
continuous pain. The work of those years was gentler
and on a smaller scale, often repeating the theme of
hen birds and their young. (BELOW)

ARCHIBALD THORBURN
The Close of a Winter's Day
SIGNED AND DATED *1905*, WATERCOLOUR, 67.5 x 161cm (26½ x 63½in)
London £100,500 ($148,500). 31.III.93
From the collection of the Thorburn Museum

The Close of a Winter's Day is generally considered to be one of Thorburn's finest
achievements and took three weeks to complete. He generally worked at an amazing
pace, rising early and preceding his labours with a cold bath, a bowl of porridge oats
and a walk in his garden in Hascombe, Surrey, where he moved in 1902. (BELOW)

MODERN BRITISH PAINTING

SIR WILLIAM ORPEN
The Roscommon Dragoon
SIGNED, OIL ON CANVAS, 76 x 63.5cm (30 x 25in)
London £139,000 ($209,800). 30.VI.93

Painted in 1913, this work and its companion piece, *The Irish Volunteer*, are generally considered to be the artist's two most famous portraits. They are the culmination of a series of pictures of Vera Hone, a celebrated beauty of the time. *The Roscommon Dragoon* shows the sitter dressed in an Armagh Infantry militia tunic, evoking the sort of Irish stock figure which Orpen had portrayed in a number of earlier self-portraits. (ABOVE)

SIR ALFRED MUNNINGS
Dragoon Guard on a Dappled Horse, facing left (one of a pair)
SIGNED, OIL ON CANVAS, 81.3 x 69.9cm (32 x 27½in)
New York $288,500 (£191,000) for the pair. 4.VI.93
Property of Senator John W. Warner

This is one of a pair of canvases of the same subject (the other is a view from the back of the dragoon). Munnings' skill in the traditional specialization of horse portraiture brought him considerable fame and success with the British public and the London art establishment, and in 1944 he was elected President of the Royal Academy. (ABOVE)

GRAHAM SUTHERLAND
Palm Palisade
SIGNED AND DATED *1948*, OIL ON CANVAS, 112 x 90cm (44 x 35½in)
London £74,800 ($166,600). 4.XI.92

In 1947 the artist visited the South of France, returning every
summer thereafter. The luxuriant flora of the area transformed his
work, allowing the introduction of new local subjects – palm fronds,
vine trellises, banana leaves and cicadas – and a fresh palette: hot
pinks, reds, yellows and vibrant acidic greens applied straight from
the tube. As Sutherland turned to these new tones, his forms became
simpler with the picture plane flattening dramatically. This was
also the period when he began to invest organic forms with a
quasi-mechanistic quality. (ABOVE)

SIR STANLEY SPENCER
The Temptation of Saint Anthony
OIL ON CANVAS, 122 x 91.5cm (48 x 36in)
London £297,000 ($463,300). 4.XI.92

Executed in 1945, this painting was the result of a competition run
by an American film studio to find a picture on the theme of Saint
Anthony to appear in the film of Maupassant's novel *Bel Ami*. Eleven
artists took part, including Dali, Delvaux and Ernst. The subject
matter, with its story of self-denial and chastity, was radically
reworked by Spencer: those from whom the saint turns away are seen
not as evil, but as representative of the artist's philosophy of free love
uniting Man, Woman and God. Elements of this painting, including
the thinly applied pale colours, mark it as the first of Spencer's late
works, prefiguring some of the great pictures of the 1950s. (ABOVE)

NINETEENTH–CENTURY EUROPEAN PAINTINGS

JOAQUIN SOROLLA Y BASTIDA
Oxen in the Sea, study for *Afternoon Sun*
SIGNED AND DATED *1902*, OIL ON CANVAS, 96 x 135.5cm (37¾ x 53¼in)
London £848,500 ($1,272,750).16.VI.93

From 1900 onwards Sorolla abandoned painting for the Salons and International
Exhibitions, looked to Velázquez for inspiration and began work on large outdoor
canvases that display broad, vigorous brushwork. This work is the most important of
the artist's preparatory pieces for his famous *Sol de Tarde* (Afternoon Sun), from
1903, now with the Hispanic Society of America in New York. It is widely agreed
that these paintings mark the point at which Sorolla achieved the pinnacle of his
artistic development. (ABOVE)

JEAN-AUGUSTE-DOMINIQUE INGRES
Don Pedro of Toledo Kissing the Sword of King Henry IV
SIGNED AND DATED *1820*, OIL ON PANEL, 48 x 40cm (19 x 15¾in) London £628,500 ($942,750). 16.VI.93

Ingres was greatly inspired by the figure of Henry IV and planned to illustrate many episodes from his life. This is one of four versions of the subject, dating from 1814 to 1831. The 1814 version is now lost; the 1819 version is in a private collection in France; and the 1831 version is in the Louvre. The appearance at auction of this work, from 1820, was a rare event. (ABOVE)

JEAN-LÉON GÉRÔME
La Reception de Condé à Versailles
SIGNED, OIL ON CANVAS, 96.5 x 139.7cm (38 x 55in)
New York $800,000 (£516,129). 26.V.93

In November 1674 the Duke of Condé was received in great honour by Louis XIV at the Palace of Versailles. Infirm from an attack of gout, Condé paused on his way up the stairs, for which the king excused him: 'Do not hurry yourself, cousin. It is not surprising that you can scarcely walk, loaded as you are with laurels.' In executing this work, Gérôme was realizing a long-held ambition to illustrate the anecdote and was undoubtedly proud of the result. He wrote: 'I have worked upon it without intermission to reach the desired end.' (ABOVE)

WILLIAM ADOLPHE BOUGUEREAU
The Virgin, Child and Saint John the Baptist
SIGNED AND DATED *1875*, OIL ON CANVAS,
200.7 x 121.9cm (79 x 48in)
New York $690,000 (£445,161). 26.V.93

To the studied synthesis of Byzantine and High Renaissance elements in this important work, Bouguereau brings a sculptural consciousness recalling the forms of Michelangelo and Bernini. The artist balances the rigid symmetry of the architectural background with flowing linear arabesques and, from a psychological point of view, the innocence and joy of the children with the Virgin's expression of melancholy and foreboding. (LEFT)

JAMES-JACQUES-JOSEPH
TISSOT
La Mondaine
SIGNED, OIL ON CANVAS,
147.3 x 101.6cm (58 x 40in)
New York $1,982,500
(£1,295,700). 17.II.93
From the Joey and Toby
Tanenbaum Collection

From 1882 to 1885
Tissot executed fifteen
large canvases, *La
Femme à Paris*, that
illustrate *parisiennes*
of various classes at
their vocations and
amusements. Common
to this series was the
emphasis on fashion,
beauty and the
increasingly complex role
of women in society.
Such scenes of modern
life were intended to
attract wealthy art
patrons of the *haute
bourgeoisie* and the risqué
subject matter of this
canvas may have been
calculated to quicken the
pulse of the elderly art
buyer. (LEFT)

IMPRESSIONIST AND MODERN ART

PIERRE-AUGUSTE RENOIR
Femmes dans un Jardin
SIGNED, OIL ON CANVAS, 54.6 x 65.4cm (21½ x 25¾in) New York $6,712,500 (£4,358,700). 11.V.93
Renoir and Monet worked together frequently in 1872-3, and the extent of Monet's influence is shown
clearly in this work of 1873 in the dominance of landscape over figures. The force of this work lies in the
dramatic brushwork: quick dashes of paint describe the flowers reflecting in the sun, long drags of wet
pigment form the trees, dark pigments crushed into the surface create the deep recesses and a brilliant
daub of pure white depicts the sun glinting off the white parasol. (ABOVE)

PAUL CÉZANNE
Nature Morte: les Grosses Pommes
SIGNED, OIL ON CANVAS, 45.7 x 54cm (18 x 21¼in) New York $28,602,500 (£18,573,000). 11.V.93

'Cézanne made a living thing out of a teacup or, rather, in a teacup he realized the existence of something alive. He raised still life to the point where it ceased to be inanimate. He painted things as he painted human beings.... He achieved expressive colour and a form that harmonizes this colour with an almost mathematical abstraction. A man, a tree, an apple are not represented but used by Cézanne in building up a painterly thing called a "picture".' (Wassily Kandinsky, *Concerning the Spiritual in Art*, 1912.) (ABOVE)

AUGUSTE RODIN
Eve
WHITE MARBLE, height 76cm (30in)
London £429,000 ($664,900). 1.XII.92

This figure was conceived as one of a pair (with *Adam*)
to flank the *Gates of Hell,* a vast Romantic creation for
the Musée des Arts Décoratifs that took over twenty
years to complete. It was first executed in a life-size
version, but it was the half-size reduction that was
exhibited publicly and quickly became one of Rodin's
most popular works. The model was Mme Abruzzezzi,
whom Rodin described – literally – in glowing terms:
'The dark one had sunburned skin, warm, with the
bronze reflections of the women of sunny lands... and
that perfect equilibrium, that simplicity of bearing
which makes great gesture.' (RIGHT)

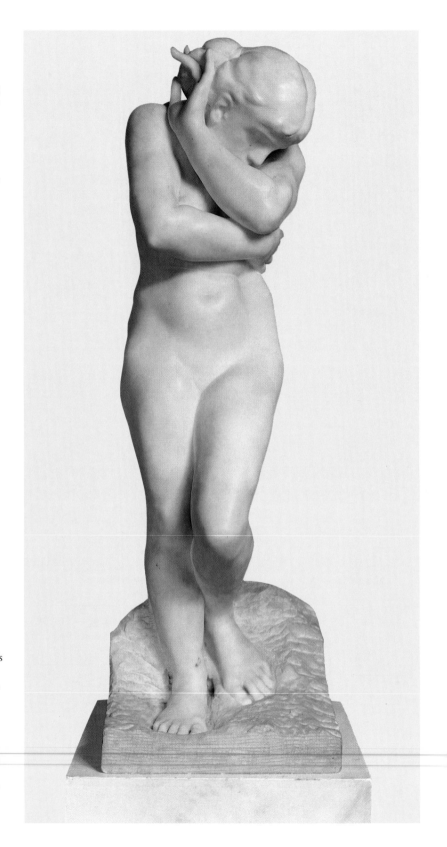

CLAUDE MONET
Femme à l'Ombrelle
SIGNED, BLACK CRAYON WITH *GRATTAGE,* 30.5 x 23.5cm (12 x 9¼in)
London £353,500 ($537,300). 22.VI.93
From the Collection of Marie-Louise Durand-Ruel.

This sensitive drawing of 1890 is a *reprise* after Monet's
painting *Essai de Figure en Plein Air (vers la droite)* of
1886, and was commissioned by Paul Durand-Ruel to
accompany Octave Mirbeau's article on Monet in
L'Art dans les Deux Mondes, 7 March 1891. Independent drawings are rare in Monet's œuvre, and the
majority were made after paintings for publication in
journals. The subject had a special significance for the
artist as the model was Suzanne Hoschedé-Butler, his
step-daughter and favourite model, who died in 1899
at the age of 33. Monet kept the painting in her
memory until his own death in 1926. (FAR RIGHT)

WASSILY KANDINSKY
Sketch 1 for Composition VII
SIGNED AND DATED *1913*, OIL ON CANVAS, 78 x 100cm (30¾ x 39⅜in) London £5,500,000 ($8,525,000). 1.XII.92
Executed in Munich in November 1913, this painting is the most definitive of six oil studies for *Composition VII*
(Tretiakov Gallery, Moscow), considered to be the most important of the artist's pre-War works. From 1911 until
1933, Kandinsky shared a close friendship with the artist Paul Klee, and they frequently exchanged paintings.
Sketch I was given to Klee in around 1925, and had remained in the Klee family until this sale. (BELOW)

HENRI MATISSE
L'Asie
SIGNED AND DATED *46*, OIL ON CANVAS, 116.2 x 81.3cm (45¾ x 32in) New York $11,000,000 (£7,284,700). 10.XI.92
From the Estate of Mollie Parnis Livingston.
L'Asie was painted in Vence in 1946. The orientalizing arabesques evoke the exotic subjects of Matisse's Moroccan
period of 1911-12. As in many of the artist's late works, the light emanates directly from the brilliance of the
colour, the perspective being flattened out to obtain decorative, semi-abstracted qualities from the image. (RIGHT)

PAUL KLEE
Landschaft mit Eseln
SIGNED AND DATED *1932*, PENCIL, WATERCOLOUR AND GOUACHE ON COTTON, 41.4 x 55.6cm (16¼ x 21⅞in)
London £1,013,500 ($1,489,800). 22.VI.93
This painting is from a series of works by Klee of the early 1930s, executed in a
method the artist described as 'so-called pointillism'. The colours and imagery loosely
refer to Klee's visit to Egypt in the winter of 1928-29 and the work is in keeping with
the mysterious and poetic compositions that the artist produced during his period at
the Düsseldorf Academy. (ABOVE)

EGON SCHIELE
Youth in a Sailor Suit
SIGNED AND DATED *1914*,
WATERCOLOUR AND GOUACHE,
47.8 x 31.2cm (18 x 12¼in)
London £429,000 ($664,900).
1.XII.92

This work is thought to depict Paul Erdmann, Schiele's nephew. Erdmann appears in a number of works of this period, either alone or with the artist's wife, Edith. Jane Kallir has pointed out that 'the drawings of Edith with her nephew, Paul Erdmann, achieve an unprecedented and bizarre degree of erotic ambiguity. At times the Edith/Egon representations seem to merge with the Edith/Paul pictures, and it is impossible to be sure who the subjects are.' In this work, however, Erdmann is alone and Schiele seems more interested in the youthful *contraposto* of the child's body than in its erotic charge.
(RIGHT)

WASSILY KANDINSKY
Milieu Accompagné (Centre with Accompaniment)
SIGNED WITH THE MONOGRAM AND DATED *37*, OIL ON CANVAS, 114 x 146cm (44⅞ x 57½in)
London £3,026,500 ($4,600,200). 22.VI.93
From the Collection of Monsieur and Madame Adrien Maeght

When the Nazis closed the Bauhaus in 1933 Kandinsky moved to Paris, where he
joined a number of artist friends, including Arp, Duchamp, Ray and Miró. One of
Kandinsky's finest paintings of this period, *Milieu Accompagné* testifies to the artist's
closeness to Miró, whose contemporary work undoubtedly helped to suggest the
stylized organic forms floating across the plane of the picture surface. (BELOW)

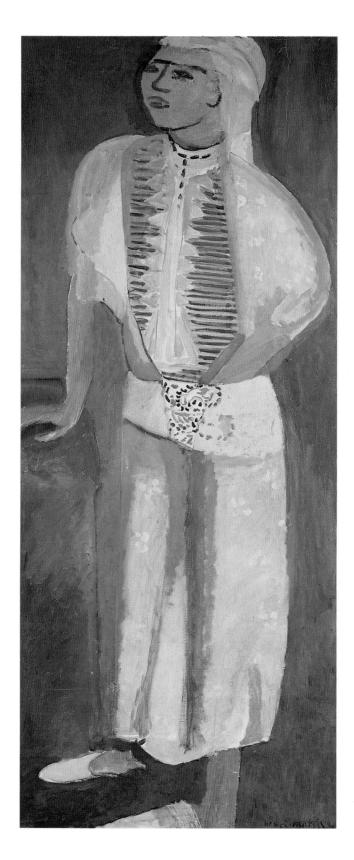

HENRI MATISSE
La Mulâtresse Fatma
OIL ON CANVAS, 146.1 x 61cm (57½ x 24in)
New York $14,302,500 (£9,287,300). 11.V.93
From the Collection formed by Joseph Müller

This work was painted on the second of two trips to Morocco. The first, in the early part of 1912, had been marred by bad weather, but Matisse returned in October the same year to stay for four months. His fascination with Morocco, which had a lasting influence on his work, was due in part to the artist's admiration for the painter Eugène Delacroix, who had visited the country in 1832. *La Mulâtresse Fatma* can be seen as a direct descendant of the work of the Orientalist painters of the nineteenth century. The artist used a number of models while in Morocco, of whom Fatma was perhaps the least favourite – he found her 'irritating'. (LEFT)

PAUL DELVAUX
La Joie de Vivre
SIGNED AND DATED *1–38*,
OIL ON CANVAS,
101.5 x 120cm (40 x 47¼in)
London £1,013,500
($1,540,500).22.VI.93

Painted a year after the death of the artist's father and in the first year of his marriage to Suzanne Purnal, this painting has an audacity and directness in its imagery that mark a new phase in the artist's work. The barriers of non-communication between the sexes, so apparent in Delvaux's earlier work, are beginning to be demolished: the naked woman and dark-suited man – both recurrent Delvaux images – here touch as they have never done before. (LEFT)

SALVADOR DALI
La Montre Molle
SIGNED AND DATED *49*,
OIL ON CANVAS,
21 x 25.4cm (8¾ x 10in)
New York $662,500 (£430,100).
11.V.93

This is surely one of the most widely known images to have been created by this most successful of surrealist painters. Dali's 'soft watch' imagery is best known from his masterpiece, *The Persistence of Memory* of 1931. *La Montre Molle* is a later variation of that work.
(RIGHT)

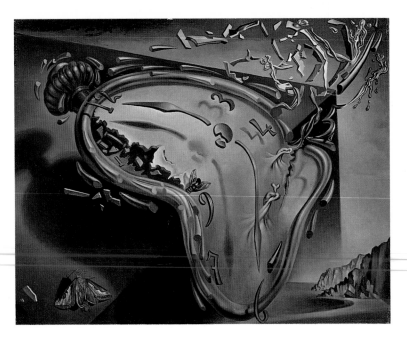

MAX ERNST
**The King Playing
with the Queen**
INSCRIBED *Max Ernst*, BRONZE,
height 97.8cm (38½in)
New York $1,210,000
(£801,325). 10.XI.92
From the Collection of Mr and
Mrs Joseph Randall Shapiro

This sculpture was executed in plaster in 1944 from which an edition of nine bronzes was cast. Ernst may have been influenced by native American art in his adoption of 'primitive', elemental forms. (RIGHT)

CONTEMPORARY ART

ROY LICHTENSTEIN
Girl with Piano
SIGNED AND DATED *63*, MAGNA ON CANVAS,
172.7 x 121.9cm (68 x 48in)
New York $1,815,000 (£1,194,079). 17.XI.92

This work is an early example of Lichtenstein's famous cartoon paintings, which are recognized as major landmarks in the history of American Pop Art, and can be considered as distillations of the artist's major artistic concerns. In common with other Pop artists of the day, Lichtenstein focused on the transformation of objects from popular culture into high art, employing a style and medium directly related to contemporary popular media. (RIGHT)

ANDY WARHOL
Marilyn x 100
SIGNED AND DATED *1962*, INK AND
SYNTHETIC POLYMER PAINT ON CANVAS,
205.7 x 567.7cm (81 x 223 ½ in)
New York $3,740,000 (£2,460,500). 17.XI.92

Marilyn x 100 is the largest version of the artist's serial image of the movie star. These posthumous portraits are perhaps the most famous result of the combination of Warhol's pioneering use of the photographic silkscreen and his discovery of media icons as subject matter. It was the public viewing of his first Marilyn paintings at the Stable Gallery, New York, in November 1962, which included this work, that finally brought the artist serious critical attention and widespread recognition. (BELOW)

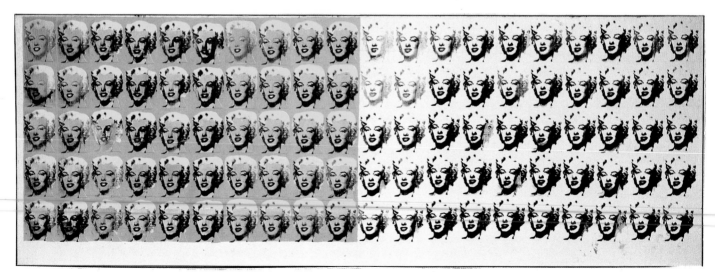

DAVID HOCKNEY
Henry Geldzahler and Christopher Scott, 1968-9
ACRYLIC ON CANVAS, 213.4 x 304.8cm (84 x 120in)
New York $1,100,000 (£723,684). 17.XI.92
From the collection of Mrs Harry N. Abrams and Mr Robert E. Abrams

Henry Geldzahler and Christopher Scott, 1968-9 is a double portrait of two of the
artist's closest friends. Having recently arrived in New York in 1964, Hockney had
attended a party at Andy Warhol's studio, where he met Geldzahler, a curator of
twentieth-century art at the Metropolitan Museum of Art, who was subsequently to
appear in a large number of the artist's sketches and paintings. Hockney was
intrigued by the pictorial possibilities of double portraits, and had just completed a
major work of Christopher Isherwood and Don Bachardy, a similarly grand and
rigorously symmetrical work. (ABOVE)

FRANCIS BACON
Study for a Portrait
OIL ON CANVAS,
51 x 41cm (20 x 16in)
London £562,500 ($826,800).
24.VI.93
This previously
unrecorded work is
closely related to a group
of four *Studies for a
Portrait* made in the
summer of 1952, which
were to lead to the
famous *Study for a
Portrait* of 1953 now in
the Kunsthalle in
Hamburg. The work does
not depict a specific
person; it is more a
statement about mankind
itself, where the figure
becomes a symbol of
human fate. Bacon once
said to David Sylvester:
'When I look at you
across the table I don't
only see you but I see a
whole emanation which
has to do with personality
and everything else. And
to put that over in a
painting... means that it
would appear violent in
paint.' (RIGHT)

LEON KOSSOFF
**Children's
Swimming Pool,
11 O'Clock Saturday
Morning, August
1969**
SIGNED AND DATED *August 1969*,
OIL ON BOARD,
152.5 x 205cm (60 x 81in)
London £209,000 ($323,900).
3.XII.92
This work belongs to an
important series of
paintings from the late
1960s and early 70s, in
which the artist depicted
everyday places and
activities in order to seize
the beauty of ordinary
life. The influence of
Monet has been noted in
Kossoff's paintings of this
period, which can be seen
as true developments of
early Impressionism,
concentrating on the
importance of light and
its effect at specific times
of the day. (ABOVE)

ALBERTO BURRI
Sacco e Oro
SIGNED AND DATED *Roma 53*, OIL, BURLAP AND GOLDLEAF, 86.4 x 101cm (34 x 39¾in)
London £309,000 ($454,965). 24.VI.93
Burri first started to use old sacking in a prisoner-of-war camp, where it was the only material
available. It was then that he realized its capacity to stretch, its subtle variations of tone and
irregular texture, and began to sew the 'sacco' together in different patterns, as a surgeon would
sew wounds. (Burri had studied medicine before joining the Italian army.) *Sacco e Oro* belongs
to the celebrated group of *Sacchi*, in two of which gold is used as an additional medium,
in striking contrast to the background. (ABOVE)

GERHARD RICHTER
Neger (Nuba)
SIGNED, OIL ON CANVAS, 145 x 200cm (57⅛ x 78¾in)
London £320,500 ($471,100). 24.VI.93

Early in the 1960s Richter began using press photographs as the direct visual source for his paintings, and those produced between 1962 and 1965 often openly display these origins, as they include captions or margins. This canvas, painted in 1964, is one of a group of paintings based on travel photographs (in the same year Richter also painted the Great Sphinx). Whereas many of the early pictures are painted in monochromatic hues of grey, *Neger* employs a much wider palette, a reflection of the artist's desire to 'add more to the painting'. (ABOVE)

ANSELM KIEFER
Dein Goldenes Haar, Margarethe!!
SIGNED AND DATED *1981*, OIL AND MIXED MEDIA ON BURLAP, 170 x 190cm (67 x 74in)
London £309,500 ($454,900). 24.VI.93
This work belongs to Kiefer's *Margarethe und Shulamith* series which was inspired by Paul
Celan's poem *Death Fugue*. The poem, which Celan wrote in a concentration camp in 1945,
contrasts Margarethe, the blond German, with the Jewish Shulamith – inseparably bound
together in the cycle of life and death. Kiefer chose to represent Margarethe through the
application of straw, reminiscent of her blonde hair, and the presence of the Jewish Shulamith
by the black shadows behind the straw. (ABOVE)

CY TWOMBLY
Untitled
SIGNED AND DATED *1956*, OIL, CRAYON AND PENCIL ON CANVAS, 117.5 x 175.3cm (46¼ x 69in)
New York $2,145,000 (£1,411,184). 17.XI.92
An outstanding example of Twombly's gestural paintings of the 1950s,
Untitled is characteristic of the artist's all-over compositions of linear 'writing'
on a luminous ground. (ABOVE)

BRUCE NAUMAN
One Hundred Live and Die, 1984
NEON TUBING MOUNTED ON FOUR PANELS, 299.7 x 335.9 x 53.3cm (118 x 132¼ x 21in)
New York $1,925,000 (£1,266,447). 17.XI.92
This is an extraordinarily ambitious neon sculpture comprising a list of a
hundred commands. The commands can be switched on and off to form
different visual arrangements and combinations of meaning. (RIGHT)

LIVE AND DIE
DIE AND DIE
SHIT AND DIE
PISS AND DIE
EAT AND DIE
SLEEP AND DIE
LOVE AND DIE
HATE AND DIE
FUCK AND DIE
SPEAK AND DIE
CRY AND DIE
KISS AND DIE
RAGE AND DIE
LAUGH AND DIE
TOUCH AND DIE
FEEL AND DIE
SICK AND DIE
WELL AND DIE
BLACK AND DIE
WHITE AND DIE
YELLOW AND DIE
LIVE AND LIVE
DIE AND LIVE
SHIT AND LIVE
PISS AND LIVE
EAT AND LIVE
SLEEP AND LIVE
LOVE AND LIVE
FUCK AND LIVE
SPEAK AND LIVE
LIE AND LIVE
HEAR AND LIVE
CRY AND LIVE
KISS AND LIVE
RAGE AND LIVE
LAUGH AND LIVE
TOUCH AND LIVE
FEEL AND LIVE
FEAR AND LIVE
SICK AND LIVE
WELL AND LIVE
BLACK AND LIVE
WHITE AND LIVE
YELLOW AND LIVE
SING AND DIE
SCREAM AND DIE
YOUNG AND DIE
OLD AND DIE
CUT AND DIE
RUN AND DIE
STAY AND DIE
PLAY AND DIE
KILL AND DIE
SUCK AND DIE
COME AND DIE
GO AND DIE
KNOW AND DIE
TELL AND DIE
SMELL AND DIE
FALL AND DIE
RISE AND DIE
STAND AND DIE
SIT AND DIE
SPIT AND DIE
TRY AND DIE
FAIL AND DIE
SMILE AND DIE
THINK AND DIE
PAY AND DIE
SING AND LIVE
SCREAM AND LIVE
YOUNG AND LIVE
OLD AND LIVE
CUT AND LIVE
RUN AND LIVE
PLAY AND LIVE
KILL AND LIVE
COME AND LIVE
GO AND LIVE
KNOW AND LIVE
TELL AND LIVE
SMELL AND LIVE
FALL AND LIVE
RISE AND LIVE
STAND AND LIVE
SIT AND LIVE
SPIT AND LIVE
TRY AND LIVE
FAIL AND LIVE
SMILE AND LIVE
THINK AND LIVE
PAY AND LIVE

AMERICAN PAINTINGS

ALBERT BIERSTADT
An Indian Encampment
SIGNED AND DATED '61, OIL ON CANVAS, 33.7 x 47.6cm (13¼ x 18¾in)
New York $695,500 (£445,830). 27.V.93

Bierstadt made his first trip west with Colonel Frederick Lander's US Government expedition in 1859. It was during this foray along the Platte River to the Wind River Mountains, Nebraska, that the artist first encountered the western landscape and the lifestyle of the native Americans. The artist wrote to *The Crayon* from the Rocky Mountains: 'We often meet Indians, and they have always been kindly disposed to us and we to them; but it is a little risky, because being very superstitious and naturally distrustful, their friendship may turn to hate at any moment.' This work is one of a small group of encampment scenes completed on the artist's return from the 1859 journey. (ABOVE)

WINSLOW HOMER
The Unruly Calf
SIGNED AND DATED *1875*,
OIL ON CANVAS,
61.6 x 97.8cm (24¼ x 38½in)
New York $1,210,000
(£775,640). 3.XII.92
Property from the
Pauline Woolworth Trust
The Unruly Calf was
painted during Homer's
visit to Petersburg,
Virginia, in the summer
of 1875. Much of the
artist's work at this time
developed subjects con-
nected with rural child-
hood, but the paintings
of this and other trips to
Virginia also tackled
themes sympathetic to
the social conditions of
the newly emancipated
southern black
population. (RIGHT)

WINSLOW HOMER
Looking Out to Sea
SIGNED AND DATED *1872*,
OIL ON CANVAS,
39.4 x 57.2cm (15½ x 22½in)
New York $706,500
(£452,800). 27.V.93
This newly discovered
work by Homer relates
to three other known
paintings by the artist
executed in 1872, all
sharing compositional
elements such as the
positioning of a flower
pot or pots on the sill
and a blonde young
woman gazing out of the
window. At the time this
work was painted,
Homer's subjects were
dominated by scenes
with a latent narrative
force taken from
memories of his boy-
hood and images of
country life. (RIGHT)

CHILDE HASSAM
The Room of Flowers
SIGNED AND DATED *1894*, OIL ON CANVAS, 86.4 x 86.4cm (34 x 34in) New York $5,502,500 (£3,527,200). 27.V.93
From the Collection of Arthur G. Altschul

Childe Hassam was one of America's leading 'Impressionist' painters. This work was painted as a tribute
to the poet, writer and gardener Celia Thaxter, who ran a summer resort on Appledore Island in New
Hampshire in the 1890s which attracted a wide circle of artists, writers and musicians. The guests were
invited to informal salons in the parlour of Mrs Thaxter's cottage, the room depicted in this painting.
Hassam regarded *The Room of Flowers* as 'one of my best things'. (ABOVE)

WILLIAM MERRITT CHASE
Peonies
SIGNED, PASTEL ON PAPER, 121.9 x 121.9cm (48 x 48in) New York $3,962,500 (£2,540,000). 27.V.93
The general scheme of *Peonies* might have been inspired by Whistler's painting *Symphony in White No. 2: The Little White Girl* (Tate Gallery, London), although it is hard to establish any direct precedent. William Merritt Chase (1849-1916) recognized the influence of a variety of contemporary painters while strongly preserving his own distinctive artistic qualities through a mastery of technique. He favoured pastels from early on in his career, a medium rarely used by his professional American counterparts. *Peonies* is exceptionally large for a pastel study and vivid proof of the artist's technical skills. (ABOVE)

CHARLES DEMUTH
Welcome to Our City
SIGNED AND DATED 1921, OIL ON
CANVAS, 63.5 x 50.8cm (25 x 20in)
New York $825,000 (£528,850).
3.XII.92

Charles Demuth (1883-
1935) spent his entire life in
Lancaster, Pennsylvania.
Until 1920 he restricted his
talents to the execution of
delicate watercolour studies,
but a subsequent change in
his choice of subject matter
encouraged him to turn to oil
and tempera. His work of this
period portrays architectural
and industrial scenes of
his native town, often
incorporating cryptic letters
and fragments of words.
Welcome to Our City features
the dome of the Lancaster
courthouse, a distinguished
mid-nineteenth-century
landmark. The subtle
anthropomorphism of the
dome itself, a device Demuth
periodically employed, hints
at the artist's doubts about
industrial progress and
development. (RIGHT)

MARSDEN HARTLEY
Abstraction
OIL ON CANVAS,
119.4 x 100.3cm (47 x 39½in)
New York $1,155,000 (£750,300).
3.XII.92
Property of Robert E. Abrams
and Michael D. Abrams

This painting of 1913
belongs to a group of innov-
ative works executed by
Marsden Hartley in the years
1913-15 which show the
strong impact of his first ex-
periences abroad. Foremost
among the new stimuli was
Wassily Kandinsky, who
Hartley had first heard about
in 1912, shortly after settling
in Paris. His interest in
Kandinsky was developed by
Der Blaue Reiter, which
Kandinsky had edited with
Franz Marc, as well as by
Kandinsky's treatise
*Concerning the Spiritual in
Art*. Early in 1913 Hartley
travelled to Germany to meet
Kandinsky in order to learn
more about his new ideas.
Abstraction was painted later
that year. (RIGHT)

EDWARD HOPPER
Gloucester Houses
SIGNED, WATERCOLOUR,
40.6 x 55.2cm (16 x 21¾in)
New York $330,000
(£211,540). 3.XII.92

Hopper sold his first
painting at the Armory
Show in New York in
1918, but it was not
until the 1930s that he
came to be hailed as a
leading exponent of the
new realism in American
painting. Between 1912
and 1928 Hopper spent
several summers in Mass-
achusetts, devoting much
of his time to painting
the local New England
architecture. (RIGHT)

LATIN AMERICAN PAINTINGS

RUFINO TAMAYO
Mujer en éxtasis
SIGNED AND DATED *0-73*, OIL AND SAND ON CANVAS, 130.5 x 194.6cm (51⅜ x 76⅝in) New York $1,485,000 (£976,900). 23.XI.92
The property of Robert E. Abrams

Female sexuality is one of the dominant themes of Rufino Tamayo's work. In this picture he seems to be celebrating the power of female eroticism, which he sees as something that needs to be deciphered in the springtime of life – hence the vivid yellow background, the yellow that he described as 'tender sun on a spring day'. (ABOVE)

FERNANDO BOTERO
La casa de las gemelas Arias
SIGNED AND DATED *73*, OIL ON CANVAS, 229 x 188cm (90 x 74in) New York $1,540,000 (£1,013,100). 23.XI.92 The property of Robert E. Abrams

Botero is one of this century's most cosmopolitan artists, yet all his work is suffused with the spirit of his native Colombia and most of his paintings display a reaction to the most exaggerated elements of South American life. This work is one of a series executed in the early 1970s on the theme of prostitutes and brothels. (LEFT)

MATTA
Psychological Morphology No. 14 (Personnages et automobile)
SIGNED, GRAPHITE, CRAYON
AND COLOURED PENCIL,
31.6 x 47.9cm (12½ x 18⅞in)
New York $104,250 (£67,600).
18.V.93

Matta was born in Chile in 1911 and trained as an architect, first in Santiago and then in Paris under Le Corbusier. In 1937 he turned to painting. He was a friend of Marcel Duchamp and an active member of the Surrealist movement, exerting a strong influence on Ernst, Tanguy, Breton and Masson. (LEFT)

JOSÉ CLEMENTE OROZCO
Acordada (Caballos y Zapatistas)
SIGNED, OIL ON CANVAS,
66 x 81.9cm (26 x 32¼in)
New York $374,000 (£246,000).
23.XI.92

The subject matter of this picture derives from pre-revolutionary Mexico. *Acordadas* were the henchmen of the landed classes, often employed to conscript farmers into slave labour. This practice led to a confrontation between the President of Mexico and the peasant leader, Emiliano Zapata, whose oppressed followers Orozco depicts here. The artist was a participant in the revolution, which broke out in 1910. (LEFT)

ARMANDO MORALES
Trois nus et voiture à cheval
SIGNED AND DATED 85, OIL ON CANVAS, 161.8 x 129.9cm (63⅗ x 51⅛in) New York $376,500 (£244,400). 18.V.93
Armando Morales was born in Nicaragua in 1927. His first one-man exhibitions were in Brazil and Peru
and in 1969 he moved to New York. His work of the 1960s incorporated informalist abstraction with
the use of canvas collage but after 1968 he returned to a more representational style, placing his figures
in semi-abstract environments which integrated volume and background. (ABOVE)

CANADIAN ART

CORNELIUS DAVID KRIEGHOFF
A Gentleman's Cutter
SIGNED, OIL ON CANVAS, 36.6 x 53.3cm (14 x 21in)
Toronto CN$49,500 (£25,390:$39,000). 19.V.93

Cornelius Krieghoff (1815-72) was an itinerant German artist who was resident in
French Canada from around 1840 to 1866. He settled first in Montreal and latterly
in Quebec, long enough to portray the landscape and the life of its people in great
detail. His paintings were sought after as souvenirs by English garrison officers, many
of whom were amateur painters themselves and responsible for much of the early
landscape art to emerge from the country. (ABOVE)

AUSTRALIAN ART

NORMAN ALFRED
WILLIAMS LINDSAY
Captured
SIGNED AND DATED *1938*,
OIL ON CANVAS,
159 x 129.5cm (63½ x 51⅛in)
Sydney AUS$145,000
(£65,300:$99,200). 22.XI.92

The work of Norman
Lindsay dominated the
closing years of Australia's
Victorian age. He was a
champion of the creative
imagination and the joys
of the flesh, and took on
his puritan detractors with
gusto. The battle was as
much concerned with
morals as with aesthetics
and, owing to Lindsay's
tireless activity, the role of
the artist in Australian
society became a matter of
vehement public debate.
Captured is a late example
of the artist's vivid fantasy.
(RIGHT)

PRINTS

REMBRANDT
HARMENSZ VAN RIJN
Jan Six
ETCHING, DRYPOINT AND BURIN,
FOURTH (FINAL) STATE,
24.4 x 19.1cm (9⅝ x 7½in)
New York $618,500 (£404,248).
13.V.93
From the Collection of
Dr Otto.Schäfer

Although he had known
members of the Six family
for some time, Rembrandt
became friends with Jan Six
during the course of etching
his portrait in 1647. It was a
time-consuming project,
requiring three separate
preparatory drawings, but
the final work is a triumph
of the printmaker's art.
Rembrandt combined
etching, engraving and
drypoint in so sophisticated
a manner that it is almost
impossible to distinguish
the different techniques. On
the plate he worked from
dark to light, using a single
point of illumination, the
window, as a frame for the
portrait. (RIGHT)

GIOVANNI BATTISTA PIRANESI
**The Man on the Rack,
plate XV from *I Carceri
d'Invenzione*, from a
collection of nineteen
volumes of the
artist's work**
ETCHING, 57.1 x 42cm (22½ x 16½in)
London £199,500 ($297,200) for the
collection. 29.VI.93

Piranesi's hallucinatory visions
of imaginary gaols, etched with
unprecedented energy, form
part of a collection of nineteen
volumes containing nearly all
of the artist's work. The
volumes were assembled by his
family in Rome shortly after
the artist's death in 1778 and
are in exceptionally fine
condition. Such sets formed
part of the libraries of many
aristocrats who had made the
Grand Tour, but most have
been broken up over the years.
(LEFT)

FRANCISCO JOSÉ DE
GOYA Y LUCIENTES
Plates from
Los Caprichos
ETCHINGS WITH AQUATINT, folio
London £111,500 ($166,100).
29.VI.93

These four etchings are
from the set of eighty
plates from a fine early
copy of *Los Caprichos*
(The Caprices), before
certain changes made for
the first edition of 1799.
Etched with the most
delicate tones of aquatint
– which soon wore out –
the fantastical and
nightmarish nature of the
images satirized the
corruption of society and
the Church in Spain.
Goya was forced to
withdraw the series from
circulation almost
immediately and only
about 300 copies were
printed in his lifetime.
(RIGHT)

El de la royona

Tantalo.

Aquellos polbos.

Que pico de Oro.

ALEXANDER
RODCHENKO
**Plate from
*Gravyuri
Rodchenko 1919*,
from a complete
portfolio**
LINOCUT, 15.7 x 11.1cm
(6½ x 4⅜in)
London £52,100 ($78,600)
for the portfolio. 30.VI.93
This work is from an
exceptionally rare
complete portfolio
of nine prints which
were executed at an
important stage in
the artist's career,
when he was begin-
ning to turn away
from two-dimen-
sional painting to
focus on the three-
dimensional design of
objects for everyday
use. Apart from a
few artist's proofs,
an edition of only
ten copies of the
portfolio was issued
at the request of the
Museum of Painterly
Culture (set up to
train and support
artists as well as to
promote the arts and
crafts design move-
ment). Of these ten,
only four complete
copies are known to
have survived. (LEFT)

MARY CASSATT
Woman Bathing or La Toilette
DRYPOINT AND AQUATINT PRINTED IN COLOURS, 47.4 x 31.3cm (18⅞ x 12⅜in)
New York $288,500 (£187,300). 13.V.93

Although born in America, Cassatt chose to spend most of her
working life in Paris. She is particularly renowned for her
extraordinarily fresh, direct coloured prints (this example is from
1890-1), which reveal her interest in Japanese woodblock prints as
well as her indebtedness to Degas. Cassatt's links with Degas were
strong, and it was he who persuaded her to exhibit with the
Impressionists. (ABOVE)

HENRI DE TOULOUSE-LAUTREC
Reine de Joie
LITHOGRAPH PRINTED IN COLOURS, 149 x 96.2cm (58⅞ x 37⅞in)
Tokyo ¥5,500,000 (£26,400:$45,400). 14.X.92

Toulouse-Lautrec's lifelong fame and success rested entirely on his
work in poster design rather than on his painting or graphic art. This
work, executed in 1892, is one of his more controversial images.
Baron Rothschild, who believed himself portrayed as the main
character of the book which this poster advertized, attempted to have
the edition suppressed. (ABOVE)

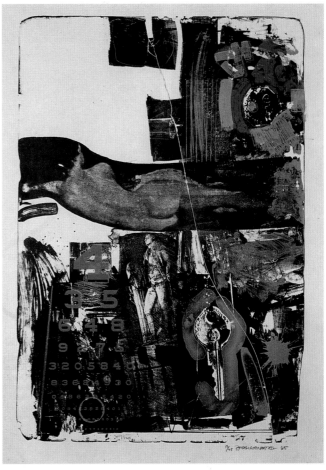

FRANK STELLA
Talladega Three II
SIGNED AND DATED *1982*, RELIEF PRINTED IN COLOURS, 168 x 132cm (66⅛ x 52in)
New York $61,600 (£40,261). 7.XI.92

Printed on handmade, hand-coloured paper, this work is from the
suite *Circuits*. The cursive black lines to which the colour appears to
cling, are made from the laser cuts left in the wood which was used as
a backboard in the foundry where Stella's large cut-out constructions
are made. When he saw the design left by the random marks overlaid
one on another, he decided to use the wood as the surface from which
this large graphic work is printed. (ABOVE)

ROBERT RAUSCHENBERG
Breakthrough II
SIGNED AND DATED *1965*, LITHOGRAPH PRINTED IN COLOURS,
111.8 x 78.5cm (30⅞ x 30⅞in)
New York $33,350 (£21,941). 15.V.93

After completing the first impression of this image in 1965,
Rauschenberg went on a worldwide tour with the Merce
Cunningham Dance Company and upon his return again took up the
stone, adding three colours and rotating the orientation by 45
degrees. By this time the stone had begun to disintegrate rapidly, so
each impression of *Breakthrough II* is slightly different. (ABOVE)

PHOTOGRAPHS

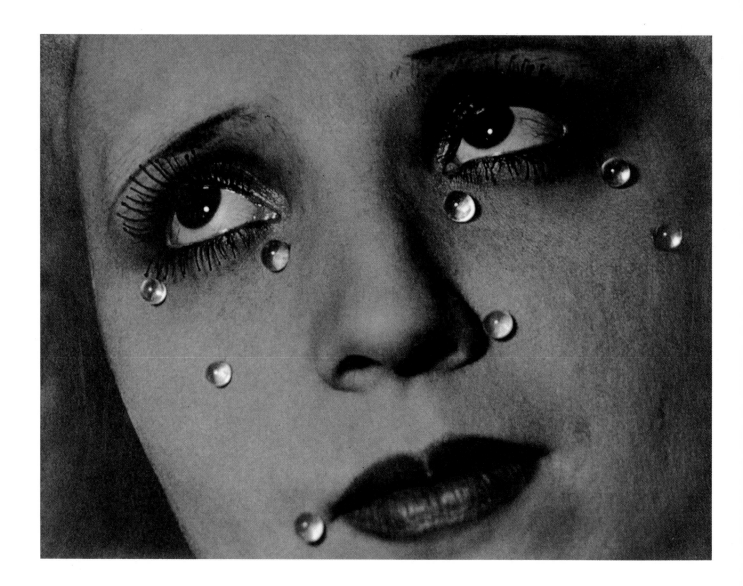

MAN RAY
Glass Tears
MONOGRAMMED, *c.*1930, SILVER PRINT, 22.8 x 29.8cm (9 x 11¾in)
London £122,500 ($190,100). 7.V.93

This work, dating from around 1930, is a little-known variant of a more tightly cropped image that has been widely published and exhibited. Its sale on 7 May 1993 achieved a record auction price for a single photograph. (ABOVE)

ROBERT MAPPLETHORPE
Calla Lily
SIGNED AND DATED *1987*, PLATINUM PRINT ON LINEN,
50 x 50cm (19⅝ x 19⅝in)
New York $63,250 (£37,426).16.X.92

This characteristic work is one in a series of studies of single blooms made by Robert Mapplethorpe during the late 1980s. (RIGHT)

quoddam cubiculum orans
quod humile erat in latitu
pedibz quattuor. & ibi multi
dieb; in oratione constanter psal
inclusis. tamen post man

LITERARY PROPERTY *by Paul Needham*

*L*iterary Property at Sotheby's is a broad umbrella, covering the written
and printed culture of the Western world and Near East from ancient
times to the present; and also the associated fields of illumination and
illustration, calligraphy, fine printing and fine book bindings. The enormous
variety of people, times, places and events encompassed by Literary Property is
the key to its fascination for those involved in these specialist areas. The
material at hand may be at one moment an early Qur'an fragment, at
another a finely illuminated Book of Hours, at another an elegant binding
commissioned by a Renaissance collector, at another Einstein's desk set of
scientific offprints, at another an early version of the game of Monopoly, and
so on; each piece contributing to our collective knowledge of the human past.

Last year, we lamented the relative dearth of single owner sales; this year
there was a 'good plenty' leading to the production of a number of catalogues
with a continuing reference value because of their unifying themes. Single
owner sales included: Darwin's Century: The Jeremy Norman Collection
(£177,600); The Jeffrey Young Collection (£441,100); The Sammlung
Rudolf von Gutmann (£1,035,000); The Otto Kallir Collection of Aviation
History ($1,014,000); The Library of Camille Aboussouan (£1,113,000) and
the Library of Alan G. Thomas (£1,531,000).

One private treaty sale deserves special notice. The entire manuscript
library of the Princes von Fürstenberg was sold through the mediation of
Sotheby's to the state of Baden-Württemberg, Germany. The Donaueschingen
Collection of some 1,200 items includes fragments dating to the seventh
century, and integral codices from the twelfth century onwards. A forte of the
collection is a group of medieval German literary manuscripts. The reported
sale price was DM48 million, establishing this as one of the largest single
book transactions in history.

An area so extensive as Literary Property inevitably breaks down into
smaller, more or less discrete collecting markets, each with its own history.

La Description des
Douzes Cesars
Abregees avecques
leurs Figures Faictes
et Portraictes
*c.*1520, TOURS, IN FRENCH,
ILLUMINATED MANUSCRIPT
ON VELLUM, 24 LEAVES,
21.1 x 13.8cm (8⅜ x 5½in)
London £165,000 ($259,000).
7.XII.92 (ABOVE)

The field of English Literature and History, which last year was somewhat thin, came back in force this season with the July London sale exceeding its high estimate. Highlights included a letter by Charlotte Brontë (£66,000), the Book of Fame *of Hannah More (£126,900), and the Reformation Collection formed by George Goyder (£313,800).*

Early printing, a traditionally strong area, showed less certainty this season, though with gratifying results for several unusually rare and fine items. In December we offered an illuminated vellum copy of the 1462 Bible, in a well-preserved contemporary Erfurt binding. Despite lacking some 26 leaves, it found strong competition, being knocked down finally at $286,000.

Travel Maps and Atlases continued the resilience noted last year, the major item being a superb copy of Blaeu's Atlas Major *in a contemporary cabinet which realized £170,000. In the sale of the late Alan G. Thomas's Collection, his copy of Stuart & Revett's* The Antiquities of Athens *made £89,500.*

In music, the season was dominated by manuscripts and letters of the great composers of the Austro-German tradition, including works by J. S. Bach, Haydn, Mozart, Beethoven, Gluck, Schubert, Brahms, Brückner and Richard Strauss. Among the highlights were the famous letter by Leopold Mozart discussing Haydn's praise of the young Wolfgang Mozart (£133,500, a record for a letter by a musician) and the autograph of Haydn's last string quartet, Op. 103 (£155,500). The market for printed music continues to hold strong; the first edition of Bach's Goldberg Variations *(Nuremberg 1714) made £18,700, and Orlando di Lassus'* Missae posthumae *(Münich 1610) £29,000 – both record prices for printed works by these composers.*

Apart from the en bloc *Donaueschingen sale already cited, Western Manuscripts and Miniatures had relatively few high profile items during the*

JOSEPH HAYDN
Autograph
manuscript of the
final unfinished
String Quartet,
Opus 103
SIGNED AND DATED *1803*,
VIENNA, 6 PAGES,
oblong folio,
London £172,500 ($265,700).
28.V.93. (ABOVE)

season, yet more modest offerings attracted considerable competition. One consignor had particularly good fortune. In February 1993 he purchased for £20 at a country house auction a miniature manuscript Psalter of the fifteenth century, which he brought to Bond Street for further study and appraisal. It was placed in our 22 June sale, and was knocked down at £9,000.

The Oriental manuscripts and miniatures market showed a steady recovery during the past season. One of the most interesting manuscripts was an early vellum palimpsest Qur'an leaf dating from the mid-seventh century, which brought £159,500.

Undoubtedly, the strongest single market within Literary Property this season was Americana, the colossus being Abraham Lincoln, whose autograph manuscripts dominated New York's auctions of Americana in December and May. Both of the two major Lincoln leaves in these sales came out of the almost legendary 'Grimsley carpetbag'.

Perhaps the most important leaf from what Lincoln called his 'literary bureau' was hitherto unrecorded and contains the earliest known formulation of Lincoln's 'House Divided' doctrine, the most historically significant Lincoln autograph to have been discovered this century. Three bidders in the 16 December 1992 sale were still active when the pre-sale high estimate was doubled at $1,000,000. The leaf was finally knocked down at $1,540,000, establishing a new auction record for any American historical document.

The second carpetbag manuscript of the season was sold in our May Americana auction. The only surviving page from a speech Lincoln gave between 1857 and 1859, this leaf last appeared on the market in 1952 when it made $1,850. This time it was sold to the purchaser of the 'House Divided' leaf for $992,500.

GEORG BRAUN AND
FRANZ HOGENBERG
Civitates Orbis
Terrarum,
volumes I-IV
1588, COLOGNE, IN LATIN,
COLOURED IN A CONTEMPORARY
HAND, 236 DOUBLE-PAGE
ENGRAVED PLATES,
39.5 x 28.5cm (15½ x 11¼in)
London £77,000 ($117,800).
19.XI.92. (BELOW)

PRINTED BOOKS & AUTOGRAPH MANUSCRIPTS

JAMES STUART AND NICOLAS REVETT
The Antiquities of Athens
VOLUMES I TO III, FIRST EDITIONS,
RED MOROCCO WITH GILT INLAY, folio
London £89,500 ($131,500). 22.VI.93
This binding represents the first
neo-classical example of its type and
has been attributed to James 'Athenian'
Stuart, making it the earliest English
binding known to have been designed
by an architect. In 1748 Stuart, along
with Nicolas Revett, discussed the idea
of publishing measured drawings of views
of Athenian buildings. The first volume
of the resulting *The Antiquities of Athens*
appeared in 1762. The works proved to
be an important early influence on the
Greek Revival movement in England.
(RIGHT)

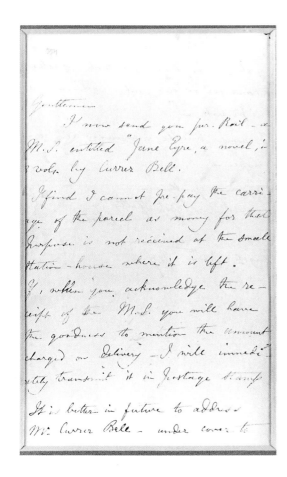

CHARLOTTE BRONTE
Autograph letter
DATED *24 August [18]47*, 2 PAGES, 8vo
London £66,000 ($102,300). 14.XII.92
From the Jeffrey Young Collection.

This letter was sent by Charlotte Brontë to her future publishers, Smith, Elder & Co, with the manuscript of *Jane Eyre*. The reaction of the firm's reader, William Smith Williams, has become legendary: he embarked on it after breakfast, broke for a sandwich and a glass of wine at lunch, cancelled an afternoon engagement to go riding, bolted his dinner and did not go to bed until it was finished. *Jane Eyre* was published on 16 October 1847 and was sensationally received, marking the beginning of Brontë's fame as a novelist. (ABOVE)

Nine first edition twentieth-century novels
STELLA GIBBONS Cold Comfort Farm (LONGMANS, GREEN AND CO., 1932)
CHRISTOPHER ISHERWOOD Goodbye to Berlin (HOGARTH PRESS, 1929)
ALDOUS HUXLEY Brave New World (CHATTO & WINDUS, 1932)
EVELYN WAUGH Vile Bodies (CHAPMAN & HALL, 1930)
EVELYN WAUGH Decline and Fall (CHAPMAN & HALL, 1930)
GEORGE ORWELL Nineteen Eighty-Four (SECKER & WARBURG, 1949)
ERNEST HEMINGWAY The Old Man and the Sea (CHARLES SCRIBNER, 1952)
MARGARET MITCHELL Gone with the Wind (MACMILLANS, 1936)
KAREN BLIXEN Out of Africa (PUTNAM, 1937)
London £6,369 ($9,999) for nine lots in total. 14.XII.92
From the Jeffrey Young Collection. (ABOVE)

ALBERT EINSTEIN
Autograph quotation beneath an early image of Einstein
DATED *1924*, 24.2 x 15.3cm (9½ x 6⅛in)
New York $66,000 (£41,700). 17.XII.92

The translation of this quotation is as follows: 'No human society can stay healthy without a common goal. This must be taken into consideration in order to understand the supreme importance of Palestine for all Jews.' In his early years, Einstein showed little interest in Judaism, but with the spread of anti-Semitism in post-First World War Germany he became a strong supporter of the Zionist movement. A committed pacifist, he opposed nationalism and thus adopted Zionism spiritually whilst rejecting its political ideologies. (RIGHT)

JOHN TALMAN
One of a collection of drawings of the various insignia of the Pontificate and other subjects
ITALY, 1702-21, TWO HUNDRED AND TWO DRAWINGS MOUNTED INTO TWO ALBUMS, folio
London £166,500 ($249,700). 2.IV.93

John Talman (1677-1726) was the son of the influential Baroque English architect William Talman. In 1710 he was in Rome with William Kent and it was then that he began collecting architectural and antiquarian drawings. The selection represented here contains examples commissioned by Talman as well as those by his own hand. It is remarkable that Talman, as an English Protestant, should have been given access to, and have been allowed to draw, objects that included those from the Pope's Secret Sacristy. (RIGHT)

LUDWIG WITTGENSTEIN
Autograph letter to C. K. Ogden
DATED *1922*, TWENTY-SIX PAGES, 4to
London £19,500 ($29,100). 20.VII.93

This letter provides detailed comments on the English translation of *Tractatus Logico-Philosophicus*, the only work by Wittgenstein (barring one short paper) to be published in his lifetime. The letter is written to the Cambridge linguistic psychologist and editor C. K. Ogden, who undertook the translation of the work. The *Tractatus* explored the dilemmas inherent in logic, which had previously exercised Bertrand Russell with whom Wittgenstein had studied, and was published in 1918 with an intro-duction by Russell himself. (RIGHT)

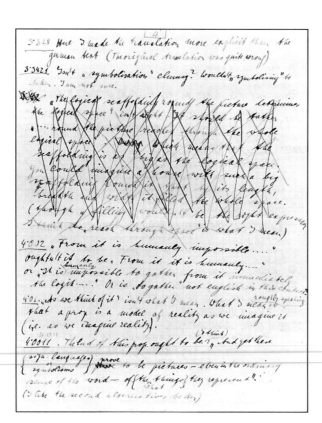

JOHANNES BLAEU
A Dutch-text edition of the *Atlas Major*
ELEVEN VOLUMES CONTAINED IN A CONTEMPORARY DUTCH WALNUT CABINET, 1649, folio
London £170,000 ($260,100). 19.XI.92

Copies of the Dutch-text edition of Johannes Blaeu's atlas are extremely rare. As with this example, they are sometimes augmented by the addition of the Dutch-text edition of Blaeu's celebrated *Townbooks of the Netherlands*. Sixteen sets have been identified within the Netherlands but only a small number exist outside the country. When coloured by a contemporary hand, as here, they form some of the most lavishly illustrated books produced in Amsterdam in the seventeenth century. (RIGHT)

ABRAHAM LINCOLN
Autograph manuscript
*c.*1857-59, 24.9 x 19.4cm (9¾ x 7⅝in)
New York $992,500 (£644,400). 21.V.93

This extract from one of Lincoln's most passionate indictments of slavery contains the lines: '… although volume upon volume is written to prove slavery a very good thing, we never hear of the man who wishes to take the good of it, by being a slave himself.' It dates to within a year of Lincoln's acceptance of the Illinois Republican nomination as candidate for the United States Senate. The manuscript is from the Grimsley Carpet Bag, which contained all of Lincoln's non-legal pre-presidential writings that he did not take to Washington. The bag was entrusted to Elizabeth Todd Grimsley, a cousin and friend of Mrs Lincoln. (ABOVE)

ABRAHAM LINCOLN
Autograph manuscript, a leaf from a speech
DECEMBER 1857
New York $1,540,000 (£974,600). 16.XII.92
Property of a descendant of Elizabeth Todd Grimsley.

This leaf can be regarded as the most historically significant autograph manuscript by Abraham Lincoln to have been discovered this century. Written in late December 1857, as Lincoln was emerging from relative obscurity to national fame, this represents the earliest surviving formulation of his 'House Divided' doctrine. The leaf is another important survival from the Grimsley Carpet Bag, most of the contents of which were widely dispersed after Lincoln's death. This leaf, however, had been kept by a member of Elizabeth Todd Grimsley's family. (ABOVE)

THOMAS JEFFERSON
Autograph letter
DATED *1788*, THREE PAGES, 4to
New York $200,500 (£130,100). 24.V.93
Jefferson's letter was written from Paris, during his term as Minister
to France, to the Comte de Moustier, his French counterpart in
America. He commiserates with Moustier on the rigours of the
six-day crossing from Le Havre to New York, and politely defends
his compatriots from the charge of deficiency in etiquette with
which Moustier had taxed them. Most significantly, Jefferson
gives his approbation of the US Constitution, which was just
approaching ratification: 'we must be contented to travel on
towards perfection, step by step.' (ABOVE)

PHILIPPE LESUEUR
Autograph letter
DATED *1783*, FOUR PAGES, 4to
New York $20,700 (£13,500). 14.VI.93
From the Otto Kallir Collection of Aviation History.
Philippe Lesueur's letter gives an exceptionally detailed account
of two famous early balloon ascents: the hot-air ascent of
J. A. C. Charles from the Champs de Mars, Paris, on 27 August
1783; and the hydrogen ascent of Joseph Montgolfier from
Versailles on 19 September 1783. The letter includes a fine
watercolour rendition of the Montgolfier balloon. (ABOVE)

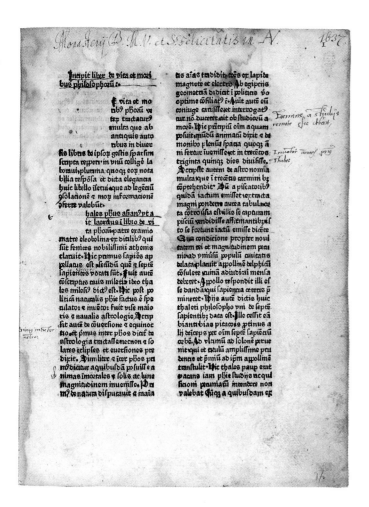

WALTER BURLEY
De Vita et Moribus Philosophorum
COLOGNE, WILLIAM CAXTON, *c.*1471-72, folio
New York $54,625 (£33,900). 14.VI.93
Burley's collection of stories about the ancient philosophers was
possibly the first book financed and published by William Caxton.
It was printed in Cologne, where Caxton lived in exile for a period of
some eighteen months, having previously spent most of his adult life
as a merchant adventurer in Bruges. The book was produced in
collaboration with the so-called Printer of Dares, Johann Schilling,
with whom Caxton formed an association that resulted in the
production of three editions. This is apparently the first copy of the
Burley tractate to appear at auction since a sale in our rooms of 1928.
(ABOVE)

Part of the library of Lord William Howard
TWO HUNDRED AND FIFTY-ONE VOLUMES (PLUS FIFTEEN PRINTED AFTER 1640)
London £35,000 ($54,900). 15.XII.92
Lord William Howard was a seventeenth-century bibliophile and
the owner of Naworth Castle in Cumbria. His library was housed
in the Castle tower and in 1844 narrowly escaped destruction from
a disastrous fire. The fire did not reach the tower, but many of the
books were thrown out of the window. Fortunately, the volumes
survived and were restored. The library has remained complete and
in situ ever since, and mainly consists of religious works, but
also includes books on history, language, poetry, science and law.
(ABOVE)

A 1462 Latin Bible
PRINTED ON VELLUM, TWO VOLUMES,
Royal folio
New York $286,000 (£181,000).
17.XII.92
Despite missing leaves, this
is one of the largest, freshest
and most elaborately
decorated surviving copies
of the famous 1462 Bible
printed in Mainz by Johann
Fust and Peter Schoeffer,
former partners of the
inventor of printing, Johann
Gutenberg. The contemp-
orary binding comes from
Erfurt, the probable source
of the Bible's finely wrought
illuminations. (LEFT)

MUSIC MANUSCRIPTS

JOHANNES BRAHMS
Autograph manuscript of the sixteen waltzes
for piano duet, Opus 39
DATED *[1]866*, 16 PAGES, large oblong folio, London £100,500 ($155,700). 28.V.93
Brahms composed this famous set of waltzes in the mid-1860s, after
his move to Vienna. He had always been attracted to the waltz
rhythm and he admired the music of Johann Strauss, although what
is distinctive about Brahms' treatment of the form is the way in which
he succeeded in investing it with a serious content. (ABOVE)

LEOPOLD MOZART
Autograph letter to his daughter Nannerl
VIENNA, DATED *1785*, 3 PAGES, 4to, London £133,500 ($205,500). 28.V.93
This celebrated and much-quoted letter from Leopold Mozart to his
daughter contains among other things the glowing testimonial of
Joseph Haydn for Wolfgang Mozart: 'I tell you before God, as an
honourable man, your son is the greatest composer known to me by
name or in person'. Haydn was at the time at the peak of his success,
and his judgement was greatly valued. (RIGHT)

Mittagmahl bis Nacht. Den anderen tag bis Frühling, und am Freytag um 1 uhr zogen wir in die Schulerstraße N: 846, im ersten Stock. Der weeg war durchaus abscheulich, den geehen, Koth, und sprüch, und aller Orth wenig arbeiter. das diese ganze schöne quartier mit aller ihren Hauptroth=weg Reutzierung hat mögt ihr daraus schlüßen, weil er 460 fl Hauszinß zahlt. Den nämlich freytag abends führen wir um 6 uhr in sein ersten subscriptions Concert, wo eine große versamlung von Menschen von Rang war. und die parten zahlt für diese 6 fastenConcert eine souverain d'or od: 3 duggath. Es ist auf d Melgnnder, in zahl für den eral ein ismahl nur ein halber souverain d'or. das Concert war unbeschreiblich, das orchester vortreflich: außer der Synfonie sang eine Sängerin von welschen theater 2 Arien. Dan war ein neues vortrefliches Clavier Concert von Wolfgang, wo der Copist, da wir anfang noch daran arbeiten, und die Bücher das Rondeau noch nicht einmal durchschreiben zeit hatte, weil er die Copiatur überall nicht durch daß nur der biele bekannte eingetrost, und nun alles zu licht, haupt der leicht Kanstalt: bey auch eben wieder aufgeführt. Am Samstag war ein abends Joseph Haydn und die 2 Baron Tindi bey uns, es wurde die neue quartett ge= =macht, die neue die er zu den anderen 3, die wir schon gemacht hat; sie sind zwar ein büsch leichter, aber vortreflich Componiert: H. Haydn sagt mir: ich sage ihn vor Gott, als ein ehrlicher Mann, ihr sohn ist d grösste Com= =ponist, den ich von person und dem Nahmen nach kenne. er hat geschmack, und über das die grösste Compositionswissenschaft. Am Sontag abend war im theater die accademie der ital: Sängerin Laschi, die ist nach Italy reiset. Sie sang 2 Arien, es war ein Violoncello Concert, ein Tenor und Bassang ein neue Aria und dann wiederstrahlt ein herrliches Concert, das er für die Paradis nach Paris ge= =macht hatte. ich war hier nur 2 Logen von d nicht schön wurdend: freuten unten ihr nahmen, und hatte das vergnügen aller verstellung d Instrumenter so vortreflich zu hören, daß mir vor vergnügen die thrän in dem aug stand.

WESTERN MANUSCRIPTS

Hebrew manuscript of festival prayers, biblical and other readings for the liturgical year

PESARO, DATED *1480*, ILLUMINATED MANUSCRIPT ON VELLUM, 18.2 x 12.5cm (7 x 4⅞in)

Tel Aviv $1,157,500 (£751,600). 15.IV.93

This is an exceptionally rich and lavishly illuminated Hebrew manuscript which bears comparison with some of the finest examples to emerge from the Italian Renaissance. It was commissioned by Elijah ben Schlomo, a native of Ferrara on the Adriatic coast. Both Ferrara and Pesaro had flourishing Jewish communities in the fifteenth century which dominated financial operations and stimulated fruitful patronage of the arts in both cities. (RIGHT)

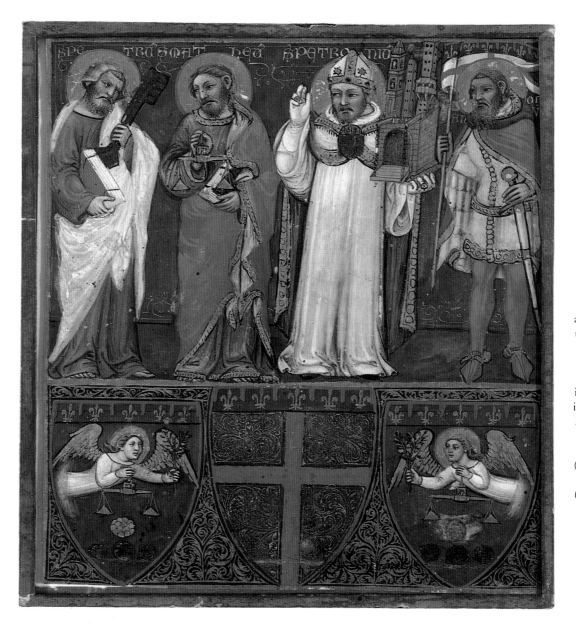

NICOLO DA BOLOGNA
Frontispiece from a register of the Guild of Money Changers of Bologna
BOLOGNA, c.1390-5,
ILLUMINATED MANUSCRIPT
ON VELLUM,
19.3 x 17.5cm (7½ x 6⅞in)
London £45,500 ($63,300).
22.VI.93

Nicolò da Bologna was highly regarded and immensely successful during his lifetime. By the late 1380s he had been appointed illuminator to the Corporation of Bologna, and was also Mayor of the district of Zappolino and Special Counsellor to the Bolognese booktrade. This miniature was painted in his official capacity as city illuminator and evidently illustrated a register of the Money Changers' Guild. It depicts Saints Peter, Matthew, Petronius (a fifth-century Bishop of Bologna) and Florian (a fourth-century Roman martyr). (LEFT)

A Book of Hours, in Latin and French

DIJON OR BESANÇON, *c.*1430-50, ILLUMINATED MANUSCRIPT ON VELLUM, 22.4 x 15.8cm (8½ x 6in) London £89,500 ($132,400). 22.VI.93

After the fall of Paris in 1420, many manuscript illuminators appear to have fled to the provinces. One group or workshop evidently settled in Besançon in eastern France, bringing with them the pattern sheets and training of the Bedford and Egerton Masters' styles. This Book of Hours, apparently unrecorded and of high quality and great richness, is an excellent example of the imported Parisian style. The folio shown here depicts Saint Thomas the Apostle dressed as a traveller (he went to India) with staff and book. (RIGHT)

Wycliffite New Testament, in Middle English

FIRST HALF OF FIFTEENTH CENTURY, MANUSCRIPT ON VELLUM, 9.2 x 6cm (3¾ x 2⅜in)
London £95,000 ($140,600). 22.VI.93

This Wycliffite Bible is remarkable not only for the fact that it is virtually complete
but also for its microscopic script. The scribe has written fourteen lines to the inch
and the entire New Testament is thus contained within 157 leaves. The book
resembles the smallest thirteenth-century Bibles, with their miniature scripts, no
longer fashionable by the fifteenth century. This could have been a deliberate attempt
to avoid prosecution: the book is small enough to be easily concealed. (ABOVE)

ORIENTAL MANUSCRIPTS

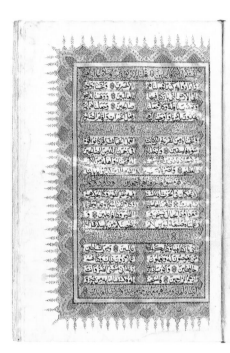

An Indian Qur'an

NORTH INDIA, PROBABLY ALWAR,
EARLY NINETEENTH CENTURY,
ARABIC MANUSCRIPT ON PAPER,
48 x 29.5cm (18½ x 11¼in)
London £106,000 ($165,300). 28.IV.93

Alwar, the Muslim state midway
between Delhi and Jaipur, was situated
on an important trade route and was an
active centre of craftsmanship. This
manuscript was possibly commissioned
from the Alwar court. By the time of its
production the mobility of artists within
the Indian sub-continent had given rise
to a relatively homogeneous style of
manuscript illumination, and the
decoration of this example owes much
to the contemporary Delhi style, itself a
descendant of the seventeenth-century
Moghal tradition. (ABOVE)

A leaf from the Qur'an

MID-SEVENTH CENTURY AD,
HIJAZI SCRIPT ON VELLUM,
36.6 x 28.2cm (14 x 11in)
London £159,500 ($258,300). 23.X.92

This leaf is one of the earliest fragments
of the Qur'an in existence. It may well
have formed part of one of the earliest
canonized copies and was quite possibly
written by one of the companions of the
Prophet Muhammad. It provides a rare
and fascinating insight into both the
early collections of the written Qur'an
and the early development of the Arabic
script, and its religious significance is of
the utmost importance. (LEFT)

A Pair of Lovers Watching the Approaching Rains
KANGRA, *c*.1820, GOLD MARGINS, 22.9 x 16.8cm (9 x 6⅝in)
New York $26,450 (£17,400). 17.VI.93
This painting is an illustration from a *Baramasa* series depicting the
month of *Bhadon* (August/September). The poet Keshav Das
describes the rainy month: 'The purple clouds are gathering, the
thunder rolls and rain pours in torrents, / The wind blows fiercely,
the cicadas chirp, the lions roar, and elephants fell the trees. / The day
is dark like the night, and one's own home is the best. / Pray leave me
not in the month of Bhadon for separation pains like poison.'
(Randhawa, *Kangra Paintings on Love*.) (ABOVE)

ATTRIBUTED TO SAJNU
The Hour of Cowdust
MANDI, *c*.1810, GOUACHE WITH GOLD ON PAPER, 30.2 x 21.3cm (11⅞ x 8⅜in)
New York $30,800 (£19,700). 5.XII.92
The artist Sajnu came to Mandi from Kangra in the first decade of
the nineteenth century, completing a *Hamir Hath* series for his new
patron, Raja Isvari Sen of Mandi, in 1810. The work shown here
depicts cattle being taken to water before their return home to the
village for the night: the 'Hour of Cowdust', one of the most
evocative moments of the day in Indian village life. Also shown is the
figure of Krishna playing his flute. (ABOVE)

A portrait bust from an album of watercolours
QAJAR, EARLY NINETEENTH-CENTURY, COLOURED DRAWINGS ON PAPER,
the album 19.3 x 11.2cm (7½ x 4in)
London £26,400 ($41,100). 23.X.92
This album contains sixty-one watercolours
depicting a variety of subjects ranging from formal
portraits of rulers, officials and grandees to lively
genre scenes. The portrait shown here depicts a lady
wearing an elaborate head-cloth and an unbuttoned
green tunic. (ABOVE)

ATTRIBUTED TO JAFAR
Portrait of Prince Muhammad Ali Mirza Qajar
QAJAR, c.1820, OIL ON CANVAS, 16.3 x 9.8cm (6¼ x 3¾in)
London £73,000 ($113,800). 28.IV.93
Muhammad Ali Mirza (1788-1821) was the eldest son of Fath Ali Shah, who
succeeded Agha Muhammad Khan, the founder of the Qajar dynasty. Ali Mirza's
mother, however, was a Georgian and his half-brother, Abbas Mirza, whose mother
was a Qajar princess, therefore became heir to the Qajar throne. (ABOVE)

SCHOOL OF BIHZAD
Manuscript decorated with miniatures
HERAT, LAST QUARTER OF THE FIFTEENTH CENTURY,
GOLD-SPRINKLED PAPER, each page 23.3 x 15.8cm (9 x 6in)
London £20,700 ($32,290). 28.IV.93

Illustrated manuscripts produced at Herat during the
reign of Sultan Husain Mirza are considered to be
among the finest achievements of Persian miniature
painting. This is a leaf from an example consisting of
40 leaves and the miniature depicted is one of three by
the school of the renowned painter Bihzad. The
calligrapher for this manuscript was Sultan Ali al-
Mashhadi, who often worked together with Bihzad on
poetical manuscripts. (LEFT)

A leaf from one of
the 'Leningrad' albums
MOGHAL, c.1660-80, GOUACHE WITH GOLD ON PAPER,
album page 47 x 32.5cm (18 x 12½in)
London £13,200 ($21,285). 23.X.92

Most of the 'Leningrad' albums are preserved in the
Institute for the Peoples of Asia in St Petersburg.
Russian sources indicate that the album to which this
leaf belongs was purchased in Tehran for Tsar Nicholas
II. The albums were originally compiled in 1739 after
Nadir Shah had sacked Delhi and returned to Persia
with a hoard of manuscripts and treasure, including
the legendary Peacock Throne. (LEFT)

THE DECORATIVE ARTS *by Philippe Garner*

A bronze figure of The Young Hercules Reading *by the Italian Renaissance sculptor Antico achieved £1,266,500 (London, July 1993); an Iznik pottery candlestick set a record for an Islamic work of art at £617,500 (London, April 1993); an Archaic Chinese bronze ritual vessel sold for £925,500 (London, June 1993); an Egyptian head of a queen or goddess made $451,000 (New York, December 1992); a Korean screen sold for $332,500 (New York, June 1993) and a fine Louis XVI* bureau plat *by Weisweiler from the estate of Hélène de Beaumont made FF8,436,000 (Monaco, December 1992). This season has seen strong prices and new records in most areas of the Decorative Arts, with fine works and impressive collections being brought to auction. Underlying the pleasing high prices for outstanding works, however, is a statistical shift which provides much comfort after a period of upheaval and uncertainty. Whilst the volume of sales may not have significantly increased, and in a business focused on the rare this should not be cause for alarm, there has been an encouraging fall in the 'bought-in' percentages.*

There have also been larger numbers of bidders taking part in the sales, with quantifiable developments in various areas of interest. Japanese buyers, for example, are again making their presence felt in the Art Nouveau glass market. Meanwhile, Chinese works of art spokesman Julian Thompson was pleased to confirm that there were no less than five bidders over £600,000 for the Archaic bronze vessel cited above. Significantly, these were from four different locations: Japan, Hong Kong, Continental Europe and London, an indicator of real depth to the market.

As an auctioneer one is uniquely placed to identify a mood swing in the market place. A price list never tells the full story. Was there only one bidder, bidding against the reserve? Were there two bidders or were there several attempting to catch the auctioneer's attention on a given lot? During the past

'Hammersmith' hand-knotted carpet (detail)
BY WILLIAM MORRIS, *c.*1895,
342 x 497cm (134 x 194in)
Melbourne A$352,000
(£158,400:$246,400). 24.V.93
From the Collection of Mrs
Tom Barr Smith. (LEFT)

A fragmentary chalcedony female head
ROMAN, 1st CENTURY AD,
height 8cm (3⅛in)
London £44,400 ($66,100).
8.VII.93. (ABOVE)

Grisailles-painted
demi-lune
commode
BY RENÉ DUBOIS,
*c.*1775, PARIS,
length 141cm (55¼in)
Monaco FF2,331,000
(£286,000:$427,700). 4.XII.92
From the Estate of Mme
Hélène Beaumont. (ABOVE)

season I for one have become increasingly aware of an upturn in the number of participants; I was frequently obliged to ignore bids, since an auctioneer should only take bidding up between two people at once, returning to an eager third bidder only once one of the contestants has stopped. There is no better measure of a healthy market place than this kind of multiple interest.

It would be foolhardy, however, to expect a resurgence comparable to that which peaked in 1989–90. We are evolving towards a new market, naturally limited by the scarcity of fine property, but driven by the scholarship of collectors and specialist dealers. Connoisseurship plays a greater role in such a market. Speculative buying will find no easy rewards. There is much reference from auctioneers in their press releases to buyers being keen but 'selective'. This is precisely what buyers should be, as indeed should auctioneers, in so far as it is in their power to control the flow and the quality of what they offer. The desirable factors remain constant whether trading in or collecting works of art – quality, rarity and provenance.

The sale of fine French furniture and furnishings from the estate of Mme Hélène Beaumont well demonstrated these ingredients. Fine pieces by Riesener, Peridiez, Dubois, Weisweiler and RVLC boasted provenances which traced their history back through very few hands over a century and a half or more. Here was the ideal mix of works of the finest quality, with specific and fascinating provenances, never before available to even the most senior of today's generation of buyers. Understandably, the auction was highly successful, with 98.4% of the works selling and a total of over FF30 million.

In the field of antiquities provenance is of particular importance because of the problems of establishing lawful origins for excavated works. The success of the sale of Important Antiquities from the Norbert Schimmel Collection, and that of works from the estate of the late Humfry Payne, doubtless owed much to the associations of these names.

Considerable interest was aroused in Melbourne with the sale of a group of carpets and furnishings from Morris & Co. These had the added appeal of being offered for sale by the Barr-Smith family, direct descendants of the Barr-Smiths who had originally commissioned these furnishings from William Morris and his company. One carpet sold for (A$352,000), and the group totalled (A$818,400).

The Decorative Arts category embraces furniture of all types, tapestries and carpets, ceramics and glass, European works of art including nineteenth-century sculpture and garden statuary, American decorative arts and American Indian and Pre-Columbian art, Islamic and Indian art, Chinese, Korean, Japanese and tribal art, and twentieth-century applied arts. In many of these fields the season has been spiced with single-owner sales. Collections of note, in addition to those already mentioned, included the Japanese sword collection formed by Field Marshal Sir Francis Festing, one of which set a new record at £265,500. The sale in New York of much of the stock of Barry Friedman, a dealer in twentieth-century works of art, attracted great interest. A dealer selling stock lacks the appeal of a collector releasing hitherto unavailable works. However Friedman's reputation is such that the sale bore no negative connotations. The results were highly satisfactory with several gratifying prices, notably the $187,000 paid for a table by Hector Guimard.

Continued success for the Decorative Arts market will depend on a rigorous approach to the selection process and on a realistic attitude towards pricing. Vendors have for the most part come to accept the need for prudent estimates to stimulate buyer interest. The great satisfaction of the 1992–93 season has been to witness so many prices set after multiple-party bidding battles. This is the surest sign of a strengthening market.

An Adam Revival cabinet on stand
By J. G. CRACE AND SONS, 1867, LONDON, height 213cm (84in)
New York $244,500 ($176,700). 17.IV.93. (BELOW)

KATSUKAWA SHUN'EI
Ichikawa Danzo IV in 'Shibaraku' attire
SIGNED AND DATED 1798, 33 x 14.4cm (13 x 5⅝in)
London £5,175 ($7,810). 11.VI.93
From the Collection of the late Prof. H. R. W. Kühne. (ABOVE)

ISLAMIC AND INDIAN ART

A Safavid tile mosaic panel
PERSIA, SIXTEENTH CENTURY, 171 x 161cm (67¼ x 63½in)
London £275,000 ($445,500). 22.X.92

At the close of the Middle Ages, the Islamic world saw the emergence of new, well-organized states. Sixteenth-century Persia was ruled by the Safavids, who gave much encouragement to the arts. The art of Islam was dominated by religion, and the ornamentation of palaces and mosques often incorporated passages from the Qur'an. In this example of painted tilework, which would originally have decorated an ornamental arch, two verses from the Qur'an are contained within the broad border surrounding the central design. (RIGHT)

A Mamluk marble and stone mosaic fountain
EGYPT, FIFTEENTH CENTURY,
approx. 430 x 430cm (170 x 170in)
London £166,500 ($259,700). 29.IV.93

The Mamluks ruled Egypt from 1450 to 1550. This spectacular fountain is said to have come from a palace in Cairo and dates from the reign of Sultan Qaitbay (1468-96). It is complete and consists of three tiered octagons with a domed superstructure and eight water-jets emanating from eight columns at each level. Fountains of this type were usually incorporated into a domestic interior where they provided a focal point for household and social gatherings. (RIGHT)

An Iznik blue and white candlestick

TURKEY, c.1480, height 25cm (9in)
London £617,500 ($963,300). 29.IV.93
Early monochrome blue and white
Iznik pottery is extremely rare and, with
this exception, all the finest examples
are in museums. The piece dates from
the time of Sultan Mehmed II, who,
having conquered Constantinople in
1453, founded Istanbul in the ruins of
the Byzantine city. Mehmed was well
known for his patronage of the arts and
it was in response to the demands of
his court that the kilns at Iznik took
on a new lease of life. (LEFT)

A Khmer sandstone balustrade finial

ANGKOR PERIOD, LATE TWELFTH CENTURY, height 123cm (48¼in)
New York $68,500 (£45,000). 17.VI.93

In the Hindu religion each of the many gods is
associated with a particular animal, which accompanies
them as an attendant or simply as a vehicle on which
the god may ride or travel. This sculptural fragment
depicts Garuda, half-man, half-bird, who was the
faithful carrier of Vishnu the Preserver. (RIGHT)

A Tibetan polychrome wood figure of the Adibuddha Vajrasattva

LADAKH, LATE ELEVENTH/EARLY TWELFTH CENTURY,
height 52.4cm (20⅝in) New York $71,250 (£46,800). 17.VI.93

Very few examples of Tibetan wood sculpture from the
eleventh or twelfth centuries survive, particularly in the
intact state of this figure. This piece retains much of its
original colouring, and depicts a Bodhisattva, the
Buddhist equivalent of a Christian saint. (ABOVE)

A Gandhara figure of Buddha
NORTH-WEST PAKISTAN, THIRD/FOURTH CENTURY, height 153cm (60¼in)
London £38,900 ($60,600). 29.IV.93

Buddhism was founded in northern India in around 500BC when Siddharta Gautama, who was born a prince but renounced material life to embark on a quest for spiritual perfection, achieved enlightenment. Gandhara, the region between the Upper Indus river and Kabul, was one of the richest sources of Buddhist art during the third and fourth centuries, art acquired by means of the vast wealth amassed by the Kushan dynasty from trade between the Middle East, India and China. (LEFT)

A Tamil Nadu bronze figure of Siva Nataraja
THIRTEENTH TO FIFTEENTH CENTURY, height 65cm (25½in) London £44,000 ($71,200). 22.X.92

The god Siva manifested himself in a multitude of ways. Here he is seen depicted as Nataraja, the Lord of the Dance, whose dancing shook the universe and created the world. Siva – Creator and Destroyer – is probably the most important god in the Hindu pantheon and this image, which represents the five divine acts of creation, protection, solace, the dispelling of ignorance and the destruction of the universe, is one of the best-known in Indian art. (ABOVE)

ORIENTAL CARPETS AND RUGS

An Anatolian dragon and phoenix carpet fragment
FIRST HALF OF THE FIFTEENTH CENTURY OR EARLIER,
approx. 66 x 48cm (26 x 19in)
New York $68,500 (£38,600).
17.IX.92
This fragment is probably the oldest example of Eastern knotted-pile weaving ever to have been offered at auction. Whilst the pattern is interpreted in a purely Turkish style, the dragon and phoenix design is probably borrowed from motifs in Chinese art. Unearthed during the 1935-36 excavations at Fostat in Old Cairo, this fragment provides a significant addition to the body of historical knowledge on early Turkish carpet production. (LEFT)

A Mamluk rug
EGYPT, c.1500,
approx. 188 x 145cm (74 x 57in)
New York $275,000 (£177,400).
10.XII.92
The Mamluk Turks were the rulers of Egypt from 1450 until 1550, when they were deposed by the Ottoman Turks. During this time the Mamluk Sultanate established court manufactories to produce the deeply coloured red, green and blue octagonal medallion rugs that bear its name. These rugs are among the oldest surviving complete carpets in the world and they rarely appear on the commercial market. (RIGHT)

An Azerbaijani rug

EAST CAUCASUS, EIGHTEENTH CENTURY, 210 x 133cm (83 x 52in)
London £26,450 ($41,300). 28.IV.93

During the early sixteenth century, the region of Azerbaijan, sandwiched between the Safavid and Ottoman empires, was an area of continual conflict and changed hands frequently. By 1588 it was firmly under Safavid control and it was Shah Abbas I who, consistent with his policy of establishing weaving centres throughout Persia, founded the textile and carpet workshops that were to embody the weaving tradition of which this rug is an example. (ABOVE)

A Tabriz silk carpet
NORTH-WEST PERSIA, 343 x 269cm (135 x 106in)
London £73,000 ($113,800). 28.IV.93
This exemplary north-west Persian carpet illustrates the high-point of nineteenth-century
Persian silk weavings. The linked double floral medallion is an unusual feature, as is the
depiction of a variety of naturalistically-drawn mythical beasts. The carpet dates from the
third quarter of the nineteenth century. (ABOVE)

CHINESE ART

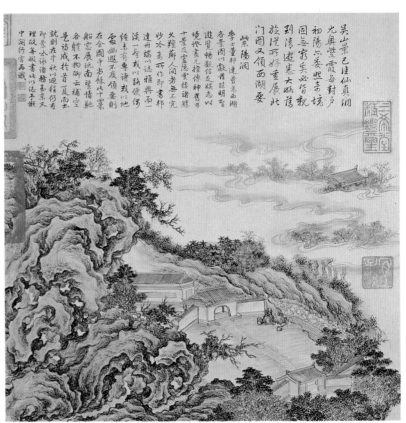

BADA SHANREN
Album of various subjects
SIGNED, INK ON PAPER, SEVEN LEAVES, each 35 x 29.2cm (12 x 11⅛in)
New York $332,500 (£214,500). 1.VI.93

Bada Shanren (1626-1705), a scion of the fallen
Ming imperial family, was forced to take refuge in
the Buddhist church for his personal safety. An
extremely educated and talented man, he created
a highly individual painting style noted for its
startling juxtapositions and abstracted brushwork.
His work is an important influence on twentieth-
century painting. (ABOVE)

DONG BANGDA
Forty Views of West Lake
c.1750, INK AND COLOUR ON PAPER, SET OF FOUR ALBUMS OF FORTY LEAVES,
each 31.5 x 30.8cm (12⅜ x 12⅛in)
Hong Kong HK$3,320,000 (£272,100:$431,100). 29.IV.93

Dong Bangda was a native of Fuyang in Zhejiang province. As well as being highly
regarded as a painter and calligrapher, he was a successful scholar and official in the
imperial court. The pictorial series *Forty Views of West Lake* was commissioned by the
Qianlong emperor. West Lake, in Dong's province, was a famous beauty spot and
the artist's treatment of the subject seems to have been appreciated by his patron. The
set of albums remained in the imperial collection until the fall of the Qing dynasty.
(ABOVE)

FU BAOSHI
Playing Go at the Water Pavilion
INK AND COLOUR ON PAPER, HANGING SCROLL,
117.5 x 67.3cm (46¼ x 26½in)
New York $134,500 (£89,600). 16.VI.93
From the Robert Hatfield Ellsworth Collection.

One of the great literati painters, Fu Baoshi (1904-65)
specialized in moody, atmospheric landscapes. Fu
studied Western watercolour techniques in Japan and
used these principles in conjunction with traditional
Chinese subject matter and brushwork. This painting,
which the artist considered one of his best, is typical
of Fu Baoshi's romantic style. (LEFT)

GAO QIFENG
An album of birds and flowers
SIGNED, INK AND COLOUR ON PAPER, TWELVE LEAVES,
each 26 x 35.5cm (10¼ x 14in)
Hong Kong HK$1,650,000 (£135,200:$219,000). 29.X.92

One of the salient features of the Chinese painting
tradition is its veneration of the past and its stylistic
emphasis on calligraphic techniques. It was not until
the early 1900s that artists in China began to free
themselves from the restrictions imposed by traditional
training and to experiment with a more Western
approach. This nineteenth-century album of bird and
flower paintings combines Western perspective and
shading with traditional Chinese brushwork, colour
and attention to detail. (ABOVE)

A jadeite snuff bottle
1780-1850, height 5.1cm (2in)
Hong Kong HK$396,000 (£32,400:$52,400). 28.X.92
From almost gem-quality jadeite, as here, to porcelain, to mammoth ivory or to dried tangerine skin, snuff bottles exhibit a greater diversity of constituent material than any other category of Chinese art. (LEFT)

A jadeite ring
The stone approx. 2.5 x 1.9 x 1.4cm (¹⁵⁄₁₆ x ¾ x ⁹⁄₁₆in)
Hong Kong HK$4,970,000 (£318,500:$477,700). 28.IV.93
Jadeite has been popular in China as jewellery since the latter part of the Qing dynasty. This magnificent emerald-green cabochon ring of exceptional translucency is mounted on reeded, eighteen-carat gold. (ABOVE)

A pair of imperial jadeite lanterns
1736-95, QIANLONG MARKS AND PERIOD, height 41.3cm (16¼in)
New York $332,500 (£214,500). 1.VI.93
From the Collection of Mr and Mrs Bernard K. Crawford.
These lanterns may well have been made for one of the Buddhist chapels built in the Forbidden City during the reign of the Emperor Qianlong. Qianlong had an interest in the decorative arts and many pieces of the finest quality were crafted in the palace workshops on his instructions. (ABOVE)

An archaic bronze ritual food vessel, the Bo Ju *gui*

*c.*1050-975BC, EARLY WESTERN ZHOU DYNASTY, height 23.6cm (9¼in)
London £925,500 ($1,388,500). 8.VI.93

The Bo Ju *gui*, so named after the pictographic inscription cast on its interior, is remarkable
not only for the quality of its casting but also for the number of directions from which its
ornament is intended to be read: from the front or back the large-eyed masks are prominent;
from the oblique angles the dragons on the corners of the base join to form masks, and from
the sides pairs of birds flank the now foreshortened handles. (ABOVE)

A *wucai* wine jar and cover
1522-66, Jiajing mark and period, height 45.4cm (17⅞in)
New York $2,860,000 (£1,845,200). 1.XII.92
From the J. M. Hu Family Collection.
The sale of this piece in December achieved the world record auction price for a
piece of Chinese (or any other) porcelain. Large jars painted in overglaze enamels
using the five-colour *wucai* palette are considered to be among the most impressive
pieces from the Jiajing period. (ABOVE)

A Ming blue and white stembowl
1426-35, XUANDE MARK AND PERIOD, width 15.6cm (6⅛in)
Hong Kong HK$3,080,000 (£252,400:$406,300). 27.X.92
Stembowls like this one belong to an elite family of
early Ming blue and white porcelain on which the
principal decoration of dragons is executed in deep
cobalt-blue and set against the lighter blue background of a turbulent sea. The number of dragons
varies, from nine, as here, to two or five. The
interior has further dragons in *anhua* ('secret
decoration'), the fineness of which is only revealed
by holding the bowl up to a strong light. (ABOVE)

An imperial *famille rose* vase
1736-95, QIANLONG SEAL MARK AND PERIOD,
height 51.4cm (20⅛in)
New York $374,000 (£241,300). 1.XII.92
The 'nine peach' subject painted on this vase in
famille rose enamels was reserved for the Emperor.
The ability to execute such a complex design on a
three-dimensional object was one of the great
achievements of the Palace Workshops under the
Emperor Qianlong, whose reign dominated most
of the eighteenth century. (LEFT)

KOREAN ART

ANONYMOUS
Ten Symbols of Long Life
INK AND COLOUR ON SILK, TEN-FOLD SCREEN,
166 x 356cm (65½ x 140in)
New York $332,500 (£221,700). 18.VI.93

The subject of this nineteenth-century
screen lies at the core of Korean art and
culture. The theme of longevity is derived
from traditional Korean nature-worship
as well as from Taoist beliefs and the
Chinese legends of the immortals. The
scene depicts the ten symbols of long life
in a continuous landscape reminiscent of
Pong Nae, the mythical island stronghold
of the gods. Symbolic dragons, qilins,
phoenix, peacocks and mandarin ducks
wander freely through the island paradise.
(ABOVE)

YANG KI-HUN
Geese in a Marsh (detail)
SIGNED, EMBROIDERY ON SILK, TEN-PANEL SCREEN,
276 x 389cm (108½ x 153in)
New York $167,500 (£111,700). 18.VI.93

Yang Ki-hun (1843-98) came from
northern Korea and spent much of his
time at the court in Seoul. He enjoyed a
good reputation as a painter and
calligrapher and it is likely that this screen
was produced for the royal palace. The
artist would have applied the ink painting
to the screen and then turned it over to
the court embroiderers, the region being
famous for its needlework and for the
high quality of the silk thread produced
there. The inscription is a prose poem
and is signed 'Your Majesty's subject,
Yang Ki-hun'. (LEFT)

JAPANESE ART

A group of two wrestlers
*c.*1680, PORCELAIN, height 31.8cm (12½in) New York $143,000
(£89,300). 4.XII.92 From the Collection of William S. Paley.
This rare pair of Sumo wrestlers was made during the
last quarter of the seventeenth century when the export
of Japanese porcelain via the Dutch East India
Company was at its height. It was around that time
that the 2,000 year-old martial art of Sumo wrestling
became a professional sport. Only a few other examples
of the subject are known. (ABOVE)

A pair of Kakiemon-style candlesticks
*c.*1670-90, height (excluding pricket) 34.2cm (13½in)
London £144,500 ($216,700). 10.VI.93
Kakiemon is the name given to a style of porcelain
decoration conceived by Sakaida Kakiemon in
around 1650. Its attenuated, asymmetrical designs in
yellow, turquoise, red and blue enamels are particularly
distinctive and were later much copied by European
porcelain makers. (ABOVE)

UNNO MORITOSHI
An inlaid shibuichi and silver tokuri
1834-96, OZEKI COMPANY, height 19.3cm (7⅝in) London £84,000 ($124,300). 31.III.93
This double-gourd wine-bottle, or *tokuri,* is inlaid in silver and shibuichi (a metal
alloy). The lower section shows the *Rokkasen,* six celebrated poets from the ninth
century. The piece bears the inscription 'Muzashiya', the contemporary name for
the part of Tokyo in which the Ozeki company was then situated. (RIGHT)

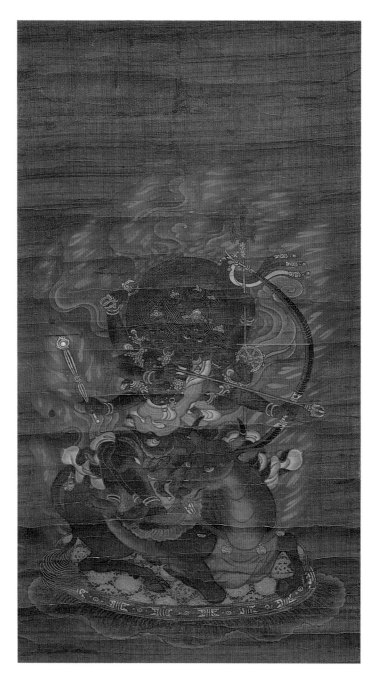

UTAGAWA HIROSHIGE
Sixty-Nine Stations of the Kiso Highway: Seba
SIGNED, WOODBLOCK PRINT, 23.8 x 35.8cm (9⅜ x 14⅛in)
New York $34,500 (£23,000). 18.VI.93
Utagawa Hiroshige is regarded as one of the great Japanese print
masters, and is particularly known for his landscape series illustrating
famous views from various regions of Japan. This print is the most
sought-after composition taken from a series featuring all the stops
along the well-travelled Kiso Highway. (RIGHT)

ANONYMOUS
Daitoku Myo-o
MUROMACHI PERIOD, HANGING SCROLL, INK, COLOUR AND GOLD ON SILK,
68.9 x 36.8cm (27⅛ x 14½in) New York $23,000 (£15,300). 18.VI.93
This work depicts one of the Four Great Wisdom Kings in wrathful
incarnation. It is an image of Esoteric Buddhism, often called 'Secret
Buddhism', as it was passed secretly from teacher to pupil. This form
of Buddhism came to Japan via China in the ninth century. (ABOVE)

RIMPA SCHOOL
Scene from the Tale of Ise
TWO-PANEL SCREEN, INK, COLOUR AND GOLD ON PAPER, 171 x 184cm (67½ x 74½in)
New York $48,875 (£35,500). 18.VI.93 From the Estate of Baron Hisaya Iwasake.
The last great flowering of Japanese art took place during the Edo
period (1615-1868). A truly Japanese style is reflected in the works
produced by the Rimpa School throughout the Edo period, which
derive their inspiration from nature and literature. (ABOVE)

KATSUSHIKA HOKUSAI
**Interior of a Theatre
with a Play in
Progress**
SIGNED AND DATED 1788,
26 x 38.8cm (10¼ x 15¼in)
London £14,950 ($22,500).
11.VI.93
This print falls into the
category of *ukiyo-e*, which
translates as 'Pictures of
the Floating World' and
was a popular movement
in Japanese genre paint-
ing in the Tokugawa
period. Theatre scenes
were a favourite subject,
arising from the develop-
ment of *kabuki* theatre
in the seventeenth
century. (BELOW)

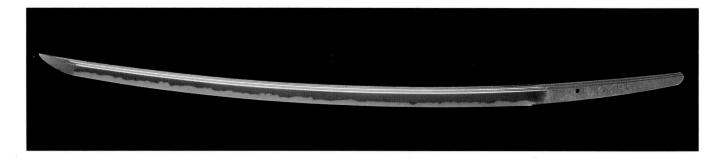

YAMAURA MASAYUKI
**A Shinshinto
Musashi Katana**
DATED 1839, 69.6cm (27⅜in)
London £265,500 ($392,200).
1.IV.93
From the Collection of Field
Marshal Sir Francis Festing.
Japanese sword-making
has been developed over
1,500 years. In the
nineteenth century a
revival of traditional
methods produced several
masters, the most famous
of whom was Yamaura
Masayuki. A Japanese
sword is appreciated both
as a weapon and as a work
of art. (ABOVE)

A black lacquer inro with metal inlay
BY HARA YOYUSAI AND HARUAKI HOGEN, NINETEENTH CENTURY,
length 8.5cm (3⅜in) London £52,100 ($77,100). 31.III.93
An inro is a seal case and comprises a box of vertically-
arranged fitted trays threaded down each side by a cord
which in turn manipulates the opening and closing
actions by means of a bead, or *ojime*. (ABOVE)

**Figure of Raigo
Kannon**
GILTWOOD, KAMAKURA PERIOD,
height 46.4cm (18¼in)
New York $30,800 (£19,200).
4.XII.92
'Pure-Land Buddhism',
which centres on the
Buddha Amitabha, Lord
of the Western Paradise,
first came to Japan in the
tenth century. One of the
most recurring images is
that of the *raigo*
(or heavenly descent) in
which Amitabha is flanked
by his two Bodhisattvas
leading a heavenly retinue
to welcome and guide the
soul of the dying to
paradise. (LEFT)

TRIBAL ART

A Raratonga Island staff god section
Height 89.5cm (35¼in)
New York $165,000 (£110,800). 24.XI.92

Raratonga, one of the Cook Islands, was converted to Christianity in 1927. John Williams, a leading missionary, claimed to have destroyed most of the indigenous religious artifacts in his crusade to eradicate pagan worship. Fortunately, Williams' purge was not as effective as he maintained, and fifteen complete staff gods are known to exist, as well as a number of end-sections, including this piece. The emergence of these sculptures suggests that a quantity of staff gods was hidden from Williams by the islanders. (ABOVE)

A Hawaiian bowl
Greatest diameter 45cm (17⅜in)
London £6,900 ($10,100). 21.VI.93
Property of Susan Mast

It was a tradition within Hawaiian communities to congregate for meals in a communal tent and to share what was known as a community bowl. The piece shown here is important in that it is considerably larger than the standard bowl used for this purpose. The particularly rich and glossy patina is also exceptional. (RIGHT)

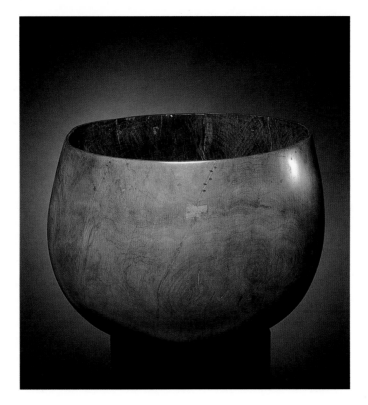

A Solomon Islands seated female figure
Height 10cm (4in)
London £3,080 ($4,840). 7.XII.92 From the Peter Hallinan Collection

This figure, fashioned from betelnut, once surmounted a limestick, a splinter of which was once attached to the base. Limesticks were used in the Solomon Islands to extract lime from containers in order to make a substance that featured regularly in Melanesian ceremonial rituals. Mixing the lime with betel vine and saliva resulted in a concoction that induced a slightly stimulating effect on the brain. (ABOVE RIGHT)

A Tellem figure
Height 34cm (13½in)
London £20,700 ($30,400).
21.VI.93
The gesture of this figure has been interpreted in different ways. The most obvious relates to its use on ancestral altars, but it has also been suggested that it could refer to the most crucial moment in the induction ritual for a Binu priest. At the high point in the ceremony the postulant would kneel before two officiating priests who would pour chicken blood and millet over a pendant held above his head. With these sacrificial liquids streaming over him the new priest would then kneel and raise his hands to wipe them away. (RIGHT)

A Fang male reliquary figure
Height 44.5cm (17½in)
New York $206,000
(£133,700). 18.V.93
From the Alexander S. Honig Collection.

The reliquary figure was of great significance to the Fang and embodied considerable power. In this example the variant surface textures of the sculpture attest to years of ritual use. The sculptural strength of the figure can be detected in the strong horizontal lines, which rhythmically break up the length of the torso, giving it a unity and plasticity which is achieved in the round by a series of corresponding lines and volumes. It was formerly in the collection of Serge Brignoni, a noted pre-War collector. (LEFT)

PRE-COLUMBIAN ART

A Mochica wood portrait mask
*c.*100BC-AD300, NORTH COAST, width 26.4cm (10⅜in)
New York $104,000 (£68,400). 23.XI.92
Ceramic portraits are one of the hallmarks of Moche art, but this sculpted example in wood
may be unique. The expressive and clearly defined features, together with the rich colours and
ornamental detail, suggest that it might originally have been the property of a high-ranking –
possibly royal – individual. (ABOVE)

A Tiahuanaco gold beaker
*c.*AD900-1100, COASTAL TIAHUANACO, height 11.1cm (4⅜in)
New York $79,500 (£51,600). 17.V.93
The Tiahuanaco region was in the southern highlands of the Andes
on the Bolivian/Peruvian border. This example of gold repoussé
work, which would have been inlaid with semi-precious stones,
depicts a puma-headed deity towering over two captives. (ABOVE)

An Olmec blackware vessel
*c.*1150-550BC, CHALCATZINGO, height 45.1cm (17⅞in)
New York $233,500 (£151,600). 17.V.93
The Olmec region was on the Gulf Coast of Pre-Columbian Mexico.
The Olmec were the first Pre-Columbian culture to combine realism
with religious symbolism. This piece is a fine example of symbolic
decoration, and includes the profile of a grimacing deity. (ABOVE)

AMERICAN INDIAN ART

A pair of quilled hide moccasins
NORTH-EASTERN, POSSIBLY RED RIVER METIS OR CREE,
length 25.7cm (10⅛in) New York $46,750 (£30,500). 12.XI.92
Property of the Earl of Harrowby
Moccasins were perhaps the most significant item of Indian clothing. This pair, made of soft hide with quillwork decoration, probably dates from the middle of the eighteenth century. (BELOW)

A pair of quilled hide moccasins
EASTERN GREAT LAKES, HURON, length 25.4cm (10in)
New York $77,000 (£50,300). 12.XI.92
Property of the Earl of Harrowby
These fine early moccasins were originally acquired by
the first, or possibly the second, Earl of Harrowby,
both of whom were travellers, art collectors and
diplomats of distinction during the nineteenth century.
The moccasins remained in the family and were
offered for sale by the present Earl. (ABOVE)

A polychrome coiled seed jar
PANAMINT SHOSHONE, diameter at shoulder 20.3cm (8in)
New York, $13,800 (£8,900). 25.V.93
From the Charlotte Butler Skinner Collection
This unusual example of Panamint Shoshone basket-
work comes from the collection of Charlotte Butler
Skinner, who, in 1905, settled in Owens Valley,
California, and during the years that followed filled her
house with Indian baskets, many of which she acquired
from Panamint Shoshone women camping nearby.
Early basketry from this tribe is highly varied in its
decoration, the result of regular contact with the basket-
makers of neighbouring tribes. (RIGHT)

A tradecloth and beadwork panel bag

NORTH-EASTERN, RED RIVER METIS OR CREE, length 60.3cm (23¾in)
New York $41,800 (£27,300). 12.XI.92 From the Collection of the Earl of Harrowby

The Red River Metis wore caps and top hats encircled with silk ribbons, knee-length leggings worn over trousers, and coats bound with sashes. The panel bag was normally attached to the sash and was commonly used as a tobacco pouch. The ornamentation was standard: a panel of woven beadwork attached to the bottom, surrounded by woollen tassels on long strings of beads. The beadwork design was geometric and often quite complex. (ABOVE)

A cloth and quillwork neck pouch

EASTERN GREAT LAKES, PROBABLY EASTERN OJIBWA, total length 80cm (31½in)
New York $71,500 (£46,700). 12.XI.92 From the Collection of the Earl of Harrowby

Pouches such as this were worn suspended from a strap around the neck. The rectangular form decorated with two parallel bands of woven quillwork is typical of the work of the natives of the central Subarctic. Such bags were widely traded, and examples similar to the one shown here have been dated to the late eighteenth century. Watercolours of the 1820s by the artist Peter Rindisbacker depict neck pouches in use at that time. (RIGHT)

ANTIQUITIES

**An Egyptian
crystalline limestone
head**
1323-1292BC, EIGHTEENTH
DYNASTY, REIGN OF
AY/HOREMHAB,
height 25.6cm (10⅛in)
New York $451,000
(£287,200). 16.XII.92
From the Norbert Schimmel
Collection.

The horizontal bands
incised across the fore-
head of this piece are the
remains of a headdress
worn by queens,
goddesses, or queens in
the guise of goddesses.
This head would have
surmounted a
monumental statue,
possibly of Horemhab's
queen, Mutnodjmet.
Horemhab served as a
general under
Tutankhamun and his
successor King Ay,
finally assuming the
throne himself as the last
king of the Eighteenth
Dynasty. (LEFT)

A Roman marble figure of Pan
c. MID-SECOND CENTURY AD, ANTONINE, height 67.6cm (26⅝in)
New York $176,000 (£110,400). 17.XII.92
This statue is a copy of a lost Hellenistic original of
the third/second century BC, and is a fine
representative of the baroque currents in the art
of the period. (RIGHT)

An Egyptian alabaster jar

c.2965-2705BC, EARLY DYNASTIC PERIOD, height 57.8cm (22¾in)
London £28,750 ($41,300). 8.VII.92

The Egyptians, like the Greeks, had no specific word
for 'art' and did not distinguish it from handicraft.
Hence the ancient Egyptian craftsman's feeling for
materials and his instinctive sense of form and
proportion are often revealed most graphically in
the applied arts. The flowing lines and classically
simple definition of this jar are a clear illustration of
the beauty that could be invested in an entirely
functional utensil. (RIGHT)

An Attic white-ground *lekythos* fragment

NEAR THE THANATOS PAINTER, *c.*440BC, height 18.1cm (7⅛in)
London £20,900 ($32,600). 10.XII.92

Attic, or Athenian, vase-painting is stylistically most
readily identified by its black- and red-figure work,
but there was also a white-ground style, of which
this fragment is a fine example. The white slip appears
to have been most commonly applied to *lekythoi*,
elongated funerary vessels normally decorated with
scenes of domestic life or farewell. The white-ground
style invited a softer, more fluid draughtsmanship than
the black- and red-figure styles, and allowed a wider
range of colours for drapery. (LEFT)

EUROPEAN WORKS OF ART

A Florentine ormolu-mounted and
pietra dura **ebonized mahogany casket**
31 x 52.7 x 45.7cm (12¼ x 20¾ x 18in)
New York $21,850 (£14,180). 12.I.93
This Florentine casket was reputedly formerly in the
collection of Empress Eugenia de Montijo of France.
The interior of the casket is fitted with red velvet trays.
(BELOW)

A north German bronze aquamanile
*c.*1200, height 29.8cm (11¾in)
London £660,000 ($1,029,600). 10.XII.92
Although a few northern European water vessels were fashioned in the shape of
equestrian knights, it is rare to find one sporting a nasal helm. Most horse-and-rider
aquamaniles therefore had flat-topped helmets, some of which were adapted into
hinged lids to receive the water. (ABOVE)

One of three north German wood reliefs of saints
*c.*1490-1500, height 103cm (41½in)
London £52,100 ($79,700) for the three. 22.IV.93

This piece and its two companion pieces have been attributed to the workshops of Hans Klocker, a renowned craftsman resident in Brixen at the end of the fifteenth century. The attribution is based on comparable works by Klocker, such as his figure of St. George, now in the Deutsches Museum, Berlin, which reveals a marked similarity in the detailing of the hands, the facial expression and the workmanship of the hair. (RIGHT)

A Paduan bronze figure of a satyr
EARLY SIXTEENTH CENTURY, height 24.6cm (9⅝in)
New York $46,000 (£29,800). 12.I.93

This piece might have served a utilitarian purpose – the figure originally supporting a standing vase in its right hand that would probably have been used as an inkpot or pen holder. (LEFT)

One of a pair of Florentine terracotta angels
SECOND QUARTER OF THE SIXTEENTH CENTURY, height 72.4cm (28½in)
New York $51,750 (£33,600) for the pair. 12.I.93

Whilst this figure is largely in keeping with the traditions of late fifteenth- and early sixteenth-century Florentine terracotta sculpture, the drapery, the style of the hair and the somewhat mannered pose suggest a date closer to the middle of the sixteenth century. (LEFT)

PIER JACOPO
ALARI-BONACOLSI,
CALLED ANTICO
**A bronze figure of
the young Hercules,
reading**
*c.*1495, MANTUA, height
22.9cm (9in)
London £1,266,500
($1,887,000). 8.VII.93

One of the great Italian
Renaissance sculptors,
Antico was born in
Mantua in around 1460.
The ruling family of the
city at that time, the
Gonzagas, were avid
patrons of the arts, and
Antico was to serve three
generations of the family
before his death in 1528.
The small bronzes
produced by Antico
adhered closely to the
forms and ideals of the
Hellenistic Roman
sculptures being
excavated at that time.
(RIGHT)

CLAUDE MICHEL, CALLED CLODION
**A terracotta group celebrating
the ascension of the Montgolfier
brothers' hot-air balloon**
SIGNED, *c.*1785, height 53.5cm (21in)
London £397,500 ($592,200). 8.VII.93

As one of the most accomplished of late
eighteenth-century French sculptors,
Clodion was patronized by such figures
as Catherine the Great and Louis XVI,
who in 1778 made him *Sculpteur du Roi.*
His reputation and popularity survived
the upheavals of the French Revolution,
to the extent that in 1791 he was created
Sculpteur de Paris. This allegorical work
celebrates the invention of the hot-air
balloon by the Montgolfier brothers,
and the first-ever ascents made in the
autumn of 1783. (LEFT)

NINETEENTH-CENTURY SCULPTURE

CHARLES SUMMERS
Cupid whispering to Venus
SIGNED AND DATED *1875*,
WHITE MARBLE,
height without column 77cm (30¼in)
London £30,800 ($48,000). 30.IV.93

Charles Summers showed at the Great Exhibition of 1851 and in the same year became the first Royal Academy student to win the Silver and Gold medals simultaneously. In 1853 he left for Australia to prospect for gold. After a sad lack of success in this venture he returned to art and achieved a formidable reputation as Australia's leading sculptor. He went back to Europe in 1867, establishing a flourishing studio in Rome. (BELOW)

SIR ALFRED GILBERT
Perseus Arming
BRONZE WITH BLACK PATINA, height including base 73cm (28⅞in) London £33,000 ($51,500). 30.IV.93

At the time the model for this bronze was made Gilbert was living in Rome. It was the first of an autobiographical trilogy, the others being *Icarus* and *Comedy and Tragedy*. (ABOVE LEFT)

SIR ALFRED GILBERT
Comedy and Tragedy: 'Sic Vita'
BRONZE WITH BLACK PATINA, height including base 78.5cm (31in) London £27,500 ($42,900). 30.IV.93

The composition of the allegorical *Comedy and Tragedy*, a dancing figure looking askance from the mask it holds before its face, is one of self-parody. (ABOVE RIGHT)

GIOVANNI GIUSEPPE FONTANA
Cupid captured by Venus
*c.*1870, WHITE MARBLE, height 132cm (52in)
Sussex £15,400 ($23,250). 1.VI.93

Giovanni Giuseppe Fontana, sculptor and watercolourist, was born in Carrara in 1821 and died in London in 1893. He specialized in classical and allegorical groups and exhibited at the Royal Academy and the New Watercolour Society. Examples of his work can be seen in the collection of the Walker Art Gallery, Liverpool. (ABOVE)

GARDEN STATUARY

CARL DORN
Leda and the Swan
*c.*1897, BRONZE,
height 193cm (76in)
New York $50,600 (£33,500).
1.VII.93
Carl Dorn was born in
1831 and exhibited
regularly at the Berlin
Academy. Mythological
subjects such as this
example were extremely
popular with sculptors and
their patrons during the
late-nineteenth century,
although Dorn's particular
specialization was in busts
and portrait reliefs. (RIGHT)

ATTRIBUTED TO EMANUELE CARONI
A female figure
THIRD QUARTER OF THE NINETEENTH
CENTURY, MARBLE, height including base
187cm (73½in)
New York $101,500 (£70,000). 18.III.93
The surge of nationalistic fervour
which swept America after the Civil
War created a demand for
monumental works of sculpture.
This work attributed to Emanuele
Caroni (born in 1826) represents the
Continent America. (LEFT)

RAFFAELE MARINI
Figure of a nude female
SIGNED, LATE-NINETEENTH
CENTURY, MARBLE,
196 x 92.7cm (77 x 36½in)
New York $31,900 (£17,800).
16.IX.92
Raffaele Marini was born in
Naples in 1868 and studied
at the city's Institute of Fine
Art, where he exhibited
from 1888 onwards. Marini
specialized in groups and
figures from Roman
antiquity. This figure,
prostrate in a field covered
with fruit and flowers, was
probably intended to
represent Persephone.
(RIGHT)

ENGLISH FURNITURE

A Queen Anne japanned bureau bookcase

SIGNED AND DATED *1713*, height 257cm (101in)
New York $231,000 (£142,593).
24.X.92
Property of Mr and Mrs Douglas Dillon
This gilt-decorated, black-japanned bureau bookcase has a double dome surmounted by three giltwood finials representing a crowned maiden, a water bearer and a trumpeter. Despite this classical detailing and the use of Corinthian pilasters, the ornamentation is consistent with the contemporary taste for *chinoiserie*: the fall-front, for example, is decorated with a procession of Chinese dignitaries. (LEFT)

A pair of George I walnut side chairs

FIRST QUARTER OF THE EIGHTEENTH CENTURY
New York $198,000 (£122,222). 24.X.92

These substantial burr-walnut chairs
have vase-form splats with carved foliage
'spilling' from their tops. The cabriole legs
are carved with classical motifs: shells at the
knee and lion's-paw feet. The floral
needlepoint seats, in tones of green and pink
on a brown ground, are a fitting
complement to the rich, mottled tones
of the wood. (ABOVE)

A Queen Anne walnut wing chair

c.1705
New York $231,000 (£142,593).
24.X.92

This rare walnut chair is
upholstered with fine
eighteenth-century
needlepoint, probably original,
depicting a seated maiden
holding aloft a cluster of grapes
accompanied by a recumbent
deer and leopard. The sides,
too, are richly embellished with
depictions of flora and fauna,
and the seat bears images of a
male and female, possibly
Adam and Eve. The cabriole
legs are carved at the knees
with shells and foliage, and end
in pad feet. (LEFT)

ATTRIBUTED TO
GEORGE BULLOCK
**An oval oak dining
or breakfast table**
*c.*1815,
top 200 x 180cm (78¾ x 71in)
London £110,000 ($168,300).
27.XI.92
Although not known to
be part of any recorded
Bullock commission, this
piece relates closely to
other attributable works
by him. (RIGHT)

ATTRIBUTED TO
THOMAS CHIPPENDALE
**A George III
lacquer-mounted
commode**
*c.*1775, height 90cm (35½in)
London £194,000 ($302,600).
14.V.93
Conceived in the
chinoiserie style of the
early 1770s, this com-
mode is related to a
small group of japanned
and lacquered com-
modes by, or attributed
to, Thomas Chippendale.
An extensive mountain-
ous landscape is depicted
on the top and a more
intimate village scene on
the panelled doors. The
four gilt-brass pilasters
have swagged rams'
heads and hoof feet.
(RIGHT)

ATTRIBUTED TO JOHN CHANNON
A George II brass-inlaid circular tripod table
*c.*1740, height 71cm (28in)
London £67,500 ($100,500). 9.VII.93

John Channon, who had established himself in St Martin's Lane by the mid 1730s, produced furniture that was strikingly Germanic in character, and it is possible that he employed German cabinet-makers in his workshop. This table has an intricate ten-lobed top with a central cinquefoil surrounded by engraved brass shells and mother-of-pearl buds. The plain baluster stem is supported by cabriole legs, with engraved brass leaf mounts. (RIGHT)

SEDDON, SONS AND SHACKLETON
The top of one of a pair of George III D-shaped painted satinwood card tables
1793, width 100cm (39⅜in)
London £67,500 ($100,500) for the pair. 9.VII.93

This card table (one of a pair) was supplied to Richard Hall Clarke of Bridwell House, Devon, as part of a commission that included chairs, a sofa, tripods and even window cornices – all intended for a suite of state rooms. Seddon established his cabinet-making business in Aldersgate Street, London, in the early 1750s and by 1786 had over 400 employees. (ABOVE LEFT)

SEDDON, SONS AND SHACKLETON
A George III painted satinwood Pembroke table
1793, top when open 81 x 95cm (30 x 37½in)
London £41,100 ($61,200). 9.VII.93

This Pembroke table is from the same commission as the satinwood card table captioned above. (LEFT)

CONTINENTAL FURNITURE

A Louis XV secrétaire à abattant, incorporating lacquer panels
STAMPED *BVRB JME*, MID-EIGHTEENTH CENTURY, width 105cm (41¼in) London £496,500 ($713,600). 11.VI.93 Bernard van Riesenburg was the son of a Dutch merchant and cabinet-maker who had moved to Paris in 1694. He enjoyed a considerable reputation, and was probably the first Parisian *ébéniste* to inset Sèvres plaques into furniture, a fashion that acquired great popularity during the reign of Louis XVI. It is likely that he also initiated the trend for end-cut marquetry, in which the inlaid decoration was cut across the grain to give a distinctive finish. (LEFT)

A Louis XVI ormolu-mounted mahogany bureau-plat, inset with painted panels
STAMPED *WEISWEILER, c.*1788-90,
width 117cm (46⅛in)
Monaco FF8,436,000
(£968,100:$1,519,900). 4.XII.92
From the estate of
Mme Hélène Beaumont.
The discoveries of
Pompeii and Herculan-
eum in the mid-eighteenth
century led to the growing
adoption of classical styles
and ideals. One of those
who capitalized on
this new taste was the
German cabinet-maker
Adam Weisweiler, whose
veneered pieces are
notable for their finely
figured wood and ormolu
mounts. (LEFT)

A Louis XVI japannned commode
STAMPED *LEVASSEUR, c.*1770-90,
width 122.5cm (49in)
Monaco FF6,660,000
(£817,100:$1,222,000). 3.VII.93
Japanning as an
embellishment to furniture
was immensely popular in
France throughout the mid-
eighteenth century, and
Etienne Levasseur (1721-98)
was one of the master
exponents of the style. The
commode shown here is an
important example of
Levasseur's work. (RIGHT)

A Louis XV marquetry cylinder bureau
STAMPED *J.F. LELEU*, *c.*1770, height 109cm (41in)
London £265,500 ($400,900). 11.VI.93
Jean-François Leleu (1729-1807) was apprenticed in the
workshop of the master *ébéniste* Jean-François Oeben,
whose furniture is renowned for the excellence of its
marquetry. After Oeben's death, Leleu's career went
from strength to strength. His patrons included the
Prince de Condé, for whom he created a marquetry floor
in the Palais de Bourbon, and Madame du Barry. He
also produced furniture for the Baron d'Ivry at the
Château d'Hénonville and probably for the Marquis
de Marigny at Menars. (LEFT)

Two from a set of six Louis XV giltwood fauteuils à la reine
SIGNED *TILLIARD*,
MID-EIGHTEENTH CENTURY,
New York $825,000 (£528,800).
31.X.92
Louis XV's preference for
living in the intimate
surroundings of the *petits
appartements* in Versailles
as opposed to the vast and
imposing state rooms did
much to encourage the
development of more
informal furniture. Design
conceits still prevailed,
however, and chairs were
often styled to stand in a
specific position in the
room in order that the
shape of their backs and
their carved decoration
could reflect that of the
panelling behind. (RIGHT)

A German painted and parcel-gilt commode

MID-EIGHTEENTH CENTURY,
width 165cm (65in)
New York $253,000
(£172,100). 27.III.93

This commode probably comes from Munich. During the eighteenth century Germany was divided into a number of separate courts, each ruled by an elector, bishop or prince. Contemporary furniture was thus extremely diverse in style. The south, and in particular the great palaces such as Würzburg and Nymphenburg, produced furniture which was frequently based on French prototypes, such as this piece. (LEFT)

A pair of Louis XVI ormolu five-light bras de lumière

LAST QUARTER OF THE
EIGHTEENTH CENTURY,
height 68.6cm (27in)
New York $396,000
(£253,800). 31.X.92

The fashion for ormolu in France began in the 1660s, when most art and decoration became focused on the glorification of the nation and of its ruler Louis XIV. By the eighteenth century gilded metalwork had come to be virtually synonymous with the refinement of the French nobility. The design of these walllights is almost identical to two pairs currently in the Petit Trianon at Versailles. (LEFT)

An Italian ormolu, burr-walnut and fruitwood marquetry commode

MID-EIGHTEENTH CENTURY, height 87.6cm (34½in)
New York $88,000 (£56,400). 26.IX.92

The *bombé* commode is perhaps the most familiar example of rococo furniture. This piece comes from Lombardy in northern Italy and was most likely made in Milan, the design elements being typical of the mid-eighteenth century in that city. The gilt-metal mounts, which completely encase the legs and then follow the outline of the apron frieze, are a particularly unusual feature. (BELOW)

An Italian walnut-veneered bureau-cabinet

SECOND QUARTER OF THE EIGHTEENTH CENTURY,
height 238cm (95¼in)
Milan L180,000,000 (£83,100:$130,500). 3.XII.92

The rococo in Italy, which was at that time still divided into independent states, was most immediately apparent in the north. In Rome, where the prime concern of the nobility was with dignity and ceremony, it was less easy to distinguish from the baroque, residual vestiges of which remained long after the formal end of the movement itself. (ABOVE)

A Neapolitan suite of painted and parcel-gilt furniture

*c.*1800, the table diameter 72cm (28½in)
London £95,000 ($146,300). 28.V.93

This suite was reputedly made for Napoleon's second wife, the empress Marie-Louise, the link with the city of Naples possibly having been formed through the city's queen, Napoleon's sister, Caroline Murat. (RIGHT)

NINETEENTH-CENTURY FURNITURE

An oak dining table
PHILIP WEBB, *c*.1864, length 260cm (102¼in)
London £26,400 ($40,300). 12.II.92
Philip Webb was a close associate of William Morris, with whom he was a founding partner
of Morris, Marshall, Faulkner and Co. This oak dining table was one of the company's
commissions, and is here seen with the appropriate accompaniment of a collection of
William de Morgan ceramics. (ABOVE)

One of a pair of German carved ivory wall plaques
*c.*1860, width 129cm (50⅞in)
London £78,500 ($119,300)
for the pair. 2.IV.93
The pair of wall plaques
of which this is one are
after the work of the
early seventeenth-
century sculptor and
ivory carver Gerard van
Opstal, who worked
under Richelieu, and
eventually became *Sculp-
teur du Roi.* Examples of
original ivory carving by
van Opstal are in the
Louvre and the Rijks-
museum. The pair
represented here show
such subjects as the
Triumph of Bacchus and
the Sacrifice to Priapus.
(RIGHT)

A pair of figural candelabra
EUGENE DELAPLANCHE,
DATED *1885,* MARBLE AND GILT-
BRONZE, height 285cm (112in)
New York $165,000 (£92,100).
16.IX.92
Eugene Delaplanche
exhibited at the Paris
Salon in 1861, winning
the Prix de Rome three
years later. He is well
known for his portrait
and allegorical sculpture,
of which these large
figures are a good
example. Each is raised
on a violet marble base
and each supports tiered,
foliage-cast candle
branches hung with
glass drops. (LEFT)

A French marquetry occasional table

*c.*1855, PARIS,
height 72cm (28½in)
London £33,350 ($51,000).
21.V.93

This occasional table has been attributed to Joseph Cremer, one of the most celebrated *marqueteurs* of the opulent Second Empire period. He supplied furniture to Louis-Philippe in 1844, also to the King of Holland, and exhibited at the 1852, 1855 and the 1862 International exhibitions. (LEFT AND RIGHT)

AMERICAN DECORATIVE ARTS

A 'Chippendale' wing armchair
*c.*1770, PHILADELPHIA
New York $321,500
(£211,500). 30.I.93
Thomas Chippendale's book of furniture designs, *The Gentleman and Cabinet-maker's Director,* was published in England in 1754, and a revised edition became available in Philadelphia in 1762. The book made a significant impression on tastes in furniture design in late eighteenth-century America, especially with New England cabinet-makers. (LEFT)

A 'Chippendale' side chair
*c.*1770, PHILADELPHIA
New York $156,500 (£102,900). 30.I.93
The rise in popularity in New England of Chippendale-style pieces of furniture encouraged an accompanying rise in the quality of workmanship. This can clearly be seen in this rare dining chair made in Philadelphia in around 1770. It is identical to two other chairs, one in the Henry Ford Museum and the other in the Karolik Collection at the Museum of Fine Arts in Boston. (RIGHT)

A Queen Anne-style balloon-seat side chair
*c.*1755, NEW YORK
New York $189,500 (£124,600). 30.I.93
On the whole the rococo movement made little impact on eighteenth-century American cabinet-makers although there is some evidence of its serpentine lines in their design of chair splats, as can be seen here. This chair is part of an original set of eight, one now being in the Metropolitan Museum of Art, New York, four in the private collection of Bernard Levy and one (previously owned by Cora Ginsburg) in another private collection. (ABOVE)

An ormolu-mounted lighthouse clock
*c.*1825, MASSACHUSETTS, height 63.5cm (25in)
New York $200,500 (£136,300). 23.VI.93
The lighthouse clock was an invention of Simon Willard and this fine and rare example is inscribed *Simon Willard's Patent*. It is of a type often referred to as an Eddystone lighthouse clock, taking its name from the Eddystone lighthouse in Plymouth, England. (LEFT)

The Martin van Buren dining table
1800-10, NEW YORK, length fully extended 474cm (186½in)
New York $189,500 (£128,900). 23.VI.93
The accordion-action construction of this rare table is based on a patent of 1800 of Richard Gillow of London and Lancaster. Most tables of this form are believed to be the work of New York cabinet-makers. This particular table was made for Martin van Buren, President of the United States. (RIGHT)

An American eagle
*c.*1880, PENNSYLVANIA, height 35.6cm (14in)
New York $38,500 (£23,700). 25.X.92

This stylized piece of American folk art was made by Wilhelm Schimmel of the Cumberland Valley, Pennsylvania, in around 1880. Decorated with paint and gesso, the eagle has a yellow comb, red mouth and yellow feet. (RIGHT)

A painted dower chest
DATED *1778*, SCHOHARIE COUNTY, NEW YORK, length 119cm (47in)
New York $46,000 (£30,200). 30.1.93

In 1710, as part of an experiment sponsored by the British Government, 2,400 Germans arrived in the Hudson River Valley. They settled in the Schoharie and Mohawk valleys of New York, and produced fine-quality furnishings for their houses, including decorated marriage chests. (BELOW)

PETER BUDENAARDE
**A House in
East Jersey on the
Passaic River**
DATED *1786*, WATERCOLOUR,
PEN AND INK ON PAPER,
20.3 x 26.7cm (8 x 10½in)
New York $26,450 (£17,400).
30.I.93
On a present-day map of
New Jersey, the area
depicted in this work is
twenty miles north-west
of New York City. It was
a region which was
heavily settled by old
New Jersey Dutch
families. Visitors to
neighbouring Bergen
County in the late-
eighteenth century noted
the use of the Dutch
language, both spoken
and written. (ABOVE)

CARL E. MUNCH
**A fraktur birth-
letter for Salome
Holtzmann**
SIGNED AND DATED *1810*,
WATERCOLOUR, PEN-AND-INK
AND GRAPHITE ON PAPER,
31.8 x 38.1cm (12½ x 15in)
New York $55,000 (£33,900).
25.X.92
Carl E. Munch was born
in Germany in 1769. In
1798 he emigrated to
America where he
became a teacher, first at
Schaefferstown and then
at Rehrersburg. In 1804
he moved across the
mountains to the Lykens
Valley. This painted
birth-letter shows angels
with a cornucopia of
flowers, wreaths and
flower-filled vases. (LEFT)

EUROPEAN TAPESTRIES

A northern Swiss tapestry fragment
*c.*1440-50, PROBABLY BASEL,
50.5 x 49.8cm (19⅞ x 19⅝in)
New York $101,500 (£65,900). 24.V.93
This early fragment depicts a lady and a gentleman in conversation and clad in courtly attire. The lady upholds a bunch of flowers, and the background is filled with scrolling vines. (RIGHT)

A London seasons tapestry
EARLY EIGHTEENTH CENTURY,
295 x 427cm (116 x 168in)
London £33,000 ($51,800). 11.XII.92
This tapestry is from a set of the seasons and depicts the months of Summer. Another version of the work is known, which is inscribed 'Julius/Augustus/September'. The two tapestries are now ascribed to the London workshop of John Chabanex, a Huguenot refugee working in England in the early eighteenth century. (BELOW)

A Brussels mythological tapestry
LATE SEVENTEENTH CENTURY,
339 x 263cm (133½ x 103½in)
New York $54,625 (£35,400).
12.I.93
This tapestry depicts
Apollo and Daphne in a
scene from Ovid's
Metamorphoses, where the
nymph is transposed into a
laurel tree to escape the
pursuit of Apollo. The
tapestry is attributed to
the Brussels workshop of
Daniel Abbeloos, who is
first recorded in 1663.
(LEFT)

APPLIED ARTS

DEMETRE H. CHIPARUS
A bronze and ivory figural group
*c.*1925, height 52.1cm (20½in) New York $151,000 (£104,100). 19.III.93

Together with Frederick Preiss, Demetre Chiparus inspired a fashion in small, decorative, female figures
which he clothed in exotic costumes inspired by the Ballets Russes, the Ziegfeld Follies or by the chorus
lines of the Casino de Paris. As with this piece, he executed the skin in ivory and the clothing in bronze.
The figures of Chiparus tend to be more extravagant and fanciful than those of Preiss. (ABOVE)

CLEMENT MASSIER
A symbolist lustre-glazed earthenware charger
*c.*1898, diameter 49cm (19¼in)
London £10,925 ($16,700).
4.VI.93
Clement Massier, who is thought to have been born around 1845, and died in 1917, was the son of a Vallauris potter and produced an imaginative body of work with crystalline and iridescent glazes at his studio in Golfe-Juan in the South of France. The work of certain symbolist painters is called to mind by the inchoate and blurred outlines of the figure emerging from the depths of this charger. (RIGHT)

JOSEF HOFFMANN
Part of a twenty-three piece porcelain tea-service
*c.*1929,
the teapot height 17cm (6¾ in)
London £7,920 ($12,300).
30.X.92
Josef Hoffmann (1870-1956), architect and designer, was the central figure in Austrian avant-garde design from around 1900 through to the 1920s. He was prolific and worked in a seemingly contradictory variety of styles, from unadorned geometric forms associated with the emergent Modern Movement to decorative, whimsical motifs of which this service is a fine and charming example. (BELOW)

A Tiffany Studios
favrile glass and
bronze mosaic
spider web lamp
1899-1918, IMPRESSED *TIFFANY
STUDIOS NEW YORK*,
height 71.1cm (28in)
New York $770,000
(£503,200). 7.XI.92
Property of the Kirkpatrick
Foundation, Oklahoma.
Louis Comfort Tiffany
(1848-1933) has become
a household name on
both sides of the
Atlantic, largely as a
result of the highly
distinctive and
innovative leaded
bronze and glass lamps
he conceived at the
beginning of this century
in America. This is a
fine example of his
work in this style.
(RIGHT)

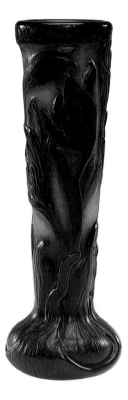

EMILE GALLÉ
A glass vase with trumpet flowers and butterflies
*c.*1900, height 34cm (13⅓in)
Monaco FF277,500 (£33,500:$50,900).
4.IV.93
Gallé was not only an artist and craftsman of extraordinary ability but he was also blessed with a strong business acumen. This enabled him to build up a large and flourishing factory in Nancy where he imposed production-line methods in order to keep abreast of the ever-increasing demand for his glassware.
(RIGHT)

EMILE GALLÉ
'Les Sept Princesses' cameo glass vase
1900, height 23cm (9in)
London £28,175 ($43,100).
4.VI.93
Emile Gallé (1846-1904) inspired a whole generation of artists and craftsmen in his home town of Nancy which soon established for itself a reputation to rival Paris as a centre for the applied arts. This important piece, which was included in the Paris exhibition of 1900, is engraved with the title 'Les Sept Princesses' and with the words 'Simplicité', 'Humilité', 'Patience', 'Fidelité', 'Douceur', 'Veracité', and 'Charité'. (ABOVE)

EMILE GALLÉ
One of a collection of documents and manuscripts
*c.*1880-1904, TWO HUNDRED PAGES, various sizes
Monaco FF166,500 (£20,100:$30,500). 4.IV.93
The dossier of notes and drawings from which this piece comes consists largely of instructions from Gallé to his associate Nicolas. They comprise annotated ink sketches, studies of plants and insects, illustrations in gouache (including the 'branch of magnolia' design for a vase shown here), details of specific projects and a quantity of personal memoranda. (ABOVE)

HECTOR GUIMARD
A mahogany gilt-bronze and glass two-tier tea table
SIGNED, height 86.4cm (34in)
New York $187,000
(£121,400). 19.XI.92
The work of the architect Hector Guimard (1867-1942) encompassed not only the design of his buildings but also the design of the artifacts to be used within them, thus creating a complete and comprehensive environment. Some of his most original furniture is that made between 1895 and 1903. This two-tier tea table is, according to current research, a unique design. (RIGHT)

ALBERT CHEURET
Figural chandelier
*c.*1925, height 38.1cm (15in)
New York $39,100 (£26,600).
19.III.93
Sculptural figures were a popular feature of Art Deco design and appeared frequently on a variety of objects. This striking chandelier by Albert Cheuret is cast as an exotic bird in flight, its wings and tail composed of sections of shaped alabaster, the rest modelled in patinated bronze. (LEFT)

EDGAR BRANDT
A wrought iron oval table with veined marble top
*c.*1925,
height 73cm (29in)
Monaco FF577,200
(£69,700:$105,900). 4.IV.93
Wrought iron enjoyed a revival during the Art Deco period. Edgar Brandt (1880-1960), who made his name in the 1920s and triumphed with his extensive contribution to the 1925 Paris Exposition, was one of the medium's most skilled exponents. (LEFT)

CERAMICS AND GLASS

A Venetian enamelled armorial goblet
*c.*1500, height 13.2cm (5¼in) London £15,400 ($26,300). 6.X.92
Glass-making originated in Egypt, Syria or Iraq before
2000BC and was introduced to Europe after the
foundation of the Roman Empire in 27BC. The earliest
significant European industry was established in
Venice, initially on the Rialto although it was later
moved to Murano when it was thought that sparks
from the chimneys might set fire to the city. (ABOVE)

An English Adam and Eve Royalist goblet
DATED *1716*, height 20.8cm (8¼in)
London £22,000 ($41,800). 15.IX.92
This goblet is engraved with a scene depicting the Fall
of Man. A similar glass, dated 1714, was sold at
Sotheby's London in 1977. The two goblets are
thought to be the earliest dated examples in English
glass of the pedestal stem. The date and the Royalist
inscription, 'God Save King George', referring to
George I, make this an extremely rare piece. (LEFT)

A William de Morgan
lustred pottery 'Sunset and
Moonlight' charger
LATE FULHAM PERIOD, PROBABLY c.1900,
diameter 46.5cm (18¼in)
London £17,250 ($26,200). 25.V.93
William de Morgan established
his firm of potters in Chelsea in 1872. In
1880 he transferred it to Merton
Abbey in Surrey and in 1888 it finally
came to rest in the Sands End Works,
Fulham, where this piece was made.
De Morgan's emphasis had always
been on lustreware, together with
pottery in the Persian and Dutch
styles, and he considered the
development of his 'Sunset and
Moonlight' triple glazes to be the
crowning glory of his career. (BELOW)

A Ruskin Pottery vase and stand
c.1915-25, total height 44cm (17⅜in)
London £12,000 ($18,500). 20.IV.93
From the Adam Ferneyhough Collection.
In 1898 Edward Taylor founded a small
pottery which became known as the
Birmingham Tile Pottery Company. Its
specialization was in unusual glass effects
applied to diverse forms of pottery. By
1903 it was enjoying an international
reputation for its distinctive mottled
and coloured glazes. (LEFT)

A Southwark delftware
polychrome drug jar
DATED 1656, height 36cm (14¼in)
London £49,500 ($85,600). 7.X.92
From the John Philip Kassebaum Collection.
Decorated pharmaceutical containers
were a feature of English seventeenth-
century apothecaries' shops and were
often embellished with the arms of the
Worshipful Society of Apothecaries.
Here, the arms appear on a shield
supported by two unicorns. (BELOW)

A Maiolica dish
FROM THE WORKSHOP OF GIORGIO ANDREOLI, SIGNED AND DATED *1531*, GUBBIO, diameter 23.5cm (9⅜in) New York $145,500 (£94,400). 24.V.93
This Maiolica dish is decorated in the *istoriato* style, which derived its imagery from religion, mythology and history. It is centred with a portrait of Fulvia, the wife of Mark Antony. (ABOVE LEFT)

A Maiolica documentary dish
DATED *1540*, URBINO, diameter 27.5cm (10⅞in) London £28,600 ($48,900). 6.X.92
This dish is by the 'Della Rovere' painter, so called because he was responsible for five known *istoriato* dishes painted with a coat of arms wrongly thought to be those of the Della Rovere family. (ABOVE RIGHT)

One of a pair of Maiolica albarelli, or drug jars
*c.*1510-20, SIENA, height 23.8cm (9⅜in)
New York $65,750 (£42,700) for the pair. 24.V.93
Tin-glazing is one of the few ceramic processes not to have evolved through the Far East. The technique spread to Italy from Spain in the late eleventh century and flourished there until the sixteenth century, when the centre of production had shifted to Holland and Britain. (LEFT)

A Le Nove porcelain écuelle, cover and stand
*c.*1765, diameter of stand 21.6cm (8½in)
New York $27,500 (£17,400). 27.X.92
This set of écuelle, cover and stand is moulded with rococo scrollwork and bowknotted floral sprays. The painted decoration depicts scenes with figures in a rural river landscape, figures watching a parade and figures by classical buildings. (RIGHT AND ABOVE RIGHT)

A Meissen porcelain pagoda figure

*c.*1725, height 20.8cm (8¼in)
Zürich SF143,000 (£65,600:$99,700). 24.XI.92

The second director of the Meissen factory, Johann Gregor Höroldt, was responsible for introducing the Chinese-style decoration by which the period is instantly recognizable. This rare figure was probably modelled by George Fritzsche, who joined the factory in 1711. The only other known example dating from the same early period of Meissen production is now in the Zwinger Museum, Dresden. (LEFT)

A Meissen porcelain 'Augustus Rex' bottle vase

1725-30, height 22cm (8⅝in) London £47,700 ($73,400). 2.III.93

The description 'Augustus Rex', sometimes applied to Meissen pieces marked with an *AR* monogram, refers to Augustus II, King of Poland, who became Elector of Saxony in 1694 and founded the Meissen factory in 1710. After the taste for *chinoiserie* of the early Meissen years, a new style was developed in the mid-1720s based on the so-called 'oriental flowers', or *indianische Blumen.* (ABOVE)

A Meissen porcelain plate

1741-45, FROM THE EMPRESS ELIZABETH OF RUSSIA SERVICE, diameter 24.1cm (9½in)
New York $20,700 (£13,400). 22.V.93

This plate comes from a service ordered by the Empress Elizabeth of Russia upon ascending the throne in 1741, and bears the Hermitage inventory number. Some of the pieces from the service have *indianische Blumen* ('oriental flowers') as the central decoration (as here), some have *Holzschnittblumen* ('flowers painted after prints'). (ABOVE)

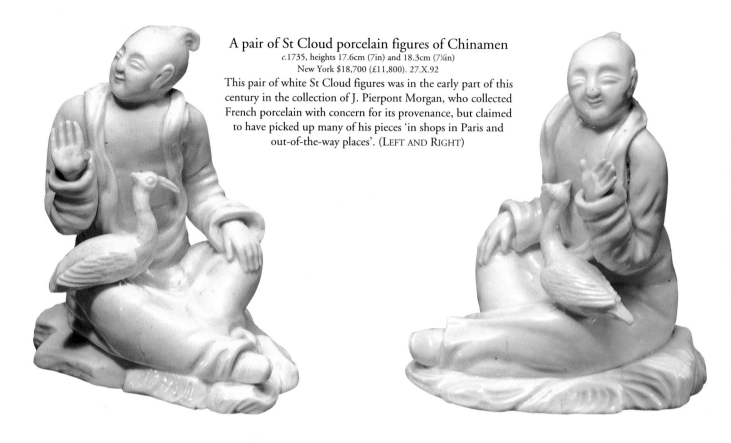

A pair of St Cloud porcelain figures of Chinamen
*c.*1735, heights 17.6cm (7in) and 18.3cm (7¼in)
New York $18,700 (£11,800). 27.X.92
This pair of white St Cloud figures was in the early part of this
century in the collection of J. Pierpont Morgan, who collected
French porcelain with concern for its provenance, but claimed
to have picked up many of his pieces 'in shops in Paris and
out-of-the-way places'. (LEFT AND RIGHT)

**A Vincennes
porcelain oval dish**
*c.*1753, width 43.5cm (17in)
London £29,900 ($47,200).
15.VI.93
Apart from the excellence
of the porcelain it
produced, the Vincennes
factory is celebrated for
being the parent of the
great Royal Sèvres
factory. The Vincennes
works moved to new
premises at Sèvres in
1756, and in 1759 it was
bought by Louis XV. At
around the time of the
move, lavish tableware
was much in vogue and
this dish is part of the
famed 'Louis XV Service',
supplied to the king
over three successive
Decembers from 1753
to 1755. (LEFT)

A Marseilles faïence turkey tureen and cover

*c.*1770, height 38.5cm (15⅛in)
London £42,750 ($61,900). 2.III.93

This rare and splendid piece was made in the Savy factory in Marseilles in around 1770, and is incised with the factory's mark of a double X. The bird has been given fine blue-black plumage and a blue-mottled red crop. It stands on a mound base with tree stumps applied with acorns. (BELOW)

A Berlin porcelain topographical vase

1832-37, height 76cm (30⅛in)
Zürich SF96,800 (£44,400:$67,400). 25.XI.92

This large, gilt-metal-mounted vase is painted with a continuous view of Potsdam. The Berlin factory was established in 1752 and its wares came to be much in demand when Meissen, the other great German porcelain-producing factory, was suffering the effects of the Seven Years War. In 1763, when the war ended, Frederick the Great bought the factory and under his ownership it achieved a monopoly in porcelain sales throughout the entire state of Prussia. (BELOW)

A pair of Paris porcelain gold-ground vases

*c.*1820, DARTE FRERES, height 36.5cm (14⅜in)
New York $19,550 (£12,600). 22.V.93

The stencilled marks on the base of this pair of gold-ground vases indicate that it was produced by the Darte brothers. Each of the vases displays a rectangular panel painted with a cluster of flowers on a russet and white marble ledge against a shaded brown ground. (BELOW LEFT)

PRECIOUS OBJECTS *by John Block*

During the 1992–93 season no area attracted as diverse, international and glamorous a following as Sotheby's Precious Objects sales. Items as varied as jewels, watches, clocks, silver, and objects of vertu attracted buyers from North America, South America, Europe, Asia, Africa and Australasia. Sales held in New York, Geneva, London, Monaco and Hong Kong offered the opportunity for collectors, dealers and institutions to acquire beautiful and well-crafted pieces wrapped in a sense of history, allure and mystery. The greater public had not seen many of these objects for decades or even centuries before they arrived in Sotheby's exhibition rooms.

The Marlene Dietrich ruby bracelet reflected the glamour, glitter and gutsiness of its original owner. The bold loop of Burmese rubies surrounded by babuette and pavé-set diamonds was an instant hit during the international pre-sale tour of the New York October sale. That the bracelet was worn by Dietrich in Alfred Hitchcock's 1950 film Stagefright, was Dietrich's signature piece of jewellery, and had not been seen for over thirty years, were all instrumental factors in the sale price of $990,000.

No name is more synonymous with the elegance of magnificent diamonds and jewellery than that of Harry Winston. Among the works in the Collection of the late Mrs Harry Winston, sold in New York in October 1992, was a magnificent pair of diamond chandelier pendant earclips, created for her in 1961 by her husband. This was the only pair of chandelier earclips made to this design, after an eighteenth-century girandole motif. The dazzling combination of pear-shape, round and marquise-shape diamonds surmounting a pair of rare elongated pear-shape diamond drops weighing over 15 carats each, had the intended effect on bidders and the earclips sold for $1,430,000.

The European season of Precious Objects also began auspiciously with the November sale in Geneva of the Thurn und Taxis Collection of silver, snuff boxes and jewels amassed by the Thurn und Taxis family over the past two centuries. King Frederick II of Prussia (Frederick the Great) was not only a

The J. P. Morgan Jr. 'Model A' Cartier Mystery Clock
SIGNED, 1913, PARIS,
height 12.7cm (5in)
New York $310,500
(£201,600). 20.IV.93. (LEFT)

Diamond bracelet
BY HARRY WINSTON, 1959,
length 19cm (7½in)
New York $473,000
(£290,100). 20.X.92
From the Collection of the late
Mrs Harry Winston. (ABOVE)

statesman, ruler and soldier, but also a major patron of the arts. Under his reign, workshops flourished creating intricate objects of vertu including a spectacular snuff box sold in November. Made in around 1770 after a design by Jean Guillaume George Kruger of Berlin, the box is encrusted with diamonds, rubies, emeralds and moulded pâte de verre. *The quality, rarity and provenance of the snuff box helped it to achieve the price of SF2,530,000.*

As with jewels and objects of vertu, the rarity of form and the importance of the artisan of a piece of silver is of great significance. One of the most unusual items sold during this season was an American silver two-handled, late seventeenth-century bowl by Cornelius Vander Burgh, New York. Not only is a piece of American seventeenth-century silver extremely rare, but also Cornelius Vander Burgh (b.1652) is considered New York's first native silversmith. The bowl brought $233,500 in New York in January 1993.

The sale of the Harcourt Collection in London included a George III silver soup tureen and cover with liner and stand for which the 1st Earl Harcourt was charged £81 16s 2d. This season the tureen achieved £20,700.

In Geneva in May a magnificent example of Napoleonic silver was sold for SF641,500. The silver-gilt soup tureen on stand by Jean-Baptiste Claude

Odiot dates from 1809–19, Paris. It is of a neoclassical architectural form, with winged female handles and decorated with figures of lions, vines and Silenian masks. When Odiot's portrait was painted by Robert Lefevre in 1822, the model of this tureen was one of three pieces placed beside the sitter.

The markets for both wristwatches and pocket watches continued to attract a wide variety of purchasers from around the world. The first stainless steel single-button chronograph to be offered at auction was sold in February in New York. Made in 1927 by Patek Philippe, the watch achieved $101,500. In London the highlight of the year was a miniature clockwatch from the Harcourt Collection. Apparently the only extant example from the seventeenth-century Hipp workshops in Kempton, the clockwatch was reputedly a gift from Queen Elizabeth of Bohemia. It sold for £133,500. Among pocket watches sold in New York was a double-dialled perpetual-calendar minute-repeating watch by Louis Audemars. Probably made for the Paris exhibitions of the late-nineteenth century, it was offered by the family of the original owner and made $255,500.

Many high-powered collectors throughout history have been fascinated by the mechanisms and beauty of clocks. Such a man was J. P. Morgan Jnr, who for Christmas 1913 ordered a clock from Cartier. Made by Maurice Couet, it was the first of the Cartier 'Mystery Clocks'. Called a 'Model A', it has a rectangular case of rock crystal with rose-cut diamond hands and is on a nephrite base. When sold in New York in April it fetched $310,500.

The economic climate has had an effect on the prices of English clocks by Tompion, Graham and Knibb and some levelling has taken place this season. Rarities such as the white marble and biscuit model by Vulliamy, which sold for £35,200, remain in demand.

The Precious Object market remained strong this season, seeming to defy recession in many countries. Sales attracted bidders from all over the world, with collectors from Asia being particularly prominent. Whether collecting these objects as works of art or amassing them as portable wealth, the buyers brought to the auction rooms an excitement that will carry over into the 1993–94 season.

A Russian gold, enamel and jewelled Imperial presentation snuff box
c.1900, ST PETERSBURG, length 8.9cm (3½in) New York $56,100 (£35,000). 8.XII.92. (ABOVE)

Silver-gilt soup tureen, cover and stand
BY JEAN-BAPTISTE CLAUDE ODIOT, 1809-19, PARIS, overall height 39.4cm (15½in) Geneva SF641,500 (£282,500:$436,300). 24.V.93 (BELOW)

JEWELLERY

A pearl and diamond tiara
1853, GABRIEL LEMONNIER,
SILVER AND GOLD MOUNT
Geneva SF935,000
(£428,800:$636,000). 17.XI.92
From the Thurn und Taxis Collection.
The pearls in this tiara came
from a parure assembled in
1810 for Napoleon's second
Empress, the Archduchess
Marie Louise. The tiara is set
with 212 pearls, weighing 2,520
grains, and 1,998 brilliants, and
was part of an order submitted
by Napoleon III to the leading
contemporary Parisian jewellers.
In 1887 the French Republican
government decided to sell the
crown jewels, and this tiara was
bought by Julius Jacobi who in
turn sold it to Prince Albert von
Thurn und Taxis. (LEFT)

A diamond brooch
LAST QUARTER OF THE EIGHTEENTH
CENTURY Geneva SF341,000
(£151,500:$231,900). 17.XI.92
From the Thurn und Taxis Collection.
This piece is set in the form of
the middle and upper sections
of the neck badge of the
Austrian Order of the Golden
Fleece and, according to the
Thurn und Taxis family
archives, was made for Fürst
Carl Anselm (1733-1805) who
became a Knight of that order
in 1775. The Thurn und Taxis
family can be traced back to the
fifteenth century. It reached
its great flowering in the
eighteenth and nineteenth
centuries, producing a host of
Hapsburg rulers. (LEFT)

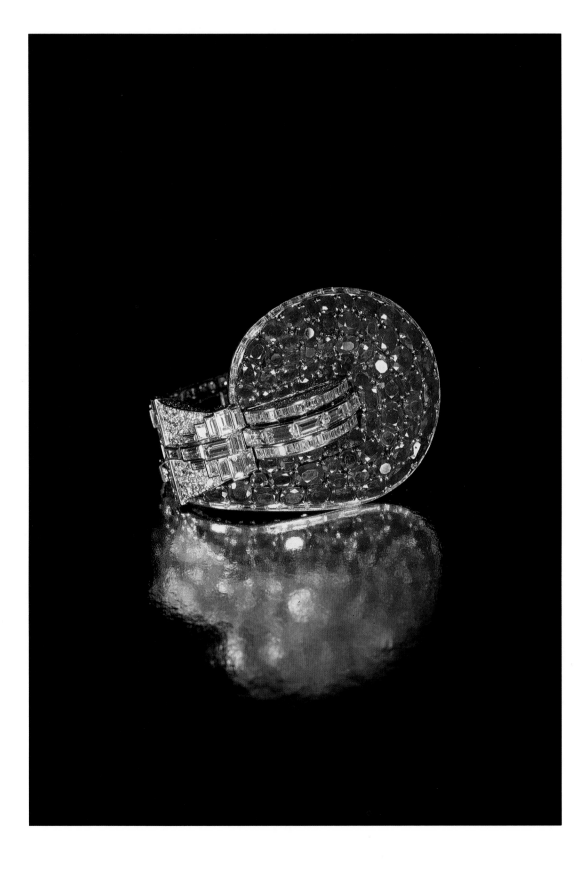

A ruby and diamond bracelet

LATE 1930S, FRENCH
New York $990,000
(£626,500). 19.X.92

From the Collection of
Marlene Dietrich.
This spectacular piece
belonged to Marlene
Dietrich and was worn
by the legendary film
star for her appearance
in Alfred Hitchcock's
Stage Fright. Dietrich's
screen persona was
largely developed by her
association with the
Austrian-American dir-
ector Josef von Stern-
berg, who persuaded her
to move from Berlin to
Hollywood in 1930. She
became his muse and he
directed her in many of
her most famous films,
including *The Blue
Angel, Shanghai Express*
and *Blond Venus*.
Dietrich died in Paris
in 1992. (LEFT)

A pair of Harry Winston chandelier pendent earrings
1961, DIAMOND, MOUNTED IN PLATINUM
New York $1,430,000 (£905,000). 20.X.92
From the collection of the late Mrs Harry Winston

These earrings are made up from 28 pear-shaped, marquise-shaped and round diamonds weighing approximately 48.75 carats, supporting two pear-shaped diamonds weighing approximately 15.9 and 15.5 carats. They were made for his wife by Harry Winston, who is widely considered to be one of the major innovators of twentieth-century jewellery design. (RIGHT)

A diamond bracelet
MOUNTED IN PLATINUM, length 17.8cm (7in)
New York $363,000 (£232,600). 9.XII.92

This bracelet is composed of seven emerald-cut diamonds weighing approximately 17.5 carats, thirty-five pear-shaped diamonds weighing approximately 37 carats, twenty-eight marquise-shaped diamonds weighing approximately 19 carats, and seven round diamonds weighing approximately 3 carats. The bracelet was reputedly bought from Harry Winston in the 1950s. (LEFT)

A Harry Winston diamond ring

SIGNED, MOUNTED IN PLATINUM
New York $1,157,500
(£751,600). 19.IV.93
This emerald-cut diamond, weighing 51.33 carats, is flanked by two modified triangular-shaped diamonds and is mounted in platinum.
(FAR LEFT)

A fancy blue diamond

MOUNTED AS A RING WITH DIAMOND SHOULDERS
Geneva SF5,283,500
(£2,348,200:$3,594,200).
26.V.93
Diamonds come in a variety of colours, blue being among the rarest and most desirable. This large example weighs 11.47 carats. (LEFT)

An emerald-cut diamond

Geneva SF5,393,500
(£2,397,100:$3,669,000).
26.V.93
This magnificent gem, which weighs 53.88 carats, is the second largest D-colour, internally flawless, emerald-cut diamond to have been sold at auction. (FAR LEFT)

A pear-shaped diamond

New York $4,732,500
(£3,134,100). 19.IV.93
Weighing 66.29 carats, this is the third largest D-colour, internally flawless, pear-shaped diamond to have been sold at auction. The largest, weighing 101.84 carats, was sold by Sotheby's in Geneva in November 1990. (LEFT)

A cultured pearl and diamond necklace
Length 43cm (17in)
New York $2,310,000 (£1,462,000). 19.X.92
Never before has a necklace made up of cultured pearls of this quality and size been
offered at auction. The pearls range from 16.0mm to 20.1mm, and the price the
necklace achieved was a world record. (ABOVE)

An emerald ring
Geneva SF1,488,500
(£661,500:$1,012,500).
26.V.93
The octagonal step-cut stone of this very important ring weighs 18.575 carats. The emerald is Colombian in origin and its extraordinary colour, brilliance and purity make it an exceptional example. (LEFT)

A ruby ring
BURMESE, THE STONE MOUNTED BETWEEN LUNETTE-SHAPED DIAMOND SHOULDERS
Geneva SF4,403,500
(£1,957,100:$2,995,500).
26.V.93
The exceptional colour and quality of this ruby, combined with its size, make it one of the rarest examples of a fine Burmese ruby to come on the market in recent years. The oval-shaped stone weighs 16.517 carats. (LEFT)

A sapphire and diamond ring
MOUNTED BY BULGARI
St Moritz SF828,500
(£368,200:$563,600). 19.II.93
The superb, octagonal, step-cut sapphire in this magnificent ring weighs 46.343 carats and, according to the Gübelin certificate which accompanies the piece, is Sri Lankan in origin. (LEFT)

A ruby and diamond bracelet
*c.*1950, MOUNTED IN PLATINUM Geneva SF311,500 (£138,400:$211,900). 26.V.93
This bracelet is made from thirteen cushion-shaped rubies framed by radiating clusters of baguette and circular-cut diamonds. (TOP)

A ruby and diamond brooch
*c.*1950 Geneva SF124,500 (£55,300:$84,600). 26.V.93
This brooch is decorated with a cluster of twenty cushion-shaped rubies bordered by alternating segments of baguette and circular-cut diamonds. (ABOVE LEFT)

A pair of Chaumet ruby and diamond earrings
*c.*1950 Geneva SF43,700 (£19,400:$29,700). 26.V.93
These earrings are signed *Chaumet London.* Each is set with with a cluster of seven cushion-shaped rubies. (ABOVE RIGHT)

A 'Tutti Frutti' Cartier brooch
*c.*1930, SIGNED, EMERALD, COLOURED STONE AND DIAMOND
Geneva SF176,000 (£78,200:$119,700). 18.XI.92
The carved emeralds frequently used as centrepieces in jewels such as this were automatically associated with India despite the fact that the best stones were Colombian in origin, having made their way east with gem traders in the wake of the Spanish Conquistadores. (TOP)

A 'Tutti Frutti' Cartier bracelet
*c.*1930, EMERALD, ONYX AND DIAMOND
Geneva SF264,000 (£117,300:$179,500). 18.XI.92
In 1911, Jacques Cartier, the head of the firm's London branch, made the first of several journeys to India, marking the start of a long and fruitful professional relationship with the East which resulted in many purchases of rare jewels in Delhi, Culcutta and Bombay. (ABOVE)

A René Boivin gold, diamond and ruby necklace
*c.*1960
New York $148,500 (£93,600). 19.X.92
From the Estate of Barbara Cushing Paley

This unusual piece comes from the estate of Barbara Cushing Paley, the youngest of the famous Cushing sisters, who were famed for their intelligence and beauty. 'Babe' was for some time fashion editor of *Vogue* in America and herself became a fashion icon, playing a dominant role in high society until her death in 1978. (ABOVE)

A Paul Brandt Art Deco brooch
*c.*1930, SIGNED, PLATINUM, DIAMOND AND ONYX
New York $43,125 (£28,750). 19.IV.93

Paul Brandt received his training in Paris with Chaplain and Allard. Although his initial designs were in the Art Nouveau style, he is perhaps best remembered for his pure Art Deco jewellery. Brandt's creations often comprise planes of diamonds against a white-metal ground, usually contrasted by geometric segments of onyx, rock crystal or lapis. (ABOVE)

An agate, gold and enamel pendant
SECOND HALF OF NINETEENTH CENTURY
London £19,800 ($31,000). 4.XII.92

This pendant was probably designed by the German goldsmith Reinhold Vasters (1827-1909). Vasters formed an enduring association with the dealer and collector Frédéric Spitzer, who inspired many of Vasters' antiquarian productions and influenced his work in the Renaissance style, of which this pendant is an important example. (ABOVE LEFT)

An agate and diamond cameo pendant
EARLY EIGHTEENTH CENTURY
London £7,820 ($11,700). 1.VII.93

Cameo-cutting was first practised in Imperial Rome. Cameos were cut out of hardstones such as onyx and agate, using the natural colours in the stones to form designs. The eighteenth and early nineteenth centuries saw a revival in the popularity of this skill, and cameos of many kinds, particularly portraits, came to be widely worn. (ABOVE)

A gold, pearl, enamel and diamond brooch
*c.*1890 London £5,060 ($7,200). 18.III.93

Gold was relatively plentiful during the late nineteenth century and designs based on natural forms were popular. In England, the Boer War prevented the supply of South African diamonds and coloured stones and enamels were widely used as substitutes. (FAR LEFT)

An enamel and diamond brooch
*c.*1890 London £1,955 ($2,800). 18.III.93

This charming brooch is designed as a spray of pansies, the petals decorated with opaque purple and lilac enamel and the centres set with cushion-shaped stones. (LEFT)

RUSSIAN WORKS OF ART, MINIATURES & VERTU

SCHOOL OF DYONYSII
An icon depicting the Anastasis, or the 'Harrowing of Hell'
THIRD QUARTER OF THE FIFTEENTH CENTURY, 51.5 x 41.5cm (20½ x 16⅜in)
London £64,000 ($95,600). 17.VI.92
The iconography of the Anastasis dates from the early Christian period. The Evangelists do not write of this mysterious event, but the image follows closely the description in the Apocryphal Gospel of Nicodemus. Christ, the new Adam, is depicted trampling the broken gates of Hell; He holds the cross which gave Him victory over death and raises Adam and Eve from their tomb. (ABOVE)

A pair of silver ten-light candelabra
FABERGÉ c.1890, MOSCOW, height 68.6cm (27in)
New York $220,000 (£141,900). 8.XII.92
Carl Fabergé, with other craftsmen of the period, was much influenced by the style of the rococo and in particular by the lavish designs of Juste-Aurèle Meissonnier, in whose manner these massive candelabra are made. Manufactured under the Russian Imperial warrant, which Fabergé acquired in 1885, they remain with their original oak case. (ABOVE)

JACQUES-ANTOINE ARLAUD
Prince James Francis Edward Stuart
SIGNED AND DATED *1703*, ON VELLUM,
oval 8.7cm (3⅛in)
London £26,450 ($37,800). 11.III.93

In 1688 Jacques-Antoine Arlaud became miniature painter to Philippe, Duc d'Orléans. His skills attracted members of the exiled Stuart family gathered at St Germain, resulting in this fine portrait of the Old Pretender. (RIGHT)

A Portuguese gold and jewelled crown
MID-EIGHTEENTH CENTURY,
height 21cm (8¼in)
New York $140,000 (£92,100). 8.VI.93
From the Richard Manney Collection.

This crown would have adorned a statue of the Madonna. It is set with diamonds, rubies and emeralds and is very close in style to a gilt ciborium (an ecclesiastical vessel) preserved in the Museu Nacional de Arte Antiga in Lisbon. (BELOW)

A desk timepiece
FABERGÉ, WORKMASTER M. PERCHIN,
ST PETERSBURG, 1899-1903,
SILVER-GILT AND ENAMEL,
height 14.6cm (5¾in)
Geneva SF132,000 (£59,700:$90,700).
17.XI.92

At the height of Carl Fabergé's success in the 1890s his St Petersburg company had branches in Moscow, Odessa, Kiev and London, with more than 500 craftsmen in his employ to help produce the exquisite objects so favoured by his wealthy patrons. (BELOW)

A snuff box made for Frederick II, King of Prussia

*c.*1770, JEWELLED GOLD AND HARDSTONE, BERLIN,
width 10cm (3⅞in)
Geneva SF2,530,000
(£1,150,000:$1,805,500). 17. XI.92
From the Thurn und Taxis Collection.

This magnificent snuff box encrusted with diamonds, rubies, emeralds and moulded *pâte de verre* was made for Frederick II, King of Prussia, after a design by Jean Guillaume George Krüger. It is said that Frederick the Great inherited a passion for snuff boxes from his mother, whose boudoir was found on her death to contain more than 300 examples. A metal snuff box saved Frederick's life during the Battle of Kunersdorf in 1759, when a Russian bullet was deflected by a box in his pocket. (LEFT)

A Dresden snuff box

BY J. C. NEUBER, *c.*1780, GOLD AND HARDSTONE,
width 9cm (3½in)
London £166,500 ($249,700). 10.VI.93

Johann Christian Neuber (1736-1808), who made this piece, was one of the most creative and talented masters patronized by the Saxon court, although by the late 1780s his large workshop had started to suffer from financial problems and, after retiring in 1805, Neuber died a pauper. (RIGHT)

CLOCKS AND WATCHES

A French quarter-striking calendar mantel clock

*c.*1840, ORMOLU, height 71cm (28in)
New York $26,450 (£18,900). 28.VI.93 From the Joseph M. Meraux Collection.

Ormolu decoration was extremely popular in France for nearly three centuries and was used to embellish a variety of objects, from furniture and porcelain to frames and clocks. The movement of the clock shown here is contained in a sphere faced with the signs of the zodiac and is supported by a winged lion, a griffin, a bull and a winged centaur for the four Evangelists. (ABOVE)

A French conical pendulum display clock

SIGNED, *c.*1865, SILVERED-BRONZE AND WHITE ONYX,
height 298.5cm (117½in) New York $134,500 (£89,600). 28.VI.93
From the Joseph M. Meraux Collection.

This rare clock comes from the collection of Joseph M. Meraux, who, by the time he died in 1992, had accumulated the largest, and arguably the finest, collection of nineteenth-century clocks in the world. (ABOVE)

An English chiming bracket clock and bracket

ELLICOTT, SIGNED, *c*.1770, MAHOGANY AND BRASS, height of clock 47cm (18½in) London £17,600 ($27,600). 17.XII.92

This fine clock reputedly belonged to William Wales (1734-98), Astronomer to Captain Cook. It was made for John Ellicott by the firm of A. & J. Thwaites and bears its stamp and number *375*, indicating that it was probably made around 1768. It is unusual to find a clock retaining its original bracket, making this a rare example of its type. (LEFT)

A spiral spring skeleton timepiece

WILLIAM SMITH, SIGNED, *c*.1850, height 40.5cm (16in) London £11,220 ($17,600). 17.XII.92

William Smith set up as a clockmaker in Musselburgh, Scotland, in 1847. Early in his career he invented a form of rubber spring which was used to drive his clocks and for which he was awarded a silver medal by the Royal Scottish Society of Arts. This rare clock was kept by Smith and came by direct descent to the consignor. (LEFT)

A French world time and annual calendar terrestrial globe clock

ANDRÉ MATHY, SIGNED, *c*.1880, SILVERED-BRONZE, GILT-BRASS AND ENAMEL, height 193cm (76in) New York $74,000 (£49,300). 28.VI.93 From the Joseph M. Meraux Collection.

The movement of this French globe clock is enclosed in a glazed rectangular case flanked with silvered-bronze figures representing the seasons. (ABOVE)

An English hunting-cased minute-repeating *grande sonnerie* clockwatch with chronograph

MARCKS & CO, SIGNED, *c.*1895, BOMBAY OR POONA,
diameter 5.5cm (2⅛in)
Geneva SF290,400 (£129,000:$197,500). 19.XI.92

The British Raj generated a market for high-quality timepieces in the sub-continent. This fine and rare example is in gold, enamel, diamond, ruby and split-pearl. (ABOVE)

An English gold and enamel verge miniature clockwatch

ATTRIBUTED TO ANDREAS HIPP OF KEMPTON, FIRST
QUARTER OF THE SEVENTEENTH CENTURY,
overall length 2.5cm (1in) London £133,500 ($200,200).
10.VI.93 From the Harcourt Collection.

This clockwatch was reputedly a gift from Queen Elizabeth of Bohemia (the 'Winter Queen') to Frederick Harcourt, and appears to be the only example of its type. (ABOVE)

An English hunting-cased minute-repeating *grande sonnerie* clockwatch with moon phases

MARCKS & CO. SIGNED, *c.*1900, BOMBAY OR POONA,
diameter 6cm (2⅜in)
Geneva SF411,400 (£182,800:$279,800). 19.XI.92

This Marcks & Co. clockwatch reflects a type of enamel design of an earlier Moghul period that can be found on a number of watches made for the Indian market. (ABOVE)

A Swiss minute-repeating perpetual calendar watch

PATEK PHILIPPE, SIGNED, *c.*1980, GENEVA,
diameter 5.4cm (2⅛in)
Geneva SF86,000 (£38,200:$58,800). 27.V.93

This fine gold watch by the Patek Philippe Company incorporates the perpetual calendar function with phases of the moon and the Equation of Time. (ABOVE)

An English verge clockwatch with astronomical dial

T. CHAMBERLIN, SIGNED, *c.*1630, diameter 5.1cm (2in)
London £34,500 ($51,700). 10.VI.93
From the Harcourt Collection.

This gilt metal clockwatch was reputedly given to the diarist John Evelyn by Charles II, whose grand-daughter Elizabeth was married to Sir Simon Harcourt. (ABOVE)

A Swiss skeletonized double-dialled minute-repeating perpetual calendar moon-phase watch

LOUIS AUDEMARS, SIGNED, *c.*1885, diameter 5.5cm (2⅛in)
New York $255,500 (£375,500). 25.VI.93

The glazed dials revealing the movement suggest that this late nineteenth-century Louis Audemars watch was probably made for exhibition purposes. (ABOVE)

A Swiss self-winding sweep seconds wristwatch

ROLEX OYSTER PERPETUAL, SIGNED, *c.*1949, diameter 3.2cm (1¼in)
Geneva SF69,000 (£30,600:$47,200). 27.V.93

This watch was reputedly made for Jawaharlal Nehru, and presented by him to Sherpa Tenzing, who, with Sir Edmund Hilary, was the first to conquer Mount Everest. (ABOVE)

A Swiss gold and platinum rectangular wristwatch

PATEK PHILIPPE, SIGNED, *c.*1938, length 3.5cm (1⅜in)
Geneva SF96,800 (£43,000:$65,800). 19.XI.92

This Patek Philippe rectangular wristwatch is typical of the wristwatches of the 1920s and 30s that have, in recent years, become so avidly collected. (ABOVE)

A Swiss gold cushion single-button chronograph wristwatch with register

PATEK PHILIPPE, *c.*1925, diameter 3.4cm (1⅜in)
New York $167,500 (£113,100). 25.VI.93

The first chronographs to be produced by the famous Patek Philippe Company were developed by Victorin Piguet in the latter part of the 1920s. This is a rare and early example in gold. (ABOVE)

A Swiss stainless-steel single-button chronograph with register and pulsemeter

PATEK PHILIPPE, *c.*1927, diameter 3.5cm (1⅜in)
New York $101,500 (£70,000). 11.II.93

Like the previous single-button chronograph, this is an early example, but also appears to be the first of its type in stainless-steel to have been offered at auction. (ABOVE)

A French gold 'cloche' wristwatch

CARTIER, SIGNED, *c.*1922, length 3.3cm (1¼in)
New York $60,500 (£38,200). 26.X.92

It is the bell-shaped face of this gold wristwatch that gives it its name. The 'cloche' style was developed in 1921, and is considered rare by collectors. (ABOVE)

A French gold calendar wristwatch with moon phases

CARTIER, SIGNED *c.*1940, length 4cm (1⅜in)
New York $99,000 (£62,600). 26.X.92

This elegant calendar wristwatch appears to be the third known example of a gold, rectangular moon-phase wristwatch made for Cartier. (ABOVE)

SILVER

A French basin and ewer

JEAN BELLON, 1768-69, MONTPELLIER,
height of ewer 27cm (10⅝in)
Monaco FF954,600 (£113,200:$175,500). 5.XII.92
From the Jourdan-Barry Collection.

Basins and ewers were popular items of
toiletware in seventeenth-century France,
although less common in the eighteenth
century when the emphasis was more on
elaborate tableware and candlesticks. The
ewer shown here is decorated in typical
rococo style with a scene depicting the
Triumph of Venus and bears the arms of
the Campan family, important magistrates
from Montpellier. (RIGHT)

A set of thirty-six French candlesticks

JEAN-JACQUES KIRSTEIN, 1781, STRASBOURG,
heights 24.5cm (9⅝in)
Geneva SF726,000 (£322,600:$493,800). 17.XI.92
From the Thurn und Taxis Collection.

This magnificent set of baluster
candlesticks bears the arms of Fürst Carl
Anselm von Thurn und Taxis (1733-
1805) and is recorded as having been
received from Strasbourg on 27 January
1782. The Musée des Arts Décoratifs in
Strasbourg possesses a pair of identical
design but without nozzles. (BELOW)

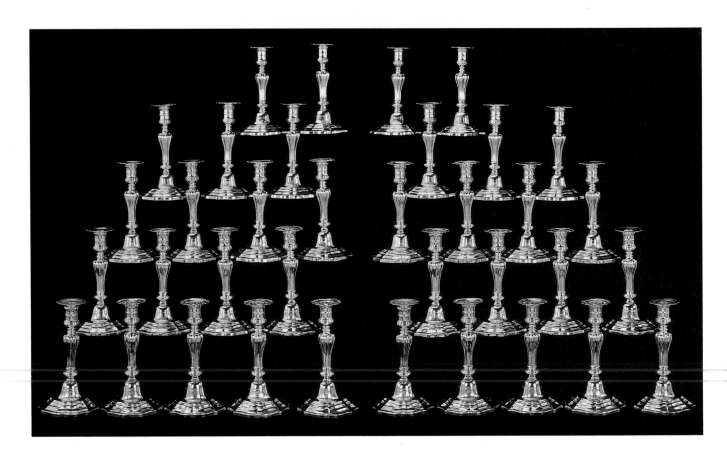

A German mother-of-pearl ewer with silver-gilt mounts

DIETERICH THOR MOYE, *c.*1640, HAMBURG, height 34cm (13⅜in)
Geneva SF366,500 (£161,400:$249,300). 24.V.93

The shape of this ewer derives from vessels produced in Persia and later during the Moghul Empire, whilst the mother-of-pearl decoration is of a type that found particular favour in Europe from the sixteenth century onwards. (RIGHT)

A Belgian silver-mounted Japanese porcelain coffeepot

MALINES, 1794, height 38.7cm (15⅛in)
New York $74,000 (£47,400). 23.IV.93

As the market for tea, coffee and chocolate expanded and prices fell during the eighteenth century, all three acquired great commercial and social importance.

This coffeepot is made of a combination of early eighteenth-century Japanese Imari porcelain mounted with Malines silver. (BELOW)

Four George II silver-gilt salvers
DAVID WILLAUME II, 1743, LONDON, diameters 34, 28.2 and 37.4cm
(13⅜, 11⅛ and 14¾in) New York $307,450 (£195,800). 28.X.92
These four salvers were made for George Booth, 2nd Earl of
Warrington (1675-1758), a renowned collector of English
silver. He started accumulating plate after his father's death,
when he inherited the family seat, Dunham Massey in
Cheshire, as well as debts amounting to some £50,000. He
worked conscientiously to discharge this huge sum but
ultimately had to resort to marrying the daughter of a
wealthy London merchant. (ABOVE)

One of a pair of French wine coolers
ROBERT-JOSEPH AUGUSTE, 1766-67, PARIS, height 23.5cm (9¼in)
London £254,500 ($381,700) for the pair. 10.VI.93
From the Harcourt Collection.
These wine coolers appear to be one of the earliest examples
of a design which Auguste continued to use, with minor
variations, for more than a decade. He enjoyed an
international reputation and supplied silver to various
European courts, including a service made between 1776 and
1785 for George III as Elector of Hanover. (LEFT)

A George II waiter
PETER ARCHAMBO, 1728, LONDON, width 15.2cm (6in)
New York $55,200 (£35,300). 23.IV.93
This waiter is decorated with a border of latticework
interspersed with cartouches in what is known as the
'Hogarthian' manner. In 1727 the famous Huguenot
silversmith Paul de Lamerie supplied a salver to
Sir Robert Walpole which he had had engraved by
the artist William Hogarth. The design was well
received and came to be frequently imitated, with
minor variations, by many English engravers. The
original Walpole Salver is now in the Victoria and
Albert Museum, London. (ABOVE)

A George II cake basket
JOHN PERO, 1735, LONDON, length 32.5cm (12¾in)
London £139,000 ($208,500). 10.VI.93
Although few items have been recorded with his mark,
John Pero was clearly one of the most skilful of
London's early eighteenth-century silversmiths. This
fine, unusual piece with panels of trelliswork and
foliage bears the arms of Pàlffy von Erdöd of Hungary.
(RIGHT)

A pair of William and Mary 'ox-eye' drinking cups
MAKER'S MARK IA, 1691, LONDON, heights 10.5cm (4in) London £68,200 ($104,300). 26.XI.92
This unusual type of cup was made almost exclusively for the colleges of
Oxford University, although there is one particularly large example in the
collection of the Mercers' Company, London. The arms displayed on this pair
are those of Queen's College, Oxford. (ABOVE)

An American two-handled bowl

CORNELIUS VANDER BURGH, c.1690, NEW YORK, overall width 31cm (12¼in) New York $233,500 (£153,600). 28.I.93

The earliest New York silversmiths were originally Dutch and the forms of the objects they created tended to be those of their native country. Cornelius Vander Burgh was born in New York, in 1652, and is considered to be the city's first native silversmith. (RIGHT)

A set of four American table candlesticks

SAMUEL TINGLEY, c.1765, NEW YORK, heights 25.4cm (10in) New York $200,500 (£136,300). 23.VI.93 From the Collection of Gloria and Richard Manney.

The construction of this rare set of four candlesticks differs from that of their English prototypes in the use of a cruciform nut at the junction of the base and stem, the English equivalent usually being joined with solder only. (BELOW)

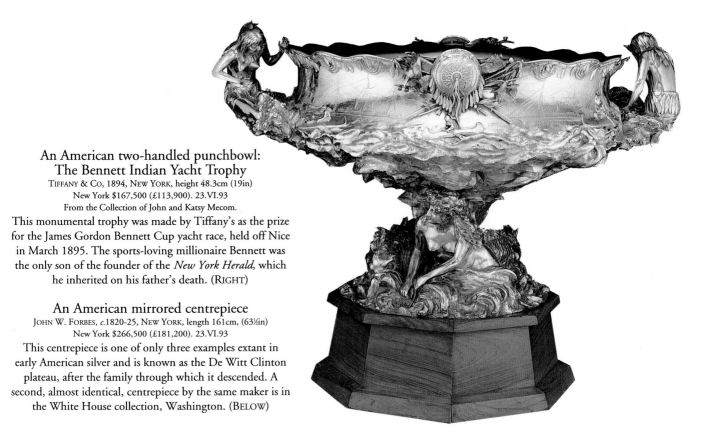

An American two-handled punchbowl: The Bennett Indian Yacht Trophy

TIFFANY & CO, 1894, NEW YORK, height 48.3cm (19in)
New York $167,500 (£113,900). 23.VI.93
From the Collection of John and Katsy Mecom.

This monumental trophy was made by Tiffany's as the prize
for the James Gordon Bennett Cup yacht race, held off Nice
in March 1895. The sports-loving millionaire Bennett was
the only son of the founder of the *New York Herald,* which
he inherited on his father's death. (RIGHT)

An American mirrored centrepiece

JOHN W. FORBES, *c.*1820-25, NEW YORK, length 161cm, (63½in)
New York $266,500 (£181,200). 23.VI.93

This centrepiece is one of only three examples extant in
early American silver and is known as the De Witt Clinton
plateau, after the family through which it descended. A
second, almost identical, centrepiece by the same maker is in
the White House collection, Washington. (BELOW)

Lou Gehrig-says...

Lou Gehrig-says...

Lou Gehrig-says...

Lou

BOB BOKEN — Lou Gehrig-says...

HAL TROSKY — Lou Gehrig-says...

FRED OSTERMUELLER — Lou Gehrig-says...

NAPOLEON

(RED) ROLFE — Lou Gehrig-says...

MYRIL HOAG — Lou Gehrig-says...

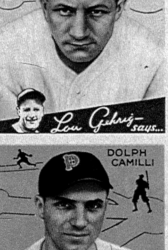
JIM DeSHONG — Lou Gehrig-says...

HOMER PEEL — "Chuck" Klein says...

LINUS FREY — "Chuck"

LLOYD JOHNSON — "Chuck" Klein says...

HAZEN (KI-KI) CUYLER — "Chuck" Klein says...

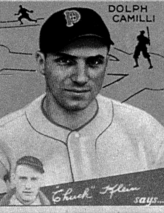
DOLPH CAMILLI — "Chuck" Klein says...

PAUL DERRINGER — "Chuck" Klein says...

"Chuck"

COMOROSKY

BILL HALLAHAN

MARTY McMANUS

GEORGE DARROW

COLLECTORS' CATEGORIES *by Hilary Kay*

Often decorative, sometimes technically sophisticated, generally of wide appeal to connoisseurs and amateurs alike, the fields included within the Collectors' Categories offer something for everyone. The 1991-92 season saw several world record prices in these categories and interest was so strong that it belied the economic recession that influenced other areas of the art market. The 1992–93 season saw a continuation of this trend.

Since 1989 Sotheby's has worked closely with the Walt Disney Company. This year we held an auction on their behalf of artwork from Beauty and the Beast. Located for the first time in Los Angeles, the sale was a tremendous success, with 100 per cent sold, realizing $1,141,650.

The film theme continued with the sale of the Stanley Caidin Collection of Hollywood movie posters, offered by Sotheby's New York in September. The result showed that, in this as yet immature market, the marketability of a poster is affected by the type of film, the fame of those appearing in it, and finally the poster's visual impact. All three factors were present in The Blue Angel, which made $27,500. The highest price was achieved by a poster for the controversial film Birth of a Nation ($49,500).

Sotheby's 1992 sale of Rock 'n' Roll Memorabilia in London was the most successful of its kind by any auction house in Europe, totalling £602,085. It featured a collection of Beatles' memorabilia from the estate of the late Mal Evans, who had been closely involved with the group from 1963 to 1970. The two highest prices achieved were £48,400 for John Lennon's autograph lyrics for A Day in the Life and £45,100 for Paul McCartney's autograph lyrics for She's Leaving Home. In the Collectors' Carousel auction in New York in June, the highlight was Dizzy Gillespie's trumpet which sold for $50,600.

**1934 Goudey
Uncut Sheet
with no. 106 Lajoie
(detail)**
SHEET OF 25 BASEBALL CARDS,
29.8 x 36.3cm (11¾ x 14¼in)
New York $74,000 (£49,300).
13.III.93 (LEFT)

**1946 Morris 8hp
Post Office
Telephone Van**
Falmouth £3,680 ($5,660).
3.V.93
From the Lamanva Collection
of Military, Commercial and
Action Vehicles. (BELOW)

Following the outstanding success of New York's inaugural sale of Sports Memorabilia in 1991, the subject has become a fixture in the auction almanac there. This season's sale included the last jersey worn by the baseball legend Mickey Mantle, which sold for $66,000.

In London, the buoyancy of the Collectables market continued this year with record prices achieved for a number of outstanding toys, dolls, automata and mechanical musical instruments. Two extremely rare 'H' pressed bisque dolls were sold in November, realizing £34,100 and £46,200, and a tinplate toy of a Russian carousel by the German company Märklin made a new world record for a European toy when it was bought for £62,000.

Auctions of instruments of science and technology held in London included a magnificent nineteenth-century microscope by Powell and Lealand which sold for £22,000, a world record price for such an instrument, while a Hahn-type mechanical equinoctial dial realized a remarkable £45,100.

Musical Instruments had some notable successes this season, with the added surprise of a saleroom duel over a violin bow by the French archetier Dominique Peccatte. Modestly estimated at £1,200 due to its various faults, it sold for £34,100. Stringed instruments by nineteenth-century Turin makers are now keenly sought after. For example, two violins by Giuseppe Rocca realized £99,000 and £78,500.

Analyses of trends in Arms and Armour revealed a transference of market strength towards continental Europe for pieces of non-British origin. In order to capitalize on this, arms and armour were sold in Zürich as well as London and New York. Highlights from Zürich included a French flintlock fowling-piece by Antoine Berthault of Paris, which was sold by private treaty to the Royal Armouries in London for SF201,960. In New York pieces such as a shanfron from 1550 and a burgonet from the 1540s were strongly in demand, realizing $36,800 and $41,400 respectively.

The Sporting Guns department held a series of highly successful sales this season with buoyant bidding in all categories. The demand is strong for high quality English guns, such as the set of three Boss & Co. 12-bore sidelock ejector guns which achieved £71,500.

A highlight this season for War Medals and Decorations was the record price set for a group of gallantry medals. This was the £132,000 paid for the VC, DSO and bar, and MC and bar awarded to Major 'Mick' Mannock, the most decorated and highest scoring British fighter pilot of the First World War.

A French flintlock
fowling-piece
BY ANTOINE BERTHAULT,
c.1670-80, PARIS,
length 117.8cm (46½in)
Zürich SF201,960
(£89,700:$137,300). 6.XI.92
From the Collection of Field
Marshal Sir Francis Festing.
(BELOW)

A German wheel-
lock sporting rifle
BY MARTIN KAMERR,
DATED 1658, AUGSBURG,
barrel length 79.4cm (31¼in)
New York $123,500 (£80,100).
24.V.93 (LEFT)

Celluloid from
Beauty and the Beast
WALT DISNEY, 1991,
29.2 x 68.5cm (11½ x 27in)
Los Angeles $18,700 (£12,300).
17.X.92 (ABOVE)

The postage stamp market was strong but selective this season, with buyers paying record prices for items and collections fresh to the market. An auction devoted to the Italian States saw a veritable invasion of Italian dealers and collectors and resulted in a 100 per cent sale, the highest price being £66,000 for the 'Borgotaro' cover. In another sale a collection from India was secured for £33,000 by a newcomer bidding over the telephone from his private jet.

The season has seen a considerable growth in coin sales with increased liaison between our London and New York departments. The sale of the 'Uruguayan Treasure of the River Plate', catalogued in London and offered in New York in March, was the largest single auction for years of gold coins, ingots and artifacts recovered from a shipwreck. The final aggregate total of $3,192,000 exceeded the sale's top estimate, with just 0.6 per cent unsold.

The Veteran, Vintage and Classic Car department saw the market poised for recovery after a period of depression. A private collection of Ferraris and Maseratis reached an international market in Zürich, with an ex-Edsel Ford GT40 sports/competition car realizing SF470,350. In Britain an ERA single-seater racing car, one of only twenty models produced, sold for £243,500.

The Wine department's tradition of selling wines from the cellars of top classified Bordeaux growths included a collection of the great classified St Julien, Château Gruaud Larose. Part of the private reserves from Château Pichon Longueville was also sold. Spanning vintages from 1908 to 1981 this section of the auction was a great success with every lot finding a buyer.

This season was another marked success for most of the Collectors' departments and, with an anticipated improvement in the world economy over the coming months, Sotheby's looks forward to further achievements within the Collectors' Categories next season.

John Lennon's
handwritten lyrics
for *A Day in the Life*
1967, BLACK FELT-TIP AND
BLUE BALLPOINT PENS,
27 x 19.5cm (10½ x 7⅝in)
London £48,400 ($75,500).
27.VIII.92 (ABOVE)

POSTAGE STAMPS

New Zealand
1906 Christchurch
1d. claret
IN HORIZONTAL
INTERPANNEAU PAIR
London £10,450 ($19,850).
10.IX.92

Produced for the 1906 Christchurch Exhibition, this pair was printed in claret rather than the vermilion which was considered a more suitable colour for the issued stamp. Most recorded examples of the 'unissued' claret shade were either sold at the Exhibition Post Office or included in Post Office presentation books. (BELOW RIGHT)

New Zealand
1915-29 6d.
carmine
'IMPERFORATE THREE SIDES'
HORIZONTAL, MARGINAL BLOCK
OF THIRTY-SIX STAMPS (DETAIL)
London £5,175 ($7,610).
26.III.93

In *The Postage Stamps of New Zealand* it is recorded that four sheets containing this variety were issued in January 1928 at the Chief Post Office in Wellington. Thus, of the forty-eight possible examples of this variety in existence, one quarter are encompassed in this block, making it probably the most important piece of the George V recess-printed series. (RIGHT)

Great Britain
1910 2d. Tyrian Plum
London £4,370 ($6,420). 26.III.93

Very few examples of the Tyrian Plum survived the destruction of the stock of sheets occasioned by the death of Edward VII on 6 May 1910. None was officially issued and this single specimen only recently came to light when a general collector saw the stamp fall out of an envelope he had just thrown on his sitting-room fire. (LEFT)

Sweden
1918 55ö light blue and 80ö black
INCLUDED IN A PRESENTATION BOOK FROM THE SWEDISH DIRECTOR
GENERAL OF POSTS London £3,740 ($7,110). 10.IX.92

The issue of 50ö and 80ö adhesives had been announced on 27 June 1918, but by 2 July it had been decided not to proceed with it. Värnamo Post Office had been sent a small supply, which was soon withdrawn, and some examples later appeared in Post Office presentation books. (LEFT)

Italy (Parma)
1859 Provisional Government 5c. verde giallo
THE BORGOTARO COVER
London £66,000 ($102,100). 4.XI.92
The stamps on this famous 1860 Borgotaro to Piacenza cover, with its unique horizontal strip of four of the 1859 Provisional Government 5c. verde giallo, were in use only between 9 June 1859 and 18 March 1860. The cover, from the collection of Maurice Burrus, is illustrated in colour in the Sassone handbook catalogue and is generally considered to be one of the most desirable items of Italian philately. (LEFT)

India
FROM A COLLECTION IN THREE OLD SCOTT SPRINGBACK ALBUMS
London £33,000 ($62,700). 10.IX.92
This selection of stamps from an exceptional collection was offered for sale intact, in three albums. Comprehensive, specialized ranges from 1817 to 1933 were included with essays, proofs, specimens, postal history and issued stamps, the last featuring one of India's rarest stamps, which appeared in 1926 with the head of George VI omitted. (ABOVE)

COINS AND MEDALS

Cob type 4 escudos
FROM THE URUGUAYAN TREASURE OF THE
RIVER PLATE, LIMA, 1750
New York $19,800 (£13,600). 24.III.93
'Cob money' is a generic term
for hand-made Spanish-
American coins, usually of crude
style. This coin is remarkable in
that one side is struck from a die
intended for the smaller
2 escudos coin.(RIGHT)

Silver medal of Doge Marcantonio Memmo of Venice
BY GUILLAUME DUPRÉ, SIGNED AND DATED *1612*
London £15,950 ($23,610). 12.VII.93
A superbly-finished original cast, this medal was executed at a
time when the French medallist and sculptor Dupré was
employed in Italy. (LEFT)

The wooden model for a medal portraying an unknown man
BY FRIEDRICH HAGENAUER, *c.*1520
London £15,840 ($23,440). 12.VII.93
An original model sculpted by the medallist Hagenauer and believed
to be one of his earliest works. (BELOW)

Bronze medal of Georg Volckhamer of Nuremberg, aged 24
BY HANS SCHWARZ, 1521
London £13,200 ($19,540). 12.VII.93
Active for only a few years around
1520, Schwarz stands out from
his German Renaissance
contemporaries for his vigorous,
individual style. This example is
only the second recorded
specimen of the medal, the other
being in Berlin where an original
drawing also survives. (LEFT)

Gold coins, ingots and artifacts from
the Uruguayan Treasure of the River Plate
SPANISH-AMERICAN, 1741–51
New York sale total $3,123,945 (£2,155,445). 24.III.93
Recovered in 1992 from the River Plate near Montevideo, the 'Uruguayan Treasure'
is believed to represent the contraband cargo of a Spanish-registered Portuguese vessel
wrecked by a violent storm in 1752. The river's notorious mud has preserved most of
the material in remarkably good condition. (ABOVE)

United States Gold Double-Eagle	Australian Silver Threepence, or 'joey'	United States Gold Stella

**United States
Gold Double-Eagle**

'EXTREMELY HIGH RELIEF' TYPE,
1907 New York $143,000
(£89,400). 9.XII.92

Research into the surface
and edge details of this
recently-discovered coin
suggest that it is a proto-
type for the celebrated
double-eagle, or $20 piece,
designed by Augustus
Saint-Gaudens. It is a
unique variety. (ABOVE)

**Australian
Silver Threepence,
or 'joey'**

OF GEORGE VI, 1937
London £18,700 ($31,600). 8.X.92

Probably the only
Australian threepence dated
1937 in private hands, this
well-used example was
recovered from loose
change in Tasmania in
1966. (LEFT)

**United States
Gold Stella**

FLOWING HAIR TYPE, 1879
New York $40,700 (£26,600).
10.VI.93

The concept of the Stella
was an unsuccessful
attempt by the United
States to issue a coin
valued at 4 dollars which
would be consistent with
the standard then in use
in Europe. (LEFT)

MUSICAL INSTRUMENTS

Violin by Giovanni Francesco Pressenda
1833, TURIN, length of back 35.6cm (14in)
London £74,800 ($114,400). 5.XI.92
Pressenda, Rocca's master (see right), was an inheritor of the
Cremonese tradition of violin making, and had studied under the
great Lorenzo Storioni. This instrument was offered at auction
completely unaltered, bearing its original contemporary fittings.
(ABOVE)

Violin after Stradivari by Giuseppe Rocca
1852, TURIN, length of back 35.6cm (14in)
London £99,000 ($151,470). 5.XI.92
The model for this instrument, as for many of Rocca's violins, was
'The Messiah' Stradivari of 1716, which Rocca would have had access
to by virtue of his acquaintance with the collector Tarisio. This
instrument was offered at auction unaltered since its production.
(ABOVE)

Chamber organ by Hugh Russell

*c.*1790, LONDON,
height 246.5cm (101in)
London £13,750 ($21,040).
26.XI.92

This chamber organ was made shortly after Russell's partnership with John England dissolved in around 1784, although a plaque above the keyboard reads *Hugh Russell London 1780.* The mahogany case contains gilded display pipes with very fine floral painted decoration.
(RIGHT)

Violin by Romeo Antoniazzi

1907, CREMONA,
length of back 35.7cm (14�16in)
London £20,700 ($30,845).
1.VII.93

The market for modern violins of quality, such as this Italian example from 1907, has been seeing particular growth of late, and the names of the makers of the first years of the twentieth century may soon be as widely-known as their earlier forerunners.
(FAR RIGHT)

Concert guitar by Francisco Simplico

1927, BARCELONA,
length 48.5cm (19⅛in)
London £9,350 ($14,300).
26.XI.92

Made to order for Maria Angelica Pedreira de Cerqueira, a pupil of Oswaldo Soares, this instrument was used by her in notable concerts in the Instituto Nacional de Musica in Rio de Janeiro (9 April 1929) and the Theatro Polythema in Salvador (20 September 1932). (RIGHT)

ARMS AND ARMOUR

An ivory powder flask
NUREMBERG OR VIENNA, LATE SIXTEENTH/EARLY SEVENTEENTH
CENTURY, 15.6cm (6⅛in)
New York $46,000 (£29,800). 24.V.93
Powder for charging a firearm was carried in a flask
suspended from the belt. This fine example, which is
engraved in the manner of Paul Flindt and retains an
early suspension cord of bullion thread, would have
been purely decorative, as flasks for use on the
battlefield had to be made of more durable
materials than ivory. (ABOVE)

A Swiss suit of half armour
c.1600 Zürich SF39,550 (£17,900:$27,600). 6.XI.92
During the sixteenth century major advances were made in the development of
firearms. This had important implications for armour design, and mobility started to
become a greater priority than direct bodily protection. (ABOVE)

A French over-and-under single-trigger carbine
DATED 1836 Zürich SF90,400 (£41,000:$63,200). 6.XI.92
This rare carbine was made for the Duc d'Orléans by Le Page and is decorated on the
butt with the Duc's monogram. It is unfired and in pristine condition throughout,
revealing that it was only ever intended for ceremonial and display purposes. (BELOW)

SPORTING GUNS

A matched set of three 12-bore single-trigger sidelock
ejector over-and-under guns by Boss & Co.
Gleneagles £71,500 ($141,600). 31.VIII.92

Boss & Co. was founded in 1812 by Thomas Boss, and the first
premises were at 73 St James's Street, London. During the 1890s the
firm was run by John Robertson, whose reputation was already
well-established as the inventor of a reliable single-trigger mechanism.
Gun numbers 7261 and 7262 in this example of Boss craftsmanship
were built as a pair in 1926, whilst number 7256 was ordered in 1927
to match the others and complete a set of three. (BELOW)

A 20-bore double-barrelled flintlock gun with
side-by-side twist barrels by Ezekiel Baker
INSCRIBED *Gunmaker to His Royal Highness The Prince of Wales*
London £14,000 ($21,800). 15.IV.93

At the end of the eighteenth century the Prince of Wales (the future
George IV) showed great interest in the work of Ezekiel Baker, one of
London's leading gunmakers, from whom he purchased several guns.
This example was given by the Prince to a close friend in 1806. (TOP)

A 16-bore/.577 four-barrelled 1884 patent
Hammer 'Cape' Rifle by Charles Lancaster
London £15,000 ($23,400). 15.IV.93

This rifle was built in 1883 and retained by the maker, presumably in
order to demonstrate his particular skills to prospective customers.
The rifle's four barrels make this a particularly rare piece. (ABOVE)

WAR MEDALS AND DECORATIONS

Russian Order of St Catherine
UNMARKED, c.1890
Geneva SF55,000 (£24,200:$37,400). 19.XI.92
The order of Saint Catherine was founded in 1714 by
Peter the Great in honour of his wife, Catherine
Alekseyevna. It came in two classes and was awarded
only to women of the highest nobility. (ABOVE)

The First World War V.C., D.S.O. and two bars, M.C. and bar
awarded to Major E. 'Mick' Mannock of the Royal Air Force
Billingshurst £132,000 ($232,300). 19.IX.92
Edward 'Mick' Mannock was the highest scoring and most decorated British pilot of
the First World War. He was finally shot down over France in 1918, and while it was
assumed at the time that his body was consumed by the flames that engulfed his
aircraft, it was later discovered that he had been buried by an unknown German
soldier, who returned his identity discs, notebook and other personal effects to the
British authorities at the end of the War. (ABOVE)

WINE

A selection of classic Champagne,
Burgundy and Bordeaux
Left to right:
A jeroboam of Louis Roederer Cristal Brut 1985
£374 ($583)
A bottle of Romanée Conti 1964
£418 ($652)
A double magnum of Château Lafite 1970
£297 ($463)
All London 21.IV.93
(ABOVE)

An historic collection of Krug Collection Champagnes
direct from the Krug cellars in Reims
Left to right:
A magnum of Krug Collection 1964
£396 ($594)
A magnum of Krug Collection 1947
£616 ($924)
A magnum of Krug Collection 1938
£660 ($990)
A magnum of Krug Collection 1953
£605 ($907)
A bottle of Krug Collection 1929
£396 ($594)
A magnum of Krug Collection 1973
£352 ($528)
All London 9.VI.93 (ABOVE)

VETERAN, VINTAGE AND CLASSIC CARS

1914 Hispano-Suiza 8/10hp four-seater open tourer
Hendon £33,350 ($51,300).
22.V.93
The name Hispano-Suiza usually summons up images of the six- and twelve-cylinder luxury cars which provided competition for Rolls-Royce and other bespoke makers. However, the company did manufacture a number of smaller models prior to the First World War. (RIGHT)

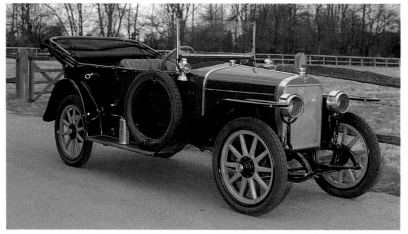

1934 ERA R1A single-seater racing car
Hendon £243,500 ($353,000).
20.II.93
The setting up of English Racing Automobiles in 1933 heralded the start of a new chapter in British motor racing history. The company aimed to produce a car that was sufficiently versatile for road or circuit racing, sprints and hill climbs. The first car to carry the ERA name was R1A, shown here. (RIGHT)

1926 Rolls-Royce 20hp three-quarter drophead coupé
Hendon £36,300 ($71,800).
5.IX.92
Introduced in 1922, the 'Twenty' was the first entirely new Rolls-Royce model since the 40/50hp Silver Ghost of 1906. This model was for some time displayed at the Science Museum, London. (RIGHT)

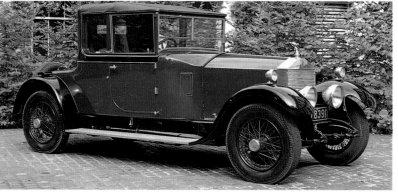

1958 BMW 507 V8 sports two-seater
Zürich SF244,300 (£108,600: $166,200). 8.III.93
The Bayerische Motoren-Werke began by building aircraft engines in 1916. Car production started in the 1930s. In 1955 Count Albrecht Goertz was recruited to style a sports car for the US market. The result was the 507. (RIGHT)

1929 Bentley 4½ litre Vanden Plas Tourer
Hendon £112,750 ($223,200).
5.IX.92
The 4½ litre Bentley was introduced in 1927. One of the most popular of body styles was the fabric-bodied Vanden Plas Tourer. This particular example was supplied new to Major E. G. Thompson and passed shortly afterwards to John C. Sword. (RIGHT)

COLLECTORS' SALES

A French *chrono-photographe* cine-matographic camera
*c.*1899, GAUMONT DEMENY
London £7,475 ($11,500).
2.VI.93
In 1896 Léon Gaumont, one of the pioneers of synchronized sound and image, asked Georges Demeny to redesign the projector he had patent-ed in 1893 to accom-modate perforated film. The result was the *chronophotographe* cinematographic camera: a major breakthrough in film projection technology. (LEFT)

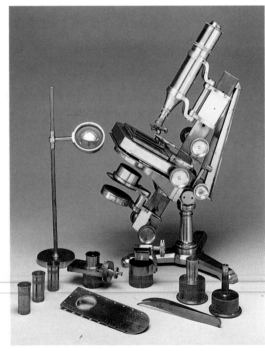

An English brass compound monocular microscope
POWELL AND LEALAND,
SIGNED AND DATED *1842*
London £22,000 ($38,000).
1.X.92
This massive microscope is signed *Powell and Lealand,* who are recorded as having worked from 24 Clarendon Street, London, between 1842 and 1846. (LEFT)

A Hahn-type gilt and silvered-brass
mechanical equinoctial dial
*c.*1805, PROBABLY SWEDISH
London £45,100 ($70,800). 1.X.92
The equinoctial dial was used to check the accuracy of clock and watch movements. This gilt and silvered-brass example is signed *F. J. Sauter,* who in 1808 is recorded as being a clockmaker working in Stockholm.
(ABOVE)

A German 'Russian' carousel

MARKLIN, c.1904, height 52.5 cm (20⅝in)
London £62,000 ($94,200). 10.II.93

This extraordinarily elaborate toy is made from hand-painted tinplate and incorporates a cylinder musical accompaniment. It was manufactured by the German firm of Marklin, one of the foremost producers of tinplate toys at the beginning of the century. A very similar toy is shown in the 1904 Marklin Hauptkatalog as item 1123. (ABOVE)

A French musical automaton

ROULLET ET DECAMPS, c.1910, height 104cm (41in)
London £67,500 ($101,200). 18.V.93

The mask-seller depicted by this rare papier-mâché automaton holds four articulated masks in his left hand and an inactive mask in his right. A sixth mask, which sticks out its tongue, appears on the sole of the clown's right foot, revealed as he lifts his leg. In addition, he lifts a mask to his face while the masks in his left hand raise their eyebrows and moustaches, stick out their tongues, look upwards or move their eyes from side to side. A devil mask, suspended over the figure's standing foot, also sticks out his tongue and closes his eyes. (LEFT)

A French bisque H-pressed doll
*c.*1880, height 46cm (18in)
London £34,100 ($52,100). 10.XI.92
A French bisque H-pressed doll
*c.*1880, height 38cm (15in)
London £46,200 ($70,600). 10.XI.92
Doll manufacture was established in Europe as an
industry at the beginning of the nineteenth century.
Early examples tended to be made of carved or turned
wood, but later on in the century ceramics were used,
as with these French bisque examples dating from
around 1880. (ABOVE AND ABOVE RIGHT)

An American cast-iron pull-along toy
*c.*1885, length 26.7cm (10½in)
New York $6,900 (£4,600). 23.VI.93
Although the American Civil War curtailed the supply of metal for non-military use,
demand was stimulated when firms returned to peacetime production. Throughout
the nineteenth century American toys were modelled closely on European imports
but from 1860 onwards the toy industry began to make a bid for overseas markets.
This 'swan chariot' dates from a little after that period.
(ABOVE)

Dizzy Gillespie's trumpet
MANUFACTURED BY KING MUSICAL INSTRUMENTS
New York $50,600 (£33,700). 23.VI.93

This trumpet was consigned with a letter of authenticity from the legendary jazz musician. Gillespie's bent trumpet was one of his hallmarks. It began as a mistake (he dropped one of his instruments) but when he heard the sound the 'mistake' produced, he decided to stick with it. The keys are finished in mother-of-pearl and the rim of the horn is inscribed *Dizzy*. (BELOW)

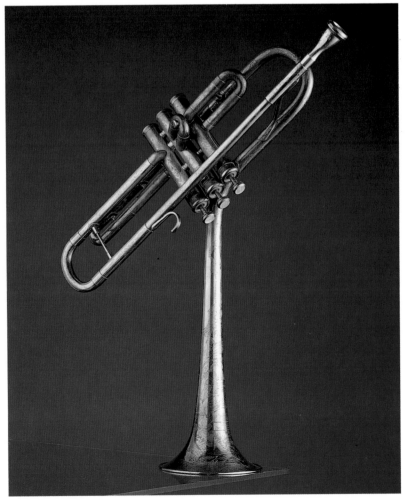

Judy Garland's dress from *The Wizard of Oz*
New York $48,400 (£30,800). 18.XII.92

What must be one of the most famous films of all time, MGM's 1939 *The Wizard of Oz* broke all box office records on its release and still remains extremely popular. This blue and white gingham pinafore is undoubtedly one of the trademarks of that film, and bears Garland's name on a label. (ABOVE)

Action Comics No. 1
comic book
JUNE 1938, PUBLISHED BY D. C. COMICS
New York $82,500 (£53,900). 30.IX.92
This completely unrestored copy of
Action Comics' number one issue
features the first appearance of
Jerry Siegel and Joe Schuster's
legendary Superman, the latter
arguably the most imitated cartoon
creation of all time. Historically,
this makes it the most important
comic book ever printed and its
appearance on the commercial
market can be considered a rare
event by any collecting standard.
(RIGHT)

CARL BARKS
Hands Off My Playthings
OIL ON MASONITE, 39.4 x 49.5cm
(15½ x 19½in)
New York $112,500 (£75,000). 26.VI.93
This was the 106th painting
completed by Carl Barks
illustrating one of Walt Disney's
most famous cartoon characters.
Here Uncle Scrooge is shown
entering his money store and
catching Donald Duck and his
nephews playing with the treasure.
(BELOW)

The Birth of a Nation poster
1916, EPOCH, 104 x 68.6cm (41 x 27in)
New York $49,500 (£31,700). 12.IX.92
From the Stanley Caidin Collection.

D. W. Griffith's 1915 work *The Birth of a Nation* is a significant landmark in the history of world cinema, and can be considered the first example of the 'epic' film, engendering a long-lasting cinematic tradition. Set in South Carolina immediately after the American Civil War, the story centres on the problems of the dispossessed white population which spawned the Ku Klux Klan. (RIGHT)

Celluloid from Snow White and the Seven Dwarfs
1937, WALT DISNEY, 33 x 40.6cm (13 x 16in)
New York $34,100 (£21,700). 19.XII.92

Snow White and the Seven Dwarfs, which was premiered in 1937, was not only Walt Disney's first feature-length cartoon but also the first to be produced in the United States. In 1938 it won a special Academy Award for pioneering animation and significant screen innovation. Half a century later it remains firmly established as a classic. (BELOW)

COLLECTIONS OF THE SEASON *by Ronald Varney*

In June and July of 1984, Sotheby's London conducted a three-part sale of paintings and works of art from the collections of the late Lord Clark of Saltwood, whose grand career in the world of arts and letters might be summarized by two particular achievements: being appointed Director of the National Gallery at the age of twenty-nine and, in later life, writing and fronting a hugely popular television series for the BBC entitled *Civilisation*.

It was perhaps no surprise that the collections he assembled over the course of his eighty years were refined and wide-ranging. Visitors to the Bond Street exhibitions in that summer of 1984 viewed civilization through the prism of Lord Clark's extraordinary possessions: there were Japanese prints and European ceramics, French nineteenth-century paintings and drawings, antiquities, Old Master paintings and drawings, Chinese vases and censers, Impressionist and Modern sculpture, and pieces of tribal art. A large group of Medieval and Renaissance miniatures, which had previously been assembled into a red morocco album by the renowned Scottish antiquary James Dennistoun, and which Clark bought around 1930, formed the core of the collection. Among the many British paintings and drawings was one of J. M. W. Turner's last great sea pictures, *Seascape: Folkstone*, which sold for £7,370,000, breaking the world record for a painting. Interestingly, it had been Clark himself who had discovered the last cache of neglected Turners in the vaults of the National Gallery in 1939, 'some 20 rolls of canvas, thick with dirt, which I took to be old tarpaulins'.

ANDERS ZORN
Portrait of Maud Cassel, Aged Seven
SIGNED AND DATED *87*, WATERCOLOUR, 99 x 59cm (39 x 23¼in)
London £99,000 ($150,400). 25.XI.92
From the Estate of the Rt Hon the Earl Mountbatten of Burma. (LEFT)

As if trying to comprehend his own lifelong passion for art, Clark once wrote, 'Why do men and women collect? As well ask why they fall in love: the reasons are as irrational, the motives as mixed, the original impulse as often discoloured or betrayed. The collector's instinct, if animals and children are any guide, has two roots; the desire to pick up anything bright and shining and the desire to complete a series.'

In reviewing the collections offered at Sotheby's during the 1992-3 season, one would have to say that the collecting instinct – whether one agrees with Lord Clark's analysis or not – is to be found at work in a most amazing diversity of collecting fields. Some of the more intriguing areas represented at Sotheby's this past season were: Melanesian art (the Peter Hallinan Collection), Hollywood posters (the Stanley Caidin Collection), postage stamps of the Italian states, Japanese prints of the Kabuki theatre (the Kühne Collection), Ruskin pottery (the Adam Ferneyhough Collection), military vehicles (the Lamanva Collection), tea caddies, Scandinavian furniture (the Bronson Pinchot Collection), metalware (the Robert M. Holland-Martin Collection) and lustreware.

To give one a sense of the importance of many of the less-heralded collections offered during the season, there was the Cavanagh Collection, sold in London in May and comprising major works on the theatre in Western Europe, Russia, Asia and the United States. It included many books, pamphlets, prints, drawings and paintings, all evoking the colour and character of the dramatic arts through the ages. Biographies and memoirs of such theatre luminaries as Garrick, Sheridan and Kean were complemented by mezzotint portraits of early English actors and actresses, stirring histories of such major theatres as La Scala in Milan, and many volumes of late eighteenth-century plates portraying costumes from the world of Parisian theatre. This treasure trove, formed over a period of fifty years, was the best collection of its kind ever to appear at auction.

Many of the collections offered at Sotheby's during the season were similarly rare and distinctive. In reviewing the highlights, one hears Lord Clark's voice as he describes the finest

JAMES MILLER
Selections from a sketchbook of drawings of London and the Upper Thames
WATERCOLOUR OVER PENCIL, each opening
20 x 32cm (7¾ x 12½in) London £24,200
($37,000). 19.XI.92 From the collection of the
late Dudley Snelgrove. (LEFT)

collectors as those who 'look at their possessions with the feelings of an artist and relive, to some extent, the sensuous and imaginative experiences which lie behind each work.'

In the centre of Verona, with its palaces of 'glowing orange and pale warm red', as Ruskin described them, lies the Palazzo Barocco, which dates back to the medieval age. The present owners of the Palazzo Barocco had, over many years, furnished it with paintings, furniture and works of art from the surrounding area of the Veneto. In late October 1992 at the Hotel Due Torri in Verona, Sotheby's offered the contents of the palazzo, as well as furniture and decorations from two villas of a noble Lombard family. The sale offered some magnificent early-eighteenth century furniture from the series of rooms that form the *piano nobile* of the Palazzo Barocco, as well as four chairs richly carved in the manner of Andrea Brustolon, one of the finest Venetian craftsmen of the period.

Two exceptional collections of twentieth-century decorative arts were offered in New York in the autumn, beginning in October with the John and Katsy Mecom Collection of European and American Art Nouveau, with its prodigious quantity of fine Tiffany glass; and the twentieth-century design collection of Barry Friedman, a New York dealer. This latter collection, which included sleek Modernist works by such designers as Marcel Breuer, René Crevel, Gerrit Rietveld and Carlo Bugatti, yielded two new auction records: $101,750 for a René Crevel Art Deco wool carpet, and $187,000 for a Hector Guimard mahogany, gilt-bronze and glass two-tier tea table, the latter a beautifully sinuous piece.

'People! Drama! Romance! What more could you want?' While these words were once used by Harry Winston to describe his own career, they might equally apply to two prominent jewellery collections offered early in the season – one of which was the collection of the late Mrs Harry Winston. Amongst the major innovators in twentieth-century jewellery design, Harry Winston included among his clients some of the most powerful and famous people in the world. One of the most dazzling of these was the Duchess of Windsor, who purchased a number of major

The Kid
FIRST NATIONAL ATTRACTION,
1921, ONE-SHEET,
104 x 68.6cm (41 x 27in)
New York $27,500 (£14,200).
12.IX.92
From the Stanley Caidin
Collection of Hollywood
Movie Posters. (LEFT)

pieces from Harry Winston which were eventually offered in the historic 1987 sale of her collection at Sotheby's in Geneva. Over one hundred pieces were included in the 1992 sale of Mrs Winston's collection, and nearly half of these had been made especially for her by her husband. This exciting auction filled the New York saleroom, and the feverish bidding in some cases drove prices to two or three times their estimate. The star lot, a spectacular pair of diamond chandelier pendant-earrings by Harry Winston, made in 1961, brought $1,430,000. The sale total of $5.1 million was well above expectations, showing once more how a famed collection can seize the public's attention.

This was again the case on the evening of 17 November 1992 at the Hôtel des Bergues in Geneva when silver, jewellery and objects of vertu from the Thurn und Taxis Collections were auctioned. The princely family of Thurn und Taxis has played a central role in the history of Europe since the days of the Holy Roman Empire, and the sale of property from their vast

THOMAS MORAN
Castle Butte, Green
River, Wyoming
SIGNED AND DATED *1900*,
WATERCOLOUR ON PAPER,
50.2 x 39.4cm (19¾ x 15½in)
New York $264,000
(£169,200). 3.XII.92
From the Transco Energy
Company collection of
American watercolours.
(ABOVE)

collections stirred the world's media into a cyclone of print, radio and television coverage. Certainly, there was a grand, sweeping story to relate behind the collections: the founding of the family fortune by Franz von Taxis (1459-1517) who established the first postal service between Brussels and Vienna; the rapid spread of this postal system, and the family's influence, throughout Europe; the establishment in 1748 of the family's principal residence in Regensburg, northern Bavaria; the move in 1812 to the nearby monastery of St Emmeram, a sprawling complex of medieval buildings; and the death of Prince Johannes, 11th Prince of Thurn und Taxis, in 1990, leading to the auction of selected items

from the family collections. These comprised around 150 lots of jewellery dating from the eighteenth to the twentieth century, highlighted by the magnificent pearl and diamond tiara commissioned by Napoleon III on the occasion of his marriage to Princess Eugénie in 1853. There were also about fifty exquisite snuff boxes, many from the finest eighteenth-century Paris goldsmiths, and an extensive collection of breathtaking table silver, mainly from Augsburg.

The auction in Geneva, in a packed saleroom that evoked the glamour and drama of the Windsor sale, yielded a total of SF19.6 million, with nearly every lot sold. The highest price in the sale, SF2,530,000, was paid for a jewelled gold and hardstone snuff box made for Frederick the Great of Prussia in 1770, breaking the previous world auction record set at Sotheby's Geneva in 1989 by a snuff box of Catherine the Great. The 'Eugénie Tiara' was acquired by Le Société des Amis du Louvre and will be exhibited with other French crown jewels at that museum.

The radiance of the Thurn und Taxis sale seemed to cast itself over a host of other auctions that took place in the late autumn and early winter, lending an air of hopeful expectation. This was quickly borne out with the sale of paintings from the collection of designer Mollie Parnis Livingston in New York in November, when for the first time in two years the $10 million level was exceeded in the Impressionist and Modern market. The painting that earned this distinction was Henri Matisse's 1946 oil, *L'Asie*, which came to Sotheby's York Avenue saleroom from the Museum of Modern Art in New York, where it was displayed in the landmark Matisse retrospective exhibition. The Kimbell Art Foundation in Texas paid $11 million for the painting, which was returned to the Museum of Modern Art for the duration of the exhibition. The Mollie Parnis Livingston Collection also included a number of important paintings by Vuillard and Picasso, as well as furniture and decorations from her Park Avenue apartment.

The Wright Ludington Collection also offered a Matisse from the Museum of Modern Art show, *La Plage Rouge*, painted in 1905, as well as works by Bonnard and Vuillard. Wright

Bureau mécanique
BY JEAN-HENRI RIESENER AND
JACQUES-LAURENT COSSON,
ROSEWOOD, BURR WALNUT
AND MARQUETRY,
height 75cm (29½in)
Monaco FF4,440,000
(£505,000:$792,800). 4.XII.92
From the Estate of Mme
Hélène Beaumont. (ABOVE)

Ludington was an avid supporter of the Santa Barbara Museum of Art, which he had helped found. During his lifetime he donated more than 300 works of art to the institution, from Near Eastern bronzes and Roman ceramics to seminal works by such Modernists as Charles Sheeler, Marsden Hartley and Joseph Stella. Born to a family that traced its roots to the *Mayflower*, Ludington had begun collecting during the early 1920s with an inheritance from his mother, buying works by such emerging artists as Derain, Picasso and Braque. He bought *La Plage Rouge* for $3,000 from the Pierre Matisse Gallery in the 1940s, while an army lieutenant. At its sale on 10 November 1992 it fetched $1,375,000.

Other paintings highlights in the autumn included the sale of the Royal S. Marks Collection in New York, which comprised nineteen works by the Latin American artist Joaquin Torres-Garcia, all of which sold for a total of $1.9 million, and the sale of the Transco Energy Company Collection of American watercolours, also in New York, which offered exceptional works by Maurice Prendergast, Thomas Moran, Andrew Wyeth and Edward Hopper.

Also offered in London over the course of the season was the collection of the late Earl Mountbatten of Burma, former Viceroy of India. The collection included paintings, works of art, furniture, antiquities, silver and other items taken from the private apartments at Broadlands in Hampshire, where Lord Mountbatten lived from 1939 until his death in 1979. Among the superb paintings was the charming *Portrait of Maud Cassel, Aged Seven* by Anders Zorn and *An Iron Forge* by Joseph Wright of Derby, which had been bought direct from the artist by Henry, 2nd Viscount Palmerston, one of the former owners of the Broadlands estate who had assembled part of the collection. This masterpiece was sold privately to the Tate Gallery in London.

Two exquisite collections were offered back-to-back in Monaco in early December, both of which conjured up images of lavish living in the great houses of France. Hélène Beaumont was one of the *grandes dames* of the Côte d'Azur, a philanthropist who owned, and generously entertained in, one of the most beautiful villas of the Cap d'Antibes. In the great French furniture sales of the 1920s, notably the Anthony de Rothschild Collection sale at Aston Clinton, Buckinghamshire in 1923, Mme Beaumont acquired the finest pieces of French eighteenth-century furniture for her villa. Many of these pieces were offered for sale in Monaco. The highlights were a Louis XVI *bureau plat* by Weisweiler, which achieved FF8,436,000, a small Louis XV porcelain-mounted marquetry table attributed to RVLC (Roger Vandercruse Lacroix), which sold for FF6,438,000, and a very rare Louis XVI *bureau mécanique* by Riesener and Cosson, which made FF4,440,000. This stunning collection, the finest of its kind to appear during the season, totalled over FF30 million, with French buyers playing a particularly active part.

The next day at the Sporting d'Hiver in Monaco saw the auction of the Jourdan-Barry Collection of silver. Comprising 250 pieces of seventeenth- and eighteenth-century silver, including some extremely rare pieces which survived the melting of plate under Louis XIV and Louis XV and during the Revolution, the Jourdan-Barry Collection was the most important of its kind to appear at auction in over two decades. The collection was formed over several generations of the Jourdan-Barry family, and a sense of connoisseurship seems to have been passed from one generation to the next. On being asked his reasons for selling the collection, Pierre Jourdan-Barry, who began collecting in 1960, replied, 'Collecting, for me, is a journey of seeking and discovery, a solitary journey because the collector is alone in his madness.... I think I have completed my long adventure in the field of French silver. I have decided to separate myself from my treasured objects with the hope that their new owners will feel the same excitement in acquiring and delight in owning them as I did.'

The autumn season drew to a triumphant close with the sale in New York of the Norbert Schimmel Collection of antiquities. One of this century's pioneering collectors of ancient art, Schimmel spent over fifty years assembling a comprehensive group of ancient Near Eastern, Egyptian, Greek, Etruscan and Roman works of art in bronze, marble, gold, faïence, terracotta and other materials. In 1989 Schimmel gave 103 works to the Metropolitan Museum of Art in New York, and in 1990 further donations were made to the Israel Museum in Jerusalem and to the Arthur M. Sackler Museum at Harvard. The 128 pieces offered at Sotheby's represented the remainder of Schimmel's famed collection. Prices in general greatly exceeded expectations, as shown by the top lot, a blue faïence inlay head of a king or god, late-eighteenth/early-nineteenth Dynasty, which sold for $484,000, three times its high estimate. The stunning sale total, $4,221,250, was as much a reflection of the quality of the individual pieces as it was a tribute to a great

An Achaemenid mirror
BRONZE, *c.* FIRST HALF OF THE 5TH CENTURY BC, diameter 21.6cm (8½in) New York $159,500 (£101,500). 10.XII.92 From the collection of Norbert Schimmel. (LEFT)

collector who exemplified the concept of old-world connoisseurship.

Archibald Thorburn (1860-1935) is widely regarded as Britain's greatest wildlife artist, and a sale in March 1993 in London offered 119 works by the artist from the Thorburn Museum at Liskeard in Cornwall. As Simon Taylor, the expert in charge of the sale, explained, Thorburn has always had a devout group of buyers because of the exquisite clarity and rendering of movement in his paintings: 'There is an almost

CHINESE SCHOOL
One of the stages in the processing of tea, from one of two albums of gouaches
CHINA, *c.* 1790, large folio London £166,500 ($249,700). 2.IV.93 From the collection of Rudolf von Gutmann. (ABOVE)

PIERRE-AUGUSTE
RENOIR
Buste de jeune fille
SIGNED, OIL ON CANVAS,
34.5 x 29cm (13⅝ x 11⅜in)
London £705,500
($1,072,300). 22.VI.93
From the Collection of Mme
d'Alayer, née Marie-Louise
Durand-Ruel. (ABOVE)

classical sense of space and peace in even his most dramatic compositions. His Highlands are wild and remote.... His England is a land of small fields and dense oak woods, of hedge-rows dotted with wild flowers, of deep snow in winter and glowing days in summer.' The lyrical appeal of Thorburn's art proved irresistible at the March auction, where, amid a packed saleroom, every single lot was sold and the total soared above the high estimate. The top lot, Thorburn's 1913 watercolour *Swerving from the Guns – Red Grouse*, made £111,500, a world auction record for the artist. The enormous success of this sale ensured the survival of the Thorburn Museum.

One of the most striking and beautiful catalogues of the season was produced in London for the sale there in April of the collection of

books, drawings and prints formed by Rudolf von Gutmann (1880-1966). The von Gutmann family owned the largest ironworks in Austro-Hungary, and Rudolf's considerable means allowed him to pursue his interest in art with studies at the Albertina in Vienna, whose directors advised on his collection. While prints were his special passion, he furnished his family houses with tapestries, porcelain, silver, glass, bronzes and paintings. In May 1938, however, von Gutmann fled Austria for Czechoslovakia, abandoning his collections, and then emigrated to British Columbia, where he died in 1966.

The Austrian Bundesdenkmalamt catalogued his collections, some of which were stored in the Hallein salt mines near Salzburg and partially recovered after the War. The print collection, which had been designated for Hitler's proposed museum at Linz, was removed to Dresden and is now in the process of being recovered. The sale of more than 100 lots from this remarkable collection was highlighted by a group of some 200 watercolour drawings of the Vatican and the various insignia of the Pontificate which had first been assembled by the early eighteenth-century architect John Talman. The collection also contained such exotica as two albums of Chinese gouache paintings depicting, among other subjects, the cultivation and production of silk and the processing of tea, and an important group of mid-eighteenth-century French water-colour designs for ballet costumes. As the catalogue to this sale observed, Rudolf von Gutmann was 'survived by collections of remark-able breadth and depth as befits one of the last of a now vanished breed of wealthy polymath.'

The season drew to a close with the sale of a number of distinguished collections in a delight-fully diverse range of collecting fields, with several achieving outstanding results. For example, the Field Marshal Sir Francis Festing Collection of Japanese Swords, which was offered in London, totalled £754,300, well above the high estimate, setting a world record of £265,500 for a sword, with a piece by Yamaura Masayuki. In New York, the Otto Kallir Collection of Aviation History, the most extensive and comprehensive collection of its kind to be sold in decades, achieved

$1,014,000, with 99 per cent of the lots sold; and the Joseph M. Meraux Collection of rare and unusual clocks, an immense assemblage of largely nineteenth-century clocks taken from the New Orleans home of a lifelong enthusiast in this field, was wildly successful, setting several records and achieving $2,738,672, with an astonishing 100 per cent of the 500 lots sold.

One of the joys of perusing a single-owner catalogue lies in reading the preface. In the brief space of a page or two, these passages often provide a wealth of biographical information on the collector, how the collection was formed, its highlights and historical resonances and the like. One of the most memorable such essays this season appeared in the catalogue for the sale in late June in London of Impressionist paintings, drawings and sculpture from the Collection of Madame d'Alayer, née Marie Durand-Ruel. Of course the name Durand-Ruel needs no introduction in the Impressionist field, and yet the story of how Paul Durand-Ruel indomitably promoted the careers of these great painters, often against daunting rejection, seemed to be a wonderful way of introducing this sale of works from the estate of his daughter. The collection included several portraits by Renoir and works by Monet, Cassatt, Boudin, Sisley and Corot, and achieved an outstanding total of £4,710,000, with every one of the twenty-two works sold. Two Renoir portraits brought around £700,000 each, and a work by Monet, *Femme à l'Ombrelle*, achieved £353,500, a record for a drawing by the artist. Offered on the same evening as the Durand-Ruel sale was an unusual group of early twentieth-century paintings from a Californian private collection, which featured a group of fifteen works by the Czech artist Frantisek Kupka (1871-1957), an early pioneer of abstraction. This was the first time that such a significant group of the artist's work had been offered at auction, and all the works sold extremely well.

In summing up the 1992-3 season, one would have to agree once more with the venerable Lord Clark: 'When all is said, the world owes private collectors an enormous debt. Without them many of the greatest works of art would have been lost or destroyed.'

FRANTISEK KUPKA
Notre Dame
SIGNED, OIL ON CANVAS, 73 x 60cm (28¾ x 25⅝in)
London £238,000 ($361,700). 23.VI.93 (ABOVE)

SLEEPERS AWAKE *by Philip Mould*

So astonishing was the discovery on 26 November 1923 that nothing since has been able to rival its impact. The account by the discoverer himself has become one of the most famous pieces of narrative journalism ever written, setting the tone for many subsequent attempts to sensationalize a great find:

'The decisive moment had arrived. With trembling hands I made a tiny break in the upper left-hand corner ... At first I could see nothing, the hot air escaping from the chamber causing the candle flames to flicker.... Lord Carnarvon, unable to stand the suspense any longer, inquired anxiously, "Can you see anything?" it was all I could do to get out the words, "Yes, wonderful things."'

And so it was, in Howard Carter's words, that the tomb of Tutankhamun was discovered. Art dealers are asked constantly whether it is still possible to find wonderful things. Surely, it is said, people know too much. It was quite one thing for the archaeologist Carter to find the tomb of Tutankhamun, but that was in 1923. How, with the massive international art trade, the huge increase in education, countless books, articles and the boundless greed of the late-twentieth century, does anyone have the remotest chance of discovering anything?

The answer is that this is exactly why discoveries are now so much more possible. The whole point about a 'find' is that it must first be 'lost'. For it to be treated as a loss, it has to be appreciated or valued; and for that to happen, it has to have been established in some way. This is precisely what happens every time an art-historical book, article or thesis is written: a new subject, or category is summoned. One reason why Tutankhamun had so much impact was that

Howard Carter and Lord Carnarvon opening the tomb of Tutankhamun in November 1923. (BELOW)

Howard Carter and Lord Carnarvon taking the effigy bust of Tutankhamun from the tomb. (BELOW RIGHT)

Howard Carter, a plausible scholar, was able to establish the antiquarian significance of his find to the world at large. A hundred-and-fifty years earlier, an undisturbed tomb from the Valley of the Kings may well have been viewed as little more than a hoard of sumptuous booty for a lucky grand tourist.

American folk art is a case in point. Much of it used to be regarded rather patronisingly as charming but lightweight: the stuff of craftsmen rather than artists in the Renaissance sense. But all that has had to change now that scholarship has taken hold. Many pieces by the better practitioners have achieved the status of hallowed artifacts, with enough attendant literature and expertise to allow the sort of drama played out recently at Sotheby's offices in New York.

It began in the autumn of 1992 when a Los Angeles seller got in touch with the American Folk Art department about a painting of an unknown lady by the mid-nineteenth-century primitive American portrait painter Erastus Salisbury Field. He had purchased it from a sale in Paris. Field is a highly regarded and greatly sought-after American folk artist, and on seeing this new example the department eagerly set about trying to identify the female sitter. In the background was a harbour scene, painted with painstaking attention to detail; emphasis on background detail to this degree is unusual and had, therefore, to be a crucial clue as to her identity. With the available recent literature the department was soon able to establish another example by Field using a distinctive port scene – a portrait of Louisa Galland Cook hanging in the Shelbourne Museum in Vermont. The hunt closed in when documentation revealed that Field had undertaken a series of paintings of all the members of the Galland family in 1838. The last time the set was remembered as being complete was in 1912 when the family moved house, but it was not exactly a happy memory. Someone had accidently placed them on rubbish barrels with the result that they were picked up and carted off into the unknown. Despite this catastrophe, by 1992 all but two had been found, and by a process of deduction they worked out that this, the unknown lady, had to be Louisa's long-lost

sister, Clarissa. With the arrival of Clarissa, all but one of the set were accounted for.

The best was yet to come. Precisely eight weeks later the department received a telephone call, this time from a client in New England who wished to sell a portrait of an unknown boy with an added ingredient – an elaborate harbour scene in the background. From the other side of the continent, Field's lost portrait of Clarissa's son, William, had surfaced to join that of his mother. Having fully proved his identity they were then reunited by the department for the sale of Fine Americana in January 1993, the fruits of modern art history and synchronicity.

Art history has developed at such a pace in recent years that it can sometimes outstrip the object of its own scholarship. In the late 1980s, Cambridge art historian J. M. Massing embarked on a detailed study of a painting that no longer appeared to exist: *The Calumny of Apelles* by the sixteenth-century Italian master Garofalo. Fascinated by the unusually extensive contemporary records of the picture, and the numerous references to it in the nineteenth century, Massing decided, in the absence of the work itself, to rebuild the image from these sources. His findings were published in *Du text á l'image. La Calomnie d'Apelles et son iconographie* in 1990.

One morning, shortly before Christmas two years later, one of the specialists in Old Master paintings at Sotheby's London opened his post to find a photograph of a large allegorical work in the style of Garofalo. It had been sent to him for comment by an American architect and collector of Old Masters. The department instantly set about researching it, and when looking into the artist and his known works inevitably came across Massing's publication. There was a flurry of excitement as it became clear that the picture Massing was describing was the one of which he was holding a photograph in his hand. As if by sorcery, Massing's exhaustive description and concentration on this one work seemed to have summoned it, spirit-like, from the unknown. A letter with a photograph was swiftly despatched to Cambridge, putting Massing quite unexpectedly in the position of coming face to face with the real life object of his hypothesis. Fortunately,

ERASTUS SALISBURY
FIELD
Portrait of William
Lauriston Cook
OIL ON CANVAS,
77.5 x 60.3cm (30½ x 23¾in).
(ABOVE)

ERASTUS SALISBURY
FIELD
Portrait of Clarissa
Gallond Cook
OIL ON CANVAS,
87 x 71.8cm (34¼ x 28¼in).
(ABOVE RIGHT)

it closely matched his expectations, providing a conclusion few scholars would dare to seek. Only rarely does circumstance corroborate academic research so neatly. Many historians would be in danger of high embarrassment should concrete evidence appear after their speculations had been published.

A painting I always think of as exemplifying the potency of academic knowledge, and one that still makes my mouth dry with feelings of missed opportunity, can be seen in a recent rehang amongst the artist's contemporaries in the seventeenth-century rooms of the National Portrait Gallery, London. It is a portrait of Charles II as a boy by van Dyck, and shows the Prince as an eight-year-old standing with a look of solemn good behaviour in a suit of armour, holding a pistol in one hand and leaning on a plumed helmet with the other. Had you been wandering through the salerooms of one of London's major auction houses just before Christmas in 1983, you may not have given it a second look. Van

Dyck had in fact painted a number of versions of this picture, and his studio and followers produced many replicas. Estimated at £400-600 and extremely dirty, it was described as one of these copies, and consequently appeared as an early lot in a routine end-of-season British picture sale – the sort of object that might have been bought by an interior designer as up-market decoration for the drawing room of some country house hotel. There was one man however, sitting not that far away in an office in Trafalgar Square, who would view it quite differently.

Dr Malcolm Rogers, Deputy Director of the National Portrait Gallery, and now one of the country's leading experts on seventeenth-century British portrait painting, inspected the sale during his lunch break. He spotted the familiar van Dyck image from across the room, and although he assumed it to be yet another late replica, decided it was worth a careful look. He was instantly alerted by some writing in the bottom right-hand corner. Both the words of the

inscription, conspicuous despite the dirt 'Charles Prince of Wales, about 1640 ... p.s. Ant: Vandike,' and the style of the lettering, a sort of primitive gothic, pointed unequivocally to its provenance as having belonged to Philip, Lord Wharton. All the pictures from this particular collection had the same style of inscription, and work that Rogers had carried out on seventeenth-century collectors told him that this was from very select company indeed. In all, the statesman 4th Baron Wharton (1613-96) owned thirty-two portraits by van Dyck, including fourteen life-size full-lengths; as the artist's patron he was quantitatively second only to the Royal family. Rogers knew that the quality of the collection was notable, and the best of them, including this composition, had been sold to Sir Robert Walpole at Houghton Hall in Norfolk, where it was noted by the eighteenth-century art commentator George Vertue: 'Charles Prince of Wales in armour at length 1640 ... all by V. Dyk.' Others from the series can now be seen in

the Hermitage, St Petersburg, having been sold to Catherine the Great later that century.

This was an illustrious stable indeed. Where it had been since, Rogers didn't know, but that was unimportant. At this stage, by this piece of academic detection he could, circumstantially at least and on the basis of early provenance, prove its likely authenticity. Certainty would not come until after cleaning. Rogers then discussed it with his colleagues and they all agreed it was a risk worth taking. Indeed, it was rare to have so much factual corroboration to hand at so early a stage in a discovery. On the morning of the sale the trustees of the Gallery purchased it for £1,965.

The picture was taken to the Gallery's restorers who then carefully removed the discoloured top layer of varnish. As Rogers expected, under the discoloured varnish had been hidden a marvellously well-preserved original, by the master himself, with some background additions by assistants. His knowledge had saved the Gallery about £500,000, and provided a further

BENVENUTO TISI, CALLED GAROFALO
The Calumny of Apelles
OIL ON CANVAS,
79 x 109cm (31 x 43in).
(ABOVE LEFT)

SIR ANTHONY VAN DYCK
Charles II when Prince of Wales
OIL ON CANVAS,
150.5 x 130.7cm (58⅛ x 51⅛in).
Now in the collection of the National
Portrait Gallery, London. (RIGHT)

example of how academia can ignite opportunity. By researching the content of a collection, a fairly novel approach compared to the more traditional method of simply listing collections through whose hands a work has passed, Rogers was in an almost unique position. 'It had always', he explained, 'been traditional to take vertical connections with provenance. Horizontal connections, however, have become increasingly interesting and it was this approach which helped establish the picture.' Were it not for his knowledge of the voracious collecting habits of the seventeenth-century Lord Wharton, it is likely that the picture would still be unrecognized today, even in a cleaned state.

Ironically, scholarship can also create extraordinary opportunities when flawed, especially for the fresh and unprejudiced eye. Shortly before Christmas 1992 the specialist flower-painting dealer Peter Mitchell, together with David Scrase, Keeper of the Fitzwilliam Museum's art gallery in Cambridge, could be found scrabbling through the racks in the Museum's basement. They were making an initial selection for a major show at Mitchell's Bond Street art gallery of still life paintings from the Fitzwilliam. The Museum's celebrated collection of works in this area is probably the most significant in the world. At the end of one rack, furthest from the light, Scrase drew Mitchell's attention to a picture which at first was very difficult to see. He could just make out the dim form of a bouquet of flowers, but it was inaccessibly stacked and surrounded by an enormous, highly ornate Victorian plaster frame. The reason for its exile to the basement was evident from the Museum's catalogue of the collection made in 1960. As number 1487, the work was dismissively described by the cataloguers as a 'copy after Jan Davidsz de Heem' and had remained in the darkness ever since. The 'experts' had gone on to state that the original composition from which this copy derived was unknown, but must date from the 1660s. Instantly intrigued, Mitchell angled himself to get a closer look. The effect then became physical. 'I felt that tingle. Despite the dirty surface and the dim light the quality seemed to be staggering.' Mitchell got Scrase to agree to cleaning the

picture for the exhibition. It turned into a revelation – a large and monumental work, a masterpiece by de Heem himself, which despite its manifest quality and extremely clear signature had had to suffer ignominious obscurity: a work that, as described by the catalogue, would have made £25,000 on a good day in a minor Old Master sale was transformed into a £2 million masterpiece. It was a startling discovery for 1993 and a reminder that the most dramatic discoveries are not, as is often believed, from the attics of old ladies, but are there before our eyes, just waiting for their names to be called.

JAN DAVIDSZ DE HEEM
Flowers in a Vase
SIGNED, OIL ON PANEL,
93.5 x 70.2cm (36⅞ x 27½in)
From the collection of the
Fitzwilliam Museum,
Cambridge. (ABOVE)

STOPPING THE CLOCK *by Edward Bulmer*

APPROACHES TO ARCHITECTURAL RESTORATION

Uppark House, Sussex, on fire on the night of 30 August 1989. (LEFT)

Containers holding the charred contents of Uppark House, Sussex, awaiting cataloguing prior to restoration. (ABOVE)

In some respects it is a sad coincidence that three of the country's most important heritage organizations have had to tackle major restoration projects concurrently. In the case of the Historic Royal Palaces Agency and the National Trust disastrous fires instigated conservation and restoration schemes on an unprecedented scale, at Hampton Court and Uppark respectively, while English Heritage, through the generosity of the owner, Mrs Williams, and the National Heritage Memorial Fund, were able to assume guardianship of Brodsworth Hall in happier circumstances. How each organization has approached and carried out their task of restoration and conservation makes a fascinating and instructive comparison in the context of the current debate on the subject.

Inevitably there were lessons to be learnt in the aftermath of the Hampton Court fire in 1986 – lessons that were put into practice at Uppark

nearly three and a half years later – yet an impressive salvage and conservation programme was in place as soon as the fire was extinguished. Palace staff and English Heritage advisors, among others, organized the archaeological recovery of objects and fragments from the sodden debris, the location of everything found was recorded and the objects then stored for conservation. So thorough was this operation that not one of the thousands of crystal beads that had made up the fine chandelier in the King's Audience Chamber was lost. Much redeemable architectural detail was salvaged along with a great proportion of Grinling Gibbons' fine carvings, though all were blackened and water-logged.

The National Trust carried out a similar operation after the more serious fire at Uppark in Sussex, storing the debris in a garrison of black bins all carefully mapped. The first priority, in both cases, was to erect a temporary roof over the building, thus preventing further damage from exposure to the elements.

In taking over responsibility for the decaying Brodsworth Hall in Yorkshire, English Heritage's first action was to make a complete survey of the house, including rectified photography. All the moveable objects were then catalogued and their conservation needs assessed, before being removed to allow structural repairs to be carried out. A large warehouse was found in which to store the house's contents, and a programme of short-term remedial work was put into action to eradicate pests which were attacking the textiles, involving fumigation and a freezing technique pioneered by experts at London's Victoria and Albert Museum. Tragic though it is, damage by fire does present certain opportunities; both in archaeological terms, in disseminating the building's history, and in practical terms, in allowing the invisible incorporation of modern technology and safety precautions in the rebuilding.

At Hampton Court, a great deal was learnt about the building methods used by Christopher Wren in his construction of the State Apartments for William III between 1689 and 1700. New information augmented an already comprehensive picture of the building provided by very detailed contemporary accounts. Hampton Court ceased to be used for courtly purposes in the reign of George III, and it was first opened to the public by Queen Victoria in 1838. Since then, the King's Apartments had gradually become a series of damask-hung picture galleries. Given the success of the salvage operation it was, in principle, feasible to restore the rooms to their appearance at any stage between 1700 and 1986. The Historic Royal Palaces Agency, in close consultation with English Heritage, decided that, although many of the Williamite furnishings were long gone, the situation represented an opportunity to restore the appearance of the King's Apartments as they were in 1700. This would involve little structural alteration and would be the most informative way of presenting the rooms to the public.

The walls had largely escaped the effects of the fire so that new structural work was limited mainly to the floors and ceilings. The floors

throughout the Apartments have been replaced with random-width pine boards, nailed and left untreated. Sea-shells were re-used underneath the boards, reinstating Wren's original solution for sound-proofing. The ceilings were similarly restored (in line with the same guiding principle) using the original method of lath and plaster. The only significant casualty of the wall decoration had been the loss of a whole 'drop' of Grinling Gibbons' carving, and damage to others. Here was a problem that might have been thought insuperable given the outstanding quality of Gibbons' work. To the surprise of many, the project organizers established a 'Gibbons workshop' in the Palace, where three master carvers and three others worked closely together, using working methods likely to have been employed by Gibbons' own workshop.

All the rooms were refurnished according to the late seventeenth- and early eighteenth-century

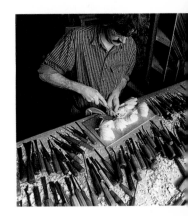

The Cartoon Gallery, Hampton Court Palace, shortly after the fire on 31 March 1986. (TOP)

A master carver at work in the workshop set up at Hampton Court. (ABOVE)

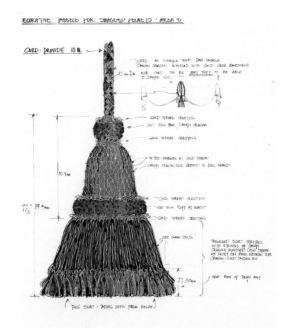

One of the designs for pelmet tassels made by the textile restoration department at Hampton Court. (RIGHT)

The Presence Chamber in the King's Apartments at Hampton Court after restoration, showing the repaired throne canopy.(BELOW)

inventories, which was possible only through a degree of reproduction. Conservation policy prevented the exact Williamite disposition of tapestries, as some would have been cut down and others obscured behind pictures. This problem has been solved by the use of bordered mohair hangings, some coloured to be evocative of tapestry tonalities. The discovery of a series of painted copies of the Raphael Cartoons in the Ashmolean Museum in Oxford, and their subsequent loan for use in the Cartoon Gallery at Hampton Court, has enabled Hampton Court's own tapestry copies of the Cartoons to be hung elsewhere in the King's Apartments. These tapestry copies were fortunately being restored at the time of the fire, and escaped damage.

The contemporary inventories indicated that there would be certain gaps that could not be filled by the Royal Collection; sconces, pier tables, torchères and curtains amongst other things. Those objects that it was felt were crucial to the understanding of the Williamite furnishing have been reproduced from appropriate models and empirical evidence. All materials and fringes have been recreated using the original constituents and levels of richness, rather than using modern, less costly, substitutes.

All surviving textiles have been carefully conserved by Hampton Court's renowned conservation studio, which had to build a special washing facility to cope with the large scale of items such as tapestries. A great quantity of molten lead had fused with the silver thread fringe of the original throne canopy that had hung in the Presence Chamber and had to be painstakingly removed. The lessons and techniques learnt have greatly endowed what is now a national resource. A computerized environmental control system has been introduced, and the previous heating system upgraded: it is now concealed under a boarded drugget, thus obviating the need for obtrusive radiators and pipe-work.

At Uppark, the National Trust, like the Historic Royal Palaces Agency, decided to use only traditional materials worked in the traditional way. This has meant finding the skills required to recarve ornamental details, to carry out freehand stucco-work, and to throw chimney

pots by hand, as well as making use of many other skills already established in conservation and restoration workshops. The National Trust's aim at Uppark is to restore the house to its appearance on 29 August 1989, the day before the fire. This, in effect, means restoring the impression of interiors unaltered since the late eighteenth century save by the passage of time. Though the wooden cornices and window frames were largely destroyed, the exterior brickwork was left all but unmarked as the fire was able to rise straight through the roof. This greatly facilitated the restoration of the previous external appearance of the house.

While the first floor contents at Uppark were entirely lost, many of the pieces from the ground floor were saved and, for the most part, remain as they appeared the day before the fire. The challenge that the Trust has taken up is that of re-incorporating as much salvaged fabric as possible, adding in new work and treating the whole so as to disguise the effects of the fire. As at Hampton Court, much of the wall detailing escaped the ravages of the fire, although subsequent storm damage took a further toll. Thus there is in most cases enough surviving material to act as an accurate guide for the finishing of the new work. New

flock papers and silks present particular problems of re-integration, unlike painted surfaces which are easily toned down by applying glazes.

The conserved contents will therefore be returned to rooms that they would recognise and feel comfortable in, particularly as the National Trust has taken the opportunity to build in sophisticated environmental control systems which should ensure optimum conditions for their future preservation. All modern necessities such as security systems are incorporated as invisibly as possible, and where new introductions are necessary, the aim is to disguise them by giving them some form of decorative articulation (as at Hampton Court).

At Brodsworth, English Heritage inherited one of the most intact Victorian ensembles in the country, but also a house in need of much structural repair work to ensure its future. Few are unaffected by the charm of faded grandeur and forgotten rooms redolent of a way of life that has passed. But it is surely short-sighted to want a decaying house not to be touched, for that is to deny future generations the chance of seeing it at all. Decay is always progressive.

Brodsworth Hall engenders just such feelings, and one cannot help thinking that they are what

The Dining Room at Uppark, Sussex, before the fire. (ABOVE LEFT)

The Dining Room at Uppark, Sussex, shortly after the fire in August 1989. (ABOVE)

Brodsworth Hall, Yorkshire, undergoing external restoration in 1992. (ABOVE)

underpin the seemingly dispassionate approach taken by English Heritage to its treatment of the house. Its policy, described as the first (and possibly the last) step, is to retain the appearance of the house as found in 1990, while carrying out all structural work necessary to render it safe and secure for the future. Decay having been arrested, the painted surfaces in the State Rooms have been surface-cleaned only. (The effect of this treatment in an area of England that has suffered high industrial pollution is dramatically apparent.) No attempt has been made to remove discoloured varnish from decorative painting, or indeed from the oil paintings, and retouching of losses has been confined to a discernible toning layer, similar in effect to the Italian picture restoration principle of hatched retouching.

The approach rules out 'improvements' save those necessitated by public safety, and so the existing heating systems will be retained, although the introduction of a security system is obligatory. The only visual changes to the interior of the house are to be in the introduction of a number of reproduced carpets, as the originals were so worn that the public would have destroyed them in the first visitor season. On the first floor the decorative state of the rooms had fared much less well and many rooms have large areas of damaged or lost wallpaper. The appearance of these rooms will be unchanged; in

fact they will be actively 'frozen in time'. Even peeling wallpaper has been 'set' in place as a hairdresser would 'set' someone's curls. Where new materials have had to be used, primarily on the exterior, English Heritage is not attempting to harmonize their appearance with the existing materials, the philosophy being to introduce minimal but honest and visible repair.

It is edifying that the Historic Royal Palaces Agency, the National Trust and English Heritage should all define particular dates at which to 'stop the clock' for the presentation of their properties to the public. Only the Historic Royal Palaces Agency chose a pre-photography period to recreate, and therefore chose the path most likely to produce problems that would require informed speculation or compromise for their solution. Even before the fire at Hampton Court there had been considerable debate as to whether it was ethical to sweep away subsequent decoration in returning to the supposed appearance of William III's Apartments. The fire obviously shifted the goalposts and a motive of public education won the day. One wonders, however, had the fire not taken place, whether the superb and elaborate model that has been made to demonstrate William's courtly use of the Apartments would not have sufficed.

A visitor's experience of any historic building is always made up of what is seen as well as what is learnt. At Hampton Court it is impossible not to speculate on whether the juxtaposition of the new dry-scrubbed pine floorboards with the unaltered dark finish of the oak panelling would have existed in 1700. Equally, the effect of the impressive electroplate silver sconces is diminished by the angle at which they hang, owing to their careful suspension to avoid puncturing the tapestries and the imbalance caused by the electrical apparatus on their backs. These are, of course, subjective matters and however objective the concept such anomalies can never be entirely avoided. English Heritage has encountered the same situation at Brodsworth where, even though the approach is one of extreme self-effacement, some decisions have had to be taken that indicate modern involvement. The National Trust steers a course somewhere in between, acknowledging

One of the bedrooms at Brodsworth Hall, Yorkshire, before restoration. English Heritage plans to alter the look of such interiors as little as possible. (LEFT)

its role as one of a succession of patrons in the evolution of a historic building, rather than attempting to impose suspended animation.

It is arguable that much of what we preserve today arose out of the rebuilding and remodelling of something that was destroyed; much of the work of Robert and James Adam is a case in point. In pursuing a policy of invisible interference one necessarily rules out the possibility of continuing the process of patronage that has produced so much of what we preserve. On the other hand, as Ruskin and Morris perceived a hundred years ago, restoration can be as destructive as neglect or accidental damage. What restoration projects on the scale of those at Hampton Court and Uppark have demonstrated is that they are very much creative processes, regenerating dormant crafts and encouraging the reproduction of first class artistic and architectural work. Perhaps the natural extension of this is to believe firmly that we have the artistic ability

to reproduce large-scale decorative work, instead of relying on technology and artifice, as was the case in the recreation of the Gentileschi ceiling at the Queen's House in Greenwich, where a photographic method of reproduction was used.

With work currently in progress at Windsor Castle after the devastating fire in November 1992, differing attitudes to restoration are now more in the news than ever. If one had to choose a universal policy for the future there is no doubt that the approaches of the three major heritage organizations outlined above would offer vital ingredients. English Heritage's approach, when viewed as a first step, is difficult to fault. If one is to allow for a next step, the meticulous regard for quality and authenticity of the Historic Royal Palaces Agency would need to be added, along with the National Trust's ability to accept that some decisions can be successfully taken only by assuming the mantle of a present-day patron with an unswerving sense of preservation.

VICTORIAN CROSSCURRENTS *by Lynn Stowell Pearson*

Collecting has been variously described as an illness, an addiction, a passion, a romance and an intellectual endeavour. Norbert Schimmel, a renowned collector of ancient art, once explained: 'The passion to chase an object, the pleasure in discovery and the exciting acquisition are the most rewarding stimuli for any possessed collector.' Today it seems as if anything is collectable – this current season at Sotheby's has seen vigorous bidding in such diverse fields as animation art, comic books, teddy bears, baseball memorabilia and even conjuring apparatus. Exploring these outer limits of the auction world can prove a highly entertaining and rewarding pastime; however, there are still many fascinating pockets within the more traditional markets capable of providing just as much interest and enjoyment. Nineteenth-century photographs and Victorian pictures are two such markets: both promise many areas for discovery and both offer excellent collecting opportunities. Yet surprisingly, neither of these now firmly established markets was an habitué of the auction rooms until the 1970s.

Photographs have been collected since the invention of photography. They had been handled primarily by antiquarian book dealers before coming to the attention of the auction-going public nearly twenty years ago. Among those who attended those first auctions of photographs were Sam Wagstaff, Curator of Modern Art at the Detroit Institute of Arts, and Howard Gilman, head of the Gilman Paper Company in Manhattan. These two visionary collectors went on to form two of the most important private collections of photographs in the world. That compiled by the late Sam Wagstaff spanned both the nineteenth and twentieth centuries, and was eventually sold in 1984 to the J. Paul Getty Museum. In 1993 Howard Gilman's encyclopaedic collection received wide-ranging attention through an

LEWIS CARROLL
Julia and Ethel Arnold in Straw Boaters
*c.*1872, ALBUMEN PRINT, 16.1 x 13.2cm (6⅜ x 5¼in)
London £5,980 ($9,020).
7.V.93. (RIGHT)

exhibition at the Metropolitan Museum of Art, *The Waking Dream, Photography's First Century*.

Philippe Garner, Director of Sotheby's Photographs Department in London, credits Sam Wagstaff with opening everyone's eyes to what photography could be. Sotheby's London held its first photographs auction in 1971. Garner, who presided over that sale, quotes a client who recalled those early days when collecting photographs was like picking up seashells along the seashore. A year before that sale, Sotheby's New York had held what is considered to be the breakthrough auction in this field: the sale of the collection of Sidney Strober. By 1975 sales of photographs had become an annual Sotheby's event.

Collecting nineteenth-century photographs in the 1990s is done in the context of a much more established market than was the case twenty years ago, and Philippe Garner feels that 'We are now confident in recognizing rarity when we see it.' It is still, though, an area ripe for exploration by the intrepid collector. 'There are so many less-explored byways, a collector can still make exciting discoveries', says Garner. Beth Gates-Warren, Director of Sotheby's New York's Photographs Department, believes that if the market for nineteenth-century photographs is ever to be more widely known and appreciated by the general public, now is the time.

Daguerreotypes – unique images fixed on a metal plate – form an area that, according to Denise Bethel of Sotheby's New York's Photographs Department, is 'probably the most undervalued segment of the nineteenth-century photography market in the US'. Excellent examples, she says, can still be found for under $1,000. In April 1993 Sotheby's New York sold Robert Vance's daguerreotype of *James King of William*, made in about 1855, for $9,200. The high price represents the historical importance of this portrait of one of San Francisco's crusading newspapermen during the Gold Rush.

Two photographers who epitomize the very essence of the Victorian era have also recently been achieving strong prices at auction – Lewis Carroll and Julia Margaret Cameron. Best known as the author of *Alice's Adventures in Wonderland* and *Through the Looking Glass and What Alice Found There*, Lewis Carroll sketched for pleasure before taking up photography in 1856, a medium he pursued for the next twenty-five years. His photographs are primarily portraits of members of his family or close acquaintances, most notably the daughters of his circle of friends. Carroll's extraordinary staging of images of childhood is evident in *Julia and Ethel Arnold in Straw Boaters*, of around 1872, which sold at Sotheby's London in May 1993 for £5,980. Carroll is well known for having made strong demands of his sitters. Ethel Arnold has recalled 'It was no joke being photographed in those days, and for a nervous child, dressed up as a Heathen Chinese, a beggar child, or a fisher maiden, to keep still for forty-five seconds at a time was no mean ordeal.' But those who leap to criticize Carroll's methods and motives should bear in mind that Ethel Arnold

also remembers that 'He was indeed a bringer of delight in those dim, far-off days, and I look back to hours spent in his dear, much loved company as an oasis of brightness in a somewhat grey and melancholy childhood.' ('Reminiscences of Lewis Carroll', *The Atlantic Monthly*, Boston, 1929.)

An equally passionate photographer, but a portraitist with quite different aims, Julia Margaret Cameron strove to capture the souls of her subjects. In many cases she preferred soft focus, which it was felt helped achieve an ethereal effect. In her portrait of the astronomer Sir John Herschel, Cameron went to his house and 'had him wash his hair so that a brilliant halo would

JULIA MARGARET
CAMERON
Sir John Herschel
1867, ALBUMEN PRINT,
32.9 x 25.2cm (12⅞ x 9⅞in)
New York $25,300 (£16,400).
6.IV.93. (ABOVE)

encircle his head' (*The Waking Dream, Photography's First Century*, The Metropolitan Museum of Art, New York, 1993). An albumen print of this photograph, dated 1867, sold at Sotheby's New York in April 1993 for a remarkable $25,300.

Collected not only for their historical importance as documents of a rapidly changing landscape, nineteenth-century photographs of the American West are also cherished as poignant and beautiful images. In October 1990 Sotheby's New York sold an album of cyanotype photographs of dam-building along the Mississippi River by H. Bosse for $66,000. Denise Bethel recalls that at the time no one had heard of Bosse and 'now prices have really taken off and people are calling about discoveries of Bosse photographs.' Mammoth-plate photographs, in the form of prints 15 x 20in, have an extraordinary capacity to capture the wide expanses of the western American landscape. One superb example from the 1870s by Eadweard Muybridge, *The Domes, from the Merced River, Yosemite Valley*, was sold at Sotheby's New York in October 1991 for $20,900.

Muybridge is best remembered for his sequential views of human and animal locomotion made with a high-speed camera in the late 1870s and 80s, which vividly demonstrated the inaccuracies of conventional representations of movement. Suddenly, and for the first time, it could clearly be seen just how a horse's legs moved when galloping, or exactly how a man's limbs were stretched when throwing a ball. This was revolutionary and invaluable information for many artists. Animal and history painters, particularly, immediately subscribed to these revelations, though, inevitably there were other artists who objected. Not what actually exists, they said, but only what can be seen to exist may legitimately become the subject of art.

The implications of photography on the art of painting were recognized from the very beginnings of photographic experimentation in the late 1830s. On the one hand it could supply artists with 'sketches' from nature of an accuracy never before known; on the other it was an open threat to artists whose sole function was to reproduce the appearance of the physical world. In a review

ROBERT VANCE
James King of William
*c.*1855, QUARTER-PLATE
DAGUERREOTYPE
New York $9,200 (£6,090).
6.IV.93. (RIGHT)

(ATTRIBUTED TO)
EADWEARD MUYBRIDGE
The Domes, from the Merced River, Yosemite Valley
*c.*1872, ALBUMEN PRINT,
39.6 x 52cm (15½ x 20⅜in)
New York $20,900 (£12,200).
9.X.91. (BELOW)

of the 1859 Paris Salon, Baudelaire famously called photography 'the mortal enemy of art'. 'Since photography gives us every guarantee of exactitude that we could wish,' he continued, 'then photography and Art are the same thing .... If photography is allowed to stand in for Art in some of its functions it will soon supplant or corrupt it completely .... It must return to its real task, which is to be the servant of the sciences and of the arts, but a very humble servant.'

Sir George Clausen and Sir Lawrence Alma-Tadema were two nineteenth-century painters who employed photography as a trusted and valuable servant, albeit in two distinct ways. Clausen studied photographs of peasants to help portray workers in the field, whereas Alma-Tadema used photographs of archaeological excavations and classical antiquities to help bring to life everyday details of ancient Rome. The extent of Alma-Tadema's use of photography in his preliminary studies can be gauged by the extraordinary collection of 164 volumes of photographs once owned by the artist that is now in the collection of Birmingham University.

The work of George Clausen came to the attention of many in 1980 with a well-attended monographic exhibition at the Royal Academy in London. Clausen is now as popular as ever among collectors, although Simon Taylor, Director of Sotheby's London's Victorian Pictures Department, believes that Clausen's watercolours are still under-priced. In his recent book *Beyond Impressionism, The Naturalistic Impulse* (New York, 1992), Dr Gabriel Weisberg describes how Clausen purchased one of the new portable cameras in the early 1880s, which allowed him to take pictures of field labourers without posing them. In November 1982 Sotheby's London sold Clausen's *Winter Work*, 1883-4, for £34,100. Now in the collection of the Tate Gallery in London, it depicts workers gathering sugar beets. One of the main figures, a peasant woman, was inspired by a photograph now in the collection of The Royal Photographic Society, Bath. Clausen's pictures from the 1880s are thought to be his most accomplished and are the most sought after. In November 1990 a record auction price for the artist was achieved by Sotheby's London with the

SIR GEORGE CLAUSEN
The Shepherd Boy,
SIGNED AND DATED *1883*,
OIL ON CANVAS,
92 x 62cm (36¼ x 24½in)
London, £78,500 ($118,500).
30.VI.93. (LEFT)

sale of *A School Girl*, painted in 1889, for £137,500. This season, the continued market interest in such works was confirmed by the £78,500 achieved at Sotheby's by another work from the 1880s, *The Shepherd Boy.*

Sir Lawrence Alma-Tadema became one of the most popular artists during the Victorian era, yet he was all but forgotten by the time of his death in 1912. During the first half of the twentieth century the work of nineteenth-century history painters and academic artists tended to be dismissed by art historians and collectors, and no one seems to have suffered quite as much as Alma-Tadema. Vern Swanson notes in his monograph on the artist in 1977 that if Alma-Tadema was referred to at all it was as 'the worst painter of the Victorian era.' One reviewer of the unpopular Royal Academy's retrospective of the artist in 1913 wrote that his 'painted anecdotes ... are about worthy enough to adorn bonbon boxes!'

A reappraisal was inevitable, but it did not begin until the late 1950s. Robert Kashey,

SIR LAWRENCE
ALMA-TADEMA
The Baths of
Caracalla (Thermae
Antoniniane)
SIGNED, OIL ON CANVAS,
152.4 x 95.3cm (60 x 37½in)
New York $2,532,500
(£1,633,800). 26.V.93.
(ABOVE)

Kirk Askew and the ballet impresario Lincoln Kirstein with influencing a new generation of art dealers like himself. In 1962 the Robert Isaacson Gallery celebrated the fiftieth anniversary of Alma-Tadema's death with an exhibition of his work. At the same time a number of young American curators were starting to buy in this field, looking for quality works without spending a great deal of money. Frank Trapp, former Director of the Mead Art Museum of Amherst College, Massachusetts, remembers that 'We [museum curators and directors] operated with a small budget, so we had to be discerning – we sometimes bought against current fashion.'

Sotheby's played an important role in bringing Victorian art to a wider audience with the opening of Sotheby's Belgravia in 1971. This pioneering effort put a spotlight on an area of the market that until then had been largely disdained. It flourished for a decade, as many dealers in nineteenth-century art opened galleries in the same neighbourhood. Successful sales, like the auction of paintings by Alma-Tadema from the collection of Allen Funt, helped to bring the art of this period into the mainstream. Funt, the creator of the television programme *Candid Camera*, had bought his first Alma-Tadema in 1967, and continued collecting until 1973, when he learned that he had been the victim of a large-scale embezzlement. Forced to sell his collection of thirty-five Alma-Tademas, Funt offered them at Sotheby's Belgravia in 1973. The sale was an extraordinary success, achieving £177,000.

One of the pictures formerly in the Allen Funt collection, *The Baths of Caracalla*, was sold again in May 1993 at Sotheby's New York for the record price of $2,532,500. In this work Alma-Tadema endeavoured to recreate a scene from Imperial Rome. To achieve this end, he relied upon the latest archaeological evidence, using the diagrams, reconstructions and photographs of surviving parts of the building that had been published in Rodolfo Lanciani's *The Ruins and Excavations of Ancient Rome* (1897). He also called upon his own extensive collection of photographs of classical architecture. The picture took two years to complete and was exhibited at the Royal Academy, London, in 1899.

Director of the Shepherd Gallery in New York, claims that 'a very select group' of dealers and collectors living in New York were largely responsible for a renewed interest in artists like Alma-Tadema, Tissot and Gérôme. 'It was very much a New York thing', recalls Kashey, who credits Robert Isaacson, of the Robert Isaacson Gallery, as well as dealers and collectors like James Coats,

SIR LAWRENCE
ALMA-TADEMA
Caracalla and Geta
SIGNED, OIL ON CANVAS,
126 x 155cm (49½ x 61in)
London £1,431,500
($2,147,200). 8.VI.93. (LEFT)

In 1907 Alma-Tadema painted another monumental work based on a scene from the life of Caracalla entitled *Caracalla and Geta*. The artist explained some of his intentions in an extremely lengthy letter to Messrs Arthur Tooth and Sons, who had commissioned the picture. 'It is therefore no wonder that so great a lover of Roman civilization as myself should have been moved to try to paint his conception of the place as it must have looked when full of people, showing in what way the seats may possibly have been filled and the arena utilized …. I have from the very outset counted the number of spectators as I painted them in, and have now reached a number approximating 2,500. Allowing that the columns and garlands hide as many more, this would give a total of 5,000 figures for that seventh part of the Coliseum which is shown in the picture, and for the entire building 35,000, the number usually believed to have found accommodation in the

auditorium.' This shows an almost bizarre level of commitment to historical accuracy, and may offer us some indication of the sort of care that Alma-Tadema took over his preliminary studies. Photography must have served him well. The picture was sold in London at Sotheby's on 8 June 1993, and made £1,431,500.

Since the early 1970s when photographs and Victorian pictures were first offered as separate collecting areas by Sotheby's, prices have risen dramatically. Nancy Harrison, of Sotheby's New York's Nineteenth-Century European Paintings Department, is sure that 'many new connoisseurs are discovering the rich rewards of collecting in these areas'. Harrison sees many opportunities for new collectors in the field of nineteenth-century paintings. 'With a variety of prices, it is still an area where a collector can trade up and the prices are not prohibitive. Masterworks by little known artists continue to be discovered.'

AMERICAN MUSEUMS AT SOTHEBY'S *by Michael Conforti*

The international art community has long been fascinated by the market activity of American museums. Since the earliest years of this century, when the *Burlington Magazine* began what soon became a European-wide protest against the export of artistic legacy to North America, the outcries have continued. While there is still political purpose to rhetoric aimed at maintaining European public awareness of the importance of enhancing national collections, real fear for the loss of cultural heritage has lessened in recent years. With the exception of the collecting activity of a dwindling number of American institutions capable of challenging Europe's larger national museums, current professional curiosity is directed more at sales *from* US museums than at purchases *for* them.

During the art boom of 1987-90 many American museums chose to rethink the nature of their collections in order to raise cash to continue buying exceptional works of art. Occasionally an institution's collecting mission was altered, as when the Kimbell Art Museum divested itself of its drawings in 1987, or when Washington's Corcoran Gallery sold its nineteenth-century European paintings in 1988 and 1989. At that time, sacrifices were also made in the depth of certain collections, as valuable works of less-than-first quality were cashed in to acquire singular masterpieces. This was the case when the Art Institute of Chicago acquired a $12 million Brancusi and New York's Museum of Modern Art bought the *Portrait of Joseph Roulin* by van Gogh. Many Europeans ask how existing collections can be compromised in this way, and question the alteration of an institution's collecting tradition to support current tastes.

The differences between American and European collecting philosophy are based less on law than on differing traditions regarding a museum's role in society. In simplified terms, American museums could be seen as educational institutions, programme-oriented and public service-directed, whereas the larger European museums, while providing educational services, are national cultural symbols housing state collections of art. Unlike the situation in Europe, the United States federal government does not restrict the export of cultural objects, feeling that the disposal of a work of art should be entirely the responsibility of its citizens and their institutions. In the early 1970s, the New York State Attorney General did become involved when deaccessioning at the Metropolitan Museum raised a public outcry, but in this instance his action was most effective in catalyzing museums and professional societies to develop deaccessioning guidelines. These ethical

JOSEPH WRIGHT OF DERBY
An Iron Forge
SIGNED AND DATED *1772*,
OIL ON CANVAS,
119 x 132cm (47 x 52in)
Sold by private treaty through Sotheby's London.
Now in the collection of the Tate Gallery, London. (BELOW)

and procedural codes now represent the parameters of deaccessioning practice in the United States today, parameters founded on the fundamental rule that money raised from selling art cannot be used to support an institution's operating expenses, and, instead, must be applied to the enhancement of collections.

In Britain, as in much of the rest of Europe, deaccessioning regulations are few in number and are usually directed at sales from specific national institutions. London's National Gallery and the Tate, for example, are not allowed to sell. The British Museum Act (1963) and the National Heritage Act (1983) only restrict certain kinds of sales from specific museum collections. In fact, recent government action in England has focused on the cost of maintaining collections, encouraging institutions to be both more independent of government and more management-conscious in their collection policies. More restrictive than any legislation has been the 1988 Museums and Galleries Commission's professional *Guidelines for a Registration Scheme for Museums in the United Kingdom* (see *Museum Management and Curatorship*, vol. 10, no. 3, September 1991; vol. 11, no. 1, March 1992).

European institutions are discouraged from deaccessioning by both explicit and implicit codes of professionalism stemming from a different public attitude towards museum holdings than in America. Collections are widely perceived as national cultural patrimony, a belief enhanced by the fact that the large majority of museums are funded by governments and overseen by some form of government ministry. The notion of cultural patrimony has a positive ring amongst influentials throughout Europe, whether generated by idealism or national pride. There has been no significant deaccessioning in Britain since the 1960s when the country was outraged over the sale of pictures from Dulwich College.

When government is involved in museum practice in America, it is usually not the federal, but civic government that exerts influence. The operations of many of the country's largest institutions are governed by private boards of trustees, but their running costs are partially funded by city or county governments. Such

CASPAR DAVID FRIEDRICH **Waldinneres bei Mondschein, vorne Leute bei hellem Feuer (A Wood by Moonlight, with People by a Fire)** OIL ON CANVAS, 71 x 50cm (28 x 19⅝in) Sold by private treaty through Sotheby's New York. Now in the collection of the National Gallery, Charlottenburg Palace, Berlin. (LEFT)

funding, generally around 10 to 40 per cent, encourages museums to be more public-service directed, and more focused on a collection's current and future use than on its nature as the preserved testament of the aesthetic assumptions of the past. Given the educational mandate implicit in most US museum charters and the pragmatic, ahistoric tradition of the country as a whole, collections are often seen as institutional assets ready to serve a museum organization in a variety of ways. The strongest forces determining the direction of assets from deaccessioned art towards the enhancement of collections (rather than towards the support of a museum's operations) are the deaccessioning codes of America's two strongest professional art organizations, the American Association of Museums, and the Association of Art Museum Directors (see *Apollo*, vol. CXXX, no. 330, August 1989, pp. 77-86).

The differences between European and American museum collecting practices are as evident in accessioning as they are in deaccessioning practices. Two of the most splendid objects to be sold by Sotheby's this past year, Joseph Wright of

Derby's *An Iron Forge* and Caspar David Friedrich's *Waldinneres bei Mondschein*, were acquired by private treaty for national collections with little possibility for American competition. Such purchasing with funds from government-directed sources has no parallel in America. Museums in the United States also look longingly at a European system that can pre-empt a picture at auction, as the Prado did to acquire the Valencian School *The Life of St Ursula* before its proposed sale at Sotheby's Madrid in October 1992. Nor do American museums always have a completely free hand when a desirable work does come to the open market. The country's civically-responsive institutions are such that most boards of trustees would have found it difficult to support the particular nudity of Renoir's *Le Jeune Garçon au Chat*, sold at Sotheby's New York on 10 November 1992, despite the painterly appeal of such early works by the artist.

It is hard for US institutions to be consistently active in the auction market for other reasons as well. Unlike in Europe, American museum trustees are appointed with the assumption that the financial stability of these precariously funded institutions are their special responsibility. Thus board consideration tends to be required for every institutional decision. Distances from salerooms and the frequent necessity of a trustee's personal financial involvement contribute to making buying at auction difficult. Not surprisingly, when purchases were made by US institutions at auction in the past year, they were generally modestly-priced additions to collections recognized for the depth of their holdings, where a potential query over an addition would not present a significant barrier. One example is the purchase of Degas' crayon lithograph *Song of the Dog* at Sotheby's New York on 5 November 1993 by the Art Institute of Chicago, which added to its outstanding collection of works on paper.

The most significant purchases by American museums at auction in 1992-3 were made by two of the richest, most accessions-directed museums in the country, the Kimbell Art Museum in Fort Worth and the J. Paul Getty Museum in Malibu. Their ongoing collecting activity is supported by a little-mentioned American museum tradition,

but one that drives most of the country's deaccessioning as well as accessioning practices. For decades the educational directive of American museum charters has been supported by an associated goal of forming 'masterpiece' collections, intended to be representative of the highest artistic achievement of whatever cultures and historical periods are covered by the institution. Ultimately deriving from the 'national school' display tradition of late eighteenth-century European museums, as well as the focus on 'object specialness' promoted by Wilhelm von Bode around 1900, the American 'representative masterpiece' ideal was catalyzed by the idealism of the early decades of this century when an unqualified critical understanding of 'masterpiece' gave special favour to Impressionist and Modernist paintings. America's National Gallery of Art was formed in the late 1930s with no interest in collecting American art, but with a commitment to building a representative

VALENCIAN SCHOOL
**The Life of
St Ursula**
TEMPERA ON PANEL
WITH GOLD GROUND,
each 184 x 67cm (72 x 26¼in)
Sold by private treaty through
Sotheby's Madrid. Now in the
collection of the Prado
Museum, Madrid. (ABOVE)

ATTRIBUTED TO PIERRE
FRANCQUEVILLE, CALLED
FRANCAVILLA
The Fountain of
Neptune, one of
two pages from a
sketchbook
PEN AND BROWN INK OVER
TRACES OF BLACK CHALK,
13.8 x 10cm (5⅜ x 3⅞in)
London £23,000 ($34,700).
5.VII.93
Now in the collection of the
Victoria and Albert Museum,
London. (RIGHT)

collection of the finest European paintings possible. The Museum of Modern Art, formed in the 1930s, still adheres to 'representative master-piece' goals within its special Modernist vision. Thus, a few years ago, paintings of considerable merit by artists better represented in the collection – including Picasso, Kandinsky and Monet – were exchanged for a work deemed superior to all, van Gogh's *Portrait of Joseph Roulin*.

The decreased availability of significant works of art over the last thirty years has not deterred institutions from continuing to interpret their educational mandate in a similar 'representative masterpiece' manner, using both deaccessioning and accessioning to achieve their goal. The philosophy has reached a particular refinement in the collection policies of the Kimbell and the Getty. The Kimbell, which reconsidered the breadth of its holdings a few years ago by selling drawings in order to concentrate on greater pictures, was successful in satisfying two areas of need this season, acquiring Matisse's *L'Asie* at Sotheby's New York on 10 November 1992 for $11 million, and the *Portrait of Jacob Obrecht*, an anonymous Flemish picture, at Sotheby's New York on 15 January 1993 for $2,422,000. While the Getty deaccessioned a less-than-first-rate Gauguin from its nineteenth-century paintings four years ago, the development of a larger nine-teenth-century collection is still taken to be a vital need, as was made clear by its purchase of Goya's 1824 *Bullfight, Suerte de Varas* for £4,950,000 at Sotheby's London in November 1992.

In spite of different collecting philosophies, there are some similarities between European and American institutions towards deaccessioning. 'Collections management' is currently a buzz phrase on both sides of the Atlantic. Most institutions sell deteriorated material, although sales are little reported as smaller auction rooms are used and modest prices realized. The educational value of copies and fakes is considered questionable in many European and American institutions, as is the worth of maintaining duplicates. The defini-tion of a duplicate can vary considerably. The guidelines laid out by the British Museum Act of 1963 allow for the sale of duplicates of identical prints and photographs, for example, but do not allow a museum to consider the equal representation of an artist, school or object type as duplication in a collection. This latter, broader interpretation recently allowed the Metropolitan Museum in New York to consider a Sano di Pietro a questionable holding, and the Brooklyn Museum to determine Rodin's *La Faunesse à Genous* to be superfluous.

'Collections management' is also the impetus for the sale of objects of distinctly lower quality, which might have been accepted as gifts when knowledge was less refined and accessions policies less restrictive. The refinement of collections in store prompted the Metropolitan Museum to sell a number of 'school' pictures this past year. The Nelson-Atkins Gallery in Kansas City and the Detroit Institute of Arts did the same, the latter also consigning a large group of modest American works. In a somewhat parallel fashion the Hirschhorn Museum sold three Rufino Tamayos at Sotheby's New York in November 1992. The money raised could then be applied to the acquisition of one greater work. Occasionally such sales from storage can produce soberingly positive results, as was the case when a double portrait attributed to van Dyck was sold by the Detroit Institute of Arts at Sotheby's New York on 15 January 1993, making an unexpectedly high $109,750. For the most part, however, sales motivated by 'collections management' transfer modest museum works into similarly modest amounts of cash.

There was less deaccessioning with a 'cash for new accessions' motivation in 1992-3 than during the market boom of 1987-90. At that time, when collectors were rushing to send their best items to auction, American museums stretched the deaccessioning guidelines to raise money for what many considered the last opportunity to buy. The Guggenheim Museum, for example, realized $47.3 million from the sale of three pictures – a Chagall, a Modigliani and a Kandinsky – at an auction on 17 May 1990 at Sotheby's New York. The cash realized this year through the sale at Sotheby's New York of three appealing works owned by the Museum of Contemporary Art in Chicago – a Klee, an Ernst and a George Segal – was allowed to be used to support operating expenses, as the works had been donated for the benefit of the Museum, but were not accessioned into the collection. Since tax concessions in the United States on donations of art for sale, rather than collection use, have not been particularly attractive to contributors in most tax years, such gifts are hard to encourage. The principle is that museums can receive works of art as gifts that are not designated to go into permanent collections. When a gift comes with this non-collection purpose, it can be sold immediately, but the donor does not get the same tax write-off as he would if he were giving it to a permanent collection. It is treated as a gift of money and the tax deductability is less. Objects of insufficient quality for the permanent collection can come to the museum in this way (or objects which the museum would rather see immediately turned into cash).

The issue of deaccessioning from museum collections to support operating expenses will be an important one over the next decade in both Europe and America. In Britain, the lingering pressure from 1980s' Conservative public policy is combining with the non-traditional perspectives of a new generation of museologists to produce a reassessment of collections management policies. In these discussions, deaccessioning to benefit the running costs of museums is fully and openly part of the debate. This is becoming true in America as well (*Museums News*, vol. 71, no. 6, November-December 1992, pp. 54 ff). Increasingly, American museum directors are being encouraged by trustees to consider collections as a financial asset, and to act as any good manager would with a convertible good that could balance operational deficits. Under pressure from two of the most publicized 'needy cases' in the last two years – the potential closure of both the Everhart Museum in Scranton, Pennsylvania, and the New-York Historical Society – consideration is being given to modifications in the deaccessioning code of the Association of Art Museum Directors. Sales of art to benefit operations might be allowed if the museum's survival is in doubt, or if part of the collection is not considered central to an institution's declared mission.

GEORGE SEGAL
Girl washing her foot on a chair
PLASTER AND WOOD,
overall 122 x 117 x 61cm
(48 x 46 x 24in)
New York $187,000
(£122,200). 17.XI.92
Formerly in the collection of
the Museum of Contemporary
Art, Chicago. (RIGHT)

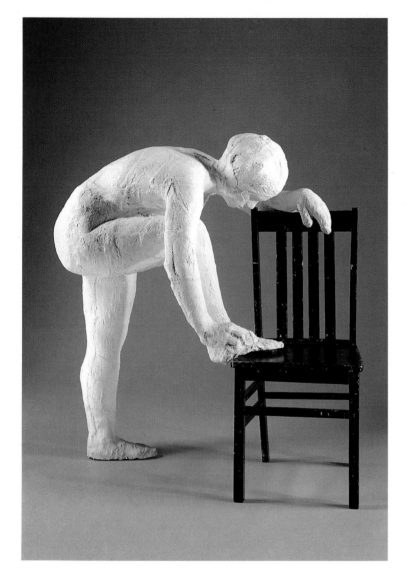

Such pressure will continue to mount as trustees and university administrators look for ways to keep their institutions alive and vital. The debate will not only involve the appropriateness of collections to a museum's mission, but also the cost and effectiveness of keeping collections in store. The discussion will extend to the question of how many museums a society can support, and how societies should deal with institutions that are no longer considered viable: those, perhaps, whose original purpose is no longer deemed relevant to today's needs. How would American trustees justify their role as a museum's fiscal agents if their institution were to feed on itself to survive? If a financially troubled museum sells a work to support operating funds, how would that affect the case for requesting further public or private support? In this largely extra-legal enterprise of collections-deaccessioning anything is possible, but any adjustments will continue to be subject to public scrutiny. Museums will constantly have to equate their needs with public expectation and trust, and any action taken will be subject to an ever-evolving code of professional conduct for ethical collection practices. It should prove to be a fascinating future.

FROM COVENT GARDEN TO MANHATTAN

THE HISTORY OF SOTHEBY'S PREMISES *by John Martin Robinson*

The understated cream stucco façade of Sotheby's in New Bond Street, with its gold-lettered name and the ancient Egyptian black-basalt head of the lion-goddess Sekhmet perched over the front entrance, is a well-known London landmark. It shares the quietly restrained self-confidence of many old-established English institutions such as Eton, the College of Arms and St James's Palace. The statement made by buildings of this type is one of discretion, scorning the need to make more of a show, and expressing a civility akin to that of an old suit made by the very best tailor.

The firm of Sotheby's is going to be 250 years old next year and has been at its present address since 1917. Before that time it was at 13 Wellington Street for a hundred years, following a brief sojourn at 145 The Strand, which proved to be too cramped for the needs of the business. When first founded by Samuel Baker in 1744, the firm was situated in York Street, Covent Garden, where it flourished for fifty years.

These earlier premises have long been demolished, though the appearance of Wellington Street is recorded in old sketches. No. 13 was on the west side of the north approach to Waterloo Bridge, facing the handsome Pennethorne façade of Somerset House. It was surprisingly similar to the present building in Bond Street, having, like it, developed out of a pair of early-Georgian houses. It was given distinction by Tuscan pilasters, a pair of flanking pediments, and moulded architraves to the first-floor windows. The central main entrance led into a small hall and stairway, which in turn led to the two top-lit salesrooms on the first floor, sandwiched between

Wellington Street in the nineteenth century, showing the firm's premises, the second building from the right.
(RIGHT)

an exhibition gallery at the front and the partners' room at the rear. An unexpected feature of the building (shared by Somerset House) was a deep double basement, made possible by the slope of Savoy Hill, which gave anybody staring absently into the front area a sharp shock of vertigo.

The Wellington Street premises were reconstructed following a terrible fire in June 1865 when the interior was gutted, and most of a collection of valuable books awaiting sale was destroyed. The fire was started in some wood shavings left by a careless workman in a yard leading to Savoy Court. J. Joseph Techner, a Parisian book-dealer whose consignment of 40,000 volumes was lost in the conflagration, wrote 'the flames ... roared up to reach every inch of the worm-eaten panelling on all sides of the antiquated premises. Within a few hours the fire had devoured everything!' *The Times* reported that, at its height, the fire could be seen 'from all the fire-engine houses in London'. Fortunately for Sotheby's, another gallery had been built ten years earlier at 21 North Wellington Street, 'as an addition to their house of business, for the more advantageous disposal

by public auction of cabinet pictures, drawings, engravings, antiquities and all works of art'. Auctions were held there until No. 13 was reconstructed, so that the interruption caused by the fire was kept to a minimum.

When first founded by Samuel Baker the firm auctioned a wide range of artifacts, yet for most of the nineteenth century Leigh & Sotheby (later Leigh, Sotheby & John Wilkinson) specialized in books and manuscripts. Wellington Street was well-suited for such a business, being close to many other book dealers in the Covent Garden area. With the increase in traffic over Waterloo Bridge, the grandiose proposals for widening The Strand, and the creation of Aldwych and Kingsway at the beginning of the twentieth century the area ceased to be a quiet, bookish backwater, and so the partners of Sotheby's decided to move to the West End. The present building in New Bond Street was acquired in 1917.

The new premises already had an interesting commercial and artistic pedigree, bearing out Lord Lytton's description of Bond Street in *The Siamese Twins* (1831) as a place 'Where each who wills may suit his wish. / Here choose a Guido – there his fish.' Nos. 34 and 35 have been in turn private houses, an inn, livery stables, the premises of royal parfumiers, commercial art galleries and art printers, milliners and wine merchants. New Bond Street forms part of the Conduit Mead Estate owned by the Corporation of the City of London, and was originally developed in the decade 1720-30. It was fashionable from the beginning. In 1749 the author Fielding had his hero Tom Jones describe it as 'a very good part of town' and that certainly remains true today. The street changed early on from residential to luxury commercial use, and handsome Georgian shop windows filled the ground floors, as recorded in a view of the street in the 1830s by Tallis.

Formerly, No. 34 was probably The Black Horse Inn. Certainly the building was known as 'The Black Horse' through several changes of use up until the mid-nineteenth century, although this name may have derived from its time as a livery stables. No. 35 was the shop of Rigge, Brockbank & Rigg, parfumiers to George IV,

Portrait of Samuel Baker, the firm's founder. (LEFT)

The Egyptian sculpture of the goddess Sekhmet, which presides above the front entrance of Sotheby's in New Bond Street. (RIGHT)

The entrance façade of Sotheby's New Bond Street offices, after the refurbishment programme completed in February 1993. (BELOW)

from 1804 to 1864. (The Tallis view shows their royal warrant displayed over the entrance.) No. 34 became a wine-merchant's shop in the 1860s when Fettoe & Sons moved in. Fettoes' were replaced in 1867 by Basil Woodd & Sons, also wine merchants. It was at that time that the two houses were combined, the present central entrance created, and large wine cellars excavated underneath. It was partly the existence of this voluminous storage space which decided Sotheby's on its choice of the building in 1917. A record of the occupation of Basil Woodd can still be seen in the form of the monogram 'B. W.' which is embossed on several of the iron piers in the basement of the building.

The first recorded artistic occupation of part of the site dates from 1861, when James Stewart, 'artist and photographer', made a brief appearance in the Post Office Directories. In 1870 Fairless & Beeforth, picture dealers, moved in and since then there has always been some artistic occupation of the building. Fairless & Beeforth came to grief over their attempt to monopolize the London sale of Gustave Doré's artistic output. In 1898 they were supplanted by the Lemercier Gallery and a succession of art publishers. Part of the premises was also occupied in the late-nineteenth century by a milliner.

It is this complex history of multi-occupation which is responsible for the fascinating, rambling – even confusing – interior, although the company has, in a series of architectural campaigns over a period of 70 years, improved the layout and imposed order on apparent chaos. When it moved in, in 1917, various alterations were made, including the construction of two new galleries in the centre of the premises and a remodelled entrance. This work was done to the design of J. G. S. Gibson (the architect of the former Middlesex Guildhall in Parliament Square and the old Debenham and Freebody store in Wigmore Street). It was at this time that the Sekhmet was moved from Wellington Street to her present position over the front door in Bond Street. This sculpture, which dates from around 1320BC, is the oldest privately-owned monument in London. It was sold in the nineteenth century as part of a

collection of Egyptian artifacts for £40, but the buyer never materialized and the goddess found a new home with Sotheby's.

Another phase of alterations was embarked upon in 1928 when the Bond Street premises were joined to the eighteenth-century houses in St George Street, on the other side of a triangular block abutting Conduit Street, most of which is now occupied by Sotheby's. The renowned firm of Mewes and Davis (architects of The Ritz on Piccadilly) were used for that work. A further small gallery at the rear of No. 35 was created in 1957, to the designs of Westmore Partners of Cheapside.

In the 1970s schemes were considered by Sotheby's for the comprehensive redevelopment of the whole complex to rationalize 'the labyrinthine and seemingly illogical geography of the premises'. A highly original design was conceived by Sir Denys Lasdun in 1975 for demolishing all the existing buildings and constructing a circular concrete rotunda in the centre of the site. This, however, was shelved on grounds of expense. Instead, a more conservationist approach has been adopted, which has woven together all the disparate elements to create a coherent and spacious interior, while retaining many fine old features which give the building its character. The first phase, in the 1980s, was the reconstruction to the designs of the Rolfe Judd Partnership of the St George Street houses to make new offices, while keeping several listed early eighteenth-century staircases and panelled rooms. The second phase, carried out during the last five years, was the addition of a new East Gallery to the main galleries on the

The main galleries at New Bond Street, after the recent programme of refurbishment. (ABOVE)

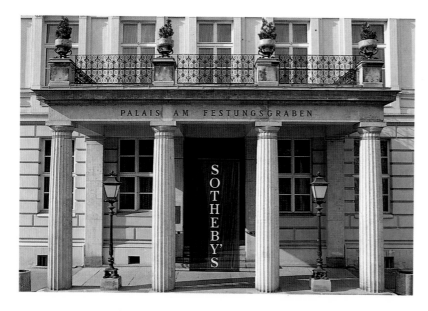

The portico of the Palais am Festungsgraben, Sotheby's offices in Berlin.(TOP)

The entrance hall of the Palazzo Broggi, Sotheby's offices in Milan. (ABOVE)

first floor, thus creating one of the largest auction house gallery spaces in the world, and a dramatic remodelling of the ground floor. This included the restoration of the original Bond Street main entrance, and created a logical sequence of communications between the different parts of the building through the new axial Entrance Hall and the Colonnade Gallery. These connecting spaces, designed by Lionel Stirgess, were conceived in a classical manner with Tuscan columns reminiscent of the low colonnaded ground floors of English Palladian country houses such as Houghton, Wentworth Woodhouse and Nostell Priory. The restored and remodelled Entrance Hall was opened in 1993.

The worldwide expansion of Sotheby's under the chairmanship of Peter Wilson in the 1960s and 70s led to the acquisition of many overseas offices. In a number of European cities these comprise notable historic buildings such as the Palazzo Broggi in Milan, with its splendid marble-pillared hall, and the Palais am Festungsgraben on the Unter den Linden in Berlin. This imposing set piece was built in 1751-3 by the architect Christian Feldmann as a Baroque palace for the Chancellor Johann Gottfried Donner, who sold it on to the Finance Ministry in 1787. In 1863 the building was transformed by the addition of a neo-classical façade and an impressive marble ballroom. In 1945, having been badly damaged by Allied bombardment, it was taken over by the Soviet military authorities, who opened it in 1947 as the Soviet House of Culture. The dramatic events of the late 1980s gave Berlin a new lease of life, and Sotheby's set up its offices there in October 1990, moving into the Palais am Festungsgraben the following May.

The major headquarters of Sotheby's outside Britain is at 1334 York Avenue, on the corner of 72nd Street, in New York City. Sotheby's had achieved a powerful presence in New York with the acquisition of the Parke-Bernet Galleries in 1964, a move which was to prove the most important development in the firm's history since the eighteenth century. Parke-Bernet had started out as the American Art Association, whose first major auction of paintings was held in 1885 at premises on Madison Square at

East 23rd Street in New York. In 1937 Hiram Parke and Otto Bernet left the American Art Association to set up Parke-Bernet. By 1949 they had moved into 980 Madison Avenue, a building that was to remain the headquarters of the company until the 1980s, when what had become Sotheby Parke Bernet was moved to the former Kodak Building in York Avenue.

Originally constructed in around 1929 for the Laure Part Company, purveyors of Chesterfield cigarettes, 1334 York Avenue became the Kodak Distribution Centre in the 1950s. The site was ideal for Sotheby's purposes as, filling a whole block between 71st and 72nd Street, it provided plenty of room for expansion and growth. Sotheby's took over the building in 1978, moving in over the next four years after an extensive programme of conversion to designs by the architects Lundquist and Stonehelm.

The conversion of the York Avenue site involved creating a block-long, four-storey building, with a façade of Canadian granite pierced by picture windows 22 feet high, through which passers-by could glimpse the activity inside. With 160,000 square feet of floor space, comprising auction rooms, exhibition galleries and offices, it is the largest custom-built auction house in the world. A full range of audio-visual devices, including large viewing screens in the salerooms and closed-circuit television, were installed to supplement the traditional saleroom procedures. The Governor of the State of New York and the Mayor of the city opened the new galleries in September 1980, and during the three Heirloom Discovery Days that followed, more than 10,000 people visited the building. It is now considered one of the landmarks of New York.

The unquestionably modern character of the Lundquist and Stonehelm conversion of the Kodak building in New York makes a startling contrast to the accretive Bond Street London headquarters with their strong English classical character. Such a contrast is entirely consistent with Sotheby's persona, as each can be seen to represent a different side of a concern which is both an eminently traditional and a vehemently modern international business.

1334 York Avenue, Sotheby's main offices in New York, opened in 1980. (TOP)

The main gallery at York Avenue. (ABOVE)

PRINCIPAL OFFICERS AND SPECIALISTS

Michael Ainslie
President and Chief Executive Officer, Sotheby's Holdings, Inc.

Diana D. Brooks
President and Chief Executive Officer, Sotheby's Worldwide Auction Operations

The Rt Hon. The Earl of Gowrie
Chairman, Sotheby's Europe

John L. Marion
Chairman, Sotheby's North and South America

Julian Thompson
Chairman, Sotheby's Asia

Roger Faxon
Managing Director, Sotheby's Europe

Timothy Llewellyn
Deputy Chairman, Sotheby's Europe

Simon de Pury
Deputy Chairman, Sotheby's Europe

American Decorative Arts
Leslie B. Keno
New York (212) 606 7130
William W. Stahl, Jnr
New York (212) 606 7110
Wendell Garrett
New York (212) 606 7137

American Folk Art
Nancy Druckman
New York (212) 606 7225

American Indian Art
Ellen Napiura Taubman
New York (212) 606 7540

American Paintings
Peter B. Rathbone
New York (212) 606 7280

Animation and Comic Art
Dana Hawkes
New York (212) 606 7424
Stephen Maycock
London (071) 408 5206

Antiquities and Asian Art
Richard M. Keresey (antiquities)
New York (212) 606 7328
Carlton Rochell (Asian)
New York (212) 606 7328
Felicity Nicholson (antiquities)
London (071) 408 5111
Brendan Lynch (Asian)
London (071) 408 5112

Applied Arts from 1880
Barbara E. Deisroth
New York (212) 606 7170
Philippe Garner
London (071) 408 5138

Arms, Armour and Medals
David Erskine-Hill
London (071) 408 5315
Gordon Gardiner
Sussex (0403) 783933
Margaret Schwartz
New York (212) 606 7260

Books and Autograph Manuscripts
Roy Davids
London (071) 408 5287
Stephen Roe (music)
London (071) 408 5300
David Park
London (071) 408 5292
David N. Redden
New York (212) 606 7386
Paul Needham
New York (212) 606 7385

British Paintings 1500-1850
David Moore-Gwyn
London (071) 408 5406
Henry Wemyss (watercolours)
London (071) 408 5409
James Miller
London (071) 408 5405

British Paintings from 1850
Simon Taylor (Victorian)
London (071) 408 5385
Susannah Pollen
(twentieth-century)
London (071) 408 5388

Ceramics
Peter Arney
London (071) 408 5134
Letitia Roberts
New York (212) 606 7180

Chinese Art
Carol Conover
New York (212) 606 7332
Jisui Gong (paintings)
New York (212) 606 7334
Julian Thompson
London (212) 408 5371
Colin Mackay
London (212) 408 5145
Mee Seen Loong
Hong Kong (852) 524 8121

Clocks and Watches
Tina Millar (watches)
London (071) 408 5328
Michael Turner (clocks)
London (071) 408 5329
Daryn Schnipper
New York (212) 606 7162

Coins
Tom Eden (ancient and Islamic)
London (071) 408 5315
James Morton (English and paper)
London (071) 408 5314

Paul Song
New York (212) 606 7391

Collectors' Department
Dana Hawkes
New York (212) 606 7424
Hilary Kay
London (071) 408 5205

Contemporary Art
Lucy Mitchell-Innes
New York (212) 606 7255
Anthony Grant
New York (212) 606 7254
Tobias Meyer
London (071) 408 5400

European Works of Art
Elizabeth Wilson
London (071) 408 5321
Margaret Schwartz
New York (212) 606 7250

Furniture
Graham Child (English)
London (071) 408 5347
Jonathan Bourne (Continental)
London (071) 408 5349
Larry J. Sirolli (English)
New York (212) 606 7577
William W. Stahl
New York (212) 606 7110
Phillips Hathaway (Continental)
New York (212) 606 7213
Alexandre Pradère
Paris 33 (1) 42 66 40 60

Garden Statuary
James Rylands
Sussex (0403) 783933
Elaine Whitmire
New York (212) 606 7285

Glass
Simon Cottle
London (071) 408 5135

Lauren K. Tarshis
New York (212) 606 7180

**Impressionist and Modern
Paintings**
David J. Nash
New York (212) 606 7351
Alexander Apsis
New York (212) 606 7360
Marc E. Rosen (drawings)
New York (212) 606 7154
Simon de Pury
London (071) 408 5222
Michel Strauss
London (071) 408 5389
Melanie Clore
London (071) 408 5394
Asya Chorley (drawings)
London (071) 408 5393
John L. Tancock
Tokyo 81 (3) 3503 2944

Islamic Art and Carpets
Richard M. Keresey
(works of art)
New York (212) 606 7328
Mary Jo Otsea (carpets)
New York (212) 606 7996
Prof. John Carswell (works of art)
London (071) 408 5153
Jacqueline Bing (carpets)
London (071) 408 5152

Japanese Art
Neil Davey
London (071) 408 5141
Yasuko Kido (prints)
London (071) 408 2042
Suzanne Mitchell
New York (212) 606 7338

Jewellery
John D. Block
New York (212) 606 7392
David Bennett
Geneva 41 (22) 732 8585

Alexandra Rhodes
London (071) 408 5306

Judaica
David Breuer-Weil
Tel Aviv 972 (3) 22 38 22
Camilla Previté
London (071) 408 5334
Paul Needham (books)
New York (212) 606 7385
Kevin Tierney (silver)
New York (212) 606 7160

Latin American Paintings
August Uribe
New York (212) 606 7290

Musical Instruments
Graham Wells
London (071) 408 5341
Leah Ramirez
New York (212) 606 7190

**Nineteenth-Century European
Furniture and Works of Art**
Christopher Payne
London (071) 408 5350
Elaine Whitmire
New York (212) 606 7285

**Nineteenth-Century European
Paintings**
Michael Bing
London (071) 408 5380
Nancy Harrison
New York (212) 606 7140

**Old Master Paintings and
Drawings**
Hugh Brigstocke
London (071) 408 5485
Elizabeth Llewellyn
(drawings)
London (071) 408 5416
George Wachter
New York (212) 606 7230

Scott Schaefer (drawings)
New York (212) 606 7222
Nancy Ward-Neilson
Milan 39 (2) 7600471
Etienne Breton
Paris 33 (1) 42 66 40 60

Oriental Manuscripts
Marcus Fraser
London (071) 408 5033

Photographs
Philippe Garner
London (071) 408 5138
Beth Gates-Warren
New York (212) 606 7240

**Portrait Miniatures, Objects of
Vertu, Icons and Russian
Works of Art**
Gerard Hill
New York (212) 606 7150
Haydn Williams
(miniatures and vertu)
London (071) 408 5326
Ivan Samarine (Russian)
London (071) 408 5325
Heinrich Graf von Spreti
Munich 49 (89) 291 31 51

Postage Stamps
Richard Ashton
London (071) 408 5224
Robert Scott
New York (212) 606 7288

Pre-Columbian Art
Stacy Goodman
New York (212) 606 7330
Fatma Turkkan-Wille
Zürich 41 (1) 422 3045

Prints
Nancy Bialler (Old Master)
New York (212) 606 7117
Mary Bartow (19th & 20th C.)
New York (212) 606 7117

Robert Monk (contemporary)
New York (212) 606 7113
Ian Mackenzie
London (071) 408 5210
Ruth M. Ziegler
Tokyo 81 (3) 3503 2944

Silver
Kevin L. Tierney
New York (212) 606 7160
Peter Waldron (English)
London (071) 408 5104
Harold Charteris (Continental)
London (071) 408 5106

Sporting Guns
Adrian Weller
Sussex (0403) 783933
Windi Phillips
Houston, TX (713) 780 1744

Tribal Art
Jean G. Fritts
New York (212) 606 7325
Jean-Baptiste Bacquart
London (071) 408 5115

Trusts and Estates
Warren P. Weitman
New York (212) 606 7198
Timothy Sammons
London (071) 408 5335

Veteran, Vintage and Classic Cars
Malcolm Barber
London (071) 408 5320
David Patridge
Rumney, NH (603) 786 2338

Western Manuscripts
Dr Christopher de Hamel FSA
London (071) 408 5330

Wine
Serena Sutcliffe MW
London (071) 408 5050

INDEX

ACKNOWLEDGMENTS

PROJECT EDITOR Sandy Mallet
ART EDITOR Ruth Prentice
ASSISTANT EDITOR Kate Sackville-West
PICTURE RESEARCH Bella Grazebrook

The publisher would like to thank Luke Rittner, Amanda Brookes, Ronald Varney, Lynn Stowell Pearson, David Lee, Peggy Vance, Antonia Demetriadi, Slaney Begley, Gail Jones and all the Sotheby's departments for their help with this book.

Prices given throughout this book include the buyer's premium applicable in the saleroom concerned. These prices are shown in the currency in which they were realized. The sterling and dollar equivalent figures, shown in brackets, are based upon the rates of exchange on the day of sale.

PHOTOGRAPHIC ACKNOWLEDGMENTS
The publisher would like to thank the following photographers and organizations for their kind permission to reproduce the photographs in this book:
17 The Tate Gallery, London © DACS 1993; 18 Courtesy of Belvoir Castle, Leicestershire/Bridgeman Art Library; 19 Reproduced by courtesy of the Trustees of The National Gallery, London; 21 The Tate Gallery, London; 22 The Shell Art Collection at the National Motor Museum, Beaulieu; 23 London Transport Museum; 26 The Ford Motor Company; 27 The Museum of American Folk Art; 28 Popperfoto; 29-31 Copyright © BBC; 32-3 Geoff Dunlop/Illuminations; 38 The 1993 Biennial Exhibition, Whitney Museum of American Art, New York; 42 Archiv für Kunst und Geschichte, Berlin; 43 Isabella Stewart Gardner Museum, Boston; 44 left By permission of the Governors of Dulwich Picture Gallery; 44 right The National Galleries of Scotland; 45 above Phil Starling/The National Gallery, London; 45 below Tim Stephens/The National Trust Photographic Library; 47 The Tate Gallery, London; 49 © The Munch Museum, Oslo, 1993/Bridgeman Art Library; 50 Stephen White/'The Ancient Art of Mexico' 1992, The Hayward Gallery, London; 51 'The Sixties: Art Scene in London' 1993, Barbican Art Gallery; 265 above, 270 © The Stanley and Frances Caidin Trust 1992; 276 Photo: Bryan Wharton/Sunday Times Magazine; 280 The National Portrait Gallery, London; 281 The Fitzwilliam Museum, University of Cambridge; 282 above Ian West/The National Trust Photographic Library; 282 below Patsy Fagan/The National Trust Photographic Library; 283 above Historic Royal Palaces; 283 below Crown copyright. Historic Royal Palaces, wood carver: David Esterly; 284 Crown copyright. Historic Royal Palaces; 285 left The National Trust Photographic Library; 285 right Tim Stephens/The National Trust Photographic Library; 286-7 English Heritage

Sotheby's Amsterdam: 63 above
Sotheby's Berlin: 304 above

Sotheby's Billingshurst: 20 left, 186 above right, 256 right
Sotheby's Geneva: 11, 221 above, 222, 225 above right and below left, 227, 228, 232 below right, 233 above, 236 above left and right, 236 below left, 237 above left and centre
Sotheby's Hong Kong: 34, 160 right, 161 right, 162 left, 165 above, 288
Sotheby's London: 1, 4-5, 6 above and below, 13, 20 right, 24, 41, 46 above, 48, 55-56, 61, 63 below, 64 above, 65, 67, 68-71, 72 above, 73-5, 76 below, 77-9, 80 left, 81, 82-3, 88-90, 92-4, 96 above, 100-3, 119-121, 124-131, 132 below, 133, 136 right, 138-9, 141-4, 146-7, 149, 151 above, 152-153, 155, 158-9, 163, 167 above right and below, 169 below, 170 above and below left, 171 below, 172, 180-1, 182 right, 183 right, 184-5, 186 above left and centre, 186 below, 190-2, 194 above, 196 below, 197, 199, 204 below, 207, 209 above left, 212-3, 214 above right, 215 below left, 216 below, 217, 220, 230, 231 left, 232 above, 233 below, 235 left, 236 above centre and below right , 245, 247 below, 248-250, 251 above and centre, 252-3, 257-9, 260-1, 262 above right and left, 268-9, 273-5, 279, 291, 293- 294, 297, 301-3

Sotheby's Madrid: 296-297 above

Sotheby's Melbourne: 148

Sotheby's Milan: 196 above left, 304 below

Sotheby's Monaco: 6 centre, 35-7, 60 above, 150, 193, 209 below left and right, 211 below, 272

Sotheby's New York: 2, 10, 12 above and below, 35-7, 46 below, 54, 57-9, 60 below, 62, 64 below, 66, 72 below, 76 above, 80 right, 84-7, 91, 95, 96 below, 97-99, 104-115, 118, 122 left, 123, 132 above, 134-136 left, 137, 145, 151 below, 154, 156-7, 160 left, 161 left, 162 right, 164, 165 below, 166, 167 above left, 168, 169 above, 170 below right, 171 above, 173-9, 182 left, 183 centre and left, 187-9, 194 below, 195, 196 above right, 198, 200-204 above, 205-6, 208, 210, 211 above, 214 above and below left, 214 centre and below right, 215 below right, 216 above, 218-9, 221 above, 223-4, 225 above left and below right, 226, 229, 231 right, 232 below left, 234, 235 right, 237 above right and below, 242-244, 246-7, 251 below, 254 above right, 262 below right, 263-5, 268, 270-1, 273 above, 278, 288-90, 292, 295, 299, 305

Sotheby's St Moritz: 227 below

Sotheby's Sydney: 117

Sotheby's Taipei: 39

Sotheby's Tel Aviv: 140

Sotheby's Tokyo: 122 right

Sotheby's Toronto: 116

Sotheby's Zürich: 215 above, 217 below right, 246, 254 above left and below